COMPUTER APPLICATIONS
IN THE BEHAVIORAL SCIENCES

Edited by HAROLD BORKO

Center for Research, System Development Corporation

PRENTICE-HALL, INC., *Englewood Cliffs, N. J.*

COMPUTER APPLICATIONS
IN THE BEHAVIORAL SCIENCES

Current printing (last digit):

12 11 10 9 8 7 6 5 4 3

Library of Congress Catalog Card Number 62–8229

Prentice-Hall Behavioral Sciences in Business Series
Herbert A. Simon, editor

Printed in the United States of America
Prentice-Hall, Inc.
Englewood Cliffs, N. J.
16558C

FOREWORD

The chapters of this book provide a demonstration by example—far more persuasive than any exhortation—of the vital role that computers have already assumed in psychological research. There is a growing consensus that graduate and undergraduate students in the behavioral sciences, particularly those who are interested in theory and in quantitative techniques, should be exposed to this new tool as an integral part of their training in research skills. There is far less agreement how this need can best be met. In this book, Mr. Borko provides us with a set of positive proposals for introducing behavioral science students to computers. The plan is one that seems to me eminently workable for students both in the basic behavioral sciences and in important areas of professional application—for example, business administration and clinical psychology.

First, the student must learn what a computer is and how it operates. He can be expected to attain some basic programing skills as a by-product of the course, but programing per se should not be the primary focus of instruction (any more than acquisition of vocabulary is a primary concern of a university language course). In addition to obtaining some skill in programing and a rudimentary knowledge of the components of a computing system, the important first objective for the student must be to acquire an understanding of the central concepts on which the organization of computers and computer programs are based. Parts I and II of the book are intended to provide this.

Second, the introductory course—whether graduate or undergraduate—must begin with fundamentals already familiar to both students and instructors. As Professors Kelly and Lingoes state in their article, the first behavioral scientists to make use of computers in most universities have generally been the statisticians and psychometricians, and, therefore, processing quantitative data is still the most common use to which computers are put by behavioral scientists. Hence, an important part of the introductory course might well be devoted to the statistical use of computers and so emphasize both the employment of computers to handle standard methods, and the significant changes that are being made in methods because of the availability of the computer.

Third, at the present stage of development of the subject, the most feasible way to give the student a glimpse of how the computer may serve as one of his important research tools is to allow him to examine some of the imaginative ways in which researchers are currently using it. A series of examples are given, which describe these examples both in terms of their behavioral science goals and significance, and in terms of the programing techniques that are employed. COMPUTER APPLICATIONS IN THE BEHAVIORAL SCIENCES, then, has been designed by Mr. Borko to serve as the textbook of a course that would direct the student's attention to three basic questions:

What is a computer?

How can computers be used in statistical data processing?

How can computers be used to produce stimuli, and to provide numerical and nonnumerical simulations of human behavior?

In teaching by example, the authenticity of the examples is a prime consideration. Mr. Borko has secured the assistance of an outstanding group of scientists who report, in Section III, eyewitness accounts of voyages of discovery; many of them, if you will permit the fancy, radioed from vessels that have not yet reached their destinations. A student who wants to know what research is like, as a living activity, will find many clues in these chapters. He will find a few answers, some powerful techniques, and many questions. Hopefully, he will find at least one of these questions so fascinating and irresistible that it will launch him on his own voyage of discovery.

I suspect this subversive intent—to attract able researchers to this area— was in Mr. Borko's mind, and in the minds of more than one of the contributing authors. It is certainly in my mind as I prefix this foreword to their articles. I share the enthusiasm of the editor and authors for the computer as a research tool in the behavioral sciences, and their assessment of its great significance. It gives me great personal satisfaction that the present volume, which introduces students to this important new tool, appears in the series of which I am general editor. HERBERT A. SIMON

PREFACE

Computers have now attained widespread use in business, industry, government, and university research centers. Many books have been written on the engineering and design aspects of computers. Other books have concerned themselves with mathematical and programing problems, and still others have dealt with business applications. Few books have been written for the researcher who is not a specialist in computers, and fewer still discuss computer applications of interest to the behavioral scientist. Yet, the social scientist is vitally concerned with the expanding computer technology, both in its effects on society and on his own research interests. This volume, it is hoped, will partially fill the void by providing the reader with information on the computer and its applications for research.

The book is organized into three parts. It begins with a general discussion of the role of computers in the behavioral sciences, which is followed by an examination of the nature of mechanical thought. Next, a brief history of automatic data processing is presented so that current developments can be viewed in their proper perspective. The concluding chapter in this first part deals with computer principles and applications.

Part II presents a somewhat detailed description of the organization of a computer numbering system, machine language, and an introduction to programing concepts.

The reader, after having completed this material, has made his acquaintance with computers and the terminology used by workers in the field. He is now ready to look into some of the original and interesting work being pursued with the aid of computers. Part III provides him with this opportunity and acquaints him with the work of a number of eminent researchers. A wide variety of computer applications are presented. The material is organized into several groups of chapters so that chapters 8 and 9 deal with general implications and review data processing in the fields of psychological research. Chapters 10, 11, and 12 are concerned with statistical computations, i.e., multiple linear regression models, factor analysis, and canonical analysis. The next six chapters, 13 through 18, discuss the use of the computer as a research technique for investigating areas of traditional concern to the psychologist such as perception, education, cognition, language behavior, and creativity. The employment of computers as a simulation technique in the creation of neurophysiological and social system models is described in chapters 19 through 24. The concluding chapter attempts to look into the future, predict trends, and anticipate problems.

A selected bibliography is included at the ends of most of the chapters so that the interested reader will be able to pursue particular topics in depth. It is the hope of all the writers that the serious student will find, in this book, some topic of special interest that will stimulate him to engage in research.

This book had its origin in a course entitled "The Use of Electronic Computers in Psychological Research" taught by the editor at the University of Southern California. The class consisted of graduate students in psychology, sociology, education, library science, etc., interested in learning about computers and their use so that they could more adequately plan their research. Not only did these students provide the impetus for the book, but they also pointed out some of the shortcomings in the original presentation and helped bring about many improvements. Their penetrating questions on specialized topics made it clear that no one person possessed sufficient detailed information on current and diverse computer applications. As a result, educators and scientists working in this field were contacted, and they graciously agreed to contribute to the writing of the book. (The editor is sincerely indebted to them.)

In terms of acknowledgments, a special debt of gratitude is due to the staff of the Psychology Department of the University of Southern California for accepting this new course into their curriculum, and to the management of the System Development Corporation, where the editor is employed, for its help and encouragement. And there are a host of other individuals—teachers, colleagues, friends, and family—who patiently and uncomplainingly participated in the creation of this volume. Special thanks are due to Catherine Kingsland and Shirley Fuson for typing the manuscript and to Louise Schultz for editorial assistance. All their help is gratefully acknowledged, and it is hoped that they will be able to take some pride in the final product.   HAROLD BORKO

TABLE OF CONTENTS

Part 1

COMPUTER SYSTEMS

1

COMPUTERS AND THE BEHAVIORAL SCIENTIST, 4

2

DO COMPUTERS THINK? 12

3

HISTORY AND DEVELOPMENT OF COMPUTERS, 22

4

COMPUTER FUNCTIONS AND APPLICATIONS, 50

Part 2

COMPUTER FUNDAMENTALS

Part 3

COMPUTER APPLICATIONS

COMPUTER APPLICATIONS
IN THE BEHAVIORAL SCIENCES

Part 1
COMPUTER SYSTEMS

Chapter 1

COMPUTERS AND THE BEHAVIORAL SCIENTIST

The behavioral scientist—by definition—studies and evaluates the complex interactions of men as individuals, within societies, and within environments. Why then should he be concerned with computers, which belong to the realm of the physical sciences? Although all the material in this book is designed to answer the question comprehensively, even the most cursory consideration must recognize the challenge to the social scientist implicit in the impact of computer technology on science and civilization.

The behavioral scientist studies man-machine relations in order to define the role of man in the control and use of the machine and thus to optimize system interactions. In the growth of computer technology, man is assigning increasingly complex tasks to the machine and, in turn, is freeing himself to assume increasingly more complex tasks. From subjects as basic as perception, learning, and thinking, through analysis of specialized social organizations, man is harnessing the capabilities of the computer as a powerful research tool. The researcher in behavioral science must learn to use this tool or risk being left behind as his discipline

4

advances. But the computer is more than a research device; it is a production tool. As such, it is being used to automate manufacturing processes, warehousing and office procedures. The applied behavioral scientist must be aware of the effects of this new technology upon industrial management, labor, and the other forces in our society.

1.1 IMPLICATIONS OF THE COMPUTER FOR THE RESEARCH SCIENTIST

As a research tool, the computer may contribute in three principal functions:

a. Organization and reduction of statistical data
b. Hypothesis seeking, by finding relationships
c. Hypothesis testing, through modeling and simulation

Research involves the accumulation of data and their eventual analysis and reduction. As our research capabilities expand, more and more data are accumulated and analysis becomes increasingly complex and time-consuming. The statistical techniques are themselves becoming more sophisticated. If behavioral science remains chained to the desk calculator, it will stagnate. High-speed electronic data processing provides a means for rigorously analyzing masses of data. While analyzing and reducing these data, special computer programs can search for patterns and relationships which, because of the number and quality of variables, might remain obscured and undiscovered. From these patterns, the researcher can develop new and significant hypotheses.

Testing hypotheses can also be facilitated through the use of automatic data processing technology, by using a computer to simulate and study human behavior. But why study simulation models rather than human beings? The physiological psychologist will immediately recognize the similarity of this question to the older, more common query: "Why do you study rats if you are primarily interested in human behavior?" And the answer is very much the same: By simulating behavior on a computer, and studying its operation in detail, we can, by analogy, make inferences about the more complex human activities. These inferences must then be validated before being applied.

By way of illustration, consider the temperature control mechanism of warmblooded animals, or more specifically of man. Normal temperature is 98.6°. The body temperature must remain constant within approximately five degrees. Yet the temperature of the environment changes from 110° or more in the heat of summer to below freezing in winter. The organism's life depends upon accurate control of heat production and heat loss. As scientists, we are interested in studying the homeostatic mechanisms in temperature control; as computer-oriented researchers, we consider simulating this process. In fact, such a model already exists, for a thermostat operates in a fashion analogous to the hypothalamus.

In a low ambient temperature, the body temperature tends to fall. The skin, which has in it receptors for heat and cold, responds to the change. Messages are sent along nerve fibers to the hypothalamus, and the organism takes action to conserve body heat—action such as shivering and/or the constriction of blood vessels near the skin. Alternately, responding to a high ambient temperature, the message sent to the hypothalamus initiates action to dissipate body heat.

The thermostat works analogously. A desired room temperature is set. A thermometer is the sensing device or receptor. Detecting that the room is too cold, the thermometer creates a message, sent along an electrical conductor, that controls and starts the furnace. When the temperature exceeds the optimal limit, the furnace is stopped. The simulation model, i.e., the thermostat, operates on a feedback principle. The similarity between the operation of the thermostat and the observable control of body heat leads to the conclusion that the human organism uses a similar principle. The hypothesis is, at the very least, worthy of additional study and testing. In the course of these interactions, the computer specialist learns to design more sophisticated machines, and the behavioral scientist achieves greater understanding of the human organism—the most complex of all machines.

Through the data organization capabilities of the computer, far more complicated relationships can be defined and enormous masses of information processed in terms of those relationships. Thus the computer becomes analogous to organizations such as those comprising another machine, a natural resource, an industry, or a social community. The computer programed to model an industry, for example, responds to controlled fluctuations in variables such as production, sales, inventory, etc., and provides a basis for generalized conclusions about the parameters and their relationships.

The analogy of the organization of the computer itself to that of the human nervous system is even more pertinent to the behavioral scientist. It has been suggested that experience leaves a permanent mark on the brain—possibly by changing the configuration of protein molecules in the brain cells. The existing memory trace permits recall of the experience. Computer memory is somewhat similar. Information is recorded by magnetizing a certain small area of core memory. The computer can recall this information by checking to determine whether the part is or is not magnetized.

During the past few years, much effort has gone into the development of a formal theory of thought and memory. Cybernetics has this basic concept: the brain is a control and communication system which can be described mathematically in the form of logical nets composed of elements and connections. Although man-made communication nets may become extremely complex, they do not approach the magnitude of complexity existing in the human organism. Certainly, if we were able to describe thought, memory, and other human processes in mathematical terms—John von Neumann has pointed out that self-reproduction is also a mathematical problem—we could achieve a much better understanding of these functions. But the development of a theoretical model is not sufficient in itself. The model must be checked and verified under various operating conditions. For testing, the use of the computer is a necessity.

Hand calculation would be infinitely laborious if not outright impossible. In research, the computer can be used:

a. To simulate a system of complex interacting variables, in order to facilitate control of the elements under investigation
b. To simulate the environment in which the system must operate, again to permit a study of the system under various environmental conditions
c. To record, reduce, and aid in the mathematical analysis of experimental observations

Yet, as versatile as it is, the computer is only a tool. By itself it can accomplish nothing, but in the hands of an imaginative scientist, its potentials are almost limitless.

1.2 IMPLICATIONS OF THE COMPUTER FOR THE APPLIED SCIENTIST

The computer has ushered in the age of self-regulating devices and automatic control. As more extensive use is made of the computer potentialities, man will receive new benefits and face new problems. Research involving these new applications is already under way, and some of the studies are reported in Part 3 of this book. Ward, Fruchter, and Koons discuss some of the recent advances in statistical techniques made possible by the electronic computer. Silberman studies the effects of automation on the teaching techniques employed in elementary schools and in universities, and Ledley applies automation to medical science. Sprowls shows how the technique could be used to study business decision making; Benson studies international diplomacy. Whether the behavioral scientist is interested in pure or applied research, he will be using the electronic computer. In addition, the applied scientist will be concerned with automation and its effects.

The trend or direction in which automation is leading us is obvious, for it is simply an extrapolation of our present practices. Just as mechanization has been a continuing process, so one can predict that automation will find ever wider applications throughout the economy. Production, the gross national product, and our standard of living will all continue to rise. New products that are the result of automated manufacturing techniques will appear on the market. Fewer people will be employed in routine factory and office jobs, but employment will increase in those concerns manufacturing automated equipment. This is the trend. It is obvious, definite and inescapable. Attempts to dismiss it or to counteract it may delay the process, but cannot change it.

Automation is on its way. How rapidly it is adopted depends upon how profitable it proves. Many objects—the small table radio for example—are already being manufactured and assembled completely automatically. Airplanes and missiles are being guided to their destination by an "automatic pilot." Soon it will be possible for a person to start his car, set the dials, lean back and read the newspaper or watch television while an "automatic chauffeur" drives him to the office.

Since automation must be economical if it is to be adopted, its greatest benefit may be considered to be the virtual elimination of expensive and unpredictable human labor in the performance of routine jobs. These economic advantages of automation were stated quite precisely and accurately by Frank K. Shallenberger,[1] President of the Shalco Engineering Corporation of Palo Alto, California, and Professor of Industrial Management at Stanford University:

> Automation has given us devices which can see better, hear better, and measure better than human operators. They think and move infinitely faster than humans. They never get tired, they willingly work around the clock, they do not make mistakes, they do not talk back, they are obedient, consistent, and fully predictable. They will not go out on strike, they do not ask annually for higher wages, and they have few personal problems.

The country's defense needs have provided another major impetus toward automation. The nations of the Communist bloc outnumber the Free World in population. To offset their numerical advantage, the free nations of the world must maintain a higher man-hour production rate or risk being overtaken in the Cold War struggle. Our government recognizes this fact, and the country's tax structure and allowable depreciation encourage capital outlay for tools and automated equipment.

Besides the many potential advantages of automation, certain deterrents and problem areas must also be recognized. Because automation means change, management must make the initial difficult decision as to why, where, and how much to automate. New equipment is expensive, and cost is a major consideration. Retooling inevitably means a change in the product design, and this raises questions of consumer acceptance, an intensified sales campaign, etc. Production problems may arise, because maximum efficiency requires that automated equipment operate continuously. In a seasonal industry, continuous production may result in a large inventory with concomitant storage and cost problems. The impact of the new machinery on the labor force must also be considered, for management neither desires nor can afford to ride roughshod over its employees. The workers must be prepared, so that they accept the change, and trained, so that they can operate and maintain the equipment. Although these are primarily problem areas for business management, they are also challenges to the industrial psychologist. To make reasonably intelligent decisions, management must have information on the anticipated effects of automation. More and more, the behavioral scientist is being relied on to provide the necessary data.

There is a need for market sampling to provide information on how new products will be received.

There is a need for improved selection of personnel to fill the newly created technical jobs.

There is a need for improved techniques of labor-management communication.

There is a need for improved training methods to develop the new skills required by automation.

There is a need for improved techniques of retraining in order to equip the semiskilled worker to handle the more technically demanding jobs in the automated plant.

The behavioral scientist must be prepared to meet these needs. Automation thus is providing new impetus for basic research in the social sciences and is expanding the industrial opportunities for the applied scientist. Fortunately, the computer—the same general purpose computer that led to the current industrial revolution and all these new problems—is providing the tool to enable the social scientist to carry on the new research.

No discussion of automation is complete without some reference to the problem of technological unemployment. The phrase "technological unemployment" has a strong emotional connotation, which often distorts objective investigation. Indisputably, automation will displace some people from some jobs. Some people will therefore be unemployed, but this does not mean that there need be any mass technological unemployment. The harness maker became unemployed when the horse and buggy was replaced by the horseless carriage, yet the over-all effect of the automobile was increased employment. History has shown that in the long run change, invention, and automation result in a higher standard of living and increased employment. "In the long run," however, the individual worker may suffer unless he receives help. Helping the displaced worker is the continual responsibility of government, industry, and organized labor. These agencies can provide the will and the means to help. The behavioral scientist must provide knowledge about retraining, counseling, and other techniques designed to ease any suffering resulting from the new technology.

Finally, one benefit that could result from automation is the shortening of the work week and increased leisure. But leisure is valuable only if it is used constructively. Misused, it can be injurious, and there is evidence that some people are misusing the shorter work week. Increased leisure has been blamed for the increase in crime in recent years. Boredom is said to be responsible for the rise in the number of people requiring psychiatric treatment. Evidently there is need for a special program of education designed to teach people to make constructive use of their leisure time and to divert energy to healthful channels of activity. But what is meant by "constructive use of leisure" and "healthful channels of activity"? How is one to decide whether it is healthier to play baseball or watch the game on television? Can the behavioral scientist, the sociologist, psychologist, and educator develop programs to help?

These are some of the challenges of automation, which eventually must be met if automation is to be a true tool of progress.

REFERENCE

1 Shallenberger, Frank K., Economics of Plant Automation, *Automation in Business and Industry,* Eugene M. Grabbe, ed. New York: Wiley, 1957, 553.

Chapter 2
DO COMPUTERS THINK?

Computers can perform prodigious tasks of computational and clerical operations, but do they exhibit the characteristics of human intelligence? In a word, do they think? There is no universally accepted definition of thinking.* Consequently, before answering the question: "Do computers think?" it is necessary to propose a definition that will form the basis for the subsequent discussion.

2.1 HUMAN THINKING

The term "thinking" will be used in this section to include *problem solving, logical reasoning, learning, creative thinking,* and *autistic thinking.* In the following paragraphs, each term is defined in relation to computing, and the limitations of a computer in accomplishing each are indicated. The definitions appear to make sharp distinctions, but it is clear that the various kinds of thinking phase into one another. Note,

---

* ". . . Thinking remains one of the unsolved problems of psychology." *Encyclopaedia Britannica* (1960), 22, 134.

too, that the term "thinking" implies both the process of obtaining results and the results themselves.

2.1.1 Definitions. *Problem solving* is a method employed in goal-seeking behavior. It involves the definition of the problem and the formulation and evaluation of possible solutions. A solution may be achieved by trial-and-error activity or insight.

Logical reasoning is a scientific method of thinking that follows certain rules and involves the manipulation of symbols. There are two major types of logical reasoning:

 a. Induction, which is the process of inferring a general principle from a number of particular instances
 b. Deduction, which is the process of reasoning from general laws to particular cases

Learning is a complex process that leads to a change in behavior as a result of practice or other experience. Learning per se cannot be measured directly but can only be inferred from a change in performance.

Creative thinking viewed both as a process and as an end result is a form of behavior characterized by flexibility, originality, and inventiveness. Our knowledge of this process is incomplete, for one cannot sit subjects down in a laboratory and instruct them to be creative and original. Most of the information available comes from the retrospective reports of great inventors, artists, and writers. Some, like Edison, are painstakingly persistent individuals who try out hundreds of possible solutions before arriving at the one which meets their rigorous requirements. The previous trials are discarded and forgotten, and the final product remains as a valuable and original piece of work. Other creative geniuses, like Archimedes, study the problem and then relax while they wait for an inspiration that will enable them to shout, "Eureka, I have found it!" The processes differ, but either technique must be considered creative if it leads to new ideas or products, for creative thinking involves the ability to organize and reorganize information into novel combinations, to bring into existence something that did not exist previously.

Autistic thinking is not based on reality considerations and does not involve plans for implementation. Daydreaming is a common example. It may, like creative thinking, be original and novel, but autistic thinking is primarily controlled by the emotional needs of the individual.

2.1.2 Comparison of Human Thinking with Computer Functions. In comparing the human activity known as thinking with computer functions, it is important to distinguish between

   a. The results obtained by
     The human
     The computer
   b. The process by which the result is obtained by
     The human
     The computer

As the succeeding paragraphs will demonstrate, it is not particularly difficult to program a computer to obtain the same results that a human would achieve in certain problem areas. Certainly, if the concept of thinking is limited to an emphasis upon results, the computer can "think," i.e., arrive at the correct solution. Computers have been programed to perform such tasks as solving problems in arithmetic and logic, playing chess, etc. Relatively little, however, has been done to simulate the *process* of human thinking by means of a computer. An outstanding exception to this generalization is the research work of Newell and Simon designed specifically to simulate the human thought process.[8] This research is particularly important because it clearly demonstrates the possibility of programing a general purpose computer to solve problems by using the same techniques, i.e., heuristics, that people use.

With these introductory remarks as a basis for judgment, let us examine various areas in which thinking can be compared with computer functions.

Problem solving. The solution of mathematical problems is one example of problem-solving behavior. How much is 2 + 2? This is a problem, and if a young child can answer it, we say that he is exhibiting intelligent behavior. The computer can solve this and similar problems of far greater difficulty. Basically, for either man or machine, solving a problem means selecting an appropriate response from a set of initially possible solutions. The information necessary for making the selection may have been previously available as a result of learning or programing, or it may be generated during the process by means of trial-and-error activities.

Problem-solving behavior of another type is exhibited by a child trying to fit together the pieces of a jigsaw puzzle or by a rat learning to run a maze. These are examples of trial-and-error behavior, and the method can be used to solve problems. There are computers (more properly, robots) in existence that can run mazes. The classic example is Ashby's Homeostat,[1] which exhibits goal-seeking behavior; a more recent example is Shannon's maze-running rat.[10] This "rat" exhibits trial-and-error behavior as it goes through the maze the first time. It then "remembers" all the turns and runs perfectly the second time. Rats do not learn as quickly or as well. In this case the machine can achieve far better results than can the living organism, but the methods are different.

The ability of a computer in problem solving is not limited to the algorithmic methods useful for deriving the correct solution to an arithmetic (or purely mathematical) problem. The work of Simon and Newell in developing a General Problem Solver program emphasizes the heuristic methods applicable to solution of logical problems. Such problems are typified by games like chess in which algorithmic methods prove impractical. That is, to reduce and analyze all possible moves contingent upon any combination of previous moves, and the possible result of each move would result in an intolerably long game. The alternate method used by humans appears to derive from analysis of a sequence of "internal plays," offering probabilities of greatest benefit or gain and execution of the play thus judged best under the given conditions. Programs modeling this probabilistic approach to problem solving are being developed.

Logical reasoning. Possibly the quintessence of human logical reasoning is found in mathematics, and the good mathematician is considered to possess great ability in this direction. Computers have been programed to prove theorems in Euclidean plane geometry in a manner "of a clever high school student." [4] Computers have also been programed to play games such as tic-tac-toe, checkers, and even chess. [11] The rules of these games involve logic and logical reasoning ability. MacCallum and Smith [6] describe a computer capable of solving the following typical problem in logic:

> It is known that salesmen always tell the truth and engineers always tell lies. B and E are salesmen. C states that D is an engineeer. A declares that B affirms that C asserts that D says that E insists that F denies that G is a salesman. If A is an engineer, how many engineers are there?

The logic machine can solve this problem, can you?

Learning. The most basic type of learning is conditioning. Pavlov conditioned his dog to salivate at the sound of a bell, thus demonstrating a change in behavior as a result of learning. Skinner used a somewhat different technique for conditioning animals. It was called *instrumental conditioning,* because the organism's response was instrumental to achieving the desired goal and the resulting gratification. A hungry rat was put in a box containing a lever and a food receptacle. At first, the rat exhibited random behavior. Eventually he pressed down on the bar and received a food pellet. Each time the animal made the correct response he received a reward or reinforcement. If the rat pressed the bar several times and received no reward, the response was extinguished. In this way, Skinner was able to demonstrate that the rat could learn and could forget. A. G. Oettinger, of the Cambridge University Mathematical Laboratory, programed the EDSAC computer to adjust its output in response to a conditioning-like stimulus. [9, 14]

The following chart compares Skinner's and Oettinger's conditioning experiments. Skinner's rat had to learn the relation between the conditioned response (bar pressure) and the reinforcement (food). He relied on the Law of Effect to establish an associative bond between the correct action and the reward. Oettinger wanted to teach the computer to print the number 3 every time it received the stimulus signal. He, too, relied on the Law of Effect. At the beginning of the experiment, the computer printed numbers at random. Every time a 3 appeared, however, the experimenter would input a strong positive signal as a re-inforcement. Every time a number other than 3 appeared, he would input a negative signal to express disapproval or negative reinforcement. The strength of the reinforcing signal varied directly with the magnitude of the difference between the given and the desired response. In a short period of time, the computer "learned" to respond to the stimulus by printing a 3.

Since computers do not ordinarily act in accordance with the Law of Effect, Oettinger had to program EDSAC to behave accordingly. His program is relatively simple. The nine possible responses are held within computer memory. They can be denoted by a_0 to a_7 and X. When the machine is stimulated, it selects a number a_r and adds to it a number representing the strength of the stimulus. If the result exceeds a given minimum value, a_r is printed. In other cases, the output is an X. The figure corresponding to a_r will then be increased or decreased in proportion to the strength of the approving or disapproving signal input by the operator. In this way, the desired number 3 is reached and stabilized. The computer has also been programed to "forget" if it receives no

	Skinner	Oettinger
Emitted behavior	The organism engages in food-seeking behavior when hungry.	In response to a stimulus, the computer will print a symbol 0 through 7 or an X. The symbol "X" means that the computer could not decide which numerical symbol to print.
Reinforcement	Food	Stimulus signal of varying intensities.
Conditioned response	Rat learns to press bar in order to receive food.	Computer learns to respond by printing the number 3 every time it receives the stimulus signal.

FIGURE 2.1 Comparison of Skinner's and Oettinger's conditioning experiments.

reinforcement. This is an example of the computer being used to simulate the methods employed by humans for learning.

Like Pavlov's dog and Skinner's rat, the computer can be programed to respond to conditioning and modify its behavioral output.

Creative thinking. For the purposes of this discussion, creative thinking was defined as the ability to organize information into novel combinations. This description implies the use of inspiration or insight as part of the creative process. Inspiration, by its very nature, cannot be planned for or programed; hence the computer cannot make inspirational guesses nor reach conclusions by insight. However, if we limit ourselves to an examination of the end result of creative thinking—namely, a novel arrangement of material or information—we find that the computer is arranging and rearranging information constantly. So far as these combinations can be formed either on a random basis or by following a logical procedure, the computer can produce novel arrangements. But in so far as creative thinking must include inspiration or some superrational element, it cannot be accomplished by a computer. One can ask whether a construct such as inspiration must be hypothesized in order to explain creative thinking. Again, the work of Newell, Shaw, and Simon [7] demonstrates that creative and original work can be understood by the application of the same laws of logical reasoning as are applied to all other effective problem-solving behavior. Indeed, they go further and state that the process of creative thinking *can* be simulated on a computer.

Autistic thinking. Like creative thinking, autistic thinking need not follow any rules or logic. Perhaps this is why some people believe that there is only a thin line separating the genius from the insane. Although computer processing must be based on definite and prescribed procedures and is not usually an end in itself, there is no inherent reason why the computer cannot be made to simulate the results of the autistic thought process and possibly even the process itself.

2.2   THE NATURE OF MECHANICAL THOUGHT

A. M. Turing [13] raised the question "Can a machine think?" and then reformulated the problem in terms of an "imitation game." This game is played by three people, a man (A), a woman (B), and an interrogator. All three are in separate rooms, and they communicate by teleprinter. The object of the game is for the interrogator to determine which of the other two players is the man and which is the woman. He does this by asking questions of the participants and evaluating their answers. He might ask, "Are you a man?" of both participants, but then he would probably get the answer, "Yes," from both, for under the rules of the game the woman must try to get the interrogator to make a wrong identification. Now what would happen if a machine such as a computer took the part of the woman? Turing suggests that if the interrogator could not distinguish between the man and the machine on the basis of the answers he receives, then for all practical purposes—as manifested in this game—the machine can think.

In the previous discussion comparing human thinking and computer functions, a distinction was made between the process of thinking and the result obtained by following that process. The varieties of human thinking, such as problem solving, logical reasoning, learning, creativity, and autism, were specified and the behavior of computers in such activities described. It was demonstrated that computers have been programed to obtain solutions to problems and achieve results which were comparable to the results achieved by thinking humans. The discussion also mentioned research which simulated the process of thinking by computer programs. One can therefore make this statement: to the extent that the researcher could specify behavior in a complete and logical fashion, the computer could be programed to accomplish similar tasks. To the degree that thinking involves no logical process, as may be the case in creativity and autism, the computer cannot think.

Shannon [12] in describing his chess playing machine makes a similar distinction. He states, "The Gordian question, more easily raised than answered, is: Does a chess playing machine of this type (i.e., a computer programed machine described in the earlier portions of Shannon's article) 'think'? The answer depends entirely on how we define thinking. Since there is no general agreement as to the precise connotation of this word, the question has no definite answer. From a behavioristic point of view, the machine acts as though it were thinking. It has always been considered that skillful chess play requires the reasoning faculty. If we regard thinking as a property of external actions rather than the internal method, the machine is surely thinking (p. 2132)."

Even this distinction may be tangential, however, for its assumes that the question, "Do computers think?" is meaningful. This is not necessarily so, for the question does not provide an operational definition of the term "thinking." If we define thinking operationally as problem-solving activity, logical reasoning, learning, etc., then the question can be answered, "Yes, computers do think because they can solve problems and perform other logically described tasks." This operational definition emphasizes the results of thinking. Alternatively, if we define thinking as a certain process or procedure used to solve problems, even then evidence could be found to support the proposition that a computer could be programed to simulate the thought process. Finally, we can take a third point of view and define thinking as an activity capable of being performed only by living organisms, and therefore, not by computers. Returning then to the original question, "Do computers think?" it is clear that a positive answer presupposes a materialistic and pragmatic view of the universe with emphasis on results, whereas a negative response must be based upon a form of philosophic dualism.[2, 3]

Although this excursion into philosophy sheds additional light on the question, it provides no final answer. Both question and answer involve a basic semantic confusion concerning the levels of abstraction with which we are dealing.[5] This is partially a confusion between the process and the end product, but it is also the confusion between the representation of an object and the object itself. One can represent a material object by a symbol, but the symbol must not be confused with the object itself. "Dog" stands for dog, but it is not a real dog. Similarly, symbols can represent thoughts, but the symbol is not the thought, and thoughts are not symbols. This is perhaps elementary, but it helps explain the confusion about thinking machines. The author contends that computers do not think, nor do they solve mathematical problems whatever the type of program employed. *The computer can only perform prescribed physical operations that the human operator correlates with thinking and with mathematics.* Machines can manipulate symbols but not thoughts; thus the computer output is devoid of all intellectual content. This output, however, can be made meaningful and useful when it is interpreted by the human operator. The computer performs mechanical and electronic operations. It is the human interpreter that thinks.

REFERENCES

1 Ashby, W. R., *Design for a Brain*. 2d ed. New York: Wiley, 1960.

2 Bunge, Mario, Do Computers Think? (I), *Brit. Jour. Philos. Science*, 6 (No. 27), August 1956, 129–38.

3 ———, Do Computers Think? (II), *Brit. Jour. Philos. Science*, 7 (No. 28), February 1957, 212–19.

4 Gelernter, H. L., and Rochester, N., Intelligent Behavior in Problem-solving Machines, *IBM Jour.*, 2 (No. 4), October 1958, 336–45.

5 Korzybski, A., *Science and Sanity*. 3rd ed. Lakeville, Conn.: International Non-Aristotelian Library Publishing Company, 1948.

6 MacCallum, D. M., and Smith, J. B., Mechanized Reasoning, *Electronic Engineering*, 23, April 1951, 126–33.

7 Newell, A., Shaw, J. C., and Simon, H. A., *The Processes of Creative Thinking, P-1320*. Santa Monica, Calif., The RAND Corp., September 1958.

8 ———, and Simon, H. A., The Simulation of Human Thought, *Current Trends in Psychological Theory*. Pittsburgh: Univ. Pittsburgh Press, 1961, 152–79.

9 Oettinger, A. C., Programing a Digital Computer to Learn, *Phil. Mag.*, 43, December 1952, 1243–63.

10 Shannon, C. E., Presentation of a Maze-solving Machine, *Trans. Eighth Cybernetics Conf.* New York: Josiah Macy, Jr., Foundation, 1951, 173–80.

11 ———, Programing a Computer for Playing Chess, *Phil. Mag., 41*, March 1950, 256–75.

12 ———, A Chess-Playing Machine, *The World of Mathematics*, J. R. Newman, ed. New York: Simon and Schuster, 1956, 4, 2124–2133.

13 Turing, A. M., Can a Machine Think? *The World of Mathematics*, J. R. Newman, ed. New York: Simon and Schuster, 1956, 4, 2099–2123.

14 Wilkes, M. V., Can Machines Think? *Proc. I.R.E.*, 41 (No. 10), October 1953, 1230–34.

Chapter 3
HISTORY AND DEVELOPMENT OF COMPUTERS

The tried, true, and trite statement, "There is nothing new under the sun," is also applicable to computers. These very modern and ingenious machines have an ancient history. Computers, in the broadest sense, are tools developed to help man calculate, standardize, and understand the events that occur in the world around him. Thus the history of computers is in part the history of man's progress in understanding his environment.

A history of that progress is beyond the scope of this text. Rather, the book presents the facts surrounding the origin and use of certain computing devices whose principles are necessary to, and incorporated in, contemporary machines. The researcher in the behavioral sciences might find a rich harvest in an investigation of the background leading to the introduction of each such device; the brief summaries in this section should be considered in the framework of an unspecified but existing social and scientific need.

Contemporary computers and their forerunners can be classified in terms of various characteristics: analog or digital, mechanical or electronic, binary or decimal, serial or parallel, general purpose or special purpose, etc. In this chapter, we examine analog devices, which calculate by using analogies, and digital devices, which count and operate on discrete digits. Of each type, we shall consider first the mechanical precedents of the electronic model. Finally, we shall discuss some of the early automatic devices and the characteristics of present-day machines.

3.1 ANALOG COMPUTERS

To compute "by analogy" requires representation of the elements of the computation by physical variables. A direct relationship is set up between a variable occurring in the problem one is seeking to solve and a physical quantity in the computation device. Numbers are represented by the magnitude of physical quantities, such as:

a. The distance between two points on a stick
b. The angular displacement, velocity, or acceleration of a rotating shaft
c. The electrical current in a conductor

From ancient surveying and map making, to mechanical devices including the slide rule and the flyball governor, to electronic differential analyzers, subsequent paragraphs will indicate the elaboration of the techniques for computing by analogy. Figure 3.1 shows the major milestones in this development.

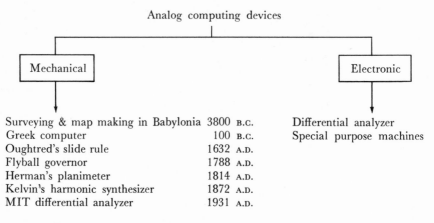

Analog computing devices

| Mechanical | Electronic |

Surveying & map making in Babylonia	3800 B.C.	Differential analyzer
Greek computer	100 B.C.	Special purpose machines
Oughtred's slide rule	1632 A.D.	
Flyball governor	1788 A.D.	
Herman's planimeter	1814 A.D.	
Kelvin's harmonic synthesizer	1872 A.D.	
MIT differential analyzer	1931 A.D.	

FIGURE 3.1 Milestones in the development of analog computers.

3.1.1 *Ancient Analogies.* Probably the very earliest form of counting or numerical manipulation was of the analog type. Primitive man scratched a line on the floor of his cave in order to represent the fact that he had killed one animal. In this case there is a one-to-one relationship between the symbol and the event. Although this is still a long way from calculating by analogy, it is a start. Perhaps many hundreds of years later, yet early in history, man measured his land and made maps. The British Museum exhibits a series of clay tablets, "circular in shape, and dating back to 2300 or 2100 B.C., which contain surveys of lands." [9] The resemblance, or analogy, between the map and the land permits computation—interpolation and measurement—without direct use of the original computation element: the land.

3.1.2 *Greek Computer.* [12] An analog computer, more than 2000 years old, was discovered around the turn of the twentieth century by a group of divers working off the Isle of Antikythera, near the Greek mainland. In a ship that had apparently been wrecked during the first century B.C., they found a gadget with a complicated set of dials, gears, wheels, and inscribed plates. Reconstruction proved this to be an analog computer of the solar system, designed to function as a mathematical model and used to calculate the motions of the stars and planets. Further study indicated that the mechanism was an arithmetical counterpart of the more familiar geometric models of the solar system which were known to Plato and Archimedes and which can be seen today in a planetarium.

A two-dimensional map provides an analogy only to a particular static condition. Mechanically variable models, such as this early analogy to the solar system, go beyond this static representation and accommodate calculations in which dynamic conditions or effects are important.

3.1.3 *Slide Rule—William Oughtred, 1621.*[6] The map, whether two-dimensional or mechanically variable, offers the opportunity to calculate only in terms of the original systems to which the model is analogous. The slide rule is an analog device at an abstract level. Familiar to most of us, the slide rule is a true analog computer in which numbers, or more precisely their logarithms, are represented by proportional distances along a piece of wood or other rigid material. Logarithms were invented by John Napier in 1614. (See Napier's Bones, Section 3.2.2.) A few years later, in 1621, William Oughtred put two logarithmic scales together and by holding one against the other was able to multiply and divide numbers directly. In the slide rule, the product of two numbers is the sum of their scalar distance. Each position along the scale represents a real number, and every number within the range of values is represented by a position on the scale. Since there is, in theory, an infinite number of points between any two scale values, the device is a continuous function computer.

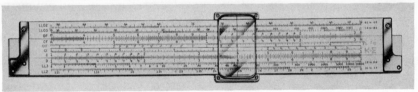

FIGURE 3.2 Log log duplex decitrig ® slide rule. (Courtesy of the Keuffel and Esser Co.)

3.1.4 *Flyball Governor—James Watt, 1788.*[11] In addition to calculating, the output of an analog device is frequently used as a control mechanism. This principle was first demonstrated by the steam engine governor, invented by James Watt in 1788. Although the flyball governor went out of use with the invention of the reciprocal steam engine, it embodies an important application of the feedback principle which is the basis for mechanical and electrical self-regulation.

Let us examine how this simple and ingenious device works. Information concerning the engine speed is conveyed to the governor in the form of the rate of rotation of a shaft. This governor shaft is linked to the output shaft of the steam engine by a gear train. The arm at the top of the shaft is linked, in turn, to the valve that controls the input of steam to the engine. When the engine is started, the shaft turns, the governor spins, and the flyball weights are impelled outward by centrifugal force. If the engine should go too fast, the outward swing of the flyballs would tend to close the input valve and slow the engine down. On the other hand, if the engine were not going fast enough, the flyballs would swing inward, i.e., toward the shaft, and this would tend to open the input valve and thus speed up the engine. After a few fluctuations, a constant speed is maintained.

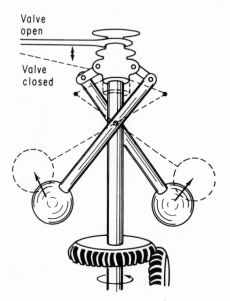

Valve
open

Valve
closed

The flyball governor is an excellent example of an analog machine in that it receives information (concerning the speed of the engine) in the form of physical energy (the speed of rotation of the shaft) and transforms this information into another physical quantity (the distance of the flyball from the shaft) in accordance with the rules of its construction. The flyball governor, however, is more than just an analog machine; it is an automatic control device that makes use of the feedback principle by linking the output to the input in order to make the engine regulate itself. Modern factories make extensive use of computers and the feed-back principle to establish automatic control of the manufacturing process.

FIGURE 3.3 Flyball governor. (Courtesy of Scientific American, Inc.)

3.1.5 *Planimeter—J. H. Hermann, 1814.*[10] As mathematics became more complex, machines were developed to solve problems of mathematical integration. If you are familiar with the calculus, you may recall that the area under a curve is determined by the formula:

$$A = \int_{x_1}^{x_2} y \, dx$$

Depending upon the complexity of the curve, this calculation may take a considerable amount of time and effort.

The planimeter is an instrument that directly measures the area bounded by an irregular curve. It was invented by J. H. Hermann, a Bavarian engineer, in 1814, and was extensively used in solving engineering problems. Jacob Amster improved upon Hermann's basic design, and in 1854 constructed the polar planimeter. Both instruments are in use today. Paralleling the relationship between a two-dimensional map and a solar system model, planimeters demonstrate the increase in degree of mechanical sophistication necessary to solve problems of greater mathematical complexity.

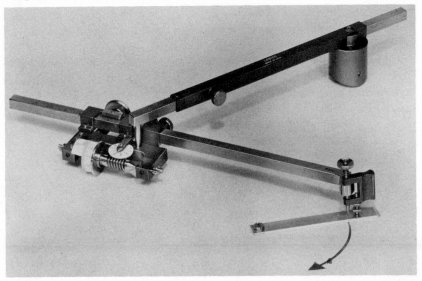

FIGURE 3.4 Planimeter. (Courtesy of the Los Angeles Scientific Instrument Co.)

3.1.6 *Harmonic Analyzers and Synthesizers—Lord Kelvin, 1892.* [10, 4]
In the early part of the nineteenth century, Fourier, a French mathematician, theorized that any complex curve could be duplicated by properly combining curves of each of the simple harmonic constituents. Since each simple harmonic curve can be expressed mathematically, any complex curve could therefore be expressed and, hence, operated upon mathematically.

Harmonic analyzers and synthesizers came into being to facilitate the use of Fourier series in analyzing waveforms. The analyzer is primarily a measuring device designed to isolate the individual harmonic components (of, for example, a musical sound) and to reveal the amplitude of each. The synthesizer performs the opposite function: it accepts information on the amplitude (or analogous relationship) of each of the components and produces the complex function. Mathematical analysis and synthesis permits controlled study of the changes in the function resulting from changes in any or each of the components.

Lord Kelvin faced this type of problem when he tried to predict, i.e., compute, the behavior of tides at different ports. The harmonic components are known, for they are the gravitational effects that the sun, moon, and planets exert on the seas at a given point in time. These can be measured and the data expressed in a Fourier series. The series can then be solved for the composite effect, which in this case is the height of the tides. To aid him in these calculations, Lord Kelvin designed an analog device in which trigonometric functions, such as sines and cosines of angles, are generated by means of pulleys and cranks of adjustable lengths. When operating, the center of each pulley describes a circular motion that is the equivalent of the sum of two simple harmonic or sinusoidal motions—one vertical and the other horizontal. The height of the tides is then calculated by adding together a number of these harmonic functions.

FIGURE 3.5 Kelvin tide predictor. (British Crown Copyright, Science Museum, London.)

3.1.7 *Mechanical Differential Analyzer—Vannevar Bush, 1931.*[2]

Mechanical instruments have been designed to solve trigonometric functions (the harmonic analyzer); integral equations (the planimeter); and differential equations (the differential analyzer). Differential equations are mathematical statements concerning rates of change rather than absolute values of quantities. The fundamental problem in the differential calculus is to measure the manner in which a function changes in value, as, for example, when computing the velocity of a falling body at any given instant. The first mechanical device for solving problems in the differential calculus was built by Vannevar Bush and his associates at M.I.T. in 1931. The basic component of this machine is the simple wheel and disc integrator plus various mechanical representations of angles and lengths (see Figure 3.6). During World War II, a large mechanical differential analyzer was built and used to help solve ballistic problems (see Figure 3.7).

Although effective in solving such problems, analog mechanical devices with their multitude of pulleys, gears, shafts, etc., are bulky and require both expensive precision tooling and considerable time to set up the individual problems. In order to change from one problem to another, a great deal of work with screw driver and wrenches is needed as the mechanical parts are changed from one set of values to another. This difficulty was eventually solved in a later model of the analyzer that incorporated some electrical components.

3.1.8 *Electronic Differential Analyzer.*

The important distinguishing feature of the electronic differential analyzer was the elimination of the mechanical gadgetry and thus reduction of needed setup time and manufacturing difficulties. Unlike the early Greek computer (see Section 3.1.2), which was a direct analogy of the solar system, a differential analyzer is not a direct analogy to anything. The distinction between direct and indirect analogy characterizes the difference between special purpose and general purpose machines. The general purpose machine is designed to solve mathematical equations, including problems involving differentiation and integration.

Insofar as one can reduce complex behavioral phenomena to mathematical formulas, whether this involves predicting the behavior of tides or calculating the trajectory of a ballistic missile or rocket, one can, by indirect analogy, solve these problems on a differential analyzer. A number of such machines are commercially available; these include BOEING, manufactured by the Boeing Airplane Company; EASE, manufactured by the Berkeley Scientific Company; GEDA, manufactured by the Goodyear Aircraft Company, etc.

FIGURE 3.6 Original mechanical differential analyzer. (M.I.T. photograph.)

FIGURE 3.7 Mechanical differential analyzer which was developed by Dr. Vannevar Bush. (M.I.T. photograph.)

The GEDA, illustrated in Figure 3.8, is installed at the Martin Company's guided missile and electronics center at Orlando, Florida. It is a large piece of equipment, 40 feet long and weighing five tons. The computer is used to solve problems connected with the design of weapon systems. In effect, it becomes an electronic analog model of a missile or craft which can then be launched or flown thousands of times under simulated flight conditions, each time providing the engineers with valuable data.

FIGURE 3.8 Goodyear Electric Differential Analyzer—GEDA (Courtesy of the Goodyear Aircraft Corporation).

3.1.9 Special Purpose Machines. In contrast to the general purpose analog computer that can operate on the mathematical expressions is the special purpose analog computer that is part of a regulatory system. This device is not designed to generate the solution to an equation in the form of a numerical quantity needed by the human. Rather, it computes its data primarily to generate a signal needed to control some other part of the system.

Included in this classification are the many specially designed devices to control temperature, pressure, density, and other parameters in the chemical and similar continuous process industries. Also included are the various speed controls (governors), directional controls (autopilots), positional controls (servomechanisms), and others. These special purpose computers are applied to the solution of many diverse problems, such as aircraft design, water flow for river and harbor control, highway traffic control, fire control mechanisms, etc. The design and utilization of these devices are highly specialized fields of study, and this book can do no more than mention their existence.

3.2   DIGITAL COMPUTERS

Just as we identified the analog device as a continuous function computer, so we may call the digital device a *discrete* computer. Whereas the analog machine measured a continuous quantity, such as the distance between two points on a bar, the digital computer can only recognize and operate upon discrete numbers.

In order to trace the history of digital computing devices back to its earliest origins, we should have to start with primitive and prehistoric man who counted with the help of his fingers or digits. Indeed, it is possible to conceive of all digital devices as extensions of the basic concept of counting on one's fingers, but it is, as we shall see, a very great extension.

Figure 3.9 lists the milestones in the development of digital computers. Subsequent paragraphs describe the contribution made by the most significant of these devices. Comptometers and mechanical calculators are not detailed, because they established no really new principles and so contributed little to the development of automatic digital computers.

3.2.1 Abacus.[1, 13]   The abacus, in its many forms, is an ancient, versatile mathematical tool in use many hundreds of years before Christ. The earliest abacus was simply a board covered with dust. Lines marked in the dust were used to represent quantities in a manner similar to lines on a slate. Later on, the dust was replaced by wax, but the purpose was the same.

At some point in history, the abacus became more formalized. A new model appeared that consisted of a tablet marked with lines. Loose counters or discs of metal, bone, glass, and other materials were placed on these lines to indicate number. Finally, these counters were fastened together on rods within a rectangular frame. Each rod represented a numerical position (units, tens, hundreds, etc.), and the value of the digit was determined by the position of the beads on the rods.

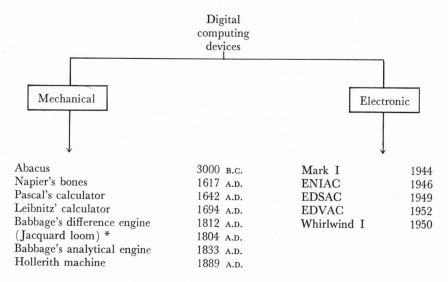

Mechanical		Electronic	
Abacus	3000 B.C.	Mark I	1944
Napier's bones	1617 A.D.	ENIAC	1946
Pascal's calculator	1642 A.D.	EDSAC	1949
Leibnitz' calculator	1694 A.D.	EDVAC	1952
Babbage's difference engine	1812 A.D.	Whirlwind I	1950
(Jacquard loom) *	1804 A.D.		
Babbage's analytical engine	1833 A.D.		
Hollerith machine	1889 A.D.		

* Though not a calculating device, Jacquard's loom contributed to the principles of representing information by the arrangement of holes in a card. This punched card method of data representation was used by both Babbage and Hollerith and is still in use.

FIGURE 3.9 Milestones in the development of digital computers.

The abacus and the Japanese equivalent, called the *soroban,* are still very much in use in the Orient. During and after World War II, many Americans had an opportunity to see and appreciate the remarkable speed and facility with which skilled operators manipulated the beads.

A unique contest, pitting the ancient skills of the Orient against the modern mechanical inventions of the Occident, was held in Japan in Novem-

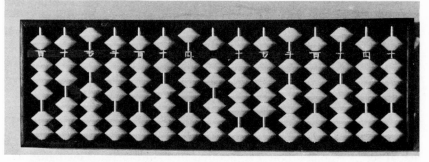

FIGURE 3.10 Abacus.

ber, 1946. "Kiyoshi Mastuzaki, a clerk in a Japanese communications department, using the abacus, challenged Private Thomas Wood of the U.S. Army, using a desk calculating machine, and defeated him in a speed contest involving additions, subtractions, multiplications, and divisions." [3] Although the most ancient of digital computers, the abacus still has a secure place in the modern world.

3.2.2 *Napier's Bones—John Napier, 1617.* [6] John Napier was the Scottish mathematician who invented logarithms early in the seventeenth century. He also developed a set of numbering rods called "Napier's Bones" which facilitated multiplication. Widely used in the seventeenth century, the device is now forgotten, or remembered only as a forerunner of the slide rule. The value of the device as an aid in multiplication can be seen from the example in Figure 3.11. Each "bone" has inscribed on it the multiplication table for the reference digit which appears on top of the rod. These two digit products are arranged so that the tens digit is above the diagonal while the units place is written below. Thus examining the no. 6 bone and reading down we find that $2 \times 6 = 12, 3 \times 6 = 18, 4 \times 6 = 24$, etc.

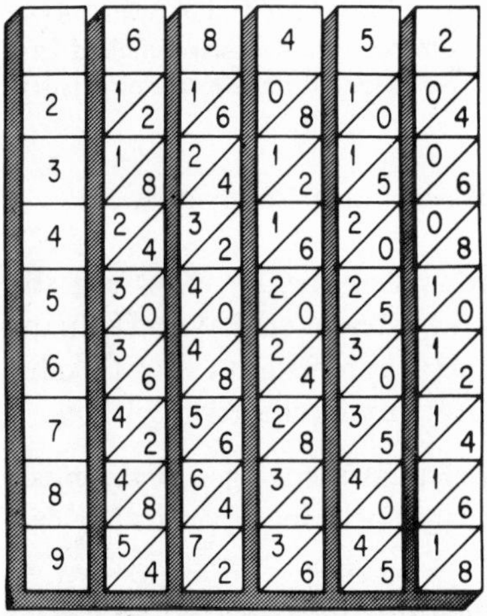

If we were to multiply 68,452 by 4 we would "throw the bones" as shown. The product is opposite the number 4 on the multiplier strip on the left. For the units place, we record the number in the lower right box under the 2 which, in this case, is the number 8. Next, we add diagonally in pairs: $0 + 0 = 0, 2 + 6 = 8, 1 + 2 = 3, 3 + 4 = 7$, and finally 2.

FIGURE 3.11 Use of Napier's bones.

The answer is: $4 \times 68,452 = 273,-808$. Should the multiplier contain more than one digit, each product would have to be recorded separately and then added together as in normal multiplication.

Napier's Bones, although not a machine in the true sense of the word, was an ingenious device making the multiplication process more mechanical and thereby decreasing drudgery and the chance for human error. (An actual set of Napier's Bones is pictured in Figure 3.12. This figure also includes a photograph of a French pocket calculator, circa 1800, which combines a Chinese abacus and a mechanized form of Napier's Bones into a single compact unit.)

3.2.3 Adding Machine—Blaise Pascal, 1642.[6]

The first true calculating machine that could add a series of numbers once the digits were set and the crank turned was invented by Pascal in 1642. Capable of doing only addition and subtraction, the machine consisted of a series of wheels on each of which were engraved the numerals 0 through 9. These wheels were mounted in a box along an axis. By using a stylus, the

FIGURE 3.12 Napier's bones and a French pocket calculator. (Courtesy of International Business Machines Corp.)

wheels could be advanced one-tenth to nine-tenths of a complete turn. The revolutionary aspect of this invention was the carrying device. When the wheel was advanced from 1 through 9 and on to 0, the carrying device advanced the next digit wheel to the left through one-tenth of a revolution; thus mechanizing the concept that $9 + 1 = 10$.

Pascal's device was the first practical adding machine—practical in that it was used by Pascal's father and other merchants to add up their accounts. The basic design was sound, but its development was interrupted because of an apparent lack of need for calculating devices at the time.

3.2.4 Multiplication Machine—Gottfried Wilhelm Leibnitz, 1671.[6]

Since multiplication is really repeated addition, Pascal's machine could

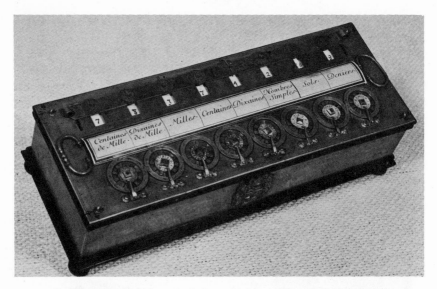

FIGURE 3.13 Pascal's calculating machine. (Courtesy of International Business Machines Corp.)

be made to do multiplication. Although possible, it would involve a slow process. Leibnitz, a contemporary of Pascal, developed a method of performing the repeated addition rapidly by use of a stepped wheel. This cylindrical wheel had on its outer surface nine teeth of increasing length numbered from 1 to 9. The concepts and the stepped wheel embodied in the early model are still used in present-day mechanical calculating machines.

Leibnitz conceived the idea of a multiplying machine in 1671, and the first operating model was actually constructed in 1694. This original calculating machine has been preserved in the Royal Library at Hanover where, at one time, Leibnitz was a librarian. Although the conception and the design were excellent, the machine's performance was not perfect, because skilled craftsmen of the period could not attain the high degree of precision needed for its construction.

3.2.5 *Punched-Card Machines—Hollerith, 1890*.[7] The development of punched-card machines for use in statistical calculations is credited to Dr. Herman Hollerith, a statistician employed by the United States government to tabulate the 1890 census data. In 1801, however, Joseph Marie Jacquard demonstrated the use of a punched-card system for controlling the alternation of colors of the yarn and thus of the fabric produced by weaving machines.[14] In modern terminology, we would

FIGURE 3.14 Leibnitz's calculating machine. (Courtesy of the Comptometer Corp.)

say that Jacquard used a punched-card program to produce a variety of patterned fabrics. These Jacquard looms are still in use today. The writer saw such a loom in operation in a silk weaving factory in Kyoto, Japan, in 1955. He was told that the pattern woven in this fashion was more complex and elaborate than one that could be woven on the more modern machines.

The magnitude of the job Hollerith had undertaken for the Census Bureau demanded a new and more efficient approach to data collection and organization. The 1880 census, using the standard manual tabulating methods to survey a population of approximately fifty million people, took seven and one-half years to complete! At that rate, the 1890 census could not have been analyzed before a new census made it obsolete. Obviously something had to be done, and Hollerith did it. He divided a standard 3- by 5-inch card into $\frac{1}{4}$-inch squares, making a total of 240 separate areas. Each one of these squares was assigned a distinct meaning. For example, a group of 20 squares were used to designate age, from 0 to 100 years in 5-year intervals. A hole punched in a particular square would indicate that the individual was between the ages of 30 and 35 years.

A photograph of the first electrical tabulating machine is shown in Figure 3.15. The punched card is inserted in the frame located at the operator's right on the console. When the handle is depressed, the points come through the punched holes in the card and come in contact with mercury cups, making electrical contact, and causing the movement of the index of a specific dial. At the close of each day, the totals reached on these counting dials had to be transcribed to record sheets by hand.

Since the machine had only 40 dials, each card had to be tabulated more than once. To facilitate the making of these multiple sorts, a box divided into compartments was placed at the side of the operator. This sorting box had 26 compartments, each closed by a lid held against the tension of a spring by means of a catch which turned the armature of a magnet. When a card was placed in the frame and the handle depressed, one of the electrical connections—referring to age, race, or any other desired characteristic—caused the lid on a designated compartment of the box to open for the reception of the card just tabulated. Thus the cards were sorted for transmission to succeeding machines. The use of these electrical tabulating machines greatly speeded up the work of the Census Bureau and their success ushered in the era of punched-card accounting methods.

FIGURE 3.15 Early Hollerith machine (Courtesy of International Business Machines Corporation).

3.2.6 Difference and Analytic Engines—Charles Babbage, 1812.[6]

The calculating devices previously discussed in this section were limited in versatility and scope of operation. Babbage's Difference Engine, conceived in 1812, was the true forerunner of the modern computer. This machine was designed to calculate and print mathematical tables, such as tables of squares. The calculations were performed by the method of differences, a standard method in numerical analysis illustrated below.

$$f(x) = x^2$$

COMPUTING THE CONSTANT DIFFERENCE								
x	1		2		3		4		5
x^2	1		4		9		16		25
d_1		3		5		7		9	
d_2			2		2		2		

x = any number in a consecutive series
x^2 = the square of that number
d_1 = the first order difference, obtained by subtracting adjacent numbers in the preceding row, i.e., $4 - 1 = 3, 9 - 4 = 5$, etc.
d_2 = the second order difference, obtained in the same way, i.e., $5 - 3 = 2, 7 - 5 = 2$, etc.

FIGURE 3.16 The method of constant differences—finding the difference.

By way of example, we will work with the function $f(x) = x^2$ and determine the value of x^2 for every value of x, or generate a table of squares. In using the method of differences, we must first determine the value of the constant difference. Note that in the above example, the d_2 is a constant value. Having found the constant difference, we may proceed to generate a table of squares. This can be done by reversing the previous process and adding the known difference to the table headings in the following manner.

COMPUTING TABLE OF SQUARES

d^2	d^1	x^2	
2	1	1	$2 + 1 + 1 = 4$
2	3	4	$2 + 3 + 4 = 9$
2	5	9	$2 + 5 + 9 = 16$
2	7	16	$2 + 7 + 16 = 25$
2	9	25	etc.

FIGURE 3.17 The method of constant differences—computing the square.

Babbage's Difference Engine could perform these successive additions and compute large tables of polynomial functions. Also, the machine was able to print out the results, thus eliminating errors of transcription. The concept of having a machine do both the calculating and the printing of the results was a great advance in the use of automation.

FIGURE 3.18 Portion of Babbage's difference engine. (British Crown Copyright, Science Museum, London.)

The British government underwrote the cost of Babbage's Difference Engine, and he began work on it in 1823. The actual manufacture of the machine was a complex engineering problem, because every part had to be made by hand. Moreover, the project was plagued by manufacturing difficulties, personality conflicts between Babbage and his chief engineer, and financial problems. The task was officially abandoned in 1842, although work stopped as early as 1833. The British government had by this time spent £17,000 or approximately $75,000, on the Difference Engine and had only received a model of a portion of the machine (Figure 3.18).

Babbage, however, was not discouraged. At the time he stopped working on the Difference Engine, he began designing a more advanced machine, which he called the "Analytic Engine." Although the newer machine included many parts of the Difference Engine, it was to be more automatic and controlled by punched cards similar to those used by Jacquard. Unfortunately, this machine, too, was never built, but from the notes still available it is clear that Babbage was the first designer of automatic computers. Like many men of genius, he was ahead of his time; the world had to wait a hundred years before Babbage's concepts of automatic computation were realized.

3.3 EARLY AUTOMATIC UNIVERSAL COMPUTERS

With the death of Babbage in 1871, the development of computers halted. Some modifications and improvements were made in the existing machines, but there were no radically new departures. All this changed in the twentieth century. This is the century of speed and material bigness, the age of coal, steel, oil, of railroads and automobiles, of big business and bigger wars. The rapid expansion in size and complexity of business and government organizations created a need for fast and accurate computing devices.

Clearly, this was the time to renew the vision of Babbage.

3.3.1 Mark I.[8, 14] It was in 1937 that Howard H. Aiken of Harvard University set to work on an automatic calculating machine. Whether he was aware of the work of Babbage is unknown and beside the point. He was clearly aware of punched cards and their use in calculating machines. He solicited the support of the International Business Machines Corporation and, in collaboration with them, built the Automatic Sequence Controlled Calculator, or Mark I as it is more commonly called (see Figure 3.19).

The Mark I is an electromechanical, not an electronic, computer. It consists of counter wheels whose rotation is controlled by electrical relays. (Basic components of an electronic computer are vacuum tubes or transistors.) The Mark I receives operating instructions by means of punched paper tape. Additions or subtractions can be performed in approximately three-tenths of a second; while multiplication takes four seconds, and division about ten. Although this machine contains more than three-quarters of a million parts and 500 miles of wire, it is only about one-tenth the size of the Analytic Engine as conceived by Babbage. For all its many mechanical parts, Mark I is a well-built and dependable machine, operational since 1944 and still in use.

FIGURE 3.19 The Harvard Mark I calculator. (Courtesy of the Harvard Computation Lab.)

3.3.2 *ENIAC*.[14] ENIAC stands for Electronic Numerical Integrator and Calculator, popularly called the "electronic brain." It was designed by J. P. Eckert and J. W. Mauchly at the Moore School of Engineering of the University of Pennsylvania and was completed in 1946. A general purpose computer, it was designed to solve differential equations of the type used in calculating the trajectories of bombs and shells.

The ENIAC is the first of the electronic computers. The Mark I, as explained previously, consists of relays, but the ENIAC has no moving parts. It uses electronic techniques exclusively to set and manipulate numbers. As a result, addition and subtraction can be performed at an extremely rapid rate. The internal circuitry was such as to require different electrical connections every time a new problem was introduced. Consequently, while the actual computations could be performed very rapidly, the preparations or setup time was long, and this tended to reduce the flexibility of the computer. ENIAC is a large machine, occupying a room 20 by 40 feet and containing 18,000 vacuum tubes. A successful machine—in that it accomplished its purpose of computing ballistic tables —the ENIAC established design principles which influenced later computer development.

FIGURE 3.20 ENIAC. (Courtesy of the Ballistic Research Labs.)

3.3.3 *EDVAC*.[14] The Electronic Discrete Variable Automatic Calculator was proposed in June, 1945. John von Neumann, on behalf of a group associated with the Moore School of Electrical Engineering, issued a report containing specific proposals for a new type of computer, new as compared with the recently completed ENIAC which was already obsolete.

EDVAC contained three major innovations:

    a. The machine was to use the binary number system, and the conversion from decimal to binary language was to be accomplished by the internal circuitry of the machine.

b. Ultrasonic delay lines were used to increase memory storage capacity.

c. The program of operating instructions was to be internally stored in the enlarged memory.

EDVAC is still in use at the U.S. Army Proving Ground at Aberdeen, Maryland.

FIGURE 3.21 EDVAC. (Courtesy of the Ballistic Research Labs.)

3.3.4 *EDSAC.*[14] The Electronic Delay Storage Automatic Calculator, EDSAC, is a British machine built at the Cambridge University Mathematical Laboratory under the direction of Dr. M. V. Wilkes. Work was begun in 1947 and the machine went operational in May, 1949. Like EDVAC, EDSAC is a serial automatic computer using the binary system of arithmetic and an ultrasonic memory storage. Whereas the earlier machines had to specify the location of each instruction, EDSAC introduced the use of the accumulator register and program counter. All arithmetic operations were performed in the accumulator; i.e., numbers were added to the sum already in the accumulator, or subtracted from the accumulator. The use of the accumulator register simplified computer logic and enabled the instructions to be read into the control unit automatically in consecutive order, thus increasing operating speed.

FIGURE 3.22 EDSAC 1 (1949–1958). Photograph reproduced by kind permission of the Director, University Mathematical Laboratory, Cambridge.

Although EDSAC is being discussed in a chapter on history, the history is by no means ancient nor is EDSAC an obsolete machine. The word format, punched paper tape input, programing by use of subroutines, etc., all make this an up-to-date computer still in use at Cambridge.

3.3.5 *Whirlwind I.*[14] Computer technology took a major step forward with the development of Whirlwind I. This machine was designed and built at M.I.T.; it contained a number of important innovations, including magnetic core storage and marginal checking.

FIGURE 3.23 Whirlwind I. (M.I.T. photograph.)

The use of small ferrite cores for storing binary digits was originally proposed by J. W. Forrester in order to achieve high operating speeds and fast memory access. The first core matrix was fitted to the Whirlwind I computer in August, 1953. (See Figure 3.23. The man in the striped suit is Jay Forrester.) It had a capacity for 1,024 words, each word consisting of 16 binary digits. Random access to any number would require only 1 microsecond, a tremendous increase in speed. Whirlwind also innovated a system of marginal checking * intended to increase the reliability of the computer by testing it under conditions more extreme than those tolerated during normal operations. In this way, weaknesses are discovered before they cause failure under operating conditions. These faults or weaknesses can then be corrected during the time normally set aside for scheduled maintenance.

The integration of high-speed components, circuit organization, and programing techniques demonstrated by Whirlwind proved to be the forerunner to the computer used in the SAGE (Semi-Automatic Ground Environment) system. This is a real-time data processing system sponsored by the United States Air Force to automate the air defense of the

* The material covered in this portion of the chapter is somewhat technical, in that various specific computer characteristics are discussed. Many of the terms used may be new to the reader. If this is so, it is suggested that he scan this section and return to it after having read the chapters on the operation and components of the computer system. The material on present-day computers is included in this section in order to complete and extend the historical treatment with some discussion of the characteristics of present and future computer models.

North American continent, and it involves the processing of large quantities of radar and other types of data. SAGE is probably the largest network of computers in the world today. The experience gained in planning and manning such a system has had an influence beyond air defense and has been an impetus for the further development and use of computers throughout our economy.

3.4   CHARACTERISTICS OF PRESENT-DAY COMPUTERS

The preceding paragraphs outlined the history of calculating machines, emphasizing innovations that advanced the state of the art. This historical review provides us with a vantage point for extrapolating into the future and predicting the characteristics of the next generation of computers.

Charles Bourne and Dan Ford at the Stanford Research Institute collected data concerning operating characteristics of approximately 200 computers presently in use.[5] They plotted the rates of change of various machine characteristics using a horizontal calendar scale for years from 1942 to 1965. Their investigation covered the number of computers becoming operational, speed of operation, memory size, and other characteristics.

Very obviously there has been a tremendous increase in the number of computer models. In 1950, only some 20 different types had been developed; ten years later, nearly 300 types were in use. Most likely this rate of increase will continue for some time into the future.

Total memory size shows a considerable degree of variability, but this range has remained relatively stable during the last ten years and will probably continue so with a fairly constant average value. Memory access time has not improved as rapidly as operating speeds. Components presently under development, however, may produce a breakthrough that would significantly increase the speed of access.

Many different types of memory devices are in use today, but drum and core memory appear to be the definite favorites; and this trend will probably continue through 1965. During this period, magnetic film memory, now under development, should become commercially available. The trend, started by EDSAC, for single-address instructions in scientific computers will probably continue, and the number of multiple address machines will become proportionally less. Index registers, a relatively new technique first used in 1951, have proved to be of great value. A large percentage of computers have one or more such registers now, and this percentage will undoubtedly increase.

From the examination of these and many other computer characteristics, the authors conclude:

> The collected data seem to suggest that the majority of the computers developed between now and 1965 will show very little change in performance from that which was obtained during the last five years. However, a few research machines will definitely advance the technology, possibly as much as one order of magnitude for some of the characteristics, such as multiply times, memory sizes, and memory access times.

REFERENCES

1 Abacus, *Encyclopaedia Britannica*, 1958, *1*, 5–6.

2 An Introduction to Analog Computers, *A Palimpsest on the Electronic Analog Art,* H. M. Paynter, ed. Boston: G. A. Philbrick Researchers, Inc., 1955, 32–33.

3 Berkeley, E. C., *Giant Brains or Machines That Think.* New York: Wiley, 1949, 19.

4 ———, and Wainwright, L., *Computers, Their Operation and Applications.* New York: Reinhold Publishing Corp., 1956, 132–39.

5 Bourne, Charles P., and Ford, Donald F., The Historical Development, and Predicted State-of-the-Art of the General-Purpose Digital Computer, *Proc. Western Joint Computer Conf.,* May 3–5, 1960, San Francisco, California. Palo Alto, Calif.: The Western Joint Computer Conference, National Press, 1960, 1–21.

6 Calculating Machines, *Encyclopaedia Britannica*, 1958, *4*, 553.

7 Gregory, Robert H., and Van Horn, Richard L., *Automated Data-Processing Systems.* San Francisco: Wadsworth Publishing Co., 1960.

8 Hollingdale, S. H., *High-Speed Computing Methods and Applications.* New York: Macmillan, 1959, 55–57.

9 Map, *Encyclopaedia Britannica*, 1958, *14*, 837.

10 Mathematical Instruments, *Encyclopaedia Britannica*, 1958, *15*, 70–71.

11 Nagel, Ernest, Self-Regulation, *Automatic Control* (a *Scientific American* book). New York: Simon and Schuster, 1955, 4, 5.

12 Price, Derek J. deSolla, An Ancient Greek Computer, *Scientific American,* June 1959, *200* (No. 6), 60–67.

13 Stibitz, G. R., and Larrivee, J. A., *Mathematics and Computers.* New York: McGraw-Hill, 1957.

14 Wilkes, M. V., *Automatic Digital Computers.* New York: Wiley, 1956.

Chapter 4
COMPUTER FUNCTIONS AND APPLICATIONS

The preceding pages presupposed some acquaintance with computers; hence various aspects of these machines were discussed in general terms. This chapter specifies more precisely what computers can do and how they are used. It presupposes no prior knowledge.

4.1 COMPUTER FUNCTIONS

As the name implies, a computer can perform all the standard *arithmetic operations*. It can add, subtract, multiply, divide, extract square roots, etc. As their great advantage over earlier calculating devices, these modern machines have tremendous speed, coupled with ability to do these operations one after the other without waiting for human intervention and piecemeal instructions. In performing a continuous series of operations, it is often necessary to *look up tables of data,* such as sines and cosines, and the computer can do this when necessary. The computer can also *store data* in tables or files for future use. Files are rarely static and must be updated periodically. For example, companies keep alphabetic files of their employees, but new employees join the company and old ones leave. The computer can *collate data* and keep the files up to date.

Although manually operated calculators compute accurately, mistakes can be made in transcribing the results. This error is eliminated by today's computers which also automatically print results and reports.

Standard office machines can perform the functions described, but the computer does them faster. Further, one function can be done only by the electronic computer and not by the desk calculator. The computer can be programed to make *logical decisions*. The decisions are very rudimentary. By comparing two sets of numbers, the computer can decide which number is larger. In the hands of a good programer, this seemingly small capability enables the machine to do tremendous work. For example, if the computer were used in inventory control and instructed to keep one dozen of a given item in stock, it could (by subtracting the latest order from the inventory) determine the number of items remaining. Programed to compare this number with 12 (the prescribed minimum shelf stock), the computer could decide whether it is necessary to reorder the item and signal this fact to the operator. The computer's capability for making this type of logical decision is one of its most valuable assets in industrial and scientific applications.

4.2   COMPUTER APPLICATIONS

Computers have many applications and diversified uses. These can be classified into the following areas:

a. Mathematical and statistical computation
b. Scientific and engineering computation
c. Business data processing
d. Military applications
e. Process control

An examination of each of these areas indicates the computer's remarkable versatility.

4.2.1 *Mathematical and Statistical Computation.* As pointed out in Chapter 3, the impetus for modern high-speed computers came from the large amounts of statistical computation required by the 1890 census. The Census Bureau remains one of the country's largest users of high-speed computers. Other large users of computers are the military agencies. During World War II computers were used to solve highly complex series of simultaneous equations. They helped determine the trajectories of bombs and shells by determining mass, velocity, wind direction, and other variables. But mathematical and statistical computations are not the province of government alone. Computers are being used to reduce computational drudgery wherever it is found. In the social science laboratory, this drudgery is often encountered in factor analytic studies. With the help of computers, months of hard calculations can be reduced to minutes. This ratio is typical of the economy of using computers.

4.2.2 *Scientific and Engineering Computation.* In the scientific and engineering fields, computers are employed in calculating aircraft performance characteristics. An experimental aircraft is flown first on a computer. That is to say, the behavior of the aircraft is determined for various flight parameters such as speed, gravitational forces, maneuverability, etc. The test results influence the final design of the aircraft. Similarly, mathematical models of other equipment and situations can be programed for testing and evaluation.

A major obstacle in scientific research results from communication and language barriers. Computers can help remove such barriers, for they can now be used to translate material from one language to another.

The techniques of machine translation are so highly developed that one company is making plans to market computer-produced language translations.

Computers are also used in the study of flood control, weather forecasting, predictions of business cycles, and the analysis of many different kinds of economic data.

4.2.3 Business Data Processing. Small businesses, large corporations, and governmental agencies are automating their accounting and inventory systems and thus increasing over-all efficiency. Insurance companies use computers to calculate dividends, premiums, and actuarial tables. Public utilities compute their customers' charges with the help of computers. The government processes individual income tax forms and Social Security records via the computer.

4.2.4 Military Applications. The military establishments of our country are entrusted with the vital task of safeguarding our nation. Maintaining an adequate degree of preparedness involves the collection and processing of quantities of data. The Army, Navy, and Air Force all use computers as part of their weapons system. The Air Defense Command, for example, operates a radar network which is constantly scanning the skies and watching for an enemy attack. Should an attack come, there will be very little time in which to take the necessary defensive measures. Time is a most critical variable, for seconds may spell the difference between survival and destruction. High-speed computers are employed to minimize the time interval between the radar recognition of an aircraft and its identification as friendly or hostile. The computers are also used to guide manned interceptors and missiles to their targets. This is the SAGE—Semi-Automatic Ground Environment—system.

Methods are being studied for using a computerized system, similar to SAGE, to control all air traffic—civilian and military—in order to reduce the danger of mid-air collisions.

4.2.5 Process Control. Process control involves a somewhat different use of computers. Oil refineries have been making extensive use of computers as control devices for some time. Without them, it would be impossible to refine enough crude oil to run our gasoline-driven economy. Computers control the input of raw materials, monitor temperature, pressure, rate of flow, etc., and perform various quality checks. In this way, it is possible to maintain production of a sufficiently high quantity and quality to meet the customer's need. Without computers, this would be impossible regardless of the amount of manpower used.

Chemical plants are operated similarly, and automobile manufacturers have automated the manufacture of automobile engines from the raw castings to the final inspection. The automated manufacturing process proceeds smoothly and with a minimum of human intervention.

4.3 COMPUTER UTILIZATION

As is obvious, computers are being used extensively in government, industry, and research installations. These expensive items of equipment range in price from less than $50,000 to more than $2,000,000. What advantages does one expect to gain from the utilization of computers? There are a number of such advantages for both the scientist in the university and the manager in a business corporation. For example, when Sir Cecil Burt, Thurstone, and others expounded the virtues of factor analysis, they found few eager followers. The computational drudgery was so great that few were anxious to use the method. The factor analysis of a correlation matrix of 35 tests (35×35) would take months of painstaking work even with the aid of a desk calculator. Now, all the computations, including the factor extractions and mathematical rotations, can be accomplished in ten or fifteen minutes of computer time.

Computers have a number of advantages:

a. *Economy:* Although computers are expensive to buy and costly to rent, they can effect operating economies in manpower costs while doing tremendous amounts of routine calculations, such as payroll, inventory control, statistical calculations, etc. The recently designed, solid-state computers are relatively compact pieces of equipment. If installed to replace punched-card accounting procedures, such a computer takes less floor space and requires fewer operating personnel. Since its files are on magnetic tape, many old records and duplicate files can be eliminated. The utilization of computer equipment will usually result in saving valuable floor space and eliminating many file cabinets. Records thus become more, rather than less, accessible.

b. *Accuracy:* In addition to, and perhaps more important than, monetary savings is the improved accuracy resulting from proper programing and utilization of computers. In a large clerical operation, a significant portion of the errors results, not from incorrect original data, but from mistakes in transcribing, typing, and filing. The computer can help eliminate these errors. Further, computer programs can be written with self-checking routines that provide even greater accuracy.

c. *Speed:* Along with economy and accuracy, rapid computation is an additional obvious advantage which can be achieved in a computerized operation.

The advantages listed are in themselves sufficient to justify the use of computers in research and industry. Still other advantages are to be gained. For the research worker, the computer provides new capabilities for studying systems previously considered too complex for investigation. Such systems can now be simulated on the computer. For industrial management, the computer can provide additional and more up-to-date information concerning the operations of the company. Computers can also be used to provide for better scheduling and maintenance procedures. An outstanding example of computerized scheduling and control is the Navy PERT (Program Evaluation Research Task) system used in scheduling the production of the Polaris missile. PERT provided Admiral Raborn with charts and time estimates, enabling him to anticipate and avoid delays and difficulties. The improved management control made possible by PERT was one of the significant factors in making the Polaris missile operational years ahead of schedule. The computer can be used to provide similar control systems for management in other governmental agencies and in private enterprise.

Utilizing computers offers opportunities, but also raises problems. Programing is one such problem. Before the computer can be put to work, a detailed list of instructions must be written in a language the machine can understand. This is the computer program, and writing it is a time-consuming and tedious task. Fortunately, relief is on the horizon. Computer manufacturers and users have developed, and are continuing to develop, simplified programing techniques and compiler systems. Programs involving basic mathematical routines and procedures can be written once and shared by all users. These shared programs and compilers are steps toward reducing the time and cost of programing.

A second major problem area in the use of computers is the lack of trained personnel. Extensive utilization of electronic computers is being restricted by the lack of people who can program and operate these machines. In this problem area, no relief is in sight. The shortage will become more rather than less severe as computers become more readily available, because programers and operators are not being trained at an adequate rate. Organizations that are planning to install an electronic data processing system should also plan to train their own personnel. However, the lack of programers is not the most serious problem. One can learn the fundamentals of programing a computer in three months or less, but it is much more difficult to learn how to make optimum use of the machine—to conceive of problems worthy of computer application. Scientists, researchers, and management personnel must be trained to reorient their thinking in terms of electronic data processing equipment and away from the desk calculator. At best, such a training program will take years, but unless these people are trained to make optimal use of the equipment, the electronic computer could become an inefficient and expensive gadget.

Programing and the need for computer-oriented executives and scientists are problem areas that must be anticipated and planned for, when installing an electronic data processing system. Since the key to a successful operation is adequate planning, this discussion is couched in terms of problems of computer utilization, rather than their advantages and disadvantages.

The behavioral scientist who is considering using computers in his research work can reap many of the same advantages and must confront many of the problems that corporate management faces. Like management, the researcher becomes capable of reducing large masses of data economically, speedily, and accurately. He also faces similar problems—how to plan suitable research and how to program the computer. He can reduce the problems involved in programing by writing in FORTRAN or a similar system, and for most machines he will find available a number of previously written "canned" programs. In planning his research, however, the scientist encounters difficulties arising as a result of using the computer and which were not present when he was reducing data by hand. Charles Wrigley, writing in *The American Psychologist*,[1] indicated a number of ways in which the computer influences research design. On the positive side, the researcher can deal with large amounts of data and apply relatively complex statistical techniques for reducing this data. In contrast, he must control a tendency to collect a large sample rather than a carefully selected one. A population sample of 1000 presents no more of a problem to the computer than an N of 100. A rigorously chosen sample of 100, however, provides more meaningful data than a biased sample of 1000. Large numbers cannot substitute for good experimental design. The researcher must also avoid the tendency to tailor his experimental methodology to conform to existing data reduction programs rather than to select the statistical procedures most suitable to the data and the problem.

Forewarned is forearmed; once alerted, the scientist can avoid these difficulties and use the computer as a powerful new tool in his arsenal of research devices.

REFERENCE

1 Wrigley, Charles, Electronic Computers and Psychological Research, *Amer. Psychologist, 12* (No. 8), August 1957, 501–508.

Part 2
COMPUTER FUNDAMENTALS

Part 1 of this book contained information designed to introduce the reader to computers, their history, functions, and applications; this part will discuss the computer itself. Part 2 includes descriptions of the data processing system and its components, the language used by the operator to communicate with the machine, and the technique of programing. Although a wide variety of material is covered, the amount of technical detail is held to a minimum. Readers who want more information can consult the bibliography for further references and the glossary for definitions of technical terms.

Chapter 5

FUNCTIONAL COMPONENTS OF A
DATA PROCESSING SYSTEM

A *computer* is a machine that is able to calculate and perform sequences of arithmetical and logical operations in accordance with preprogramed instructions, thus eliminating the need for human intervention at each step. A *data processing system* consists of a combination of units, including the arithmetic processing unit (which is the computer proper) plus input, output, and storage devices. See Figure 5.1.

Data are brought into the system by means of the *input unit*. The devices that make up this unit must be able to sense information, as coded on some medium, and transfer it to the storage unit. Information enters the system as holes in punched cards or paper tape, as magnetized spots on magnetic tape, as letters and numbers printed on paper in magnetic ink, or directly from the keyboard of an electric typewriter connected to the computer.

The *storage unit* is the computer's memory facility. Storage devices must be prepared to receive information from the input unit and to file it according to a prearranged indexing scheme. The items stored in the computer may be the instructions needed to solve a problem or the data these instructions will manipulate. The size or capacity of the memory and the

60

speed with which its contents can be located and transferred to the central processing unit are important variables which determine the adaptability of the total system for particular commercial or scientific uses.

The *control unit* directs and coordinates the timing and operation of the entire processing system as it performs various arithmetic and logical operations and transfers the data into, and out of, storage. Although control circuits are usually dispersed throughout the system, the diagram shows the function as centralized in the control unit. By means of the control console and its many switches and signal lights, the operator starts and stops the computer and maintains cognizance of the step-by-step progress in the solution of a problem.

The *arithmetic processing unit* is the operational heart of the data processing system. This unit adds, subtracts, multiplies, and divides. It also performs logical operations, such as determining whether or not a number is zero, whether one number is larger than another, or whether a quantity is positive or negative. These determinations may seem trivial but—as will be seen—properly programed, a computer can do a great deal with these few decision capabilities.

COMPUTER UNITS

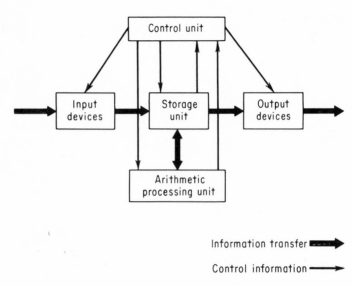

Information transfer ▬▬▶

Control information ▬▶

FIGURE 5.1 Functional components of a data processing system.

Finally, after a problem has been solved and the answer computed, the *output unit* provides the means for getting the results out of the computer

FIGURE 5.2(a) UNIVAC SS80 data processing system. (Courtesy of Remington Rand UNIVAC Division, Sperry Rand Corporation.)

FIGURE 5.2(b) IBM 7090 data processing system. (Courtesy of International Business Machines Corp.)

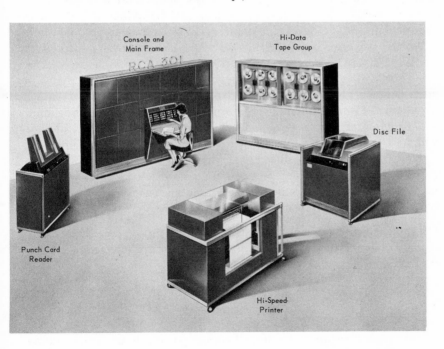

FIGURE 5.2(c) RCA 301 data processing system. (Courtesy of the RCA.)

and into a form readable by humans. Output devices are similar to the input units and include equipment that handles punched cards, paper and magnetic tape, and printed information.

A few commercially available data processing systems are pictured in Figure 5.2.

5.1 INPUT AND OUTPUT DEVICES

The units that function as input devices can often do double duty as output equipment, as their basic structures are the same. In one instance, the device is used to read unprocessed data into storage; in the other, it records the results of the computation. In both cases, the information is recorded in code on cards, tape, or other media, which the unit interprets. The methods of coding information are presented in later chapters. This chapter is primarily concerned with developing some familiarity with the equipment and its operating characteristics.

5.1.1 *Punched Cards.* The punched card is the most common input medium, probably because it is an excellent and versatile means of storing information. Installations using punched-card equipment can continue to use it even after converting to a more rapid electronic method of processing data. Both numerical and alphabetical information can be coded for card punching. Names, descriptive labels, and other items of either a numerical or non-numerical nature can be reproduced on the card from the punched holes. The card itself contains 80 or 90 columns in which information is stored. The information can be read into the computer at rates of 100 or more cards per minute depending upon the type of card reader. Considering the speed at which a computer can operate, however, this rate is not fast enough. Few computers rely on a direct card input; most convert the information from cards to paper or magnetic tape, for these can be processed at higher speeds.

The punched-card input unit consists of equipment for punching, verifying, and collating the cards. The Remington Rand Photoelectric Verifying Punch is illustrated in Figure 5.3.

5.1.2 *Punched Paper Tape.* Long before computers came into existence, punched paper tape was used in connection with teletype equipment. It was adopted for use with the early electronic computers and remains a popular input medium. Tapes are available in various widths and can have five, six, seven, or eight channels. Ordinarily, one character

FIGURE 5.3 Remington Rand photoelectric verifying punch. (Courtesy Remington Rand UNIVAC Division, Sperry Rand Corporation.)

occupies a row across the width of the tape. The normal speed of reading varies from 150 to 500 characters per second.

Paper tape is a faster input medium than the punched-card system. It has a further advantage: the coding can be done as a by-product of regular typing. Using a Flexowriter (Figure 5.4), or an attachment to an electric typewriter, a typist can produce a coded tape while she is preparing her standard typewritten copy. Prepared in this fashion, punched paper tape is a very efficient input device, for it eliminates the duplication of effort involved in preparing the coded data separately.

Verifying the accuracy of the tape is facilitated by preparing the tape and printed copy simultaneously, for an error in one means an error in the other, and proofreading the printed page is relatively simple.

Punched paper tape offers a third advantage: the machines needed to punch and read paper tape are cheaper than those required to handle cards or magnetic tape.

FIGURE 5.4 Flexowriter. (Courtesy of Friden, Inc.)

5.1.3 *Magnetic Tape.* Like the punched cards and punched paper tape equipment, a magnetic tape unit can function as both an input and output device. Magnetic tapes are also used for bulk storage of data that is to be filed for future use.

The magnetic tape looks very much like the tape used in home recording devices. It consists of a plastic ribbon with magnetic surfacing. A magnetic read-write head reads or records the information. The data are recorded as magnetic spots on the tape in a prearranged seven-channel code. Computer magnetic tape differs from audio tape in that for audio recording, the signal varies with the degree of magnetization, whereas in

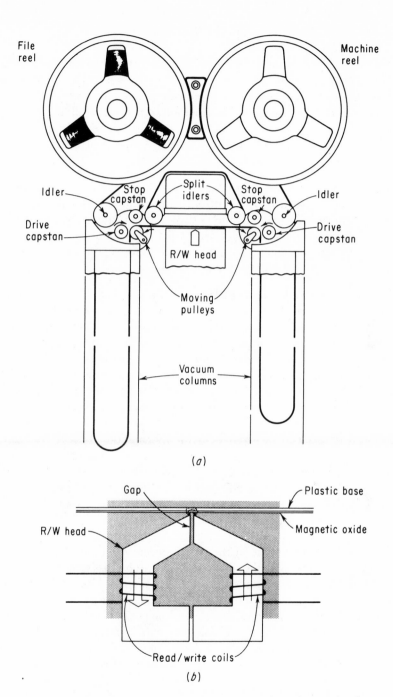

FIGURE 5.5 Diagram of magnetic tape unit and read-write head:
(a) Tape feed unit; (b) One-gap read-write head. (Courtesy of
International Business Machines Corp.)

the most popular scheme for computer application, the direction of magnetization carries the intelligence. The data are recorded in binary code; one direction of magnetization represents binary 1, and the opposite direction represents binary 0. This method of recording allows for a high signal-to-noise ratio and excellent reliability. Alternate techniques of recording, offering other advantages (such as amount of information per unit length) are also in use.

The data are recorded in blocks of information, each approximately one inch long and separated by about one-quarter inch of blank tape. This arrangement aids in locating the desired data. Commonly, counters on the tape drive equipment keep track of the blocks and activate the read heads when the specified information is located. Again, different equipment utilizes alternate identification methods.

The prime advantage of magnetic tape input is the speed with which information can be read into the computer. High-speed, high-density tapes have an effective "read rate" of more than 50,000 characters per second. A single foot of such tape, read into a computer in a fraction of a second, bears as much information as fifty punched cards (which require half a minute or more to be read into the computer). Not only is it possible to store large quantities of information on tape, but it is easy to manipulate this material and to update it. Unlike cards and paper tape, magnetic tape is reusable. Its major disadvantage is the relatively long time needed to locate a given item of information. This is basically a mechanical problem arising from the fact that one item may be on the front end of the tape whereas the next required item may be at the tail end. It takes time to move a few hundred feet of tape. Nevertheless, the great storage capacity of magnetic tape makes it an efficient medium when used to input data for high-speed computer processing.

5.1.4 *Magnetic Ink.* One of the recent developments in data input systems was designed by the Stanford Research Institute for machine processing of letters and numerals printed in a special magnetic ink. The system, designed primarily for banks, has enabled them to process paper checks mechanically and with less clerical help. This innovation heralded a great advance in data processing technology, for it involved a compatible system understandable to both men and machines. In other systems, special coding for machine processing must be employed.

Still other equipment has been developed capable of reading symbols written in ordinary ink. Eventually, it will be possible to supply the computer with both the data and the instructions for solving a problem, in ordinary printed English. These machines will be able to recognize,

FIGURE 5.6 Magnetic character sensing. (Courtesy of International Business Machines Corp.)

understand, and follow natural language instructions to obtain the desired solution. Some day, too, it may be possible to input data to the computer verbally. Results of recent research on machine recognition of sound are encouraging, and great progress is being made in this area.

5.1.5 *Direct Keyboard Input.* When a relatively small amount of input and output material is required, an electric typewriter can be connected directly to the computer. Obviously, this is a very slow method of providing data, but by using the techniques of buffering and time sharing, it need not delay computer processing. The typewriter keyboard contains many numbers and symbols: a feature not possessed by other input devices. As an output device, the electric typewriter enables the computer to supply the results in printed language for immediate interpretation and utilization.

5.1.6 *Printers.* The internal operation of the computer takes place in millionths of seconds. The time-consuming aspect of the work is transferring data into, and out of, the machine. Solving a problem may take a few thousandths of a second, but obtaining a readable answer may introduce a wait of several seconds. Printing speeds are critical. They vary from 10 characters per second on the typewriter to 2000 or more per second on high-speed printers.

The typewriter is a slow printer because time is consumed in raising the key to the paper and returning it to its original position. These inertial effects are minimized in high-speed printing by using a print wheel, print chain, or matrix printer. In both the print wheel and chain, the type revolves rapidly. When a letter is properly positioned, a small hammer strikes the paper against the type. A maximum speed of up to 500 lines per minute may be obtained using this system.

Faster speeds—about 1000 lines per minute—are possible using the wire matrix printer. In this device (see Figure 5.7) each character in the printing line is formed by pressing the ends of selected wires (in rectangular, 5 by 7 matrices) against the paper. This procedure does not result in solid type, but the printing is legible.

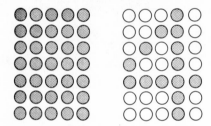

FIGURE 5.7 Matrix printing pattern. (Courtesy of International Business Machines Corp.)

An even faster method of printing is one that operates on an electronic principle and employs no mechanical moving parts. In the electronic printer, a stream of electrons from a cathode ray tube is passed through a selected character aperture. The resulting character is displayed on the face of the tube and projected on a revolving, light-sensitive drum. A sheet from the roll of printing paper is placed in contact with the electronically charged drum, and a black chemical material, which acts as the ink in this printing process, is electrostatically transferred to the paper and is fixed there by the heat of the drum (see Figure 5.8). Electronic printers are capable of attaining a speed of 100,000 words, or 5000 lines, per minute. (A printed page in a book contains approximately forty lines.)

5.2 STORAGE DEVICES

Storage is classified as external and internal, and the internal or main storage is further specified as static or dynamic.

External storage may be compared to a file cabinet of data not in active use. Characteristically, external storage devices have high capacity (i.e., they store great quantities of material) and a slow access rate; hence, it takes a comparatively long time to find the information desired. Further, data contained in external storage must first be transferred to internal storage before they can be operated upon by the computer. In this sense, external storage devices are used by the input unit; in a similar manner, they may be used by the output unit for storing data after the computer operations have been completed. Examples of external storage devices are punched cards, punched paper tape, and magnetic tape. Since the external storage devices were described previously as input-output units, the discussion will not be repeated.

Internal storage must be directly accessible to the arithmetic processing and control units of the data processing system. Access time is rapid, but capacity is somewhat limited. In *static storage,* the information is held in a fixed location in space and is always instantaneously available. Electrostatic and magnetic core memories are static. Information stored in *dynamic memories* circulates and therefore changes position and storage location with time. As a result, the stored information is not always available for instant recall. The data must be properly positioned before they can be read. Examples of dynamic memory storage devices are the

FIGURE 5.8(a) The S-C 5000 high-speed electronic printer. (Courtesy of Stromberg-Carlson, A Division of General Dynamics.)

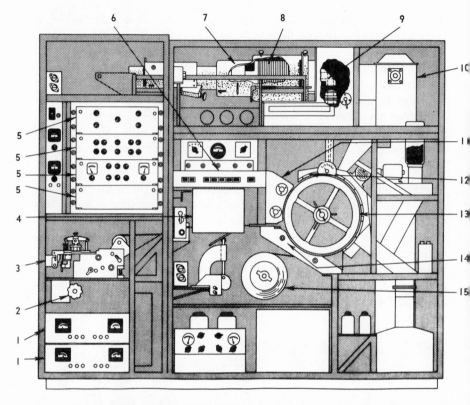

FIGURE 5.8(b) The S-C 5000 high-speed electronic printer: schematic. (Courtesy of Stromberg-Carlson, A Division of General Dynamics.)

1 Power supplies
2 Paper roll take-up spindle
3 Paper cutter (accessory)
4 Fuser
5 Tube control circuits
6 Push-button controls
7 Metal shield
8 Charactron shaped beam tube
　(7-inch diameter) (cutaway)

9 Split prism (cutaway)
10 Developer section
11 Cleaning chamber
12 Charge grid
13 Xerographic drum
14 Transfer grid
15 Paper roll

magnetic drum, disc, and acoustic delay lines. The term "memory" may be somewhat confusing and anthropomorphic. It is used interchangeably with "storage" and refers to that unit in the data processing system which holds information for later use. The information may be instructions, data, reference tables, or the results of intermediate and final calculations.

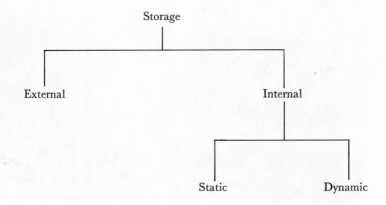

FIGURE 5.9 Classification of computer storage devices.

All this information must necessarily be stored in code form on some medium.

All memory units have the following characteristics, and they can be rated on these dimensions:

a. *Capacity:* The term refers to the number of words of data that can be stored in the memory device. Capacity may vary from a few hundred to a few hundred thousand digits.

b. *Complexity of the machine logic:* The ease with which the computer can move information in, and out of, storage is generally a function of the complexity of the logic (or organization) of the machine. This complexity is reflected in the variety of instructions the machine can recognize and execute. At a minimum, all computers must have a "read-into-memory" and a "read-out-of-memory" instruction. This may be a series of instructions rather than a single command word. In addition, some machines have indexing features and provide a means for setting up temporary storage tables that can be read out as a block of data rather than one item at a time. These features serve to increase the effective speed of operation.

c. *Speed of access:* Access time is that time required to locate a particular memory address and transfer data either into, or out of, the specified location. Access speed is measured in milliseconds (thousandths of a second) or in microseconds (millionths of a second).

(a)

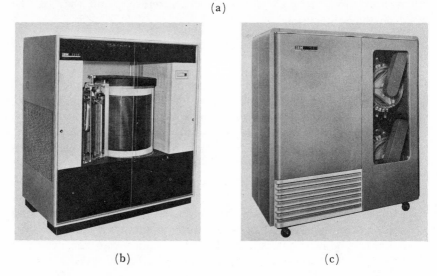

(b)   (c)

FIGURE 5.10 Common internal storage devices: (a) magnetic core storage; (b) magnetic disk storage; (c) magnetic drum storage. (Courtesy of International Business Machines Corp.)

d. *Cost:* The dollar value of the memory unit is a function of the construction, i.e., core, drum, disc, etc., and is directly related to the capacity of the unit and access speed.

e. *Volatility:* Memory in which data remain intact despite power failure or equipment shutdown is called *non-volatile.* In contrast, items stored in volatile memory are lost when the power is shut off. Electrostatic storage tubes and delay line memories are examples of volatile memory; magnetic recording is non-volatile.

Before specifying the differences in storage equipment, it is useful to consider the function of the storage unit in general. A computer must have the capability of receiving information, holding it until ready, using the information (data, reference tables, or instructions) to solve the problem, and then storing the computed results before printing out the solution. When large quantities of information are to be stored, each item must be labeled and indexed so that it can be located when needed. Computer storage systems use a very simple method of indexing. The storage space is divided into a series of "bins," called *words,* in a manner analogous to the rows and columns of individual mail boxes found in most post offices. Each "bin" is given an address, and information is referred to by the address in which it is located. For example, computer instructions are written in the form: "Take the information in address no. 306 and add it to the data in address no. 307, then store the result in address no. 101." This basic reference scheme of providing each piece of data with an address holds true for all types of storage equipment.

5.2.1 *Magnetic Core Storage.* Magnetic core memory is a static and non-volatile storage system offering random access to any item in its relatively large capacity.

The core is a tiny (less than one-tenth of an inch in diameter) ring of ferrous material. It can be magnetized in less than a millionth of a second by a few millionths of a watt, and it retains its magnetism indefinitely. A wire is passed through the hollow center of the core; when an electrical current flows through the wire, the core becomes magnetized in one direction.

If the current is reversed, the polarity of the core magnetization is likewise changed.

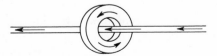

These two directions of the magnetic polarity can be called "plus" and "minus," or "1" and "0." This binary or two-state system of coding is used as a basis for storing all information in the computer.

The cores are strung together like beads in a frame. These frames (or planes) vary in size, with the more popular sizes containing approximately 4000 cores (see Figure 5.11). These planes are then stacked one on top of the other; a given core address being the aggregate of cores in all planes at a particular column/row position. Each core is located at the intersection of a vertical and horizontal wire. Such an intersection can be identified (as the coordinates in a plane).

In order to magnetize a particular core in the desired direction (i.e., to record the desired 1 or 0), it is necessary to send one-half the needed current through the horizontal wire and one-half through the vertical

FIGURE 5.11 Magnetic core plane. (Courtesy of International Business Machines Corp.)

wire. As can be seen from the diagram (Figure 5.12), this procedure produces full current at one and only one core. The process of recording coded information by magnetically orienting selected cores is called "reading into memory." Once the information has been stored, some means

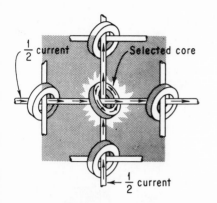

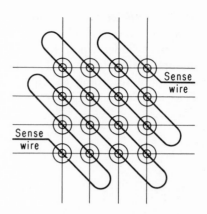

FIGURE 5.12 Selecting a core. (Courtesy of International Business Machines Corp.)

FIGURE 5.13 Core memory plane showing core detection. (Courtesy of the Remington Rand UNIVAC Division.)

for reading it out of memory must be provided. To read out, the directions in which a specific core has been previously magnetized are determined by use of a third wire, called the "sense wire." It connects each of the cores on a plane (see Figure 5.13).

By activating a set of cross wires, current is directed to a specified core and orients its magnetic field. In reading out, however, our goal is not to orient that core but to determine its orientation. If the core was previously magnetized in the direction representing a zero value, the reading out process effects no change in the magnetic orientation. Hence, the detector circuit senses no change—or a zero. But had the core been magnetized in the 1 state, application of readout current produces a change in orientation, which induces a current in the sense wire. Such a current is detected as a 1.

Because it involves applying a current, reading information out of core destroys the data, or more accurately, the reading out process alters orientation of cores storing 1's. It is therefore necessary to regenerate the data. This is accomplished by an inhibiting pulse, which may be sent through the sense wire or through a fourth wire following the readout pulse and which restores the status of the core orientation. In summary, each core has a number of wires passing through its center, and these provide the capability for writing and reading information into, and out of, core storage. The system is efficient, reliable, has very fast access time, but is comparatively expensive and used in the more costly data processing systems.

5.2.2 *Magnetic Drum Storage.* The most frequently employed internal computer storage device is the magnetic drum. The drum is a rapidly rotating cylinder whose ferrite-coated surface can be readily magnetized in minute discrete areas. The drums vary in diameter and in length. The number of recording channels and capacity depend on the drum size. For example, the magnetic drum in the UNIVAC Real-Time Computer

FIGURE 5.14 Magnetic storage drum. (Courtesy Remington Rand UNIVAC Division, Sperry Rand Corporation.)

System (Figure 5.14) is a very large piece of equipment. It has 128 recording bands across the length of the drum and a total capacity of 3,800,000 alphanumeric characters. A more common size of magnetic drum is the storage unit of the UNIVAC SS 80 Data Processing System. A line drawing of this piece of equipment is shown in Figure 5.15. There

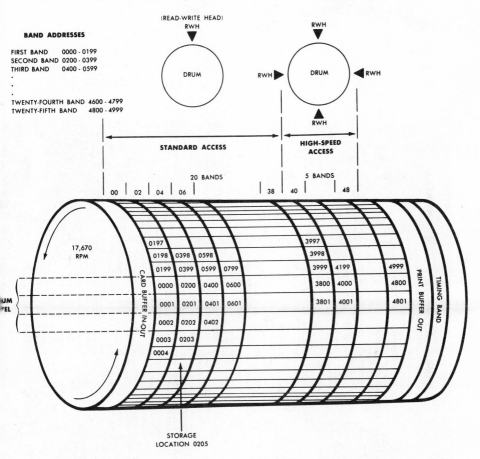

FIGURE 5.15 Storing data on a magnetic drum. (Courtesy Remington Rand UNIVAC Division, Sperry Rand Corporation.)

are 25 recording bands on the magnetic drum, each containing 200 word locations for a total of 5000 words. Twenty of these storage bands are called "normal-access bands" and are provided with one read-write head per band. The remaining five bands are called "fast-access bands," because they are equipped with four read-write heads per band, spaced 50 words apart, and have an information access time four times as fast as

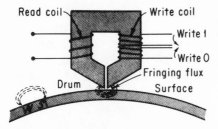

FIGURE 5.16 Magnetic drum recording read-write head. (Courtesy of International Business Machines Corp.)

that of the normal-access band. Also recorded on the drum are permanently magnetized control tracks, which enable the computer to locate and interpret any given address.

Information is recorded by read-write heads, which magnetize small areas (called cells) on the drum surface (Figure 5.16). Electrical cur-

FIGURE 5.17(a) Magnetic disc recording. (Courtesy of International Business Machines Corp.)

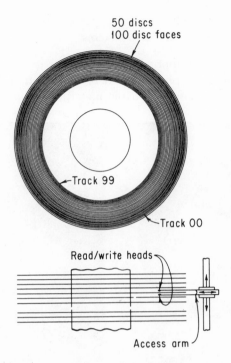

50 discs
100 disc faces

Track 99

Track 00

Read/write heads

Access arm

FIGURE 5.17(b) Magnetic disc recording; schematic. (Courtesy of International Business Machines Corp.)

rent is sent through the writing coil. The direction of the current flow determines the resulting polarity of the magnetic cell, which in turn is used to represent the binary digits 1 and 0. For reading data, the magnetic state of the cell is detected by the reading coil, in which the magnetic orientation induces a correspondingly polarized current. In the magnetic drum system, reading is not destructive, because the condition of the cell does not change when it passes under the magnetic head.

Besides its somewhat limited storage capacity, the rotating magnetic drum system has another important disadvantage: namely, the recording and sensing of information can take place only when the specified location is passing under the read-write head. This means that access is not instantaneous but, in fact, varies with the distance that the specified cell must travel to reach the head. To increase the access speed, some drum systems use more than one head per track.

5.2.3 *Magnetic Disc Storage.* Magnetic tapes have large storage capacities but slow access to specified data. Magnetic drums offer faster access time, but a much smaller storage capacity. Magnetic discs combine the best features of these other two systems.

The magnetic disc is approximately two feet in diameter and resembles an oversized phonograph record. It is made of thin metal and is coated on both sides with a ferrous oxide material similar to that used on the

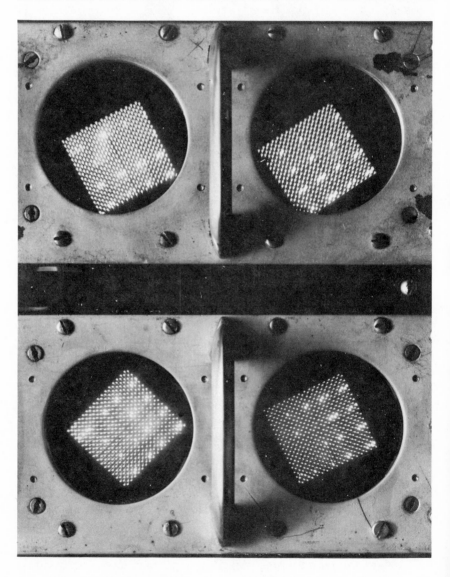

FIGURE 5.18(a) Detail of electrostatic memory. See Figure 15.8(b).

FIGURE 5.18(b) Electrostatic memory. (Courtesy of International Business Machines Corp.)

magnetic drum. Each side of the disc contains 100 concentric tracks in which the data can be stored. Fifty discs are mounted on a rotating vertical shaft. The magnetic read-write heads are mounted on an access arm that can be moved, under the control of the computer, to any track on any disc. (See Figure 5.17.)

The magnetic disc storage system can hold large amounts of data and provides for relatively fast access on a modified random basis. This method of storage is particularly desirable for business accounting systems, which need relatively inexpensive, large capacity, random-access storage devices. The operating speed need not be extremely fast. Magnetic disc memory meets these specifications. The access arm, with its read-write heads, takes approximately a tenth of a second to move from one track to another. This is many times longer than the access time of core memory, which is measured in microseconds.

5.2.4 *Electrostatic Memory.* In electrostatic memory systems, information is stored on the surface of cathode ray tubes. These tubes are similar to the type used in television sets, but are generally approximately three inches in diameter. Such a tube can store a total of 256 bits. Total memory may be increased by using an array of tubes.

As in all computer memory systems, information is stored in binary code form. In the magnetic memory systems, the critical variable was the direction of magnetization, positive or negative, 1 or 0. In electrostatic memory, the presence or absence of an electrical charge on a specified portion of the surface is interpreted as 1 or 0, respectively.

The face of the cathode-ray tube is divided into a 16 by 16 matrix, which provides 256 small squares or storage positions. To record information on the tube face, an electron beam is directed to a particular square, and an electrical charge is placed on a portion of the phosphorous coating. The presence of this charge is interpreted as binary number 1. To read information out of memory, the electron beam is again directed to the selected location. If a 1 has been stored there, however, the area is already charged, and additional electrons have no effect. The lack of an output charge indicates that a 1 had been stored in that location. On the other hand, if a 0 has been stored in the selected location, the electron beam charges the area, causing an electrical pulse at the output circuitry. As in core storage, the reading out process destroys the data, which then must be regenerated.

In addition to the destructive readout, a number of other problems are inherent in electrostatic storage devices. One such problem centers in the fact that the areas in which the electrical charge must be placed are quite small, and the angle of deflection of the electronic beam is very critical. Should the electron beam be directed to one spot on the surface of the tube for any length of time, it "digs a hole" in the phosphorous coating, damaging it. Finally, differences in adjacently placed electrical charges tend to neutralize one another, producing a state of equilibrium.

(a)

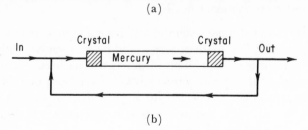

(b)

FIGURE 5.19 Acoustical delay line: (a) Photograph of UNIVAC I; (b) schematic. (Courtesy Remington Rand UNIVAC Division, Sperry Rand Corporation.)

This means that information stored as differences in electrical potential must be constantly regenerated to prevent loss. In summary, electrostatic storage is very sensitive—being subject to many operating difficulties—and expensive. Consequently, this type of memory system is not usually used in today's computers.

5.2.5 *Acoustical Delay Line.* Data can be stored as a series of electrically initiated, mechanical pulses traveling at low speed through a conducting medium. This device is called a "delay line."

Mercury-filled tubes with crystals on either end are commonly used as the storage medium. When an electric impulse is applied to the input crystal, it is converted to mechanical energy, transferred along the mercury column as an ultrasonic wave. At the other end, the output crystals reconvert the wave to a corresponding series of electrical pulses. An interval of time elapses from the moment the impulse enters the storage medium until it leaves. In a 30-inch tube of mercury, this interval is approximately 250 microseconds. This interval constitutes the "delay" that gives the storage device its name. At any given instant, a number of pulses are in transit in the mercury tube. Approximately 180 alphanumerical characters may be pulsing in the 30-inch tube at one instant, and this is the storage capacity of the unit. The storage is dynamic, for the data are constantly recirculating. As a pulse emerges from the output crystals, it may be used, and, unless modified, it flows back into the input end, recirculating as long as the equipment is powered. When needed, specific data can be located by maintaining an identification with respect to regularly spaced standard pulses (called a "clock") and transferring the information to the control unit.

Mercury ultrasonic delay line storage is volatile and relatively expensive. Although the mercury tube was successfully used in EDVAC and UNIVAC I (see Figure 5.19), it is being superseded, in today's computers, by faster and more compact devices.

The ideal computer storage system should have a large capacity in a small equipment volume, fast random access, and be inexpensive both in initial production and in operation. This ideal has not yet been reached; therefore, many different systems, some of which have been described, are in use. The storage device is selected for a given data processing system on the basis of the particular feature the designer chooses to emphasize. Each system has its strengths and weaknesses.

5.3   ARITHMETIC PROCESSING UNIT

The arithmetic unit processes data in accordance with programed instructions and can add, subtract, multiply, and divide. Besides these basic operations, computers can interpret many other instructions—such as "Clear and add," "Shift right," "Branch on zero," etc. The instructions are built into the circuitry of the arithmetic unit. A variety of instructions simplifies the computer operations and provides for greater operational flexibility and speed. (See Figure 5.20.) In performing its functions, the arithmetic unit must be furnished with information as to what operation to perform, the location of the data to use, and a place to store the results. Commonly, the same series of instructions incorporates the location of the next instruction. Thus, the computer can operate without interruption until instructed to "Halt."

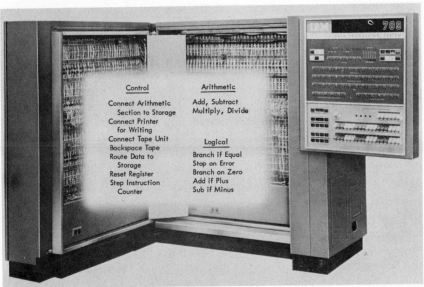

FIGURE 5.20 Arithmetic processing and control units. (Courtesy of International Business Machines Corp.)

In addition to arithmetical operations such as can be performed by any desk calculator, the arithmetic unit of the electronic computer is able to carry out logical operations. Logical decision making is utilized in the "Branch" instruction. Normally (i.e., without branching), the computer performs a series of operations in a prescribed sequential manner. The process starts with the computer examining instruction no. 1, and the work continues sequentially through instructions no. 2, no. 3, no. 4, etc. The computer performs a logical decision when instructed to deviate from the sequence in accordance with the results of a prescribed test. Such an instruction is called a "conditional branching instruction" and may be considered similar to a branch or fork in the road. A traveler, reaching a fork in the road, reads the signposts. Using the information thus obtained and considering his known objective, he decides which road to follow. Computer logic is similar. For example, in calculating an arithmetic mean, we may want the computer to add an indefinite series of numbers (N cases). The computer, like a human operator, detects when the series is ended, for then all the cases have been tallied. The next, or $(N + 1)$ case, will be equal to zero. In a manner analogous to looking for signposts, the computer is instructed to examine the contents of each new register before adding the data to the subtotal of the series and to branch on contents equal to zero. The "Branch zero" instruction provides that, if the register contains all zeros, the computer should—instead of continuing with the normal sequence of instructions—branch, or skip, to register X and follow the instruction located there. In this manner, the computer decides, on the basis of the information it possesses and without human intervention, when to stop adding and to divide by N in order to obtain the arithmetic mean. This decision-making capability is part of the logic built into the arithmetic processing unit, and it helps account for the computer's tremendous versatility.

5.4 CONTROL UNIT

Although the arithmetic processing unit may be the heart of the computer system, the control unit is the brain inasmuch as it directs the operation. It selects and interprets the instructions to be performed; it moves information from one part of the computer to another as needed; it coordinates the performance of all the computer elements and insures that the system functions as an integrated unit. Specifically, the control unit must monitor the timing of every operation, and it must interpret the coded instructions. The console provides a method by which the operator communicates with the computer, and the computer with the operator.

5.4.1 Timing. Electronic digital computers perform arithmetical operations in microseconds, i.e., millionths of a second. Accurate timing is critical to effective computer operation. Correct information must be in the correct location for the results to be meaningful. Required timing is accomplished by a device variously called a "clock" or "pulse generator." The basic functional unit of computer time is the time needed to process one digit of information. If this interval is fixed at one-millionth of a second, the computer is said to operate at a 1-megacycle rate, and the clock may be a fixed frequency pulse generator, such as a crystal-controlled oscillator. This mechanism is often found in computers with magnetic core storage. When magnetic drum storage is used, the computer clock is synchronized to the rotation of the drum, to insure that the timing will not be out of phase should the speed of the drum rotation vary slightly. Other timing devices may also be used, but the basic principle of controlling the time sequence of the computer operation remains inviolate.

5.4.2 *Decoding.* Before information can be processed by the computer, it must be put into a numerical code (only numerically coded information can be stored in the computer). It is the function of the control unit to interpret the coded instructions and signal the other parts of the computer to take the required actions. An instruction word * may be divided into two parts: the operation code, and the data address that specifies the storage location of the data, or operand. The instruction word ⎡ 52 | 0364 ⎤ may be interpreted to mean, "Add (code 52) the contents of storage location 0364 to number in the accumulator." As the control unit decodes this instruction word, it sets up the proper circuits to perform the addition operation as specified.

5.4.3 *The Control Console.* Every computer is equipped with a control console, and the operator and machine communicate with each other by means of the console equipment. By appropriate switch action, the operator starts and stops the computer. Other switch actions enable the operator to control the input and output units, to read the contents of a storage register, to examine the contents of the arithmetic unit, to transfer information from one location to another, and to actuate manually any operation of which the computer is capable. Through the console, small amounts of data can be entered directly into storage. Communication is a two-way channel, and the computer communicates with the operator by means of flashing lights, bells, and other signals that are part of the console. This is especially important when a malfunction occurs, for computers can be programed to recognize errors and to signal the condition to the operator. The console lights indicate the reason why the machine stopped—a program error or a mechanical failure—and enable the operator to trace the cause of the difficulty.

---

* The chapter dealing with machine language and word structure presents more detailed information on such items as instruction words, data words, and methods used in instructing the computer.

Many computer consoles have a special maintenance panel with switches and meters designed to help the engineering personnel service and maintain the equipment. Under test conditions, the computer can indicate the unit that is not operating properly. Since these components are often assembled on boards readily plugged into frames, any malfunctioning part can be quickly replaced.

The computer is an integrated system of input and output devices, an internal storage unit, a central processing unit, and a control section that directs and coordinates the operation of all the parts. Together these components make up the electronic data processing system.

FIGURE 5.21(a) IBM 7080 control console. (Courtesy of International Business Machines Corp.)

FIGURE 5.21(b) IBM 7070 control consoles. (Courtesy of International Business Machines Corp.)

Chapter 6

DATA REPRESENTATION

Chapter 5, which deals with the functional components of computers, states that before data can be processed, they must first be coded into a language which the computer is capable of manipulating. This need for translation is not a new concept; the citizens of one country must translate their thoughts if they wish to be understood by the natives of another country. In the United Nations, for example, speeches are translated into five official languages, and even this does not guarantee universal understanding. Equally, for communication with a computer, still another language, and symbols other than the spoken or printed word, must be used in order to convey meaning. Concepts can be represented in many different symbol systems, for a concept is distinct from the symbols used to represent it.

This chapter contains a discussion of the concepts and symbols of *machine language;* i.e., the language that the computer can manipulate. Just as one does not necessarily learn a foreign language before traveling abroad, however, one need not learn the machine language in order to understand and use the computer. The material presented in this chapter is important for those who wish to understand the inner workings of the computer, but it is not a necessary prerequisite for the reader who is solely interested in learning to use the computer as a tool for solving various research problems.

In this chapter, the decimal, binary, and octal numbering systems, and some variations thereof, are explained, and the methods for converting one system to another illustrated. The principles of binary arithmetic are described, as is a basic computer circuit for binary addition. Also included are the standard codes for representing data on cards, paper, and magnetic tape. Together, this material provides the reader with a knowledge of the essential elements of machine language. But users of electronic data processing systems need not code in machine language. As a matter of fact, most users program the computer in a problem-oriented language. The essentials of programing are discussed in Chapter 7, and those readers who do not find the mathematics and logic of computers interesting may turn immediately to that chapter.

6.1   NUMBER SYSTEMS

Numbers are symbols. The numerical concept *eighteen* may be written as the decimal number 18—as it commonly is throughout the Western world—but it can also be written as the Roman numerals XVIII, the Hebrew character ʼח (pronounced *chai*), the Japanese character 十八 (pronounced *juhachi*), and as other symbols as well.

Even this is an oversimplification, for numbers have different meanings. Numbers may be used *to denote quantity*—as in "2 apples" or "4 pencils." Numbers may also be used *as addresses in an ordered series,* and when used in this fashion the numbers need not connote quantity. The house at address 84 is not necessarily bigger than the house at address 82. The house number enables us to distinguish a given address from all others and to locate it. Finally, numbers may be used solely *for identification,* with no implication of quantity or serial location. This is true in the case of telephone numbers, Social Security numbers, Army serial numbers, etc.

This introductory discussion emphasizes that symbols can be used to carry information, that the same information can be conveyed by different symbols, and that the same symbol can convey different information, depending upon how it is used. The meaning of the symbol is determined by convention. In communicating with computers we use some familiar symbols, but we determine their meaning by a new convention. First, let us examine the common convention of numbering called "the decimal system."

6.1.1   *Decimal.* The decimal numbering system probably had its origin in the accident of nature that provided man with ten fingers or digits. The common numbering system is composed of ten symbols: 0, 1, 2, 3, 4, 5, 6, 7, 8, and 9. With this system, we can count up to 9 using one symbol at a time. In order to count past 9, it is necessary to combine two symbols. By using two symbols together, the person counting can represent up to 99 objects. To count further, three symbols must be used, and so forth.

Mathematically, the decimal system is described as being based on powers of 10. For example, the number 8463 can be written:

$$8463 = ? \text{ (in powers of 10)}$$

$$(8 \times 10^3) + (4 \times 10^2) + (6 \times 10^1) + (3 \times 10^0)$$

$$8 \times 1000 = 8000$$
$$4 \times 100 = 400$$
$$6 \times 10 = 60$$
$$3 \times 1 = 3$$
$$\overline{8463}$$

In the foregoing example, only whole numbers were used. It is also possible to write fractions and mixed numbers in the decimal system and in the powers-of-10 convention. For example $92\frac{5}{8} = 92.625$, which can be written:

$$(9 \times 10^1) + (2 \times 10^0) + (6 \times 10^{-1}) + (2 \times 10^{-2}) + (5 \times 10^{-3})$$

$$9 \times 10 = 90$$
$$2 \times 1 = 2$$
$$6 \times 0.1 = 0.6$$
$$2 \times 0.01 = 0.02$$
$$5 \times 0.001 = 0.005$$
$$\overline{92.625}$$

It is obvious that any numerical quantity can be expressed in this manner, but it is obvious only because we are so accustomed to dealing with decimal numbers.

In summary, the base 10 of our most commonly used number system is probably an accident of nature related to the biological fact that human beings have ten fingers. The decimal convention is a useful system and one which can be applied to the design of mechanical or electronic computers. Mechanical calculators and the early electronic computers did, in fact, calculate in the decimal system. Mechanical computers are composed of gears, each with ten teeth, representing the ten decimal symbols. These gears are designed to mesh together so as to produce a cumulative effect when one number is added to another.

An electronic computer is composed of vacuum tubes or their equivalent. One might visualize a series of numbers represented as an array of electric light bulbs arranged ten in a row, thus:

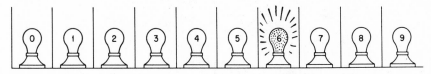

The number 6 is tallied when that bulb, and no other, is lit. The computer will operate with such a system, but it requires an extremely complicated circuitry in order to add or otherwise manipulate these numbers. There are simpler ways of doing things.

6.1.2 *Binary*. Had nature provided man with eight or two prehensile digits, we might have developed different numbering systems. The electronic computer is not necessarily restricted to the use of a particular numbering system. As the example of the electric light bulb array shows, the computer can operate on a decimal numbering system. To simplify computer circuitry, we take advantage of an obvious characteristic of the electric light bulb: that it is either on or off—that it can exist in one of only two states. Not entirely by coincidence, this leads us to a consideration of a numbering system, called the "binary system," which has only two symbols: 1 and 0. The sparsity of symbols necessitates large combinations of digits, or "bits" as they are called, to express quantity. For example, the binary expression for the number 18 would be 10 010, or five binary bits as compared to two decimal digits.

When counting in the binary system, we start as in the decimal system and assign the symbol 0 to zero and 1 to one. Having now used up all the permissible symbols, the first symbol, namely 0, appears again in this position, while the next position to the left advances one symbol. Thus binary 10 (read one-zero and not ten) is equivalent to decimal 2. Figure 6.1 compares the first twenty binary and decimal numbers. Just as the decimal system is based on powers of 10, so the binary system is based on powers of 2, and any binary number may be written as a sum of powers of 2. Figure 6.2 gives an abbreviated list of the powers of 2. Note that fractions can be expressed as negative powers of 2.

Analyzing binary 010 010.101 into powers of 2, we get:

$$
\begin{aligned}
0 \times 2^5 &= 0 \\
1 \times 2^4 &= 16 \\
0 \times 2^3 &= 0 \\
0 \times 2^2 &= 0 \\
1 \times 2^1 &= 2 \\
0 \times 2^0 &= 0 \\
1 \times 2^{-1} &= 0.5 \\
0 \times 2^{-2} &= 0.0 \\
1 \times 2^{-3} &= \underline{0.125} \\
&\ 18.625
\end{aligned}
$$

In order to convert a binary number into its decimal equivalent, it is only necessary to write it as the sum of its powers of 2, as was done in the example above. Thus, one calculates that binary 010 010.101 is equal

Binary	Decimal
0	0
1	1
10	2
11	3
100	4
101	5
110	6
111	7
1 000	8
1 001	9
1 010	10
1 011	11
1 100	12
1 101	13
1 110	14
1 111	15
10 000	16
10 001	17
10 010	18
10 011	19
10 100	20

FIGURE 6.1 Binary and decimal numbers.

2^n	n	2^{-n} Fraction	2^{-n} Decimal
1	0		
2	1	1/2	0.5
4	2	1/4	0.25
8	3	1/8	0.125
16	4	1/16	0.062 500
32	5	1/32	0.031 250
64	6	1/64	0.015 625
128	7	1/128	0.007 813
256	8	1/256	0.003 906
512	9	1/512	0.001 953
1024	10	1/024	0.000 977
2048	11	1/2048	0.000 488
4096	12	1/4096	0.000 244

FIGURE 6.2 Positive and negative powers of two.

to decimal 18.625. Conversely, a decimal number may be converted into its binary equivalent by successively subtracting the powers of 2. This is readily accomplished by repeated division of the decimal number by 2. The remainder of this step of the process becomes the binary digit. An example will make this clear.

EXAMPLE: Convert the decimal number 106 into its binary equivalent.

Remainders

2/106	
2/53	0
2/26	1
2/13	0
2/6	1
2/3	0
2/1	1
0	1

= 1 101 010

Note that in reading the answer, we read from the bottom up, in the direction of the arrow.

In summary, the following points concerning the binary numbering systems are to be stressed:

  a. 0 and 1 are the only two symbols used.

  b. It is a base 2 numbering system as compared to the decimal system, which is derived from a base 10.

  c. Any number or quantity may be expressed in the binary system, although to do so generally requires a longer sequence of symbols than is the case in decimal numbers.

  d. It is possible to convert from decimal numbers to binary and from binary to decimal. The two systems are equivalent, and the same numerical concept can be expressed in both symbol systems.

6.1.3 Octal. Whatever its advantages for use by a computer, the binary number system, with its large combinations of digits, is awkward for human use. Errors are likely to be made in the transcription and transmission of a long series of 1's and 0's. Fortunately, the octal system provides a method for reducing the number of binary bits to one-third while still maintaining all the advantages of that system. Figure 6.3 compares the three number systems.

A close inspection of the table reveals that there is an obvious relationship between the octal and the binary numbers such that one system can be

Decimal	Binary	Octal
0	000	0
1	001	1
2	010	2
3	011	3
4	100	4
5	101	5
6	110	6
7	111	7
8	001 000	10
9	001 001	11
10	001 010	12
11	001 011	13
12	001 100	14
13	001 101	15
14	001 110	16
15	001 111	17
16	010 000	20

FIGURE 6.3 Decimal, binary, octal conversion table.

converted to the other by inspection. For the numerals 0 through 7, the octal is identical with the decimal system, and both have the same binary equivalent. Since the octal numbers are derived from powers of 8, only eight symbols are utilized; the numerals 8 and 9 do not appear in this system. Octal numbers go consecutively from 7 to 10 and from 17 to 20 (see Figure 6.3). It should also be noted that each octal digit has its three-bit binary equivalent and this equivalence holds true regardless of the number of octal digits, so that octal 5 = binary 101, and octal 15 = binary 001 101, and octal 55 = binary 101 101.

To convert octal to binary, or binary to octal, one must simply express the octal number as a combination of three binary bits.

EXAMPLE: Convert octal 367 to binary.

$$3 = 011$$
$$6 = 110$$
$$7 = 111$$
$$367 = 011\ 110\ 111$$

EXAMPLE: Convert binary 100 101 001 to octal.

$$100 = 4$$
$$101 = 5$$
$$001 = 1$$
$$100\ 101\ 001 = 451$$

It is also possible to convert an octal number into a decimal equivalent by writing it as the sum of its powers of 8.

EXAMPLE: Convert octal 3075.2 to its decimal form.

$$
\begin{aligned}
3 \times 8^3 &= 3 \times 512 &&= 1536 \\
0 \times 8^2 &= 0 \times 64 &&= 0 \\
7 \times 8^1 &= 7 \times 8 &&= 56 \\
5 \times 8^0 &= 5 \times 1 &&= 5 \\
2 \times 8^{-1} &= 2 \times 0.125 &&= 0.250 \\
\hline
&&& 1597.250
\end{aligned}
$$

8^n	n	8^{-n}
1	0	1.0
8	1	0.125
64	2	0.015 625
512	3	0.001 953
4,096	4	0.000 244
32,768	5	0.000 031

FIGURE 6.4 Positive and negative powers of eight.

6.1.4 *Binary-coded Decimal.* Computers operate most efficiently using a binary code. The electronic circuitry is simpler, and the calculation can proceed at a faster rate if the computer is designed to operate with binary rather than decimal numbers. Input data are typically in decimal format, however; and so are the output data. For the human operator, conversion from decimal to binary is tedious, time-consuming, and subject to error. The computer would require additional circuitry to do its own converting, and this would tend to increase the size, complexity, and cost of the equipment. The solution to this dilemma was the development and utilization of a compromise and combinatory code called the "binary-coded decimal" (BCD). In this BCD system, the decimal number is converted to binary on a digit-by-digit basis using 4-bit binary equivalents for each decimal digit. Thus 379 would be expressed as 0011 0111 1001. In pure binary, 379 would be 101 111 011. Both pure binary and binary-coded decimal are based on a two-symbol system, but the conventions that give meaning to these symbols are different and should not be confused. To the human operator, the main advantage of the binary-coded decimal system is that conversion from one system to another can be made by inspection. Computer conversion is handled on a digit-by-digit basis and requires very simple circuitry. Yet this code provides the computer with the capability for performing calculations in binary arithmetic, with its attendant advantages of simplicity and speed.

6.1.5 *Biquinary*. Several forms of biquinary codes are in use. The name applies to a code in which a single bit represents the quantity 5, and three or more other bits represent quantities 0 through 4. In the classic system, the biquinary code requires seven positions to represent a decimal digit. Two of these positions, the binary component, have an assigned value of 0 or 5. The other five, or quinary, positions have values of 0, 1, 2, 3, and 4. The abacus is a familiar use of one variation on this biquinary code.

	Decimal value	0	1	2	3	4	5	6	7	8	9
Binary {	0	1	1	1	1	1	0	0	0	0	0
	5	0	0	0	0	0	1	1	1	1	1
Quinary {	0	1	0	0	0	0	1	0	0	0	0
	1	0	1	0	0	0	0	1	0	0	0
	2	0	0	1	0	0	0	0	1	0	0
	3	0	0	0	1	0	0	0	0	1	0
	4	0	0	0	0	1	0	0	0	0	1

FIGURE 6.5 Biquinary code.

Figure 6.5 illustrates how numerical data can be represented in biquinary. For example, the number 7 requires a binary code 5, plus a quinary code 2. The coding of alphabetic data requires two biquinary words. The 90-column punched card of the Remington Rand UNIVAC division uses a modified biquinary code.

6.2 BINARY ARITHMETIC

We all know how to perform the basic decimal arithmetic operations, but how does one calculate in binary? Actually, it is very simple, for we use only 1's and 0's.

6.2.1 *Addition*. The basic operations for binary addition are illustrated in Figure 6.6.

ADDITION TABLE
$0 + 0 = 0$ $0 + 1 = 1$ $1 + 0 = 1$ $1 + 1 = 0$ and carry 1 $1 + 1 + 1 = 1$ and carry 1

FIGURE 6.6

As one would expect in any system of addition, $0 + 0 = 0$, and $0 + 1 = 1$. In binary, because there are only two symbols, when we add $1 + 1$ we do not get 2 (for this does not exist). Rather, $1 + 1 = 0$, and it is necessary to carry 1, i.e., add 1 to the next column on the left. Should that column contain a $1 + 1$, and we add 1, we are in effect adding $1 + 1 + 1$ which equals 1, with 1 to carry. An example will make this clear.

EXAMPLE: Add the following binary numbers.

Binary		Decimal equivalent
100 110		38
001 111		15
110 101	=	53

6.2.2 *Subtraction*. Subtraction is equally simple, and the rules are the same as those used in decimal subtraction.

BINARY SUBTRACTION TABLE
$0 - 0 = 0$ $1 - 0 = 1$ $1 - 1 = 0$ $0 - 1 = 1$ and borrow 1

FIGURE 6.7

EXAMPLE: Subtract the following binary numbers.

Binary		Decimal equivalent
101 011		43
010 110		22
010 101	=	21

6.2.3 *Multiplication*. Binary multiplication is similar to decimal multiplication as the table and example illustrate.

BINARY MULTIPLICATION TABLE
$0 \times 0 = 0$
$0 \times 1 = 0$
$1 \times 0 = 0$
$1 \times 1 = 1$

FIGURE 6.8

EXAMPLE: Multiply the following binary numbers.

Binary	Decimal equivalent
100 110	38
101	5

```
    100 110
  0 000 00
 10 011 0
 10 111 110        =        190
```

6.2.4 Division. Division is reduced to a process of successively subtracting the divisor from the dividend. If the result of the subtraction yields a positive remainder, a 1 is written in the quotient. If the remainder is negative; i.e., if the divisor is too large and cannot be subtracted, then a 0 is placed in the quotient.

BINARY DIVISION TABLE
$0 \div 1 = 0$
$1 \div 1 = 1$
(Division by 0 is not allowed).

FIGURE 6.9

EXAMPLE: Divide the following binary numbers.

Binary   *Decimal equivalent*
1 000 001 $\div$ 1 101 $65 \div 13 = 5$

```
              101
  1 101/1 000 001
        110 1
        001 101
          1 101
              0
```

6.3   BOOLEAN NOTATIONS AND COMPUTER CIRCUITRY

Section 6.2 has shown how the basic arithmetic operations of addition, subtraction, multiplication, and division can be accomplished in the binary system. It has also been stated that the basic reason for using binary numbers is to simplify the electronic circuitry of the computer. It is therefore appropriate to examine a computer circuit and to determine how the process of addition is actually accomplished in the computer. But first it is necessary to learn a few symbols of logical diagraming. These symbols provide a type of shorthand notation for expressing the function of a circuit without having to draw the complete circuit diagram. The specific symbolic notation most often applied to digital computer systems is called "Boolean algebra." It was devised by George Boole, an English mathematician, in 1849 and is really a system of symbolic logic. Its application to computers is a recent development and is based upon the fact that Boolean algebra deals with functions that are either true or not true; i.e., it deals with binary conditions and therefore conveniently describes the logical circuitry of digital computers.

Without going into excessive detail, it can be briefly stated that in this application of Boolean algebra, alphabetic characters are used to represent the electrical impulses, and other symbols represent the interrelationship of the signals. For example, A and B are designated as signals. The absence of these signals can then be indicated by $\overline{A}$ and $\overline{B}$, variously read as "A bar" or "not A."

If the presence of either of two input signals yields an output signal, a condition exists which can be expressed by the following Boolean notation: $A \cup B = C$. This is read as "A or B equals C." On the other hand, if both A and B must be present in order to produce an output signal then $A \cap B = C$ is the Boolean description of that condition. It is read "A and B equals C." In diagraming the logical operation of digital computer circuits, a few special symbols based upon the Boolean equations have been devised. These are illustrated in Figure 6.10. The OR circuit will produce an output signal if there is an input on either A or B. In order for a signal to appear at the output of an AND gate, input signals must be present at both A and B. If the AND gate is combined with an INHIBITING INPUT signal device, then an output will be produced if and only if there is an input signal on A and no input for B, or vice versa.

These three types of units can be combined to form a logical diagram of a *half adder* circuit, a basic computer circuit for performing binary

OR circuit

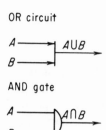

AND gate

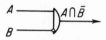

AND gate with inhibiting input

$A \cap \bar{B}$

Half adder

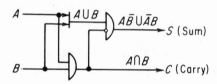

FIGURE 6.10 Logic diagram of a half adder. (Courtesy of the RCA
Service Company.)

addition. When a signal is applied to either input A or input B, an output
signal is produced at the sum output line.

$$A \cup B = S$$

In binary addition, this represents $0 + 1 = 1$ or $1 + 0 = 1$. A signal
applied to both inputs A and B would be the same as adding $1 + 1$, and
the answer should be 0 and carry one; that is, no signal should appear
at the "sum" output, but one should appear at the "carry" output. Following the various possible inputs in the diagram of the half adder, it
will be seen that if there are inputs at both A and B, then there will be
but one output to "carry."

In Boolean algebra terminology, this can be expressed as follows:

$$(A \cup B) \cap (\overline{A \cap B}) = A\bar{B} \cup \bar{A}B = S$$

The expression above is read as A or B, but not both A and B, equals A
and not B, or not A and B, which equals S, or sum.

$$A \cap B = C$$

means that if there is an input at both A and B, there will only be an output at C, or carry.

The half adder is one of the circuits used in the arithmetic unit of the digital computer. Other circuits provide the capability of performing other calculations. For our purposes, it is enough to know that both people and computers can calculate in binary arithmetic.

6.4   CODING INFORMATION

It has been shown that numerical concepts can be represented in a binary as well as in a decimal convention and that the computer can manipulate and perform arithmetic operation with binary numbers. Obviously, information must first be read into the computer, and this is accomplished by means of the various input devices. These data recording media can now be re-examined in order to study the methods used for coding information.

6.4.1 *80-Column Punched Card.* The 80-column card with rectangular holes is one of the most popular devices for recording data. The card contains 80 vertical columns and twelve rows. The twelve positions in each column, i.e., the rows, contain the decimal digits 0 through 9 (with 9 being in the row nearest to the bottom edge of the card). The uppermost two rows, sometimes called X (row 11) and Y (row 12), are the zone positions. In actual practice, the 0 row may serve the dual role of both a numeric value and a zone position.

From this brief description and illustration (Figure 6.11), it is clear that the numerals 0 through 9 can be represented, in this code, by a single punch in the proper row. To represent alphabetic data—i.e., the letters of the alphabet and other nonnumerical symbols—two punches in a single vertical column are necessary. The letters A through I are coded by punching the twelfth zone and the numerical location 1 through 9 respectively. For the letters J through R, the eleventh row and again the numerical positions 1 through 9 are used. To code S through Z, zone 0 and positions 2 through 9 are used. Special characters, such as $+$, $-$, $\%$, $*$, etc., can be coded by using unique combinations of two or three punches, such as zone 12, 11, and number 1. In this manner, all numerical, alphabetic, and special characters can be represented by the 80-column punched card code.

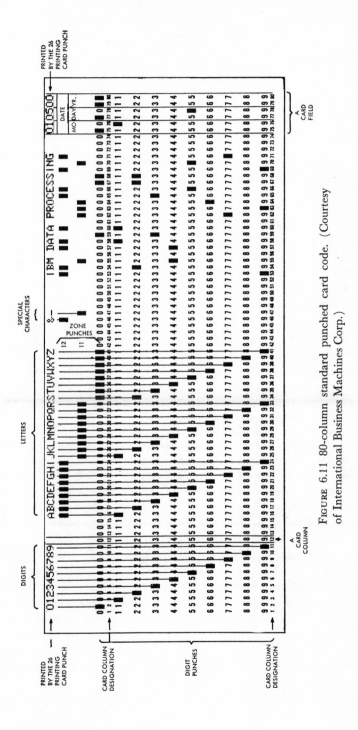

FIGURE 6.11 80-column standard punched card code. (Courtesy of International Business Machines Corp.)

The holes are punched by a special card punch machine and interpreted by a card reader. In planning the coding of information onto a card, certain columns are reserved for specific information. Thus, columns 1 through 4 may be used for an identification code number. Age may be put in columns 5 and 6, sex in 7, etc. In the illustration, columns 75–80 were reserved for the date. Should more than 80 columns be necessary, the record can be continued by using additional cards. Continuity would be established by means of identification and sequence numbers.

Storing data by means of holes punched in cards has many advantages. It is simple and accurate, for the punches can be verified. The coded data can be printed directly onto the card as the holes are punched, facilitating identification. The cards can also be sorted into many sequences or arrangements on the basis of the data; thus it is possible to sort alphabetically by name, numerically by age, by test score, etc. By use of the card accounting machines, arithmetic operations can be performed and reports printed, all derived from the little holes in the cards. For electronic data processing, however, direct card input is too slow, and the cards are used most often as an external supplementary storage device.

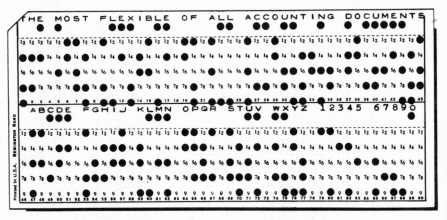

FIGURE 6.12 90-Column card code. (Courtesy Remington Rand UNIVAC Division, Sperry Rand Corporation.)

6.4.2 90-Column Punched Card. This card is arranged into two identical banks of 45 columns each. Each bank has six rows numbered as follows: 0, 1_2, 3_4, 5_6, 7_8, 9. A hole punched into the row labeled 1_2 may represent, or so it would appear, either the odd or the even digit. To make the differentiation positive, the following convention is used: a single punched hole serves to represent the 0 and all odd digits. Two punches are used to represent the even digits: one punch in the row as marked, and the other punch in 9. Figure 6.12 illustrates this method.

To represent the number 5, one punch in the 5_6 row is all that is necessary, but to represent the even digit 6, two punches are required; one in row 5_6 and the other in row 9. Alphabetical data is equally easy to code, although, as can be seen from the illustration, three punches are often required to represent a single letter.

All the advantages, previously described, of the 80-column card are equally true of the 90-column card. The choice is dictated by the manufacturer's preference and equipment.

6.4.3 Punched Paper Tape. One of the few disadvantages mentioned in connection with punched cards concerns the fixed size of the card. Each card can contain only a limited amount of information, and it is sometimes necessary to use more than one card to record all the pertinent data. Punched paper tape is a continuous recording medium not subject to the limitations of fixed record size. The only restriction concerns the size of the reel on which the tape is to be stored. Paper tape offers other important advantages: the record is less bulky and easier to store; it can be read at a fast rate; and by using a Flexowriter or similar device, punched paper tape may be coded at the same time the copy is being typewritten.

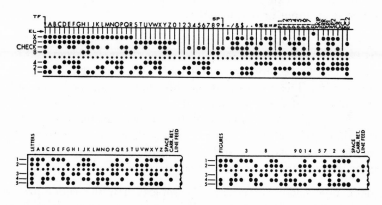

FIGURE 6.13 Punched paper tape codes. (Courtesy of International Business Machines Corp.)

Data are recorded as a special arrangement of punched holes along the length of the tape. Figure 6.13 illustrates portions of coded five- and eight-channel tape. Other types use six and seven channels. Although the specific codes may vary, the system is essentially the same. Using five channels, a maximum of 32 combinations of holes (i.e., $2^5 = 32$) is possible. But if one of these combinations is used to indicate a shift—

comparable to the shift from lower to upper case in a typewriter—the number of possible code positions can be nearly doubled. Note the different combinations of holes for letters and figures. This code also has the additional advantage of providing a method for indicating the space between words, carriage return, line feed, and a large selection of special characters. The five-channel code is also used for sending teletype messages, which makes this form of data input particularly valuable in an integrated data processing system where information may have to be sent from the branch office in one city to the main office in another via teletype.

6.4.4 Magnetic Tape.

The information coded on cards and paper tape is visible to the human eye as holes in the recording media. In magnetic tape recording, we lose this knowledge, for information is recorded by magnetizing selected areas on coated plastic tape. Once recorded, this information is retained permanently, if desired. Should the information no longer be useful, however, it can be erased and new data recorded on the same tape. This reuse capability results in considerable savings. Another advantage of magnetic tape recording is the speed at which data can be recorded and read. At the present time, magnetic tape provides a data system that can be directly and efficiently tied to the high-speed computer as an input or output device.

Magnetic tapes are available in different widths. One of the more popular sizes is $\frac{1}{2}$ inch wide and has seven recording channels. From 100 to 500 characters can be recorded on 1 inch of tape, depending upon the recording density. This means that the information punched onto one 80- or 90-column card could be stored in considerably less than 1 inch of tape. A full reel of tape contains 2400 feet and can be read at the rate of more than 100 inches per second. These figures provide some indication of the storage capacity and speed with which information can be made available to the computer for processing.

Magnetic tape codes are no more complex than the codes previously discussed. Figure 6.14 contains an illustration of a seven-bit alphameric code. The A and B zones of the tape code correspond approximately to the X and Y zones on the 80-column punched card and are used for recording nonnumerical data. Numbers are recorded in a four-bit binary-coded decimal system. Special symbols are used to identify the end of a word and the end of the message. A valuable feature of this form of tape recording is the incorporation of a check or parity bit. In the code illustrated, "even parity" is used; i.e., the number of magnetized bits in any vertical column must add up to an even number. If in the course of processing the tape, the parity check does not prove out and a column contains an odd number of bits, the computer alerts the operator to the fact that an error has occurred. This check helps insure against the loss of data as a result of mechanical difficulties in the input-output units, and it provides accurate information quickly accessible for computer processing.

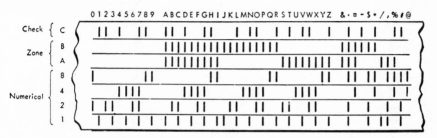

FIGURE 6.14 Magnetic tape code. (Courtesy of International Business Machines Corp.)

The different coding techniques described in the preceding sections enable one to represent alphabetical and numerical information in a form amenable to automatic data processing.

Chapter 7
PROGRAMING FUNDAMENTALS AND
MACHINE LANGUAGE

Chapters 5 and 6 described the physical structure of a computer and the methods of coding data for machine use. They also presented some basic principles of the decimal numbering system and introduced other numbering systems—binary, octal, binary-coded decimal, and biquinary —as being more useful in automatic data processing. Besides having the coded data available, however, the computer needs a program of operating instructions. This chapter will discuss the programer, concepts of programing, and coding techniques.

7.1 THE PROGRAMER

The profession of programing has existed for less than two decades. Those presently in this relatively new field have varying educational backgrounds. Mathematics and engineering predominate, and with reason, for a knowledge of mathematics and a familiarity with digital computer hardware is desirable for optimal utilization of the computer's capabilities. In addition, the programer must understand the content of the problem to be solved. In the past, most computers were used to solve

112

mathematical and engineering problems. Today, computers have much wider applicability, and more people are learning to program and use these machines. This is especially true of the research scientist who has special problems to solve. In order to plan his work effectively, he must have some knowledge of programing, although he does not have to become an expert coder. Fortunately, the modest programing goals of the scientist user can be met with relative ease.

Programing can be divided into four phases: analysis, program design, coding, and testing. A brief discussion of each of these will help clarify the functions of the programer.

7.1.1 *Analysis.* In seeking to solve any problem, the first step usually consists of making a precise formulation of the question. This is a most difficult step, and an adequate solution requires a thorough knowledge of the content area, a knowledge of the modern mathematical techniques applicable to the specific type of problem, and enough familiarity with computers to recognize how this equipment can be most economically

113

applied to the solution of the problem. Let us assume, for example, that as behavioral scientists we are given the task of investigating creativity by simulating the process on a computer. This is the problem as it would be presented by a researcher. How would we go about solving it? As a first step, the problem must be formulated more precisely and the area of investigation delimited. Operational definitions of such terms as "creativity" and "simulation" must be worked out. The hypotheses must be clearly stated, along with the experimental design and the statistical techniques that would be used to reduce the data to be collected.

The analysis of a problem for computer programing requires knowledge far beyond specific programing skills. The "system analyst," as he is often called, must be an expert in his field as well as in computer techniques. Business organizations frequently call in consultants—operations research personnel—to help in the program analysis phase of the work. In scientific research, this phase remains the responsibility of the principal investigator and cannot be delegated. Since one cannot be an expert in all fields, however, the problem formulation phase of the program preparation is usually carried on by a team including trained mathematical programers. Their function is formulating the problem in mathematical terms and designing a mathematical model capable of solution.

7.1.2 *Program Design.* Once the programer has an operational statement of the problem, he proceeds to reanalyze the formulation in terms of the sequence of computer operations to be performed. The solution of a problem by means of a computerized data processing system is comparable to a factory production line. The input, or raw material, is the data to be processed; the output is the finished product or solution. The data processing system, which is science's production line and factory, transmutes the raw materials into the finished product. The programer determines the operations that are to be performed on the input in order to achieve the desired output.

Part of the task is making efficient use of time and equipment. Hence, the programer is concerned with simplifying the coding, reducing execution time, and minimizing the number of storage registers required. In order to help obtain an overview of the entire problem and, as an aid in visualizing the steps involved in the solution of the problem, the programer commonly designs a program flow chart. This chart is a visual presentation of the movement of data through the computer. It labels each stage of the process and the operations that are to be performed. It also indicates the task assigned to each computer component at every stage of the operation. Thus the flow chart helps the programer to systematize his thinking and optimize the use of his equipment. The preparation of a flow chart is a salient feature in program design. In large organizations where there is a division of work, the person classified as a programer is responsible only for flow chart preparation. The formulator does the analysis; the programer prepares the flow charts; the coder writes out the machine instructions.

Flow charts must be detailed and comprehensive, but the level of detail is determined by the purpose for which the chart is drawn, and this varies. A management level, or systems analysis, flow chart graphically summarizes the major routines of the system and provides a comprehensive picture of the data-processing stages. This type of flow chart provides an over-all systems view of the problem; however, it is not detailed enough for coding. The detailed flow chart, as the name implies, contains a complete analysis of all the steps, in their proper sequence, which are to be followed in order to achieve the desired solution. In this detailed flow chart, the physical form of records (punched cards, paper or magnetic tape, etc.) is shown by special symbols, and there are additional chart symbols for the hardware (drum memory, processor, printer, etc.) and the processing operations. This chapter and succeeding chapters on computer applications use flow charts designed for systems analysis and not detailed coding.

The chart in Figure 7.1 and others like it have been in circulation for some years. It is part of the folklore of the programing profession, and is of unknown origin. Although somewhat facetious, it does illustrate a number of important aspects of flow charting. Looking first at the upper right-hand corner, we see a flow chart that is highly oversimplified and provides insufficient information. Getting up in the morning is a fairly complex process, and it is precisely this process that we wish to chart and specify. Therefore, a single box labeled "get up" is inadequate for our purpose. Looking now at the main chart, we see depicted some of the procedures and behavior involved in getting up. The behavior is not linear, for it involves certain repetitions or loops, as in the case of groaning and shaking wife. There are also certain decisions to be made. These decision points are recorded as questions in oval-shaped enclosures. Note, too, that this system-oriented flow chart does not indicate the precise means by which the computer would be programed to make the decision.

Flow Charting a Program for Decision Making. A flow chart indicating the type of logical problem solving and decision making which can be performed by a computer is illustrated in Figure 7.2. Let us once

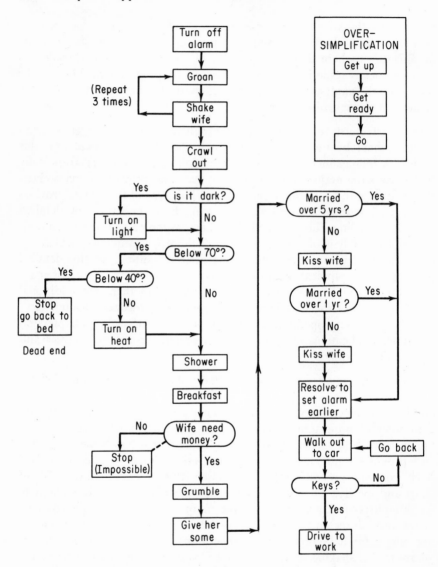

FIGURE 7.1 Flow chart: How to get to work in the morning. (A similar flow chart appeared in McCracken.[21])

again pick up the adventures of our friend who woke up in the morning, kissed his wife good-bye, and walked to the car with keys in hand. He has three keys on the key ring: a house key, a garage key, and a car key. The keys are easily distinguishable by size. The car key is the smallest. The man—a man who thinks for himself—knows which key fits into

THE KEY PROBLEM

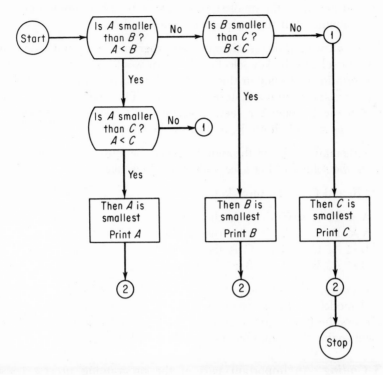

FIGURE 7.2 Flow chart for the key problem program.* (Courtesy Remington Rand UNIVAC Division, Sperry Rand Corporation.)

his automobile ignition. Our problem is programing the computer to select from among the three keys the one that fits the car. We know that the three keys are of different sizes, and the car key is the smallest of the three, so that logically the solution hinges upon comparing the three keys and selecting the smallest.

This seems simple enough, but the question remains of *how* we shall do this. How can the computer "look at," sense, or measure, each of the three keys, and then compare the measurements, decide which is the smallest, and select that one? One possibility is to put into the computer the size characteristics of the car key, use this as a standard, and compare all given keys to this standard. The key that matches would be the one selected. Another possibility is to compare two of the three keys and

* The key problem is described in "Programing a New Profession For You," Remington Rand UNIVAC, Educational Series 2, 1958.

eliminate the larger, compare the remaining two, again eliminating the larger, and thus have the smallest, or car key, left. There are undoubtedly other possibilities, but for our purposes, these suffice.

At this point, we ask our mathematician programer to help decide which method for solving the key selection problem would be the most efficient. The criteria for efficiency in this case are simplified coding, reduced execution time, and minimized storage facilities. The mathematician makes a mathematical model for each possibility and selects the simplest. In this case, the second choice is, by far, the best solution.

Our mathematician is not through, however; he must write a set of equations for the solution. Let's see what these look like.

Let A, B, and C = the three keys

a. $A < B$, $A < C$ $\therefore$ A is the smallest
b. $A < B$, $C < A$ $\therefore$ C is the smallest
c. $B < A$, $C < B$ $\therefore$ C is the smallest
d. $B < A$, $B < C$ $\therefore$ B is the smallest

The systems analysis of the problem ends with the writing of the mathematical model of the problem and its solution. The program designer now draws the flow chart, Figure 7.2, and the coder writes the program that will enable the computer to solve the problem.

7.1.3 *Coding.* An important part of the programing process consists of translating the mathematical formulation of a problem into machine language. Coding is exacting and detailed, but it is not difficult. To understand coding, one needs to be aware that the computer, in contrast to the human being, cannot think for itself. In order to function at all, the computer must be given precise instructions for every operation. Writing these instructions is the coder's job.

Computer instructions are written as a combination of letters and numbers in accordance with a predetermined code. This code differs for the different computer systems, although the basic concept remains the same. The coder must be well versed in the logic of the computer system, the purpose, the use of each code symbol. He must follow the machine logic precisely and systematically.

7.1.4 *Testing.* Once the program has been coded, it must be tested to insure that it operates properly and arrives at the correct solution to the problem. Program testing, or "debugging" as it is usually called, involves trying the program in a properly operating computer and observing the results at various stages in the computation. Occasionally the program will not "cycle"; i.e., an incorrect instruction will cause the computer to stop prematurely. The error must be located and corrected. In other instances, the program may go into a continuous loop, repeating the same few instructions over and over, and not process all the required data. As can be imagined, many types of coding errors result in improper cycling of the program of instructions. All of these errors must be located and corrected.

After determining that the program does cycle, it must be tested to insure that the results of computer processing are accurate. One might process a problem having a known solution by the, as yet, untested program. If the end results agree, it can be assumed that the program is accurate. To be sure, this assumption will not necessarily hold true in all cases. It is possible for a program to function properly with one set of data and not with another, for there may be an aspect of the program that was not exercised by the trial data. These intermittent errors are very difficult to locate. The situation is analogous to the problem faced by an automobile owner who takes his car to a garage because he hears a "knock." When the mechanic drives the car, the "knock" is not there. To locate this type of difficulty, more rigorous systematic testing than simply comparing results is necessary. A new program is checked by using programed test routines, which print out the contents of selected registers as each instruction in the program is completed, and by other similar techniques.

The four phases of system analysis, program design, coding, and testing together constitute the programing process from the start to the finished product.

7.2 COMPUTER WORDS

Both the program of instructions and the data to be processed are stored in the internal memory of the computer. The basic unit of information is the computer word, which is a series of binary digits stored in a register. Each register has its own address. Commonly, the size of the computer word, i.e., the number of bits, is constant for a given computer, but different machines may have larger or smaller words. Computer words are of two kinds: instruction words and data words. In memory, these are indistinguishable from each other. If an instruction word is entered into the arithmetic unit, it will be treated as a data word. When the instruction word enters into the control unit, however, it is interpreted as an instruction and executed. Having instructions and data in the same format adds to the versatility of the computer, for instruction words can be processed and modified in the same manner as data words. This is another way of saying that the computer can be programed to modify its own instructions—an extremely interesting concept and one that has many ramifications.

7.2.1 *Instruction Word Format.* Computer instructions can be classified, on the basis of function, into three general categories: transfer of data, arithmetic operations, and branching or conditional instructions. At the start of the computing process, the data and the instructions for solving the problem have been coded on to external storage media, such as punched cards, paper, or magnetic tape. *Transfer instructions* direct the transfer of information from these storage devices to the internal memory system on which the computer can operate. This category of instruction also transfers data out of internal storage to output tapes or printers. Other uses involve the transfer of information from the main memory area to the arithmetic registers, between registers, and back to memory.

Instructions for *arithmetic operations* direct the computer to add, subtract, multiply, and divide. Normally, computation moves sequentially from one instruction to the next on the program list. *Conditional instructions* provide a means for interrupting sequential processing and allowing the program to skip to a designated place in the list of instructions. Conditional instructions compare the contents of two registers, and the branching is contingent upon the results of this comparison. For example, instructions may be written to compare A and B, and if A is larger, continue the normal sequence; but if A is smaller, branch to a predetermined instruction, which would then start a new sequence (see Figure 7.2).

Computer instructions consist of two parts: the operation and the address. The operation portion specifies the action the computer is to perform; the address specifies the location in memory of the operand—i.e., the data word on which the operation is to be performed.

Instructions of the type described may be written in the following form:

One-address word format

OP	*a*

The rectangular box represents the word as stored in a register. "OP" stands for operation, and "*a*" for address. This schema is called a "one-address" word format, or one-address logic, and the instructions are interpreted as, for example, add (the operation) the contents of register "a" (the address) to the accumulator. It is implicit in the logic of this system that the results of the operation will be retained in the accumulator until transferred. The *accumulator* is a working storage register located in the arithmetic unit. Having performed the specified operation, the control unit locates the following instruction in the next address location; that is, if the first instruction was in memory location "m," then the next one would be in location $(m + 1)$. To accomplish this sequencing of instructions, the machine stores the address of the instruction being executed and, by means of a sequence counter, adds a "1" to that address in order to obtain the address location of the next instruction.

The basic components of the computer are the input and output units, the storage unit, the control unit, and the arithmetic unit (see Figure 5.1). Let us examine the basic computer operating cycle in terms of the function of each of these components.

The *input and output units* are peripheral equipment used to bring data into the main storage or to transfer or print out information from storage.

The *storage unit* is the repository of all information, both instructions and data.

The *control unit* contains an instruction register. Most machines also contain one or more sequence or index registers.

The *arithmetic unit* contains one or more accumulator registers.

The computation cycle is regulated by the control unit and is divided into a "fetch" phase and an "execute" phase operating as follows:

Fetch: The fetch phase is under the guidance of the sequence register; the address of the next instruction is located; the information (namely, the operation to be performed and the address of the operand) is transferred into the instruction register; and the operand is fetched.

Execute: The execute phase is under the direction of the instruction register which sees to it that the instructions are carried out and the sequence register updated.

If one wanted to add X to Y using one-address logic, the sequence of instructions would be:

Fetch: Transfer the instruction to the instruction register.

Execute: Clear the accumulator and add the number X to it. Add 1 to the sequence register.

Fetch: Transfer the next instruction to the instruction register.

Execute: Add Y to the accumulator.

The sum of $X + Y$ is now stored in the accumulator. If we were interested in this sum, our next instruction would be to transfer the contents of the accumulator to a specified register located in the main memory storage. Then, if we wished, we could have the contents of that register printed out.

Keep these points clearly in mind: the control unit contains the instruction to be executed and the sequencing needed to locate the next instruction. The computational work is done by the accumulator register of the arithmetic unit; this work includes the arithmetic processing and also the various logical tests and branching instructions.

The IBM 709, Burroughs 220, and Packard-Bell PB 250 are examples of computers that use a one-address word format. Instruction word formats differ in other machines. The more common systems and their interpretations are listed below. In the examples, the operation part of the word (OP) will, for purposes of simplicity, be considered as an add instruction.

One-and-one-half-address word format *

OP	a_1	a_2

In the one-address format, the instructions are stored and processed in sequence; in the one-and-one-half-address format (since instruction words are not stored sequentially), the location of the next instruction word must be specified. IBM 650 and UNIVAC Solid State 80 and 90 computers use the one-and-one-half-address logic.

Two-address word format †

OP	a_1	a_2

Even though the word format is the same for both the one-and-one-half- and the two-address words, the computer logic that interprets the instructions is different. The IBM 305 and the RCA 301 use the two-address instruction word.

---

* Add the contents of address a_1 to the accumulator, and locate the next instruction in address a_2.

† Add the contents of a_1 to the contents of a_2 and store the result in the accumulator.

Three-address word format *

OP	a_1	a_2	a_3

Three-address logic is used by Honeywell 800 and National Cash Register 304.

Four-address word format †

OP	a_1	a_2	a_3	a_4

The National Cash Register 390 Data Processing System uses the four-address word format.

The very diversity of instruction word formats in use by different manufacturers indicates that no one system has a clear advantage over any other. The one-address machine operates at a relatively fast rate, but requires a number of instructions to perform a particular function, such as adding two numbers together. A three-address machine could perform this same addition in one instruction, but the over-all execution time might be slower. At any rate, for most machines, the computer logic is fixed, and it is the responsibility of the programer to know his computer and to make optimal use of its capabilities.

7.2.2 Data Word Format. In contrast to the relative complexity of the instruction word, the data word format is simplicity itself. The sign and the magnitude constitute the only information necessary to represent numerical data. The data word can be represented schematically:

Sign	Magnitude

So, with reference to the instruction, "Add the contents of a_1 to the accumulator," a data word or number, in the form indicated above, would be the contents stored in address a_1.

Depending upon the computer, the data word format can become somewhat more complex by using variable word length configurations, floating point numbers, overflow bits, and similar items. Each computer has its own special idiosyncrasies, which the programer must learn and use in coding the machine.

* Add the contents of a_1 to the contents of a_2 and store the result in a_3.
† Add the contents of a_1 to the contents of a_2, store the result in a_3, and locate the next instruction in a_4.

7.3   PROGRAMING LANGUAGE

Machine computation is carried on by means of a set of programing instructions that precisely define every step in the computational process. As was pointed out, the program must be written in a code called the "machine language." Each of various computers has its own unique machine language, and a program written for one type of computer does not operate in another machine. All this adds to the complexity of programing. To help alleviate this difficulty, a number of more abstract symbolic programing languages have been developed, enabling the user to communicate with many types of computers. Programs are written in the symbolic language and then translated automatically, by the computer itself, into the specific machine language to process the data.

Machine language consists of the specific codes and formats directly interpretable by a given computer. In most cases, the representation of alphabetical or numerical data in machine language is simply the binary expression for each letter or number. Nevertheless, enough variation exists in the word format of the different computers to make the machine language relatively unique. In dealing with instructional codes, there is even greater variability. The very strangeness and preciseness of machine languages tend to decrease computational flexibility and cause clerical errors in programing.

Problem-oriented languages are designed to be more meaningful to the human writing the program than to the machine processing the codes. For example, the instruction "add" in machine language might be written as binary 23 (010 111), but in problem-oriented language it would be written as ADD. Obviously, the latter symbol is easier for a person to understand and remember. The task of programing any given machine is simplified by this procedure and made relatively independent of the computer hardware. Before executing the program, the symbolic instructions must be translated into machine code. The translation is accomplished by a large set of machine-language instructions, which convert the problem-oriented language symbols into machine language. Writing this translator program is a very difficult and time-consuming process requiring skilled programers, but once available, it can be used with ease. FORTRAN, coined from "*for*mula *trans*lation," is such a problem-oriented language developed for the IBM 700 series computers. An example of its use will be given in a subsequent section of this chapter.

At present, each problem-oriented language requires a translator to convert it into a suitable machine language. In addition, since not all computers can use the same problem-oriented language, various manufacturers develop their own versions of these symbolic languages. The entire procedure is very inefficient, because it requires many translators and monopolizes the talents of skilled programers (who are in short supply) to develop these automatic translation programs. One possible solution to this dilemma lies in the creation of a common computer-oriented language. This would be a synthetic language into which all problem-oriented languages would be translated, and from which all machine languages would be translated.

The present procedures can be diagramed as follows:

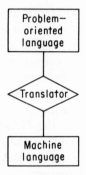

It has been suggested that a more generally applicable, and therefore more efficient system, would have the following form:

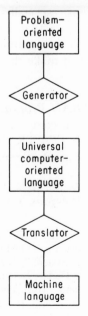

A program written in problem-oriented language would be processed, by means of a "generator" program, into the universal computer-oriented language. Since a number of problem-oriented languages exist, different generator programs would be required to convert them into the universal language, which would be the same for all computers. When a given computer was selected for use, the universal computer-oriented language would be processed through a translator program into the proper machine language. The universal type of language has, as its main advantage, potential ability to make every computer program, originally written in a problem-oriented language, usable in all computers.

The concept is excellent, and although many difficulties must be overcome before it becomes a reality, the initial research is already under way. At the System Development Corporation, a special research project called UNCOL is investigating the programing feasibility of a *un*iversal *c*omputer-*o*riented *l*anguage. Other organizations are also working toward the standardization of computer languages. One of the most significant of these efforts was the proposal made by the ACM (Association for Computing Machinery) and the GAMM (German-Swiss Applied Mathematical Society) for an international standard *algo*rithmic *l*anguage (ALGOL) for use in scientific numerical work. In a similar vein, a conference on data system languages, sponsored by the U.S. Department of Defense, helped prepare the specifications for COBOL—*c*ommon *b*usiness *o*riented *l*anguage—for business data processing.

For the average computer user, especially the scientist who is less interested in programing techniques than in the computer applications, these developments in symbolic programing languages help take the drudgery out of programing and make the computer a more useful and usable tool.

7.3.1 *An Illustrative FORTRAN Program.* To illustrate the ease and simplicity with which a modern, complex, high-speed, electronic digital computer can be programed, a FORTRAN program for the IBM 709 is analyzed in detail.* The program chosen as illustration involves the

---

* The author is indebted to Mr. John Tauchi, Research Associate in Biomedical Statistics at the Medical School, University of California at Los Angeles, for his help in preparing this program.

For additional information on FORTRAN programing see "IBM General Information Manual, Programer's Primer for FORTRAN Automatic Coding System for the IBM 704 Data Processing System," Form 32–0306–1; "IBM Reference Manual 709 FORTRAN Automatic Coding System for the IBM 709 Data Processing System," Form C28–6054–1; and "IBM Programer's Reference Manual for FORTRAN," Form 32–7026.

calculation of an arithmetic mean, variance, and standard deviation for a set of data. Although these calculations are simple enough to be performed on a desk calculator, they can become tedious and time-consuming. At any rate, the example is a useful one to illustrate FOR-TRAN programing. FORTRAN is a problem-oriented language designed for use with the IBM 704 and 709 data processing systems. It enables the programer to write instructions in a relatively simple language, which resembles ordinary usage. This FORTRAN language is then automatically translated into an efficient 709 machine language by use of a special program called a compiler. The programer need not know, and does not use, the machine language.

As was pointed out earlier in this chapter, programing consists of four phases: analysis, program design, coding, and testing. Let us examine these phases in terms of the example.

7.3.1.1 *Analysis.* Analysis consists of the precise formulation of the problem and a design of a mathematical model to be used in its solution. The problem under consideration is the calculation of an arithmetic mean and standard deviation. The formulas for these calculations are already well known and no special analysis work is needed. The formulas selected are those designed for use with the original, ungrouped data.

$$\text{Arithmetic Mean: } M = \frac{\Sigma X}{N}$$

$$\text{Standard Deviation: } \sigma = \frac{1}{N}\sqrt{N\Sigma X^2 - (\Sigma X)^2}$$

$$\text{Variance: } \sigma^2 = \frac{N\Sigma X^2 - (\Sigma X)^2}{N^2}$$

$\Sigma =$ the sum of
$X =$ the individual measurements
$N =$ the number of cases
$\Sigma X^2 =$ each measurement squared and then summed
$(\Sigma X)^2 =$ all measurements summed and the total squared

7.3.1.2 *Program Design.* Program design involves the analysis of the mathematical formulas in terms of the computer operations to be performed. The flow chart represents the movement of the data through the computer. The flow chart as drawn (Figure 7.3) is more elaborate than necessary for FORTRAN coding. The chart shows each stage of the data processing as a discrete step. The FORTRAN language, how-

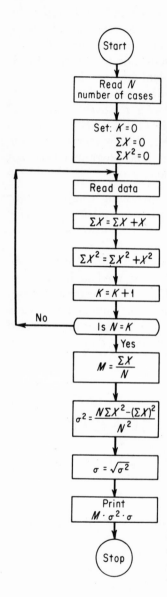

FIGURE 7.3 Flow chart of program to compute arithmetic mean, standard deviation, and variance.

ever, is powerful enough to combine a number of these steps, and the actual coding is simpler than the flow chart indicates. For example, the chart shows the reading into the computer of one item of data, i.e., one test score, at a time. In practice, six or ten scores are punched on one card and read into memory simultaneously and then processed in the same way. Nevertheless, for clarity each logically separate procedure is illustrated.

In examining the chart, we see that the first item of business after "start" is to read into memory the number of cases in the sample. Then three accumulator registers are set to zero. One (K) keeps a record of the number of data cards processed; a second accumulates the sum of X by adding the score value (X) to the ΣX accumulator; and the squared X value (X^2) is summed in the third register. When these steps have been completed, a test is made to determine whether the value of N equals the number of cards processed (K). If the two numbers are not equal, the computer control loops back to read in another data card and the process is repeated. When $N = K$, all the cases have been processed, and so the next step calls for the computation of the arithmetic mean (M). Then the value in the register containing ΣX is squared $(\Sigma X)^2$, and the value in the other accumulator (ΣX^2) is multiplied by N. All the figures needed to compute the variance and the standard deviation are now available, and so these statistics are computed. M, σ^2, and σ are printed and the machine stopped.

7.3.1.3 *Coding.* To write the coding for this problem in machine language would pose a fair-sized problem. The programer would have to assign each item of data in the sample to a particular storage location in memory and then transfer the information from memory to the accumulator for processing. A long series of instructions would be required. With the FORTRAN problem-oriented language, all this is unnecessary. One simply states the problem in accordance with the formal rules of FORTRAN, and the compiler program translates the statement into machine language.

	1	2 5	6	7 FORTRAN *program* 72	80
1	C			JØHN JØNES PRØGRAMER	
2	C			PRØGRAM TØ CALCULATE THE MEAN,	
3	C		1	VARIANCE, AND STANDARD DEVIATIØN	
4	*			FØRTRAN	
5				DIMENSIØN DATA (1000)	
6		900		FØRMAT (I 5)	
7		901		FØRMAT (5F 10.2)	
8		902		FØRMAT (3F 20.2)	
9				READ INPUT TAPE 5, 900, N	
10				READ INPUT TAPE 5, 901 (DATA (I), I = 1, N)	
11				SUMX = 0.0	
12				SUMXX = 0.0	
13				FLN = N	
14				DØ 10 I = 1, N	
15				SUMX = SUMX + DATA (I)	
16		010		SUMXX = SUMXX + DATA (I) ** 2	
17				AV = SUMX/FLN	
18				VAR = (FLN * SUMXX − SUMX ** 2)/	
			1	FLN ** 2	
19				STD = SQRTF (VAR)	
20				WRITE ØUTPUT TAPE 6, 902, AV, VAR, STD	
21				CALL EXIT	
22				END	

FIGURE 7.4 FORTRAN statement of program to compute arithmetic mean, standard deviation, and variance.

7.3.1.4 *Analysis of the FORTRAN Program.* All the alphabetical characters written in FORTRAN language must be in capital letters. The letters "I," "O," and "Z" are handwritten as I, $\emptyset$, and $\not Z$. The asterisk followed by FORTRAN signifies a message to the FORTRAN compiler indicating the start of the compilation. This form of notation is a FORTRAN convention standard throughout most of the country. A "C" punched in column 1 identifies the card as a comments card, which is not to be processed by the FORTRAN compiler, but is to be listed as part of the program printout.

Line   1 :   gives the name of the programer and other identifying data, if any.

Line   2 :   contains the title of the program.

Line   3 :   The 1 in column 6 indicates that the statement on this card is a continuation of the previous card. Up to nine continuation cards are allowed.

Line   4 :   is the word FØRTRAN, indicating that the translation is to be accomplished by the FORTRAN compiler.

Line   5 :   DIMENSIØN DATA (1000) : reserves 1000 memory locations for input data.

Line   6 :   900 FØRMAT (I 5) : means that the data are in the *I*nteger mode, literal notation, and occupy the first 5 columns on the punched card. This FORMAT is used to read in sample size; see line 9.

Line   7 :   901 FØRMAT (5 F 10.2) : means that there are 5 data items in the *F*loating point mode, literal notation; each variable occupying a *10*-column field; and there are 2 digits following the decimal point.

Line   8 :   902 FØRMAT (3 F 20.2) : means that there are 3 data items in the *F*loating point mode, literal notation; each variable occupying a *20*-column field; and there are 2 digits following the decimal point.

Line   9 :   READ INPUT TAPE 5, 900, N: names the Input Tape unit No. *5;* the *900* refers to the statement number at the associated FORMAT; *N* is the variable denoting the sample size.

Line 10 :   READ INPUT TAPE 5, 901 (DATA (I), I = 1, N): names the tape unit no. *5;* the *901* refers to the statement number of the associated FORMAT; and the rest of the statement indicates that a list of variables is read into the array labeled *DATA; I = 1* sets Index register *I* to *1*, and the index register is incremented until it reaches limit *N*, which is the sample size. This instruction reads all input data into the memory locations reserved by the statement on Line 5.

Line 11 :   SUMX = 0.0: is an arithmetic statement; *SUMX*, the expression to the left of the equal sign, is a variable meaning the sum of the X's. The equal sign means compute the value of the expression to the right of the equal sign and assign this value to the variable on the left of the equal sign.

The expression to the right of the equal sign, 0.0, is a constant chosen so as to convey a meaningful mathematical computation. This expression sets the value of $SUMX$ equal to zero at the start of the computations.

Line 12: SUMXX = 0.0: is an arithmetic statement and is interpreted in a manner similar to that of the preceding statement. $SUMXX$ is the sum of the squared X values. $SUMXX$ is set to zero at the start of the computations.

Line 13: FLN = N: is an arithmetic statement that converts N, originally written in the *I*nteger mode, into the *F*loating point mode for use in *F*loating point arithmetic.

Line 14: Dϕ 10 I = 1, N: is a *DO* statement which is an instruction for a loop or sequence of statements to be executed one or more times. It means *DO* all the following statements up to, and including, statement 10; set I (the *I*ndex register) = *1*, then repeat the process, incrementing the index by 1 each time the loop is repeated, until $I = N$ which would mean that all of the data in the sample had been processed. When $I = N$, the loop is broken, and the next instruction is the one following statement 10 which, in this case, would be on line 17.

Line 15: SUMX = SUMX + DATA (I): is an arithmetic statement and part of the *DO* loop. It is an instruction to read an item of *DATA* in the *I*nteger mode and to add this value to $SUMX$ which had been set to zero at the start of the problem. In the next iteration of the loop, a new value will be added to $SUMX$, and so on.

Line 16: SUMXX = SUMXX + DATA (I) **2: is referred to in the program (Line 14) as statement number 10. It is an arithmetic statement and is part of the *DO* loop. *DATA (I)* **2 is an instruction to read an item of *DATA*, written in the *I*nteger mode, and square it. The symbol ** indicates an exponential expression and the 2 specifies the power. The entire expression is an instruction to read the data, square the value, add it to $SUMXX$ (which had been started at zero). Then iterate and read the next value, etc.

Line 17: AV = SUMX/FLN: is an arithmetic statement in FOR-
TRAN for computing an arithmetic mean. *AV* is the
*AV*erage or mean which is obtained by dividing the sum
of the *X*'s by the sample size. $M = \Sigma X/N$.

Line 18: VAR = (FLN * SUM XX − SUM X **2)/FLN **2: is
an arithmetic statement containing the FORTRAN instructions for computing the *VAR*iance or, σ^2.

$$\sigma^2 = \frac{N\Sigma X^2 - (\Sigma X)^2}{N^2}$$

Note the use of a continuation card.

Line 19: STD = SQRTF(VAR): is an arithmetic statement which
says that the *ST*andard *D*eviation is to be obtained by taking
the *SQ*uare *Root*, using *F*loating point mode, of the
*VAR*iance: $\sigma = \sqrt{\sigma^2}$

Line 20: WRITE ØUTPUT TAPE 6, 902, AV, VAR, STD: is an
output statement and provides for the transmittal of information from computer memory to an output tape and
from there to the printed page. In this case, *TAPE* Unit *6*
is specified as the output tape. The variables to be written
on this tape are the *AV*erage, *VAR*iance, and *ST*andard
*D*eviation, and the spacing is to be as specified in FORMAT
902.

Line 22: CALL EXIT: is a termination statement used at the computer center for the subroutine that terminates the execution phase of the program and transfers control back to the
executive program. In this way, the next FORTRAN program can be processed without loss of computer time.

Line 23: END: is the statement used to conclude all instructions in
this program. The statement notifies the executive routine
to initiate the compilation phase of this program.

7.3.2 *Floating Point Arithmetic*. One of the troublesome details in
numerical computation concerns the handling of the decimal point. In
ordinary hand multiplication, the decimal point in the product is located
so that it is to the left of the sum of the decimal places in both the
multiplier and the multiplicand. This is illustrated in the following example:

$$
\begin{array}{r}
741.9527 \\
\times \quad 62.834 \\
\hline
46619.8559518
\end{array}
$$

In multiplying numbers either by hand or in a digital computer, it is possible to set the number of decimal places in advance and decide to treat all numbers as having, for example, three decimal places. This system has certain disadvantages, however, as the following example illustrates.

$$
\begin{array}{r}
0.034 \\
\times\ 0.025 \\
\hline
0.000850
\end{array}
$$

Since we are limited to three digits to the right of the decimal point, we lose all the non-zero digits.

To avoid this type of difficulty, most computers engaged in scientific computational work use floating point arithmetic. Although the term may be strange, the procedure is familiar. Basically, the numbers are so arranged that the decimal point precedes the first digit; they are then multiplied by a power of 10 in order to locate the decimal point in its proper place: 0.7419527×10^3. In computers designed with special circuits for floating point operation, the floating point numbers are aligned so that the exponents are equal before addition and subtraction. In multiplication, the exponents are added; in division, the exponent of the divisor is subtracted from the exponent of the dividend. All this is done automatically, requiring no special programing instructions, and is therefore fast and efficient.

7.4   SUMMARY

Chapter 7 on programing fundamentals and machine language is an introduction to the concepts of programing and the functions of the programer. As an example of the programer's work, a problem involving some statistical calculations was analyzed. This analysis included a flow chart and a FORTRAN statement. These were studied in detail. Although such a brief discussion cannot serve as a substitute for a course in programing, it does provide necessary basic information and is helpful for understanding the programs and computer applications described in Part 3 of this book.

BIBLIOGRAPHY, PARTS 1 AND 2

1 Bell, W. D., *A Management Guide to Electronic Computers*. New York: McGraw-Hill, 1957.

2 Berkeley, E. C., and Wainwright, L., *Computers, Their Operation and Applications*. New York: Reinhold Publishing Corp., 1956.

3 ———, *Giant Brains*. New York: Wiley, 1949.

4 Booth, A. D., *Automation and Computing*. New York: Macmillan, 1959.

5 ———, and Booth, K. H. V., *Automatic Digital Calculators*. New York: Academic Press, Inc., 1953.

6 Bowden, B. V., ed., *Faster Than Thought*. London: Pitman, 1953.

7 Canning, R. G., *Electronic Data Processing for Business and Industry*. New York: Wiley, 1956.

8 Chapin, N., *An Introduction to Automatic Computers*. Princeton, N.J.: Van Nostrand, 1957.

9 Eckert, W. J., and Jones, R., *Faster, Faster*. New York: McGraw-Hill, 1956.

10 Fahnestock, J. D., *Computers and How They Work*. New York: Ziff-Davis Publishing Co., 1959.

11 Goodman, L. L., *Automation Today and Tomorrow*. London: Iota Services, Ltd., 1958.

12 ———, *Man and Automation*. Baltimore, Md.: Penguin Books, 1957.

13 Gotlieb, C. C., and Hume, J. N. P., *High Speed Data Processing*. New York: McGraw-Hill, 1958.

14 Grabbe, E. M., ed., *Automation in Business and Industry*. New York: Wiley, 1957.

15 Gregory, R. H., and Van Horn, R. L., *Automatic Data-Processing Systems*. San Francisco: Wadsworth Publishing Co., Inc., 1960.

16 Hartree, D. R., *Calculating Instruments and Machines*. Urbana, Ill.: Univ. Illinois Press, 1949.

17 Hollingdale, S. H., *High Speed Computing: Methods and Applications*. New York: Macmillan, 1959.

18 Jeenel, J., *Programing for Digital Computers*. New York: McGraw-Hill, 1959.

19 Mace, D. and Alsop, J., *A Simplified System for the Use of an Automatic Calculator.* New York: Watson Scientific Computing Laboratory, 1957.

20 McCracken, D. D., *Digital Computer Programing.* New York: Wiley, 1957.

21 ———, *et al., Programming Business Computers.* New York: Wiley, 1959.

22 Murphy, J. S., *Basics of Digital Computers.* 3 vols. New York: John F. Rider, 1958.

23 Nett, R., and Hetzler, S. A., *An Introduction to Electronic Data Processing.* Glencoe, Ill.: The Free Press, 1959.

24 Paynter, H. M., ed., *A Palimpsest on the Electronic Analog Art.* Boston: Geo. A. Philbrick Researchers, Inc., 1955.

25 Rogers, J., *Automation, Technology's New Face.* Berkeley, Calif.: Institute of Industrial Relations, Univ. California, 1958.

26 *Scientific American Book: Automatic Control.* New York: Simon and Schuster, 1955.

27 Sluckin, W., *Minds and Machines.* Baltimore, Md.: Penguin Books, 1954.

28 Stibitz, G. R., and Larrivee, J. A., *Mathematics and Computers.* New York: McGraw-Hill, 1957.

29 Wiener, N., *The Human Use of Human Beings.* New York: Doubleday, 1956.

30 Wilkes, M. V., *Automatic Digital Computers.* New York: Wiley, 1956.

Part 3
COMPUTER APPLICATIONS

Before turning to the studies dealing with research application of the computer, let us take stock and review our aims and accomplishments. We began our presentation by introducing the reader to computers and examining their capabilities and limitations. In order to provide background on the development of this new tool, we reviewed the history of computers—from ancient times to the present. By becoming acquainted with the early ancestors of the computer and recognizing its family resemblances to the familiar slide rule and desk calculator, we began to find this new tool less mysterious. Knowledge of the various components of a data processing system, what they do and how they do it, helped further to dispel the mystery. By learning a little of the language of the computer and the fundamentals of programing, we began to understand the concepts and procedures for using this device to solve problems. We are now ready to examine the impact of the computer, as used by the scientist, to expand the areas of research and study. Part 3 of this book contains a series of reports by scientists who are actively engaged in important and original research involving the use of the computer.

The various applications fall naturally into several groups. Chapter 8, on the university computing center, sets the stage for the subsequent material. Chapter 9 reviews the historical antecedents of data processing in psychological research and some of the methodological problems inherent in this area of study. Specific techniques of psychological data processing are also reported in terms of their previous applications. The next three chapters (10, 11, and 12) deal with statistical calculations. Chapter 10 describes a general model for multiple linear regression analysis, along with illustrative examples of psychological applications and computer procedures for solving regression problems. Chapter 11 on factor analysis opens with a discussion of the questions that can be investigated by means of this technique and then describes computer methods of calculating intercorrelations, factoring, rotating, and associated problems. The chapter also considers the effect of computers on factor analytic methods of research. The concluding chapter (12) of the statistical portion of computer applications is concerned with canonical analysis. Although this is not a new technique, it is one which has become practical only since the advent of large-scale digital computers. The history of canonical analysis is reviewed, and the computational methods are described in detail. This very powerful device for analyzing psychological data, with their many interacting variables, will be increasingly used by researchers.

Chapters 13 through 18 constitute a section devoted to computer applications in experimental psychology. Chapter 13 establishes the use of the computer to study perceptual processes by disclosing the techniques for programing the computer to generate visual and auditory displays and to recognize patterns. Chapter 14 describes the "teaching machine" as an aid to education and as a research tool for investigating problems of learning and retention. The application of the computer to explore cognitive processes is considered in Chapter 15. Binary choice behavior is used as an example, and the steps in writing a program for simulating problem-solving behavior, as well as testing and evaluating this program, are described in detail. Chapter 16, "Synthex: An Approach toward Computer Synthesis of Human Language Behavior," contains an excellent introduction to the use of a computer for solving language problems of both a syntactic and a semantic nature, as well as a description of a simple, non-computer, question-answering device. Research in automatic language data processing continues in Chapter 17, but here the emphasis is on machine translation of languages. Finally, and in a particularly interesting example of the use of the computer to investigate cognitive and creative behavior, Chapter 18 discusses computer studies of musical composition.

The next six chapters (19–24) deal with system simulation studies. The section begins with the work of Ashby on the simulation of the human brain. He defines "brainlike" behavior, sets up a model, and discusses the value of simulation. Chapter 20, on nerve net theory, describes the properties of artificial neurons and shows how they can be combined into nets which can count, recognize patterns, and exhibit other forms of behavior. Extending the concept of small neural nets to larger systems, Chapter 21, "Advances in Biomedical Science and Diagnosis," describes how computers can be used to simulate complex biomedical systems, such as the human circulatory system. This chapter also includes material on computer applications to medical data processing, as in the analysis of electroencephalograph patterns, and to medical diagnosis. Chapter 22 gives a detailed description of "Leviathan," an ongoing research project which uses a computer simulation model to develop and test a theory of large social systems. The next chapter is concerned with simulation of the complete operations of a business firm as a means of studying the effect of management decisions and policies. Chapter 24 expands the size and complexity of simulation models into the area of international relations and diplomacy; it describes a program for "A Simple Diplomatic Game," along with its advantages and limitations. The concluding chapter (25) offers some predictions about the future of computers in behavioral science research.

The advent of the computer and its general availability is broadening the research interests of the social scientist, for he now has the means by which to investigate the more complex and vital aspects of human behavior. The research reports in Part 3 of this book are designed to acquaint the reader with the work of prominent investigators and to suggest ideas and methods for further research. Most of the chapters allude to areas in which additional research is necessary, and many suggest topics for investigation. Each reader should find in this material some area of special interest which he can pursue.

Charles Wrigley
8/THE UNIVERSITY COMPUTING CENTER

*Charles Wrigley was born in 1917
in New Zealand. He received both B.A. and M.A. degrees
at the University of Auckland. Following service
in World War II he attended
the University of London, where he studied with
Sir Cyril Burt and received a Ph.D. in 1949.
After a two-year teaching assignment at McGill University
in Canada, he came to the United States as a Research Associate
with the University of Illinois, and there he
received his first computer experience with ILLIAC.
From Illinois he went to the University of California
as Visiting Associate Professor,
where he had the opportunity to use the IBM 701.
He is now Professor at Michigan State University,
working with the MISTIC Computer.
During these years he has published some two
dozen papers on quantitative and political psychology, and
much of this research involved computer applications.*

The scientific utility of an electronic computer is great, but so also is the expense. In the fifteen years since ENIAC was built, scientists and administrators have had to become accustomed to computers which may cost hundreds of thousands or even millions of dollars, and where the rate that has to be charged to the user in any self-supporting installation may amount to hundreds of dollars per hour. The needs of the early behavioral scientists were much more modest. In the laboratory experiments in psychology in the nineteenth century, equipment often consisted only

I should like to express my thanks to my present and former associates from whom I have learned a great deal about the application of computers to psychology, and whose ideas have shaped my own and are therefore reflected to some extent in this chapter: Dr. Donal S. Jones, Harvard University; Mr. James A. Clark, Mr. M. Gordon Howat, Mr. Donald F. Kiel, and Mr. Kenneth W. Terhune, Michigan State University; Dr. Paul B. Koons, Ohio University; Dr. David J. Fitch, Personnel Research Branch, Adjutant General's Office; Dr. Peter W. Hemingway, Southern Illinois University; Mr. Raymond J. Twery, Stanford Research Institute; Mr. Jack O. Neuhaus, University of California; Dr. Kern W. Dickman and Dr. Henry F. Kaiser, University of Illinois; Dr. James C. Lingoes, University of Michigan; Mr. Donald M. Wilkins, Kansas State University.

of a pencil, a stopwatch and some paper. Subjects were usually volunteers and unpaid; if outside subjects were unavailable, psychologists could always experiment on each other. At that time, the scientist who was sufficiently dedicated could meet his expenses from his own pocket. The philosophy of self-support extended into the twentieth century. In the nineteen-thirties and the nineteen-forties, punched-card machines began to be rented by universities. The researcher would then pay hourly charges for the privilege of using the machines. If he had research funds of any sort, the costs were probably charged to that source. Failing that, he paid the bills himself.

This method of financing was obviously inadequate for electronic computers. Even the most dedicated of scientists could not hope to purchase his needed time on a computer from his personal income. Some system had to be devised whereby some central organization provided a machine free of charge to those scientists who were unsupported by research grants. Hence, there have been two problems in making computers available to scientists. The first is the obvious technical one of providing machines which possess the requisite speed, reliability, and storage. The second has been the administrative one of developing organizational and financial arrangements so that the machines are effectively used by researchers. At the university level, the answer has proved to be the Computing Center operated on the Robin Hood principle of charging those who have research funds, but of supplying the machine free of charge to those who do not. This chapter will be concerned with some of the administrative and technical problems involved in building up these centers.

The part played by instrumentation in the history of science will be considered in Section 8.1. The next three sections will be devoted to the three M's of the University Computing Center: machines, men, and methods. Machine selection and financing will be discussed in Section 8.2, and the training of computer specialists in Section 8.3. Methods are the next ingredient; existing ones have to be revised, and new ones created. This topic forms the subject of Section 8.4. Finally, in Section 8.5, the current role of computers in the behavioral sciences will be examined and assessed.

Examples are often drawn from the experience of the University of Illinois. This is partly because of my own familiarity with that experience, but primarily because Illinois was the first university to own its computer on an unrestricted basis and therefore was able to give scholars in all fields easy access to a computer. As a result, the first computer analyses in many areas of science were carried out at the University of Illinois. An electronic computer has been available there since 1951. Hence, there is by now ten years of experience in the problems of transition to computers. The lessons of the decade may serve as a guide in our charting of progress for the next ten-year span.

8.1   INSTRUMENTATION IN THE HISTORY OF SCIENCE

The Platonic tradition bequeathed to us by the Greeks has stressed the role of ideation and theory in the history of science. It is not surprising, therefore, to find historians of science emphasizing the epochal new theories, for instance, the Copernician view of the solar system, the Newtonian laws of motion, the Darwinian evolutionary theory. These are presented as the great landmarks in the development of science, the dramatic moments which every schoolboy is expected to know about.

Each of these theoretical reconstructions, however, has been preceded by a long period of accumulation of factual knowledge. Darwin's field studies of island floras and faunas made during his voyage on the *Beagle* preceded by twenty years his promulgation of the theory of evolution; Kepler's and Newton's insights depended upon the planetary observations of Tycho Brahe, made years before; and the stimulus to Copernicus' heliocentric astronomy was the increasing body of astronomical information which led to frequent amendment of the original Ptolemaic system of epicycles and deferents.

The rate of scientific fact finding, in turn, has been influenced by the discovery and improvement of scientific instruments. A history of science is needed which focuses not upon the theoretical reconstructions but upon the instrumental inventions and their scientific outcomes. Following the invention of glass, there is the birth of modern chemistry; the telescope is the forerunner of modern astronomy; the microscope, of cellular physiology and of microbiology. In each case, the order of scientific development has been (a) the invention of the new instrument and its perfection, (b) the meticulous accumulation of scientific observations—e.g., by the early observatories, by the seventeenth-century microscopists—and then, perhaps a century or more later, (c) the theoretical reconstruction. The twentieth century has added its own important share to the instruments designed to supplement man's unaided power of observation and analysis, e.g., the betatron, the radio telescope, the electron microscope. Judging from past scientific history, these instruments will provide a vast accession in our store of factual knowledge, and from this knowledge will arise the theories of the future.

The electronic computer bids to rank as one of the great twentieth-century inventions. It stands as man's latest and so far his most successful effort to supplement his powers of calculation. Viewed from the wider perspective of history, its rate of expansion has been remarkable. In 1946, there was only ENIAC; five years later, when psychologists first caught up with electronic computers, they were to be counted by tens; ten years later, by hundreds; and now, only fifteen years later, by thousands. They are being used in all areas of science, physical and social. Calculations impracticable only twenty years ago are now routine. Initially designed to aid in computation, computers are taking over an increasing range of clerical duties. It is probably not exaggerating to speak of this as a second industrial revolution, when the menial chores of the clerk will be lightened, as were those of the laborer in the Industrial Revolution of a century or more ago; and the hope is increasing that these machines created by man will even be able to supplement his powers of problem solving and decision making. If generality of application is taken as the criterion for evaluating the importance of any scientific invention, then the computer promises to be one of the most important inventions of all time.

This book is concerned with only one part of this history-making change. It is restricted to one segment of the scientific effort, namely, that of the behavioral sciences, and to only a ten-year time span, so that we are still actively engaged in finding answers for some of the initial technical problems. It is, in effect, a case study of what happens when social scientists try to adapt to the challenge of a new scientific instrument which promises to offer almost unlimited powers of calculation, relative to the tools of a decade ago.

Let me remind those who are sceptical, and who consider that this may overstate the influence of a scientific instrument, of the experiences of Galileo. Upon hearing of the invention of the telescope by the Dutch lensmakers, he set to work to construct his own. His task completed, he trained his homemade telescope upon the heavens and was rewarded with an unparalleled burst of discoveries. He saw the shadows of the rising and the setting sun cast by the mountains of the moon upon its plains; he observed the phases of Venus and saw four satellites of Jupiter; sunspots and the rings of Saturn became visible; and turning from the planets to the stars, he found multitudes of them not visible to the naked eye, so that only a small part of the assemblage had previously been known. In awe, he wrote, "I am quite beside myself with wonder, and infinitely grateful to God that it has pleased Him to permit me to discover such great marvels."

There is a danger, of course, in random fact finding. Perhaps the most amusing reminder of this danger is to be found in the words of Gulliver when he visited the scientists of the Grand Academy of Lagado:

The first professor I saw was in a very large room, with forty pupils about him. After salutation, observing me to look earnestly upon a frame, which took up the greatest part of both the length and breadth of the room, he said perhaps I might wonder to see him employed in a project for improving speculative knowledge by practical and mechanical operations. But the world would soon be sensible of its usefulness, and he flattered himself that a more noble exalted thought never sprang in any other man's head. Every one knew how laborious the usual method is of attaining to arts and sciences; whereas by his contrivance the most ignorant person at a reasonable charge, and with a little bodily labour, may write books in philosophy, poetry, politics, law, mathematics, and theology, without the least assistance from genius or study. He then led me to the frame, about the sides whereof all his pupils stood in ranks. It was twenty foot square, placed in the middle of the room. The superficies was composed of several pieces of wood, about the bigness of a die, but some larger than others. They were all linked together by slender wires. These bits of wood were covered on every square with paper pasted on them, and on these papers were written all the words of their language, in their several moods, tenses, and declensions, but without any order. The professor then desired me to observe, for he was going to set his engine at work. The pupils at his command took each of them hold of an iron handle, whereof there were forty fixed round the edges of the frame, and giving them a sudden turn, the whole disposition of the words was entirely changed. He then commanded six and thirty of the lads to read the several lines softly as they appeared upon the frame; and where they found three or four words together that might make part of a sentence, they dictated to the remaining four boys who were scribes. This work was repeated three or four times, and at every turn the engine was so contrived that the words shifted into new places, as the square bits of wood moved upside down.

Six hours a day the young students were employed in this labour, and the professor showed me several volumes in a large folio already collected, of broken sentences, which he intended to piece together, and out of these rich materials to give the world a complete body of all arts and sciences; which however might be still improved, and much expedited, if the public would raise a fund for making and employing five hundred such frames in Lagado, and oblige the managers to contribute in common their several collections.

He assured me, that this invention had employed all his thoughts from his youth, that he had emptied the vocabulary into his frame, and made the strictest computation of the general proportion there is in books between the number of particles, nouns, and verbs, and other parts of speech.

How useful a computer would have been to this good professor!

Any scientific instrument can be, and sometimes will be misused. Perhaps that does not matter too much in the full course of scientific history. The futilities are winnowed out like chaff. To try to strike some balance between Galileo and Lagado, let us turn to Richardson's treatise on weather forecasting [6] written in 1922. The meteorologist is attempting to make the best estimates of future weather that he can from the known weather of the present and the past. With observations from all over the world, if he needs them, and from the upper atmosphere as well as from the ground, the voluminousness of his records can be oppressive. In the midst of a book that is mostly technical and mathematical, Richardson devoted two pages to a fantasy. He pictured the weather forecasters of the future working in teams in a huge circular room resembling London's Albert Hall. Each team was analyzing one segment of the data. The weather director was in the center of the assemblage. Like the conductor of some immense orchestra, he would shine a green light of approval upon those teams which were up to schedule, but a red light of disapproval upon those who had fallen behind in the race to finish the calculations so that the forecast could be available ahead of the weather being predicted. Less than forty years later, the fantasy is actuality, but instead of teams of clerks and their conductor, meteorologists have had recourse to a computer and its programers.

8.2   MACHINE ACQUISITION AND CONTROL

Obviously, the first stage in computer adaptation is getting a machine. Because of their low cost, desk calculators spread rapidly through university laboratories; it was feasible for each administrative unit to acquire its own machines. An electronic computer presents a much more formidable problem. University administrators were faced with a dilemma. Financially, they felt they could not afford a computer, but scientifically, that they could not afford to be without one. It is a tribute to their resourcefulness that within ten years almost all research-oriented universities have accepted the computer as a legitimate piece of scientific equipment and have found the means to acquire one. The financial support given by the National Science Foundation, the generous discount policies of the commercial firms, and the "build-your-own-machine" movement have each played their part.

8.2.1 *Achieving Computer Acceptance*. In order to win acceptance of the computer as part of the research support facilities of the university, four early misconceptions had to be cleared away:

a. Early estimates of potential computer usage were much too conservative. It was thought at first that a single university could not support a high-speed computer with sufficient workload, so that a few machines located on a regional basis across the country would be better. For example, Hartree, a pioneer computer designer at Cambridge University, believed that four or five computers would suffice for all British needs in scientific computing. I must confess to the same misjudgment. When I started using ILLIAC in 1951, I was so impressed by its high speed—since it operated at what then seemed to me the fantastic speed of 1400 multiplications per second —that I failed to foresee that within less than five years this machine would prove to be too limited for the university's needs and that a supplemental machine would have to be obtained to handle the overload.

b. Some administrators wanted to charge the heavy hourly machine rates directly to the scientist, so that the computer might be self-supporting. On the cheaper punched-card machines, this policy had worked moderately well. Fast computers, however, might cost $100 or more per hour, so that under this policy only those adequately provided with research funds would have gained access. Computers would have been priced beyond the means of the independent researcher or the graduate student. The University of Illinois seems to have been the first to promulgate the enlightened policy of charging those supplied with research funds, but providing the machine free of charge to those without. This procedure seems to have become standard by now.

c. Many administrators, including some computer directors, thought machine time to be so valuable that it should be used only for tasks which could not be carried out with any other calculating aid. For example, one administrator questioned the desirability of using a computer to calculate a series of fifty matrix inversions of order six. His grounds were that the scientist could work each one with the aid of a desk calculator in an hour or two. In psychology, this policy would have meant use of a computer for principal axes factor analysis and for analytic rotation, but not for calculation of correlations or preparation of contingency tables; the latter tasks seemed to be regarded as insufficiently respectable. This philosophy of computer scarcity deified the machine, overlooking the primary purpose of a computer, i.e., saving men's time and supplying them with much needed research assistance not previously available. Perhaps the extreme of this philosophy is represented by the university which imposed a nominal charge, as computer rates go (about $10 hourly for the use of a fairly fast computer), not to add appreciably to revenue, but mainly to dissuade any frivolous or wasteful use of the machine. Admittedly, any heavily loaded machine must be carefully scheduled to avoid waste and inefficiency, but this was a machine still only partly loaded. Such a charge deters the scientist from experimenting. He tends to keep to his old ways when, as we shall see later in this chapter, a main problem in using computers is finding better methods of analysis. At the worst, he may not use the computer at all but may prefer to stay with the desk calculator, thereby saving his money and wasting only his own time. Once again, the Illinois administration set a most valuable precedent by the liberality of its provision of machine time.

d. Some physical scientists were of the opinion that computers should be reserved primarily for mathematicians, physicists, and engineers, who might be expected to have the appropriate level of mathematical sophistication and rigor. Behavioral scientists were regarded (often correctly) as mathematically rather naive. The volume of the behavioral scientist's input was often surprising, and that of his output even more so. (I share the critics intuitive distrust of those researches sometimes found in our area where output is larger than input.) However, the voluminous input so often found should be regarded as a challenge rather than as an occasion for merriment by computer engineers. The computers of the nineteen-forties and of the early nineteen-fifties, designed both by and for physical scientists, were ill balanced, with input and output facilities much inferior to the main arithmetical unit.

8.2.2 *Computer Obsolescence*. In dealing with issues involving machine acquisition, it is necessary to comment on the question of computer obsolescence. This problem may be worded thus: Since rapid technical advances continue in machine speed, storage capacity, machine reliability, and input and output systems, is it better to acquire a machine immediately, despite the obsolescence risk, or to wait for the brave new models of the future?

There are two stages in obsolescence. The first occurs when some scientific analyses, not practicable upon current machines, become feasible upon newer machines of greater capacity and speed. Rather than disrupt the over-all research effort by changing a computer so as to cope with these problems, it may often be preferable to give the scientist concerned funds with which to buy time at some other computing center. The second stage occurs if and when the cost per calculating unit has become sufficiently lower on some newer machine to justify the effort of changing facilities, with its associated chores of reprograming. Provided that the university has started with as modern and as powerful a machine as is available at the time of acquisition, this second stage is reached only after quite a long time. The University of Illinois started with what was then one of the best machines in the world. In terms of the standards of the nineteen-sixties, its storage capacity is limited (1024 immediate-access locations, 12,800 memory drum locations). Those who need large storage space will need to look elsewhere until ILLIAC II, currently under construction, is ready. This means that the first stage of obsolescence has been reached. But it is doubtful whether the Illinois machine is yet at the second stage. After ten years of service, ILLIAC remains a comparatively economical machine.

Two features of computer economics are relevant here. It has been an American tradition to change last year's model for a new one. Should the same be done with computers? In my judgment, the answer is emphatically "No." Changing a computer is much more disruptive than trading in an automobile because of the labor of preparing the standard programs for a computer and of getting researchers familiar with them. It is not always realized that the programs may cost as much as or even more than the machine itself. Frequent computer changes mean that the same programs are written over and over again, and for a large part of the time the installation is not effectively used.

Another aspect of computer transition should be stressed. It is a false economy to take out the old machine at the same time as bringing in the new. Until a program library is established for the new machine, it will be of limited usefulness. The old machine retains its value so long as there are programs available for it which have not yet been written for the new one. This labor of reprograming will probably be substantially reduced, or possibly eliminated, as newer machines are built which have program compatibility with the older machines they are intended to replace, and as more programs are written in languages, such as FORTRAN, applicable to various machines. But in the past decade, the evidence seems clear that institutions, such as Illinois, which have stayed with one machine have fared better, with respect to building up a substantial library of programs, training graduate students in machine use, and widespread scientific application of the computer, than have the installations which changed computers frequently.

The second factor in computer economics is that the more powerful and more expensive machines are cheaper per unit of calculation than the less costly but less speedy ones. Increases in machine speeds have more than offset the increased expense, provided there is the workload to keep the giant busy.

These two factors mean, in my estimation, that a university spends its money most wisely if it concentrates upon one centralized installation, equipping it with the most modern and powerful machine available at the time of acquisition. Many universities have had separate punched-card facilities for business and for research use, but it is likely that this tradition will have to be abandoned. A machine of the sixties is so fast that with proper scheduling a wide variety of work can be handled. The cost of a modern computer is so formidable that it would be a financial luxury to have two of these giants on a campus until such time as the first becomes overloaded. There remains the possibility of getting two smaller machines, one for business use and one for research, instead of the one large one. One disadvantage of this course of action has already been pointed out: namely, that the two machines jointly cannot handle the same workload that the one centralized installation can. A second disadvantage is that, if both have smaller capacity, some campus analyses then cannot be handled on either machine.

An administrative consequence is that determined efforts must be made to avoid factionalism among the various units of the university affected by computer developments. Because computers represent a new area for universities with few established precedents, factionalism seems to be found rather frequently. At present the punched-card equipment is often under different control from the electronic computer, and the two organizations may view themselves in a competitive rather than in a complementary role. Separate schools, such as the School of Business or the School of Engineering, may hope to acquire their own machines. The Director of the Computing Center should be given sufficient authority to insure that a consistent university-wide computational policy is followed. His position requires that he should be responsive to the special needs of the various groups for whom computers are important. Computers have been shown relevant to so many areas of scholarship that there are inevitably going to be many differences of opinion and need.

Two trends have been evident during the last ten years: (a) a great increase in the volume of work emanating from any campus as the computer becomes better known and a versatile program library is established, (b) a great increase in the volume of work which can be handled by one computer. Presumably these two curves will sooner or later change to plateaus, but this still seems to be a long way off. So far, the two increases seem roughly to have balanced each other, as the experience of the University of Illinois appears to show. One general purpose machine, ILLIAC, sufficed for the computational needs of the early fifties; ILLIAC II will probably suffice for the early sixties. Present indications are that each of the twenty or thirty major universities with extensive research programs and large numbers of doctoral students (Big Ten, Ivy League, etc.) will be able to use at least one machine of present maximal power (such as the Bendix G-20, the Control Data Corporation 1604, or the IBM 7090). Smaller universities which do not have sufficient work to keep one of these machines occupied—even when allowing for a dramatic upsurge in demand once a computer is installed—face a difficult problem of machine selection. Computer economics indicate the financial advantages of the regional machine. Yet there remains a great research convenience in having a computer close at hand upon one's own campus. The best answer may prove to be a compromise, with a medium-speed machine handling most analyses on the campus, and a transfer of those problems requiring greater speed or storage capacity to one of the major universities.

If the upward curve of machine speeds should exceed the upward curve of usage, this argument for a regional machine might hold even for the larger universities. When machines of the power of LARC and STRETCH become generally available, we may find that a single university, even the largest, cannot keep the computer fully occupied. The pattern for the future may then become that of each university maintaining its own machine for the tasks less demanding of speed and storage, and a regional group of universities supporting one of the larger computer installations. This would be equivalent to the present library system by which each Middle Western university maintains its own library, but transfers some less used titles to the Midwestern Library Center rather than retaining them locally. The position is complicated by the fact that for numerical operations which only take a few minutes, a speed gain by a factor of ten does not make much difference. What does it matter whether a large set of correlations takes fifty seconds or five? That is why I think we are more likely to go to a mixed system than to the complete regionalism originally prophesied by Hartree. The convenience of getting most of one's calculations on one's own campus is simply too great to be sacrificed.

However, prophecies in any area of rapid technological advance are always risky. An effective system of satellite machines might be organized over an entire state or an even larger region, where inputs are flashed to a central machine in some convenient location and the outputs are flashed back to the campus of origin.

If the curve of usage heads upward faster than the curve of speed, then the answer is easier. If and when any university can maintain one of the most powerful current machines and this too becomes overloaded, then the university can add to its computer installation with the aim either of diversifying or of decentralizing its facilities.

8.2.3 *Computer Construction, Rental or Purchase?* Any computing center has to decide whether it is better advised to rent a commercial machine, or to buy one, or to build its own machine. Early centers had no choice. Until the Remington Rand UNIVAC was marketed in 1952, high-speed commercial computers were not available. Each computer before that had to be custom-built. Even after that, universities usually acquired a computer more cheaply by building their own than by getting a commercial machine. The universities that have built copies of ILLIAC have found themselves equipped with fast computers and extensive program libraries for comparatively low cost.

As computers have become progressively larger and more complex, the disadvantages of individual effort and the advantages of commercial production have become increasingly apparent. The task of successfully building a computer becomes more and more formidable, and the economics of mass manufacture are more evident. For most universities, the effective choice is therefore between buying or renting a commercial machine.

Rentals are high in comparison with purchase prices. A machine may be purchased for no more than three or four years' rental. The reason for this rapid depreciation is, of course, the obsolescence issue. With a rented machine, a change can be made whenever an improved new model becomes available, while a purchased computer has to be held for a longer period. A secondary advantage of rental is that computer maintenance is then generally supplied free of charge, whereas with purchase either a maintenance contract is needed at comparatively high price, or, alternatively, the university's engineering school has to have or to add qualified computer technicians to its own staff.

The viewpoint expressed in this section has been that a university should aim at getting a very good computer and holding it for probably at least ten years. During the early part of the period, it will have an outstanding installation relative to other centers, and even in the latter part, any university with a machine such as a G-20, a 1604 or a 7090 is certainly not going to be saddled with what can in any sense be called an inferior machine, no matter what the technical progress may have been during the period. A machine that makes many thousands of multiplications and divisions per second remains in an absolute sense a very impressive acquisition. Over the ten-year span, purchase will have proved markedly cheaper than rental. The money so saved could with advantage be devoted to strengthening the consultancy and programing services of the center, the topic to be discussed in the next section. More important perhaps than the financial saving will be the program stability so achieved. At least until full program compatibility is achieved, any university which rents a machine with the express aim of changing its computer each two or three years is going to spend a disproportionate amount of its effort upon the writing and rewriting of programs.

8.3   PROGRAMING AND PERSONNEL

Now that many universities have good machines, the main emphasis must turn to their effective use. This includes recruiting and training good programers, reporting programs in a foolproof way, providing courses for both graduate and undergraduate students in numerical methods appropriate for computers, and supplying consultant services to insure that machines are used efficiently. Most universities have already recognized this need to some extent by offering programing courses and by making computer staff available for consultation with would-be users. It is my opinion, however, that we have not done enough in this direction.

8.3.1 *The Program Library.* The key to effective use of a computer is a good program library. The problem is deciding where the responsibility for building it should lie. Salesmen sometimes suggest that there is no longer any problem; their company is said to be able to supply all programs that are needed. Likewise, organizations such as SHARE—the Society to Help Avoid Repetitive Effort—have been launched to place programing efforts on a cooperative basis. Yet the national practice seems still to be greatly inferior to the national aspirations. Universities have had IBM 650's for many years now; yet the social scientists who use these machines find that their programing needs are still formidable. Either they cannot secure copies of the programs which have been written elsewhere, or the reports are not intelligible, or the other university's machine is not compatible with their own. The commercial firms seem to me to be to some extent culpable in this sorry state of affairs, since they have the financial resources needed to set the matter right, and it would also appear to be entirely in their own self-interest to do so. I doubt whether any one of them has so far spent even a tiny fraction of 1 per cent of its budget upon this coordinating effort. If they will not take the lead, then perhaps some national foundation may be willing to do so. Two journals in our area (*Behavioral Science* and *Educational and Psychological Measurement*) now include computer sections, including brief reports upon newly prepared programs. This is a helpful development, but it does not go far enough.

Sooner or later there will come the recognition that a computer program is just as important a part of our scientific effort as a research report and requires as careful dissemination and preservation. Indeed, it will probably be regarded as more important than the average run-of-the-mill article, because it is used by so many more persons. When that time arrives, what is written here will be out of date.

Some central organization might meanwhile fruitfully undertake the same sort of responsibility for computer programs that the American Documentation Institute has accepted for the care and distribution of unpublished research material. A charge should be made for each program sent out. The system would still be much cheaper for the recipient than the present one where he may in the end have to write his own program. The organization might also try to insure that program reports follow a uniform format whenever possible and that the directions are intelligible. Authorship and date should also be indicated. Not only is this fair to the author, but any doubtful points can then be checked with him. In the past, there have probably been many cases where recipients have not used programs which they have been sent because of obscurities in the operating instructions.

At present, however, the issue remains as to the policy a university should adopt to insure an adequate program library. The University of Illinois has followed the practice of arranging for the computer staff to write a few staple routines, but for the most part expecting the user to write his own. This policy has had its merits. Not only have a number of social scientists learned to write programs, but also their library remains probably the most extensive one available at present in the social sciences. This is remarkable when it is remembered that Illinois has had to rely upon its own efforts and upon those of the three other universities with compatible machines, namely, Iowa State University, Michigan State University, and the University of Sydney. Yet I doubt whether the Illinois policy provides the long-term answer. This collection of programs is somewhat one-sided, reflecting too much the research interests of those who participated in its preparation; e.g., factor analysis and pattern analysis are well represented, but analysis of variance and covariance is not.

Furthermore, computer programs serve the interest of so many researchers that I am uncertain about the wisdom of expecting every man to become his own programer, any more than we expect him to become his own librarian. In many calculations and clerical tasks, use of a computer can save much time when a program is available, but the task can be carried out more quickly by hand than by writing a special program. The calculation of correlations is one example; the clerical operation of transposing matrix rows and columns is another. Yet programs for these, once written, will be very widely used. Likewise, it is doubtful whether the research director, who can be assumed to be a man of high productivity, should take time away from his researches to teach himself the specialized skill of programing. It seems better for this skill to be delegated to a specialist. Discussion will therefore turn to the training and employment of computer personnel.

8.3.2 *Personnel.* In my opinion, each larger department of psychology should include a computer specialist. Perhaps he could also serve other departments with similar computational needs, e.g., sociology, anthropology, communications, political science, if they do not have sufficient work for a programer of their own. Colleges of agriculture, of business, and of education seem to me to use computers enough to train and employ their own specialists. Duties of a computer consultant should include (a) writing basic programs; (b) training and assisting other members of the department in their program writing; (c) maintaining the program library, i.e., insuring adequate reporting of local programs and obtaining copies of programs written elsewhere; (d) helping machine users in the mechanics of card and tape production; (e) acting as a statistical and mathematical consultant for those who need such help (many poor theses in psychology are attributable to mathematical and statistical inadequacies; the computational adviser invariably finds himself giving statistical advice as well); (f) training a few especially selected graduate students to handle other computational consultancies similar to the one which he holds. The appointee should have academic rank, because the best men will not usually be willing to accept non-academic positions. This rank should be held jointly in the psychology department and at the computing center. If possible, he should be supported by graduate assistants who can help with the consultancy and programing, and can themselves be trained as computer specialists. This would help overcome the present growing shortage of qualified men in the field.

Administrators may ask whether we can afford such appointments. We cannot afford to be without them. The computer has become so well accepted that universities, with the willing support of the National Science Foundation, are prepared to spend as much as a million dollars on a machine; and the giants of the future, such as LARC and STRETCH, may cost many times as much again. Having made this immense investment, universities will then have to be prepared to supply a staff of data processing specialists to insure effective use of the machine. At each university (Michigan State University, Pennsylvania State University, University of California, University of Illinois, University of Michigan) where I have first-hand knowledge of computer operations, there has been the same pattern: some social science departments have had vigorous and efficient computer leadership; others were ineffective and wasteful in their use. The difference seems to depend upon personnel—whether anyone in the department has computer interests and skills and whether he has been willing to devote part of his time to training and helping others.

Some might urge that this assignment should be left entirely to the central computer staff. However, there are two reasons why the task should be kept at the departmental level. First, the amount of consultancy across the university is too great. Even within one department, the work can be burdensome. At Michigan State University, there is a list of 88 articles, theses, and convention papers in psychology which include computer results, and the list may not be complete. This holds for a period of less than four years since MISTIC (the Michigan State computer) became available. Secondly, the usual computer mathematician or engineer is not well qualified to advise a behavioral scientist upon his computations. He cannot be expected to know psychological theories and objectives or standard psychological methods. Obviously, the best consultant is one who has an intimate knowledge of the area of research.

European visitors have commented that American universities do not encourage men to give their maximal effort to consultancy. The reason, no doubt, is the emphasis placed in the United States upon personal publications in deciding upon promotions. The person who can adequately fill a computer consultancy such as has been outlined must be highly qualified, and as a rule such men will be available only if we insure that they have as good opportunities for advancement as do their competitors.

Should personal publication be expected from these men before they are promoted? My inclination is to think it should. The best consultant is probably one who has first-hand experience in research; his own efforts help him appreciate the problems of others. So long as personal production is expected from him, it is only fair that anyone appointed as computer consultant be guaranteed a proportion of uninterrupted time for his own research. The alternative is for administrators to be willing to judge and promote computer consultants in terms of their catalytic effect upon others' research production. Two or three of the best computer men I have known have been singularly unselfish persons who seem able to get just as interested in the research of others as in their own. Perhaps a place should be reserved in our larger universities for persons of this temperament, just as it seems generally agreed that there is an important place for those whose gifts lie in the field of university administration rather than individual research. Perhaps, so as to maintain good academic form in the matter, it might be arranged for them to appear as highly productive by (a) including computer programs among their publications—this would be just, since as much creative thinking is likely to go into a program as into a research manuscript—(b) listing them as co-authors in all research publications in which they have played an advisory role; they will then appear to be unusually productive researchers.

Computer programing and the organization of computer analyses have gone beyond the reach of careful clerks with high school education. There seems to be a growing demand for persons who are simultaneously competent researchers, experienced in the use of multivariate methods, and skilled as computer users and programers. To try to meet this demand, behavioral science departments should introduce courses in the numerical methods appropriate for computers both for graduate and undergraduate students and should recruit and train good programers. Most universities have already recognized this need to some extent by offering programing courses and by making the computer staff available for consultation with would-be users. These efforts have usually been made by the computing center. It is my opinion that their work should be supplemented by the behavioral science department themselves. All graduate students nowadays should know of the existence and potentialities of computers; many should be given an opportunity of using a computer for the analysis of their own data; some of the more enthusiastic should be encouraged to try their hand at the writing of programs; and occasional ones with the requisite ability, temperament, and mathematical knowledge should be trained specifically as computer specialists to act in the roles already discussed.

8.4 INNOVATION IN NUMERICAL METHODS

The good programer in the behavioral sciences also has to be a numerical innovator, expert in his knowledge of the use that is going to be made of his work, and willing to break away from customary statistical practices. Old techniques have been revised to make them convenient for computers, and completely new methods are being created that would not be feasible were it not for the existence of computers. Factor analysis provides a striking example because of the historical role played in it by subjective judgment. Ten years ago each factorist had to rely upon his own experience and wisdom in deciding upon the number of factors to extract, where to locate axes on his graphs, how to estimate communalities, and so on, so that two persons who started from the same data could never be guaranteed to reach the same answer. By contrast, factor analysis now can be applied with all judgment eliminated. Computers have provided the spur to these technical changes, and these revisions had to be made before effective programs could be prepared. Since factor analysis is considered in detail in Chapter 11, the steps of such an objective system will merely be itemized here. The principal axes method gives a unique initial factoring; Guttman's communalities [2] provide exact rank-reducing values for those concerned only with the common variance; the Kiel-Wrigley criterion provides a logical basis for the decision upon the number of factors to be rotated; analytic methods have been developed both for orthogonal and for oblique rotation; and matrix algebra methods are now available for the matching of factors. The important point in this context is that, associated with the programing effort, there has had to be a series of technical and logical reappraisals of factor analysis. Factor analysis may seem to be an exceptional case, because it has traditionally been more judgmental and imprecise than any of our other main procedures. To show that these technical revisions apply to even the most standard of methods, I should like to illustrate by the staple of psychological statistics, the correlation coefficient.

8.4.1 *Calculating the Correlation Coefficient (A Case Study).* As an undergraduate, I was taught to plot the bivariate frequency distribution of x and y on graph paper. Numbers were kept to single digits so far as possible by use of class intervals and assumed means. A slide rule was available for the final multiplications and divisions, and a table of squares for extraction of the square root. Special work sheets were available to systematize the order of operations. This procedure could be successfully taught to any reasonably intelligent clerk with a high school education and a patient temperament. Two hours might be needed for a correlation when the sample was large.

Several years later, I was introduced to desk calculators. Formulas convenient for desk calculators were not yet in the textbooks, but were presented in a small book by George W. Snedecor and Henry A. Wallace (later Vice President; surely the only one who ever wrote a book on statistics). Squares and products could be calculated directly from the scores without introducing class intervals and assumed means to simplify the figuring. Various dodges were available for calculating and checking sums of squares and products, such as the now well-known one of entering x on one side of the keyboard and y on the other, and then squaring, thereby getting x^2, y^2 and $2xy$ in different parts of the upper register. Once again, the operation could be successfully taught to any reasonably intelligent and careful person. Thirty minutes might be needed for a correlation.

My next transition was to punched-card machines. An entirely different method was used for calculation of squares and products; known in the United States as *progressive digiting* and in Britain as *summary multiplication,* it apparently was originally devised by a Danish actuary, Tetens, in 1785. The procedure enables the square of x and the product of x with a number of other variables to be obtained simultaneously. The procedure reduces multiplication to a series of additions. The operator using this method requires more than a rote understanding if he is to be efficient. He must be familiar with plugboards and maintain good organization. By working with duplicate sets of cards, he can arrange for tabulations to proceed on one set, while the sorter is getting the cards ready for the tabulation to follow. A couple of hundred correlations may now be calculated and checked in a period of eight or ten hours. That means perhaps twenty completed correlations per hour.

Twery's method for calculating correlations, devised in 1952, seems to be the best for an electronic computer. All scores for one person are input, and then every square and product is formed for that person, each being stored in a different location. It is as if a large number of desk calculators were placed around a hall, with a separate one used for accumulation of each square and each product, and then a clerk went from one to the other, recording one square or product on each. This unconventional order of work has two advantages. First, data in the behavioral sciences are usually arranged with all scores for one person together; punching of card or tape is therefore easier. Secondly, scores for any individual are no longer needed, once squares and products have been formed from them. The method accordingly permits a practically unlimited number of persons in the sample, even when storage capacity of the computer is quite limited. With this procedure, a set of 700 correlations can be calculated in ILLIAC for a sample of 500 persons in about twenty minutes, i.e., 35 correlations per minute, with most of the time required for input, so that with more modern machines with faster input systems, there is a further appreciable reduction in the time.

This example has been introduced to illustrate the extensive changes often needed even in the most standard computations in order to take advantage of the special characteristics of a computer. There may well be a negative rather than a positive transfer from knowledge of the traditional desk calculator and punched-card methods.

8.4.2. Patterns and Types. Whereas the correlation coefficient ranks among the older of the techniques of psychological statistics. McQuitty's [4] method of agreement analysis is among the newer. This procedure handles problems which remained unanswered before the computer period. Specifically, it is designed (a) to provide a method of classification for dichotomous and categorical data based directly upon the responses and the point frequencies, with no reference to correlation; (b) to group persons into types at the same time it is assembling items into patterns; (c) to identify configurations of items (referred to here as *syndromes*) in which non-linear relations as well as linear relations between the elements can be identified.

The traditional multivariate methods have adopted a linear and compensatory model. Variables have been assumed to be additive, both in predicting some outcome (as in multiple regression) and in determining a man's standing upon a factor (as when calculating factor measurements). Any deficit on any one variable can always be offset by a surplus upon another. Computational convenience seems to have been the main reason for this linearity assumption. Non-linearities are quite often found in meteorology and other physical sciences, and no convincing logical reasoning or empirical evidence has ever been provided to show that they will not be found in psychology. Indeed, this possibility can hardly be put to the test so long as we do not have satisfactory non-linear methods.

Variables can be conceived as either disjunctive or conjunctive rather than compensatory in their effects. To insure a certain favorable outcome, either *a* or *b* may suffice. Since elementary school work is not very hard, either reasonable ability *or* a modicum of hard work may enable a child to perform well. This is the disjunctive situation.

Alternatively, both *a* and *b* may be needed if the favorable outcome is to occur. A Ph.D. is probably unobtainable unless the candidate has reasonably high ability *and* is willing to work hard. This is the conjunctive situation. On this view, genius might be hypothesized to be a total configuration of aptitudes and traits, each playing an essential part in the man's realizing his fullest achievement. With any key element lacking, the configuration would no longer be appropriate, and performance might then be relatively undistinguished. Political history indicates that neither a female nor a Negro may at present be elected to the American presidency, no matter how talented the person may be in other respects. There is no overcoming the single biological disability. The logic is conjunctive rather than compensatory. (Political configurations change. There was a time when a Catholic was also automatically excluded from Presidential consideration.) Davison [1] discovered that frustration tolerance of nursery school children was sharply lowered whenever (a) they were blocked by some situation which they were unable to master, *and* (b) they were very persistent in trying to reach their goal. Frustration was very much less whenever inability and persistence were not conjoined, i.e., when they failed but were not very highly motivated to accomplishment, or when their prolonged effort led eventually to the desired outcome.

The practical difficulty is the considerable number of patterns to be found in any empirical analysis. If the sample of items is large, one often cannot find two identical patterns, e.g., no two senators in the United States 83rd Congress voted in exactly the same way. The great step forward, introduced by McQuitty in agreement analysis, has been to shift the focus to the acceptance of partial patterns, so that persons are classified in terms of their predominant patterns of responses. Operationally, this means extracting the largest person-item submatrices characterized by perfect agreement that can be found in the data. Each submatrix consists of a subset of persons and a subset of items. The group of persons may be defined to form a *type*. The items upon which they agree are defined to be the *pattern*. The technique is one of multiple classification. Any person can appear in more than one type, and any item can appear in more than one pattern. There are several different ways in which these submatrices can be isolated. This description applies to the system recently worked out and programed by Hemingway. [3]

His first step is formation of the agreement matrix. The computer, having been supplied with the responses for n persons, calculates the number of items on which each person agrees with each other. There are accordingly $n(n-1)/2$ agreement scores. Items may be either dichotomous or multichotomous. The data matrix remains in the computer, since it will be referred to again and again.

The machine next finds the two persons with highest agreement, and they are grouped together. (Special rules which will not be given here deal with ties.) The computer prepares a scoring key itemizing the responses on which the two persons agree. The logic is that items on which they disagree cannot be essential to the pattern. All other persons are then scored with respect to the scoring key, which contains the items provisionally accepted as belonging to the pattern. The person who has the highest score on this key is obviously the one who has most in common with the two persons already provisionally grouped into a type, so that he is added to the group. The scoring key is once more revised, now including only those responses on which all three persons agree. Remaining persons are scored in terms of this further revision, and the person with highest score joins the type in his turn. Thus, as the number of persons in the type increases, the number of items in the pattern declines. The process of building the type and more precisely defining the pattern continues until the maximal product of accounted-for responses is reached, i.e., when the product of the persons provisionally in the type and items provisionally in the pattern is at a maximum. The maximal product of persons times items is found empirically. The computer continues adding to the provisional type as long as any remaining persons have any items in common with those in the type, and then selects the stage in the chain when the persons times items product is largest. These product functions seem characteristically to reach a mode, and thereafter decline rather rapidly, as losses of items outweigh gains of persons. The computer then prints the $j \times k$ submatrix and deletes the $j \times k$ responses from the data matrix.

Other submatrices are calculated in the same way as the first. A new agreement score matrix is formed for the unused item responses. The pair of persons with highest agreement form the nucleus of a second type. There is the same process of revising the scoring key after the addition of each person, and next adding to the type the person with highest score on the key. At any stage of building up the submatrix, the key, by its method of construction, consists of responses on which there is perfect agreement among subgroup members.

Here is a procedure with the simplest of arithmetic, consisting only on counting and of finding the highest agreement score. Yet agreement analysis is feasible for any large set of persons and items only on a computer. Indeed, even for a computer the operation is a lengthy one. MISTIC probably ranks as a high-speed computer, even in these times of faster machines, with its speed of about 10,000 additions per second. However, about 15 minutes may be needed to extract one submatrix from a group of 100 persons and as many items. An agreement analysis for the

United States 83d Senate, based upon the voting records of the senators, disclosed as many as forty type-patterns; about ten hours were needed for its computation. The machine indicates the number of responses included in each submatrix at the time of printing it out, so that at any stage it is easy to determine how much of the data matrix has been used and deleted. If the machine is needed for other work, the residual data matrix can be punched on cards, and the operation can start again later.

Any item may appear in more than one submatrix; so may any person. In analysis of voting records, this multiple classification enables one to recognize the varying affiliations and alliances. For example, a senator may vote with the civil rights advocates on one group of votes, with the economy bloc on another, and with agricultural interests on a third. Likewise any one roll call vote can appear in more than one pattern, i.e., it has different meaning and significance for various Senate groups.

Thus, briefly, we may see the interplay between the computer, the programer, and the methodologist. For effective computer use, methods often have to be drastically revised. There is also a greater incentive to create completely new procedures, in the knowledge that the computer can readily complete the calculations, even if a human would be loath to do so. Results provided by the computer enable new techniques to be evaluated much more quickly, providing a spur to the methodologist to revise and to reformulate. Computers are demanding radical changes in our numerical methods. That will be illustrated again and again in this book.

8.5 COMPUTERS AND THE SCIENTIFIC EFFORT

My prediction is that the electronic computer will prove to be the most versatile and influential scientific instrument so far invented and that it will play a larger role in the scientific histories of the future than even such obvious challengers as the microscope and the telescope. There are two reasons for this judgment: (a) the large number of sciences that are benefiting from computers, (b) the very varied numerical, clerical, and logical activities which form part of the computer workload. To the scientist with limited time and energy, the computer means extra research assistance. Unlike its human counterparts, this assistant is indefatigable. incredibly fast, and remarkably accurate; but it shares, with the humans it is superseding, the need to be given extremely precise instructions. It is moronic in the literalness with which it does what it is told to do. In this chapter, our concern has so far been with the problems of transition. We are still learning how to handle the facilities available to us. This section deals with the long-term influence of computers upon scientific method and experimental design in the social sciences, once our problems of machines, of men, and of methods have been resolved.

8.5.1 *Functions of the University Computing Center.* The modern American university has become so complex that it threatens to divide into a set of small empires, made up of its various departments and institutes, each encircled by high walls and too preoccupied with its own problems and affairs to have any time left for effective scholarly communication with its neighbors. In this fissioning, the computer center stands out as one centripetal force and the university library as another. If I were the architect designing a functional twentieth-century campus, I should place these two institutions at the two main vantage points, with all roads leading to them. These are the two central organizations to remind us of the unity of scholarship and science.

Nearly every computing center has been preoccupied so far with hardware problems. The dream of acquiring a computer has been realized at most universities. Now, faced with the nightmare of an overloaded facility, committees are writing their memoranda to urge the case (and it is generally a good case) for computers of higher capacity and power. The pattern of hardware change therefore continues. If one inquires about the computer position at University X, a rather stock reply is: "At present we have only Machine Y, but Machine Z is on order." Viewed at the microcosmic local level, computer policy sometimes seems bedevilled by politics. The over-all view, however, shows an amazingly rapid international acceptance of computers. There may be controversies about the machine to be acquired (there will be many complaints that the current machine is not good enough) and as to how it should be controlled (criticisms are often heard that the current administration is insufficiently helpful and does not fully realize the scientific and economic importance of getting analyses completed as rapidly as possible), but there seems to be virtually complete acceptance that any university with pretensions to scientific respectability must have some reasonably fast computer. I do not have the facts, but my guess is that telescopes and microscopes never spread around the scientific world at this rate; I doubt if even Caxton's momentous discovery of printing did.

The duties of university computing centers must gradually be widened to include the dissemination of knowledge about computer numerical techniques, language translation, computer simulation models, Monte Carlo methods, and all the other new procedures emerging as a result of computer development. Alternatively, this work will have to be initiated in other departments of the university. Before the introduction of computers, numerical analysis was a somewhat unpopular subject. It was unattractive, for example, to study solutions of equations which were either too involved for any practical use or which required an unreasonable amount of time and effort in their application. Likewise, matrix algebra, after its golden nineteenth-century days, had settled down into a rut. The field has now come alive again and is bustling with activity. There is, however, a formidable problem in getting this information into an intelligible form for the computer user. Clearly, behavioral scientists must be better trained in calculus, matrix algebra, and mathematical statistics than in the past.

Quite a large proportion of graduate students in the behavioral sciences, and perhaps even the undergraduates, should be expected to take mathematics as a minor. Computing activities will help by showing students the utility of mathematics and providing an incentive for its study; the interdisciplinary coteries which form around computing centers are often mathematically very stimulating. While improvement of mathematical standards should proceed as fast as possible, a generation or two may be required for behavioral scientists to reach the standards currently found in the physical sciences. In the interim, mathematical and statistical information must be presented in simpler form. Special textbooks are needed for those with limited mathematical training, even if this means an expansive and verbal style that is irksome for professional mathematicians. The need for improved consultancy services at the university has been discussed earlier. Because of these augmented functions, the time may not be very far distant when the computing center will have to be allocated as large a proportion of any university's budget as the library currently gets.

8.5.2 The Interplay of Theory, Method, Experiment, and Instrumentation in the History of Science. We can now return to the problem of the role of instrumentation in the history of science. There is an elaborate interweaving of theorization, of fact finding, of method construction, and of instrument development. No one technique can be assigned a logical or a chronological primacy over the others. The response to one problem in science is generally the stimulus for another. Any advance in methodology leads to more fruitful fact finding; better experimental evidence means theorization is more likely to be relevant; and so on.

Instrumentation plays its part in determining the form, not only of the methods and the experimental results, but even of the theories. The differences between the American and the British view of factor analysis may have been the product of their different computational facilities. For historical and cultural reasons, psychological research has not been as generously financed in Britain as in the United States. There has been less research assistance and fewer punched-card machines and electronic computers. Factor analyses have generally been conducted with smaller test batteries, so that fewer factors have been extracted. It is not surprising, therefore, that Vernon's [8] description of human ability is more parsimonious in its admission of factors than Thurstone's.[7] British reluctance to accept the desirability of rotation may be attributable to the same circumstance. As long as one operates with only three or four factors, the main groups of tests can be discerned readily enough by inspection of the centroid sign pattern, so that there is no need for rotation. Once twelve or sixteen factors have been extracted, however, the sign pattern becomes so complicated that a rotated solution with many near-zero loadings becomes essential if the test clusters are to be clearly distinguished.

This interplay between method, experiment, and theory can be illustrated from the British history of the study of individual differences.

Here are some landmarks:

a. Darwin: We have already seen how years of painstaking observation preceded his theory. His sequence is: observation $\longrightarrow$ theory.

b. Galton: Stimulated by the Darwinian theory to examine the evidence upon human inheritance, he devised the correlation coefficient to measure resemblances in persons with varying amounts of common inheritance; then he made a multitude of observations. His sequence is: theory $\longrightarrow$ method $\longrightarrow$ observation.

c. Karl Pearson: His professional career was devoted to elaborating upon the idea of correlation and other statistical techniques relevant for biological research. He stayed with method throughout. Instrumental consideration influenced his results. Tables in his articles appear to eight decimal places because that was the capacity of his hand-activated Brunsviga.

d. Spearman: He started with his concept of general intelligence, then devised a method intended to establish its existence, and then collected the data on which to test his theory. His sequence is: theory $\longrightarrow$ method $\longrightarrow$ observation.

e. Burt: He seems to have been of a more empirical temperament, concerned initially with certain educational problems. His observations led him to considerations of refinement of psychological measurements. His sequence is: observation $\longrightarrow$ method.

There is no general order. What happens seems to depend upon the temperament of the man, upon his times, and upon what his predecessors have done.

Our interest in computers has sprung from the time-consuming nature of our multivariate methods. The initial sequence has been: method $\longrightarrow$ instrumentation. I have tried to show how the computer transition is not a rote process of programing the extant methods. The need now is for revision of methods to meet the computer requirements. The sequence has become: instrumentation $\longrightarrow$ method. My prediction is that computers will also bring us a great accession in empirical knowledge (remember Galileo and his telescope). Behavioral science theories hardly ever seem to fit the facts well; the facts are generally too complex. Any spate of fact finding will inevitably reveal discrepancies in our theories, and there will then be a heroic attempt to restate them so as to overcome their defects. The later computer sequence will therefore be: instrumentation $\longrightarrow$ fact finding $\longrightarrow$ theory.

Biological history is informative about the effects of new instrumentation and the time span over which this operates. The compound microscope was invented at about the beginning of the seventeenth century. By the middle of the century, decisive advances began to be made in technique. Red blood corpuscles were seen; then bacteria; then spermatozoa; and then muscle striations. Thus blood chemistry, bacteriology, embryology, and histology had their origins. With accumulation of vast amounts of data, there was an impetus to classification which culminated in Linnaeus' *Systema Naturae* in the middle of the eighteenth century. In the nineteenth century, with the empirical foundations of biology so much better established, there came a period of great theories and generalizations. Thus two hundred years or more lapsed from the invention of the microscope to its theoretical harvest. The intervening period had been devoted to perfection of the microscope as a research instrument, to observation and to classification, which provided the seeds for the theoretical accomplishments to follow. The computer impact on science may be expected to take a similar course, but with more compressed time span because of the greater proportion of human time and energy being given to scientific research.

8.5.3 *The Scientific Paradigm in the Behavioral Sciences.* The scientific task in the behavioral sciences is isolation of functional relations. Much has been written about the stimulus-response sequence. This has been oversimplified. Except for reflexes, there is not usually a one-one correspondence between stimulus and response. Behavior in any situation depends in part upon the set of stimuli impinging on the organism and in part upon the organism, i.e., its present state, its inheritance, its prior learning, and its expectancies. Any single segment of behavior is generally the resultant of a large number of determinants pertaining both to the stimulus configuration and to the organism itself. Stimuli and organismic variables will be called the *antecedents,* and the sequence of behavioral responses will be called the *subsequents.* The functional relations needed are those which link a set of antecedents and a set of subsequents. These neutral terms have been selected to avoid imputation of causality and its metaphysical problems.

The functional relations will generally be both multivariate and probabilistic. The reason for their multivariateness is obvious; many determinants affect the outcome. They are probabilistic because not all determinants can usually be accounted for. Meteorology provides an analog from the physical sciences. The outcome, which is the weather, is the product of many atmospheric and geophysical factors, so that its predictions are probabilistic.

Probably no one will have disagreed to this point. The controversies about method occur mostly at the tactical level of how best to attain to these multivariate functions. There are those who support the univariate procedure by which only one antecedent is varied, with all others held constant. This procedure has been favored not only by experimental psychologists but throughout the natural sciences, and it is probably unequaled for its precision and ease of interpretation.

The multivariate methods are the product of twentieth-century statistics. Several chapters in this book deal with them—multiple scalogram analysis is considered in Chapter 9, multiple regression in Chapter 10, factor analysis in Chapter 11, and canonical analysis in Chapter 12. With these methods, various aspects of the stimulus-and-organism configuration can be considered jointly. The complexity of the experimental situation is disentangled by the multivariate statistics. Until recently, these methods have had the common characteristic of being extremely laborious computationally. Despite this, multiple regression and factor analysis came into regular use before the arrival of computers. Because behavioral scientists were already familiar with these techniques, they have been first to be programed. Canonical analysis involves finding the best linear functions between a set of antecedents and a set of subsequents, an objective which is essentially similar to the formal scientific one of finding the functions which link stimulus and organismic variables with the behavioral responses. Combining as it does some elements of multiple regression and some of factor analysis, canonical analysis was extremely laborious, and hence was hardly ever used in our desk calculator period. Because it is not well known, it remains little used even though we have the computers to handle it. The multiple discriminant function, designed to achieve the best classification into known groups (surely similar in form to the objective of the clinical psychologists), is another method that was developed before computers, but even now remains practically unused. There are the new multivariate techniques, such as McQuitty's [4] agreement analysis and Lingoes' multiple scalogram analysis, which have been devised since the advent of computers, and whose calculations have been organized in such a way as to make full use of computer capabilities. The era of invention of new multivariate techniques is evidently not yet over. We are likely to see many more during the next half century.

Experimental designs may be classified in yet another way. The variables can be controlled and manipulated, or they can be observed in some systematic way in real-life observations in the field. We are accustomed to think of laboratory experiments as having some sort of intrinsic merit not possessed by material gleaned in the field. Astronomy, however, serves to remind us that high rigor can be attained even when the scientist must rely upon observation. Until the ascent of Sputnik in 1957, there had been no manipulated experiment in astronomy.

Thus there is a two-by-two classification: univariate-controlled, univariate-observational, multivariate-controlled, multivariate-observational. We are dealing here with oblique rather than orthogonal factors. Not all designs are equally likely. Instead, controlled laboratory studies are more likely to be univariate, and field studies to be multivariate. The distinction should not, however, be made too sharply. The k-way analysis of variance has been used increasingly in the laboratory. By suitable balancing of the numbers of subjects receiving the various experimental treatments, the effects of each factor can be examined independently from the others. The economy of a procedure in which several variables are experimented upon simultaneously is one advantage of the design. Another is the feasibility of examining the interactions (non-linearities) between the variables, in which the outcome is influenced by the simultaneous level on two variables. The laboratory psychologist is evidently willing to adopt multivariate techniques whenever he can get the controls and the precision he wants.

The strengths of the multivariate field experiment lie in its realism. Behavior is observed *in situ*. Applications of psychology will incline toward multivariate designs, because in making predictions and recommendations, we shall always want to utilize our information as fully as we can.

It is not helpful to have behavioral scientists feuding about which is the right method to follow. The complexity of behavior is sufficiently great to warrant trying all roads which may add to our knowledge. The extremes are clear. The univariate laboratory experiment excels in precision; the multivariate field investigation is strong on realism. Both are admirable goals, and each investigator has to use his own judgment as to the best balance between the two. His decision will no doubt be influenced by his temperament and his training as well as by his objective appraisal of the situation.

There is one fundamental difference between the methods. So far as the history of modern science goes, the univariate method is comparatively old, extending back to Galileo or before. The multivariate method is much newer, with its main development occurring within about the last hundred years (although I believe the resolution of forces into components goes back several centuries before that). The multivariate logic seems to have owed its formal inception to John Stuart Mill's[5] canon (1843) of concomitant variation. Galton's discovery of correlation came forty years later, at a time when there was an intensive search in progress for a reliable method of measuring association (Walker,[9]); *Biometrika*, the statistical journal, dates from the beginning of the twentieth century; and the multivariate statistical procedures considered in this book have emerged since then. This is not a long period in terms of the history of science. The preoccupation with methods which has characterized a number of multivariate researchers is explicable in terms of the infancy of their field.

Computers are significant because they have opened the way to easy use of multivariate statistics. We can now readily take a multivariate approach to the search for functional relations. The tactical routes open to us have been widened. It is entirely premature to say what proportion of future behavioral science research will be multivariate and what proportion will be univariate. Multivariate analysis is still too new, and both its logic and its techniques are insufficiently elaborated. That there will be some significant place for multivariate analysis and for the computer as its instrument does not have to be argued.

REFERENCES

1 Davison, J., Master's thesis, University of California, 1957.

2 Guttman, L., An Estimate of Communalities That is Imagewise Consistent and Structure-free. University of California Contract AF 41 (657)–76, Research Report *20*, 1958.

3 Hemingway, P. W., Multiple Agreement Analysis. Ph.D. thesis, Michigan State University, 1961.

4 McQuitty, L. L., Agreement Analysis: Classifying Persons by Predominant Patterns of Responses, *Brit. Jour. Statist. Psychol.*, 1956, *9*, 5–16.

5 Mill, J. S., *A System of Logic*. London, 1843.

6 Richardson, L. F., *Weather Prediction by Numerical Process*. Cambridge: Cambridge Univ. Press, 1922.

7 Thurstone, L. L., *Primary Mental Abilities*. Chicago: Univ. Chicago Press, 1938.

8 Vernon, P. E., *The Structure of Human Abilities*. New York: Wiley, 1951.

9 Walker, H. M., *Studies in the History of Statistical Method*. Baltimore, Md.: Williams and Wilkins, 1929.

E. Lowell Kelly & James C. Lingoes

9/DATA PROCESSING
IN PSYCHOLOGICAL RESEARCH

*E. Lowell Kelly received the doctorate in psychology
from Stanford in 1930 and taught psychology and statistics at
the University of Hawaii, the University of Connecticut,
and Purdue before World War II. During the war,
he was an aviation psychologist in the U.S. Navy, where he worked
in problems of pilot selection and flight training.
In 1946, he joined the staff of the University of Michigan,
where he is now Professor of Psychology, Chairman of
the Department of Psychology, and Director of
the Bureau of Psychological Services. His primary research
interests include personality assessment, the selection
of professional personnel, and psychological factors in marriage.*

*James C. Lingoes received the doctorate in psychology
from Michigan State University, in 1960. He holds a joint appointment
as Assistant Professor of Psychology and Research Associate
in the Computing Center of the University of Michigan. His major
areas of interest are in clinical psychology
and in the applications of computers to clinical problems.
His present research is concerned with the development
and application of a new statistical technique, called
"multiple scalogram analysis,"
to diagnostic tests.*

9.1 HISTORICAL ANTECEDENTS AND METHODOLOGICAL PROBLEMS

Psychologists were among the first behavioral scientists to recognize and utilize the high-speed digital computer in data processing. The modern computer was developed by mathematicians and engineers primarily for application in their own fields (and in the physical sciences). At most universities, responsibility for the operation of computers is usually assigned to mathematicians or engineers, yet the records of such centers show that psychologists rank high in actual use of computer time. Furthermore, this high level of use occurs even though, in the early days at least, psychologists found that using the computer demanded that they first spend hundreds or even thousands of hours in writing new programs for the particular types of data analysis they wished to carry out. There seem to have been two reasons for this development:

a. Psychologists are typically better grounded in statistical methods than persons with primary training in other of the behavioral sciences. Many widely used statistical techniques were developed by psychologists; psychologists have written several of the standard textbooks in the field, and at most universities at least one course in statistics is a minimal requirement for all graduate students in psychology.

173

b. Psychologists had been heavy users of earlier electromagnetic equipment originally designed primarily for data processing in business operation but later adapted to scientific data analysis. This equipment, although pitifully inadequate by present-day standards, was a godsend to many psychologists who needed to analyze large bodies of data. Furthermore, experience with such equipment and its operation led to familiarity with all the basic ideas and procedures involved in the actual operation of computers and to an appreciation of their tremendous promise as a research tool.

But the readiness of psychologists to adopt the computer as a tool and their widespread use of computers point to a prior question: Why have psychologists historically been so active in the development of statistical methods, in the use of aids to computation, and in concern with experimental design? The answer to this question appears to lie in the unique problems faced by psychologists and in the nature of their subject matter. Whether the psychologist is primarily interested in theory or in application, certain special problems make his task both difficult and complex. These problems confront all social scientists, but psychologists are peculiarly sensitive to them, perhaps because they are more concerned with their status vis-à-vis their colleagues in the physical sciences. Four of the most critical of these problems are (1) sampling of subjects, (2) experimental controls, (3) selection of variables, and (4) the measurement of variables.

9.1.1 Sampling of Subjects. The psychologist is concerned with behavior, but he cannot study behavior in the abstract; he must study a behaving organism, whether it be a rat, a cat, a monkey, or a human subject. But even after he has selected the species, he still must choose a sample. From the standpoint of simplicity, it would be pleasant to have a ready supply of "standard subjects" of each species, much as the chemist can reach for chemically pure reagents. As every one knows, however, no two living organisms are identical, not even litter mates or identical twins. Instead, individual differences are the rule and are especially pronounced among higher organisms. Every psychologist, then, is forced to restrict his study to a sample of subjects selected from the larger population of possible subjects and to be concerned with the adequacy of that sample for any particular investigation. For experimental psychologists interested primarily in psychological processes, this means using a sample sufficiently large to yield stable estimates of population parameters and adequate tests of hypotheses. For many other psychologists, the primary focus of interest is individual differences among subjects, their origin, their interrelationships, and their relationships to life criteria. In either case, the research psychologist is likely to be confronted with a considerable amount of statistical analysis. Computers permit him to process his data far more efficiently and accurately than was heretofore possible.

9.1.2 *Problems of Experimental Controls.* An investigator interested in studying the factors involved in the linear acceleration of an object, for example, needs to know certain facts, e.g., the mass of the object, the force applied and its point of application, the inertial properties of the object and of the medium through which it must pass, and many others besides. Next, he must vary each of the relevant variables, systematically, one at a time, in order to generate some laws about linear acceleration as a function of these variables. Having measured, controlled, and observed, he can then analyze and formulate. A fairly simple set of mathematical expressions in the form of general and special laws would result from these procedures. Finally, he must test his formulations, i.e., replicate the experiments.

In essence, the foregoing exemplifies the experimental model of the physical sciences. Control of all but a single variable is the essence of experimentation in the physical sciences and the ideal in psychology as well. For a variety of reasons, some of which are indicated below, such experimental control often is not possible or not acceptable in experimentation with human subjects. Thus, the psychologist finds it necessary to permit several or even many variables to covary as in nature and can no more manipulate them than can the astronomer. In such instances, the univariate model must be replaced or supplemented by the multivariate; probability and the use of statistics then must supplant the isolation and manipulation of variables. The physical scientist comes closest to this problem in the fields of meteorology, astronomy, and quantum physics. But even though he cannot control, isolate, or accurately measure the relevant variables in these areas, the physical scientist's knowledge of them far surpasses the equivalent knowledge of the behavioral scientist.

There are still other differences: Human objects differ from other objects in a number of respects, not the least of which is in our attitudes toward them. Social and moral restraints, the evidence from the Nuremburg trials notwithstanding, deter the scientist from inflicting pain or discomfort upon another person, however noble the cause or intent.[9] Further differences from physical objects relate to the variability, complexity, and highly reactive nature of human organisms. A psychological probe into the inner emotions of another may result in a blank stare or a poke in the nose. (How unlike the well-behaved physical object!) Here no simple laws are possible and certainly none with the esthetic elegance of a mathematical equation.

Opportunities for direct manipulation of variables are limited, not only because of ethical reasons or emotional involvement [33] but also because such control either introduces artificiality or destroys the variables we wish most to assess. We always stand the chance of losing what we seek, almost in direct proportion to our efforts to reach it. The probabilistic model, rather than univariate experimentation, is thus the most obvious and natural choice of the psychologist for many problem areas. With this choice goes a necessary tolerance for ambiguity and indeterminacy, a need for passive rather than active control, for sampling, and for satisfaction with approximation rather than certitude.

When samples are used instead of populations, where parameters require estimation, where natural experiments replace laboratory control, when likelihoods need evaluation, in short, when we operate within the confines of the multivariate probability model, a computer becomes a potentially powerful ally. It can free the social scientist of a great deal of drudgery in the organization of data; it can allow him to use what were, B. C. (before computers), forbidding statistical techniques. With some ingenuity on his part, computers offer the opportunity for testing models and simulating behavior. This last area, as yet not fully explored, is extremely exciting and challenging for the behavior scientist concerned with thinking, emotional, and motivational processes. It is likely that clinical psychologists of the future may find it necessary to utilize computers for situations requiring more than a crude diagnostic evaluation. [22] Currently, it seems unlikely that computers will be used in psychotherapy, but with the development of language translation programs, it is not inconceivable that a future computer could serve as a valuable aid in therapy.

9.1.3 *Plethora of Psychological Variables.* The nomenclature of variables in psychology is almost as bewildering as their number. Thus, we have molecular variables and molar ones, those which are environmental and organismic, quantitative and qualitative, observable and inferred, complex and simple, stimulus and response, independent and dependent, etc. It would be interesting to speculate on the reasons for this meta-language. Does it reflect the complexity and range of variables required for understanding human behavior—as opposed to those needed for physical objects, our incomplete comprehension of what is relevant, or our frustration? Possibly all three. In any event, the number of variables is indeed large, many are difficult or impossible to isolate, some defy analysis, and quite a few are vague and lack operational significance. A Linnaeus is needed to identify a psychological hierarchy of behavior-relevant variables. Short of finding this genius, we can employ the limited capabilities of a computer to help us discover the underlying dimensionality of this universe (see Chapter 11 on factor analysis, for example). Having done this, we will be in a much better position to measure the variables and to design experiments to test their effects. [1]

9.1.4 *Problems of Measurement in Psychology.* Last, but certainly not least, are the multitude of problems connected with measurement of psychological variables, once they have been selected. How does one go about measuring a complex variable: for example, anxiety? But first, what is meant by this term? The psychological literature is replete with definitions, operational and otherwise, of this central concept. Almost as much has been written on this "variable" as on love, and with about as much understanding. Psychologists not only do not agree upon the "meaning" of this term, but they set about measuring it in different ways. As a consequence, several studies have shown little or no relation between alternative measures and symptoms of anxiety. This is clearly an unsatisfactory state of affairs for research, even though the use of this term and others like it often suffices for action in a clinical setting or in the everyday world.

Perhaps one of the chief difficulties in this area exists because we carry many of our language habits over into the research setting, even though it is chimerical to suppose that the complexities of psychological reality will correspond to the forms of language. An obvious, but unpalatable, solution of this dilemma is giving up our theoretical pretensions and matching our research language with the complexity and often highly specific nature of life. Another, and related, solution is the painful and long-drawn-out process of empirical investigation. Integral to this enterprise is reliable and meaningful quantification.

For variables that are either too complex or difficult to isolate from the observation matrix, as well as for those discontinuous in nature, some numerical value can be assigned. The important thing, however, is not the number as such, but the intra-individual and inter-individual reliability with which it is given. Although some information is lost by having too few categories, even dichotomous data can yield valuable insights. A number of techniques are available to the clinician for quantifying even the most recalcitrant variable, e.g., scaling methods, Q-sorts, check lists, etc. That old standby, rating scales, although subject to a number of distorting influences, can also be used to good advantage. Despite our best efforts, there will be variables which we feel are important but which elude quantification. If we can accurately specify what the variable's presence means for any given bit of behavior and what its absence indicates, and if we can do this reliably, then it can be quantified. On the other hand, if we cannot do these things, we are either working with an epiphenomenon or are confused in our thinking. In any event, a computer does not as yet have the logical powers of a human. It is restricted in its manipulations to machine representations (often binary) of the data we input. The output, or results, can be no better or worse than our conceptualizations.

Before turning to illustrative examples of the extremely profitable and often necessary use of digital computers by psychologists for data processing, it is important to note what the modern computer cannot do and what it can.

The computer cannot design an experiment, select the variables to be studied, select the measuring instruments, or collect the data. It cannot specify which among alternative methods of statistical analysis are to be applied. It cannot even read data until they are coded and punched in a specified language and format. It cannot do anything with the data it reads until supplied with a set of specific sequential instructions called a "program." But with the appropriate program stored in its memory, the computer can read large amounts of data rapidly, carry out elaborate sequences of computations at high speeds, with almost complete accuracy, and then print out the results in an easy-to-read format specified in the program. Taken together, these operations are termed "data processing."

Because of both the cost and the capacity of modern computers, psychologists are rarely the sole users of any computer. Usually they process their data through a general purpose computing center, so highly automatized that not even the immediate operator of the computer is aware of the specific type of problem the computer is working on at any given moment. As noted above, psychologists who pioneered in the application of computers had to write entirely new programs for the special types of data analyses in which they were interested. Preparing and debugging such programs typically required far more time than the particular statistical analysis for which they were written. Once written, however, a program could be used over and over again. More important, the program could be made available to fellow psychologists at other universities, with access to the same type of computer; thus it became possible to develop libraries of shared programs. In spite of the variety of computer types and the rapidity of technological change in the computer field, most computer centers are now supplied with a library containing tested programs for carrying out the most frequently used techniques of statistical analysis. Thus the tremendous advantages of the modern computer in routine data processing are immediately available to the research psychologist who need only (1) prepare his data in the proper format, (2) specify to the computer operator the particular program (or programs) to be used in processing his data, and (3) specify certain parameters which must be inserted before a generic program can begin computing on a specific problem. A few hours (or even minutes) later, depending on the demand for computer time, he picks up his printed results of a data analysis, which only a few years ago would have required several man-weeks or even months of hand computation, and in many cases would have been completely unattainable at any cost.

The foregoing picture of the psychologist's almost effortless use of the computer in data processing is admittedly somewhat rosier than that which exists in many localities. Unfortunately, many psychologists work in institutions without a computer. Those with access to a computer may discover that only a limited number of needed programs are available for the particular make and model locally available; hence they are forced to learn to write programs. And with the rapid technological changes, one finds that just about the time an adequate library of programs is established, a decision has been made to acquire a new computer. Even though the new model may have a much larger memory and compute many times faster than the old one, the user now must write or otherwise acquire an entirely new library of programs; consequently, it may be months before he can take full advantage of the potentiality of the new computer. Finally, like all man-made machines, computers both new and old are subject to operational breakdown. Although breakdowns rarely result in inaccurate computation, they can result in annoying delays, especially after one has become accustomed to high-speed data processing.

For these, as well as other reasons, it is hardly surprising that the most extensive and most effective use of computers occurs in institutional settings, where one or more staff members specialize in the application of computers to the particular sorts of problems and analyses of interest to behavioral scientists. To be maximally effective, such a specialist must be thoroughly familiar with both the terminology and techniques employed by behavioral scientists on the one hand, and with the programming and operation of the local computer on the other. Although he need not (and perhaps should not) serve as a consultant in research design or in decisions regarding statistical analyses of data, he must be at least sufficiently well grounded in both mathematics and statistical techniques to establish and maintain an up-to-date library of programs, to write new programs as needed, to recommend the most appropriate and efficient programs for carrying out analyses as specified by the research scientist, and generally to assist the would-be user to make maximal use of the computer. In a few university settings, specialists of this sort hold joint appointments on the staff of the computer center and the staff of an instructional department. Several of the larger psychological research institutes have found it necessary to appoint one or more such full-time specialists to facilitate computer use by other research personnel.

The great potentialities of the computer in data processing seems to have been first realized by psychologists at the University of Illinois. Its School of Engineering had built the ILLIAC for university use at the same time it built the ORDVAC for use by the Ordnance Department of the United States Army. Thanks to the cooperative attitude of the engineers in charge of this installation, to the vision and diligent programing efforts of Charles F. Wrigley, J. Neuhaus, K. Dickman, and others, and because of the computational needs of R. B. Cattell, Charles Osgood, L. L. McQuitty, and others of the department of psychology, a most effective data processing facility was developed by 1955. For the first time, psychologists were able to complain, not about finding time to analyze their data, but about having so many analyzed results available that they could not find time to prepare them for publication!

The influence of this pioneering development at the University of Illinois was far more than local. Because of the size and speed of the ILLIAC, local scientists could not utilize its full capacity in the early years, and the University of Illinois generously made the computer and its programs available to scientists from other universities. Thus, many psychologists first learned of the real potentialities and the actual necessity of computers in present-day research. Today, all major universities have some type of computer installation available for data processing; for present-day psychological research, it is as essential as is a good library for historical research.

The remainder of this chapter presents illustrative examples of data analysis of special interest to psychologists. No effort has been made to assess systematically the impact of computers on published research; rather the authors have attempted to select a variety of problems and techniques in order to emphasize for research psychologists the range of application and ability of computers.

9.2 PSYCHOLOGICAL DATA PROCESSING

9.2.1 *Factor Analytic Studies.* Even a cursory survey of the literature indicates that the most extensive application of computers in psychology has been in factor analytic studies (see Chapter 11). There are at least two reasons: (1) the versatility of the technique, and hence its utility in a wide variety of research designs, and (2) the extremely large number of computations required for factor analysis and analytic rotational solutions. In fact, before the development of computers and of appropriate programs for factor extraction and analytic rotation, psychologists were unable to undertake any but relatively small problems, i.e., those involving relatively few variables. Now, because of these developments, it is entirely feasible for an investigator to complete, within a matter of minutes, a factor analysis that formerly would have required two or three man-years of laborious computation. In fact, several such analyses may be carried on as a part of a doctoral dissertation.

The most ardent proponent of factor analytic techniques in psychology is Cattell, who was also one of the first to employ computers extensively in his research.[4] Cattell was also the first to clarify and label the distinction between three types of factor analysis—all of potential interest to the psychologist. These are designated as R, P, and Q and are characterized as in Figure 9.1.

Careful study of Figure 9.1 shows that the essential differences between the R and P techniques are (1) in the number of persons or cases studied, and (2) in the number of occasions on which observations are made. Both the R and P techniques represent an effort to identify basic or underlying sources of covariation among a larger number of observed variables. In R technique, the correlation between variables is based on the covariation of individual differences of the several variables across many individuals. The resulting factor (or underlying variable) is thus said to be a common factor across persons. In P technique, the correlation is based on the covariation of correlated changes in variables *for the same person* on many successive occasions. The resulting factor is thus common to the variables, but it may be unique to the individual. Q technique, on the other hand, is designed to identify subgroups of persons who have such similar scores on a sample of variables as to justify treating them as a common type of person.

All three of these factoring techniques are used by psychologists, and as was indicated earlier, in most instances, their extensive use is feasible only

Data matrix	R	P	Q
Each row is an: Each column is an:	Entity (person or subject) Attribute (variable or test)	Occasion Attribute (variable or test)	Attribute (variable or test) Entity, person or subject
Scattergram plotted column vs. column	Variable against variable. Each entry refers to the paired scores of one person on two variables.	Variable against variable. Each entry refers to the scores on two variables made by the same person on that occasion.	Person against person. Each entry refers to the scores of two persons on the same variable.
Correlation matrix	r between variables	r between variables	r between persons
Resulting factors:	Underlying dimensions common to two or more variables.	Underlying dimensions common to two or more variables.	Underlying types common to two or more persons.
Factor loadings is correlation of:	A variable and an underlying dimension on which persons vary.	A variable and an underlying dimension on which the individual varies from time to time.	A person and an underlying type representing a subgroup of persons.
Typical N of: Persons Attributes Occasions	Many (100–1000) Several (10–50) One	One Several (10–50) Many (100 if possible)	Several (10–50) Many (100 if possible) One

FIGURE 9.1 Essential characteristics of R, P, and Q factor analyses.

with computers. R technique has been most widely utilized in the development of personality assessment devices of interest to clinical psychologists and in studies concerned with the empirical identification of theoretical constructs. Examples of the use of the R technique in the development of psychological tests include the well-known tests of Primary Mental Ability (Thurstone),[39] the 16PF Personality Test (Cattell),[5] and the Guilford-Zimmerman Temperament Test.[13] In addition, Cattell has made extensive use of factor techniques in developing his O-A Battery,[6] objective personality tests, and in seeking to find matchings among the personality factors found in different domains of personality test variables: self-ratings, ratings by others, objective tests.

A number of investigators have utilized R-factor analysis in an effort to identify the dimensions underlying observed behavior of neurotic and psychotic patients, regardless of their psychiatric diagnosis. The first one developed by Wittenborn [44] reduces 52 symptom-ratings to 9 cluster scores established by factor analyses. Later Lorr, Jenkins, and Holsopple [20] developed the Multidimensional Scale for Rating Psychiatric Patients. Some 40 rating scales provide 11 "factor" scores. A still later form devised by Lorr, Rubinstein, and Jenkins [21] for use with psychotic outpatients provides scores on ten personality and symptom variables. Each of these instruments has proved extremely useful in providing relatively objective scores in a series of relatively uncorrelated dimensions.

Of considerable interest and utility to psychologists has been the extensive series of R-factor analytic studies of Osgood and his students [29] concerned with the development of the connotative dimensions of meaning and utilizing the technique known as the "Semantic Differential." This technique first requires the subjects to rate objects, concepts, or people on a series of adjectival bipolar scales; the resulting ratings are intercorrelated, and then the matrix is factored. Small,[34] in a doctoral dissertation, followed these procedures to study age and sex differences in semantic stimuli of fourth, eighth, and twelfth grade boys and girls. Shortly thereafter, Smith [36] applied the same technique to identify the dimensions of the self-concept of neuropsychiatric patients; he was able to identify clearly five such dimensions and replicate them on a second sample of patients. In a doctoral dissertation under the senior author's direction, Lin is following the same general procedures in studying age and sex differences in the self-concept of fourth, eighth, and twelfth grade boys and girls.

The second most widely used of the three factor analytic techniques by psychologists is Q technique in which some index of association (r, tau, coefficient of profile similarity, etc.) is computed between all possible pairs of individuals in a group, and the resulting matrix of coefficients is analyzed in an attempt to find natural clusters (families or types) of persons. The first such application seems to have been the study by Moore, Stafford, and Hsu [28] in 1947 (long before the availability of computers) aimed at identifying pre-psychotic syndromes in a population of college students. More recently, Guertin [12] utilized what he termed "inverted factor analysis" to identify types of schizophrenic patients, but failed to find any evidence of a general factor of schizophrenia. Borko [3] also used an inverse or obverse factor analysis to determine clusters or types of patients based on MMPI responses. And still more recently, by means of a cluster analysis of a group of poor readers, Smith and Carrigan [35] identified five types of reading cases, each of which they regarded as requiring different kinds of remedial treatment.

P-factor analytic technique is most similar to the type of intuitive analysis represented by the intensive case study so much preferred by clinical pyschologists. In fact, it is a method for doing systematically what the clinician attempts to do intuitively, i.e., to identify the essential (or basic or genotypic) variable(s) influencing the day-to-day fluctuations in the behavior of a single patient. The reader may therefore be surprised to learn that P technique has been but rarely used by clinical psychologists. Why is this so? There are at least three possible reasons:

a. Like all types of statistical analysis, P technique requires that the observational data be quantified, i.e., expressed as numbers, and unfortunately, many clinical psychologists object to any form of quantification of their observations of patients, arguing that it is impossible to express in symbols or numbers the complexities of the phenomenon which they observe. Actually, this is not a well-justified concern, since the investigator is free to use as many variables (symptoms, traits, mechanisms) as he wishes and may rate each on as many categories as he chooses.

b. Unfortunately, a great many clinicians are antagonistic to any proposal to apply statistical techniques of any kind to the single case. Because of this orientation, they often fail to acquire any real competence with the methods of multivariate statistics and hence could not utilize P-factor analysis even if they wanted to. If their training has included some familiarization with the technique, they are apt to argue that since the assumptions underlying it are not met (e.g., linear relationships among variables), the technique is not applicable to real clinical problems, where interactions and curvilinear relationships supposedly abound.

c. The most rational reason for the paucity of P-factor studies is the admittedly serious problem involved in securing meaningful data on enough variables on enough successive occasions for a single case to provide reliable correlations and a stable factor structure. It requires considerable testing time on each occasion to obtain scores on each of several variables. More important, since the goal is determining the covariation in the day-to-day fluctuations of states of the subject, it is essential that the measures obtained not be influenced by virtue of repeated measurements. Unfortunately, this requirement is not easily met in psychological measurement, because of practice effects, memory, boredom, etc. Ideally, one would use tests for which there were 100 equivalent forms, but unfortunately, none exist.

It is not surprising, therefore, to find that the most extensive use of P-factor analysis has been in the analysis of physiological and psycho-physiological variables, for which the measures are presumably relatively uninfluenced by repetitive testing. Thus Williams,[43] in a single subject tested on 100 occasions, identified a cyclical factor, or state, characterized by low cholinesterase in serum, high pulse pressure, high pH of saliva, low pH of urine. Another factor was characterized by high per cent lymphocytes, low per cent neutrophils, high blood glucose, and small difference flicker fusion thresholds. A third factor, perhaps the best substantiated of all factors defined by the P techniques, is one characterized by large PGR deflections, high initial skin resistance, low glucose concentration, marked upward drift in skin resistance during relaxation, short dark adaptation, high daily urine volume, and other variables.

But P-technique studies of the single case need not be limited to physiological variables. Cattell and Luborsky [8] have shown that ingenuity on the part of the investigator permits the inclusion of often repeated measures of needs, moods, and attitudes in P-technique studies. Furthermore, Cattell and Cross [7] present rather convincing evidence that certain personality factors originally identified by the R technique with many subjects also appear in a single case analyzed by the P technique.[6]

An interesting application of R technique of factor analysis to the single case occurs in a study recently completed by Rosenthal,[32] who explored its possibility as a technique for discovering the implicit personality theory utilized by a judge in his assessment of others. In this study, Rosenthal asked each of several subjects (judges) to rate a number of others (targets) on some 40 variables, utilizing each target's autobiography as a basis for the ratings. For each judge, correlations were computed between all pairs of rated variables, the N being the number of targets rated. Thus, it was possible to carry out an R-technique factor analysis for each judge. Rosenthal found marked differences in the resulting factor structures, e.g., differences in the number of factors required to account for 95 per cent of the variance, in the relative amount of variance accounted for by the most salient factor, and also in the loading of specific variables. Equally important from the standpoint of methodology, he found that, with 50 or more targets, intrajudge factor similarity (i.e., replicability) was considerably greater than interjudge factor similarity.

9.2.2 *Multiple Regression.* Perhaps some of the best examples of the use of the regression model for prediction can be found in the studies by Horst and his associates at the University of Washington.[17] This source has issued a series of publications which are truly impressive in the thoroughness of their documentation. Particularly noteworthy is the excellent reporting of many IBM 650 computer programs needed for such analyses. A cursory glance through these articles and the program write-ups will clearly demonstrate the close interdependency of research and computers.* A major part of the work done at this center relates to predicting college success differentially for a number of different course areas. The analog for the clinician might be the differential prediction of therapeutic success as a function of type of therapy, therapist-patient similarity, initial status of the patient, diagnosis, etc. Quite typically, because of the problems involved, the clinician attacks this type of research in a piecemeal fashion. Nothing comparable to the number of cases (Horst reports using as many as 15,000) and variables (up to 46) has been attempted in the clinical area.[15] Let us here illustrate the procedures involved in one kind of predictive study and how the computer is integral to the analysis.

As Talbott [38] has pointed out, batteries composed of intellective measures have reached a certain point of predictive efficiency relative to the complex criterion of college success. The search for additional variables tapping aptitude and achievement does not offer much promise of raising the level of prediction. Not altogether unfamiliar to the personality psychologist has been the suggestion that personality and interest variables might result in a significant improvement in predicting college grades. Talbott rightly anticipates, however, a prior problem, i.e., that of the predictive value of normative versus ipsative measures. Common sense,

* Wrigley (see Chapter 8) has aptly pointed out the role of instrumentation in scientific progress.

mathematics, and empirical findings suggest contradictory answers to this problem. Talbott addressed himself to this issue by comparing the relative predictive efficiency of an ipsative and a normative personality measure for college grades. The responses of 171 University of Washington college students to Edwards Personal Preference Schedule [10] (the ipsative measure) and Wright's Rating Scale [45] form of this same test (the normative measure) served as the basis for predicting college grade point averages in nine different course areas plus the all-University grade point average. His principal finding was that the two measures did not yield significantly different predictions, although it was expected that the normative measure would be superior.

The following steps in the analysis of these data nicely demonstrate the advantages of having a computer as helpmate. First, there is the time-consuming and often boring matter of scoring the test protocols. It is much cheaper, quicker, and quite probably more reliable to let a machine do this for us. Second, each variable from both forms of the test (15 on each) must be correlated with every other and with the 10 criterion measures, representing some 750 correlations. Third, the two 15-order matrices must be inverted in order to obtain the regression weights and the multiple correlations. Fourth, vectors of criterion correlations must be estimated by multiplying the inverse obtained by vectors based upon subsamples of Ss in the nine course areas. Finally, some test of significance must be devised and calculated for the differences between the predictions of the two forms of the test for the ten criteria. Although each of these steps has been separately programed, efficiency would dictate an integrated program,* starting with the new data and ending with the various tests of significance. On a high-speed computer, a job of this magnitude would probably not exceed 30 minutes in time. This saving would mean that the researcher could easily investigate many different hypotheses in the space of a week or a month.

In those cases where one has many criteria or a complex multidimensional criterion and a number of predictors, the regression model is wedded to the factor model to yield what has been called "canonical analysis" by Hotelling. (See Chapter 12 for the procedures and examples.)

The next example illustrates a complex analysis employing a principal-axis factor analysis and a least-squares multiple regression analysis in yet another manner.

* See the last section of this chapter for an example of such a program.

9.2.3 *Factor Space D² Analysis.* The method of multivariate analysis to be described is particularly appropriate in those cases where there is reason to believe that the treatment effects we are evaluating may be a function of a small number of underlying factors. Overall and Gorham [30] report on the use of such a method for clinical experimental data. Briefly, the particular project reported by these investigators was a double-blind study of 12 weeks' duration using drugs administered to 80 newly admitted schizophrenic patients, randomly assigned to six different drug groups. Three psychiatric evaluations were made using Lorr's Multidimensional Scale for Rating Psychiatric Patients, i.e., before treatment, 4 weeks after initial administration, and after 12 weeks. Since it could not be assumed that the 11 "factor" or scale scores used on this test represented independent dimensions for this particular sample of patients, *factor space D² analysis* offered a potentially powerful tool for evaluating significant treatment differences, which might not otherwise become apparent from a univariate analysis. For any sizable sample of cases and number of groups and/or variables, such an analysis would be prohibitive with a desk calculator.

The kinds of calculations, rather than a detailed procedure, will be outlined here. As reported by Overall and Gorham, the essential steps involved in this type of analysis are (1) the calculation of the correlation matrix, based upon the within groups sums of squares and cross products, corrected to the treatment means and summed over groups; (2) a principal-axis solution of the correlation matrix to yield a few orthogonal variates accounting for the maximum of variance; (3) the rotation of the reference axes to meaningful structure; (4) estimation of factor scores by regression analysis; and (5) the testing of differences among the various group means on the underlying dimensions, which is provided by Mahalanobis-D^2 statistic. [31]

Two factors resulted from the seven Lorr scales analyzed, four having been omitted from the study because of previous findings. The first factor was interpreted as representing improvement in ward behavior; the second related to improved mental processes. Factor scores were differentially related to drug treatment. With the increased accessibility of computers, this method of analysis with many more variables may well prevail in the clinical literature.

9.2.4 *Pattern Analytic Methods.* Two general classes of techniques will receive attention here: (1) those methods which relate to *ordered data,* e.g., testing, classifying, and comparing profiles or patterns of standings on linear continua; and (2) those which relate to *unordered data,* e.g., discovering that set of elements or items which has a predictive validity not possessed by its constituent parts.[40] The first class of methods has come to be known as "profile analysis"; the second has unhappily assumed the generic term of "pattern analysis," or one of its cognates, e.g., "configural analysis." We shall use the latter term for the second class of procedures.

9.2.4.1 *Profile Analysis.* As Gengerelli and Butler [11] state the issue, "The problem of profile analysis is essentially a matter of specifying by means of a single real number the mutual quantitative discrepancies existing among a set of measures or scores x_1, x_2, x_3 . . . earned by a given individual." The authors then proceed to generate unique, unambiguous numbers to describe any profile of scores. This is accomplished by obtaining rank differences among the set of variables and adding a fractional portion to each coefficient from a table of prime numbers. The latter maneuver insures that to each profile there corresponds one number and to each number there is but one profile. By these procedures, profiles can be ordered in a discrete replicable series, thus permitting the use of a statistic to describe the average profile of a group of Ss. One is then able to determine whether any particular group of Ss can be discriminated from any other. It is also possible to classify any particular profile as being more like another (group or individual) profile than unlike it. Gengerelli and Butler report that, in their experience, where the difference between the mean profile scores of two groups was significant at better than the .01 level, misclassification of profiles did not exceed 30 per cent.

Although it is not known whether this method has been programed for a computer, it is a very simple program to write. Here is one case where the clinician can easily gather thousands of protocols, set up norms, test differences, and then proceed to classify test protocols individually in the clinical setting. The authors cite a study of five nosological groups: (1) paranoid schizophrenics, (2) manic depressives, (3) alcoholics with psychosis, (4) alcoholics without psychosis, and (5) college students, who were tested on the MMPI. Each group was found to have an average profile which significantly differed from the *null* or flat profile at better than the .001 level. When significance tests were applied to the differences among groups, only one group was found to be discriminable from the others, i.e., the college group. Having established essentially two classes of profiles, i.e., disturbed and normal, classification was then attempted. The percentage misclassified was 16.7 for the disturbed patients and 20.0 for the college group. The addition of the *elevation* variable did not improve the differentiations; i.e., there were still two classes of profiles. This method treats *shape* and *elevation* separately and hence leaves open the question of a possible interaction between the two as contributing to discriminations.

Other methods have been suggested for profile analysis, e.g., an analysis of variance technique by Block, Levine, and McNemar [2] and the use of intraclass correlation by Haggard.[14] The latter technique offers a very interesting application as illustrated by the author, i.e., determining the reliability over time of a set of profiles taken from one individual. One of Haggard's findings was that the profiles of different persons were more similar than that of the same person (five MMPI testings of a psychiatric patient, admitted many times), over a period of $3\frac{1}{2}$ years. If this were not so, one would begin to question seriously either our treatment methods or the test employed. Haggard suggests many other applications which would interest both the clinician and the personality psychologist.

A somewhat different use of the profile matching technique was used by Kelly and Fiske [18] in an analysis of the relative accuracy of qualitative (judgmental) and quantitative (objective) matching of personality descriptions of subjects assessed first as beginning graduate students in clinical psychology and assessed several years later on the basis of professional performance. In brief, it was found that the purely statistical matching of all possible pairs of rated personality profiles resulted in 74 per cent of the cases being correctly matched, as compared with 70 per cent correct matches by judges using two verbal descriptions of the same subjects. This example is included less because of the resulting findings than to indicate the range of applicability of computers to research of interest to clinical psychologists. The *tau* statistic used is perhaps the most appropriate statistic for comparing the shapes of profiles, but its hand computation is laborious if more than a few variables are included in profiles to be matched.

Another example of the utility of a computer in computing *tau* is a study by Hoffman who was interested in comparing the problem-solving abilities of small homogeneous and heterogeneous groups.[16] All members of a pool of potential subjects in this experiment were administered the Guilford-Zimmerman Temperament Survey, which yields scores on 10 variables. Hoffman used a computer to obtain the *tau* of each subject with every other subject in a large subject pool and then assigned his Ss to experimental groups on the basis of their similarity or dissimilarity.

All the foregoing methods presuppose the existence of some group or groups from which the analysis proceeds. The techniques to be discussed below are designed to *find* these groups empirically. Thus, logically and experimentally, the procedures of configural analysis should precede those of profile analysis. The order of presentation was reversed because of the greater familiarity of profile analysis as contrasted with configural analysis.

9.2.4.2 *Configural Analysis.* Basic to the methods to be discussed is what is known as the Meehl Paradox; [23] i.e., two or more test items can severally have a zero correlation with a criterion and yet jointly be perfectly correlated with it. This possibility arises from the statistical definition of independence, i.e., two or more items are independent if, and only if, each variable has a zero relationship with every other item when taken separately and with every combination of variables. McQuitty [24] has clearly outlined the issues involved and has offered many different methods for analyzing data configurally. In this chapter, we shall content ourselves with illustrating but two configural techniques: *agreement analysis* [25] and *similarity analysis*. [26]

Agreement analysis is a method excellently suited for solving those problems which are of utmost significance to the clinician, i.e., patterns of behavior. Implicit in the pattern or configural approach is the assumption that other than linear relationships may exist among variables. Based on Zubin's [48] agreement score, McQuitty has devised a general method for classifying or clustering persons or items in terms of patterns. An agreement score based on two or more persons is simply the number of items responded to in the *same* way. Thus, e.g., if at least 2 Ss gave "true" responses to 10 items of an inventory and "false" responses to 4, the agreement score would be 14 for those persons.

In one of its simplest versions, agreement analysis involves the following five steps:

a. Calculate agreement scores for all pairs of persons; this basic symmetric matrix represents the common components of agreement existing among the N individuals.

b. Select the highest entry in the matrix as a basis for combination.

c. Reduce or condense the agreement matrix by one row and column and use the common answers of the preceding combination to score all individuals not in the pattern.

d. Substitute this array of agreement scores for the one deleted and note who is included in the new combination; e.g., if *A* and *B* were combined, the column and row designations could be represented as *AB*.

e. Reiterate steps b to d, successively combining individuals, groups, or individuals and groups, until all Ss have been classified or until all patterns merge into one.

The foregoing procedures result in a hierarchical organization of the data not unlike that of a Linnaean system. Although it is not too difficult to perform an agreement analysis, addition being the most complex of the mathematics involved, any sizable sample of Ss and items would soon tire the most ambitious researcher. The scoring, re-scoring, and counting are well adapted to computer operations.*

Despite the method's adaptability to clinical and personality problems, not much research has been done in this area. McQuitty [27] has shown in one study on psychological well-being that mental hospital patients differ from other persons primarily in terms of their response patterns. Further work with this method is needed.

In contrast to the version of agreement analysis presented above, the method of *similarity analysis* differs in three main respects:

a. It has a generality beyond qualitative or ordinal data.

b. Indices of association form the basis for determining all higher-order relationships (one does not refer back to the actual responses for combining).

c. A classification assumption is involved based on similarity rather than identity of response patterns.

The basic matrix from which an analysis proceeds can contain frequency counts (e.g., agreement scores), correlations, or other indices of association or concomitance. The method can be used on continuous or discrete variables, where the relationships are either linear or curvilinear. Thus, as a clustering method, similarity analysis is more general than agreement analysis. To the degree, however, that its assumptions are in error when combining individuals, items, or variables, then agreement analysis would

* Dr. Kern Dickman at the University of Illinois has programed many versions of agreement analysis for the ILLIAC series of computers. Peter Hemingway of Michigan State University has computed yet another version for MISTIC.

seem to be the more powerful method. Let us see how the method works by giving an illustration.

Wrigley [46] has presented a study on the divisional structure of the American Psychological Association, which had been previously analyzed by both factor and cluster methods. The first step, after having obtained indices of membership for the 17 APA divisions, was to reduce the order of the matrix by 1. This was done by combining the two divisions of Personality-Social and SPSSI, representing the largest coefficient in the matrix. One row and column is then deleted from the matrix and an *average* is calculated for the newly combined division and substituted for one of those deleted. The procedure is then identical with the foregoing version of agreement analysis for further combinations. Each time a reduction is made, average indices are calculated, based upon the number of elements in the pattern. This method resulted in a number of groupings, which were then compared with the results of two factor analyses and a cluster analysis.

After having made these comparisons, Wrigley proceeded to list the advantages of similarity analysis in comparison with factor analysis. Briefly, he concluded that similarity analysis: (1) allows one to select the number of groups after analysis; (2) is quicker; (3) is more objective; and (4) has an immediate appeal to the uninitiated. Factor analysis, on the other hand, uses more information, allows for multiple classification (another version of similarity analysis also provides for this), and probably yields more stable results.

To conclude this section on pattern analytic methods, it seems obvious that clinical psychologists now have the opportunity for extensively testing their beliefs about the pervasiveness and importance of patterns. The methods just described represent only a small proportion of those available for research use.

We now turn to an illustration of a technique from scaling theory, whose development was materially aided by a computer.

9.2.5 *Multiple Scalogram Analysis.* Multiple scalogram analysis [19] (MSA) represents a generalization of Guttman's [37] scaling method. As such, its aims are (1) to provide an empirical and statistical basis for scaling items, (2) to produce as many unidimensional scales as is consistent with the underlying dimensionality of the matrix. The kinds of items which are particularly appropriate to scale analysis are cumulative in nature: when either endorsement or passing of an item implies the endorsement or passing of another item which is more popular or less difficult. Thus, for example, the following three items are cumulative in respect to the underlying ability of arithmetic knowledge: (1) $3 + 2 = 5$; (2) $a + b = b + a$; and (3) $x^2 - 9 = (x + 3)(x - 3)$. That is, a person passing the third item would in all likelihood pass the other two, and a person failing the first would fail the two more difficult ones. Each item is assumed to represent increasing amounts of arithmetic knowledge.

Based on Ss' responses to such items as the above, we can order the people in respect to their possession of the trait being measured. To the extent that a univocal ordering of Ss and items can be obtained, the items are said to be "scalable" or to form a unidimensional scale. Such scales have these important formal properties: (1) scale scores permit a reconstruction of the Ss' answers to all items; (2) maximum predictability with relatively few items is attained for *any* external criterion; and (3) error of measurement is minimized for both scale scores and responses to individual items.

The following five formal criteria were employed for linking items and for testing the scale hypothesis:

a. *Positive manifold.* All adjacent items in a Guttman-Lingoes scale are required to be positively related. If the items are negatively related, one of them is reflected, i.e., 1's are changed to 0's and 0's to 1's, where 1 represents an endorsement or passing of the item and 0 its converse.

b. *Mononicity* of item marginals. The proportion of 1's is not allowed to increase when items have been ordered from easy to difficult or from popular to unpopular. If a positively related item (or one that has been made positive by reflection) fails to meet this criterion, that item is not considered a candidate for the scale.

c. *Minimum distances* between adjacent items of a scale. The measure of distance is the symmetric set difference, i.e., items are as similar as possible in their 11 and 00 correspondences.

d. *Minimum errors.* The number of 01's, when items have been ordered from easy to difficult, should be the smallest value obtainable for the smallest distance. If one minimizes the following function of distance and error, the third and fourth criteria can be collapsed, i.e., the square of the distance plus the number of errors.

e. *Statistical significance.* The fourfold table resulting from any two adjacent items must be significant at or beyond the .01 level as evaluated by either the χ^2 or Fischer's exact test. This last criterion provides a test for rejecting the scale hypothesis, sets a lower bound on the coefficient of reproducibility, and requires differential reproducibilities for items with extreme marginals and for varying sample sizes.

The first item of any scale is chosen on the basis of that item marginal that is largest when all items whose marginals are less than $N/2$ have been reflected. Scales are terminated either when there is no positively related item with the preceding item of a scale when the marginals are required to be monotonic decreasing or, if there is such an item, when the relationship is not significant, according to the fifth criterion above.

Without going any further into the theory of scale analysis, suffice it to say that many different kinds of items have been found to scale, from fear symptoms [37] to the voting behavior of United States senators.

Lingoes [19] has presented an excellent example of a configuration or pattern possessing validity not possessed by its constituent parts. In an analysis of a personality inventory (MMPI), it was found that although scale scores on selected variables could not discriminate patients from nonpatients (identical means and variances), a measure based on the concept of deviation from perfect scaling did so significantly ($P \leqslant .003$).

Without going into great detail, the MSA procedure is based on what might be called "chain theory." The essential premise of this theory is that variables may concatenate in many different ways other than the linear for which we have adequate measures. A more general measure of relationship has been used based on probability considerations. What this entails for the MSA technique is a calculation of exact probabilities for multivariate distributions. In the dichotomous case, this means that Fisher's exact test must be applied between each and every item (a substantial enterprise even with tables of log factorials). Two items are considered to be relevant to the same domain if, and only if, they yield a significantly small probability value. As each successive link in the chain is developed, an order emerges among the elements of the chain which can be described sometimes as a Guttman unidimensional scale, sometimes as a factor, as a cluster, or as of some other form. Thus, it can be seen that no restrictions are imposed on the data, be they linearly related or otherwise, qualitative or quantitative, etc.

Computers are essential to the use of this technique with even moderately large matrices. An analysis of 100 items and 100 Ss took only three minutes on an IBM 704, but would take at least a month to do by hand.

We conclude this chapter by presenting an illustration of an integrated set of computer programs (an example of an executive routine) for multivariate analysis.

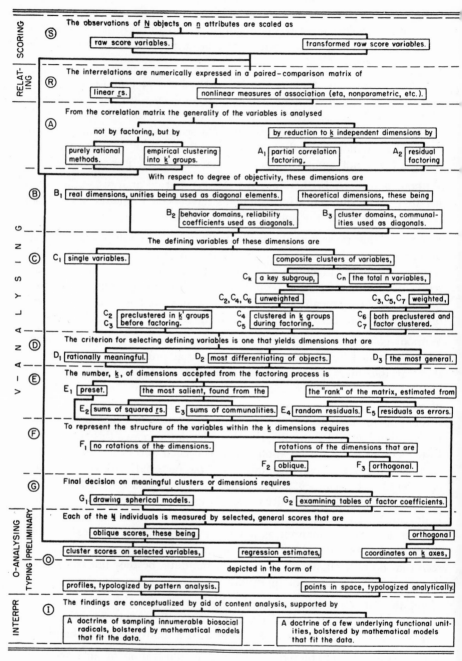

FIGURE 9.2 Multidimensional analysis of individual and group differences—executive program.

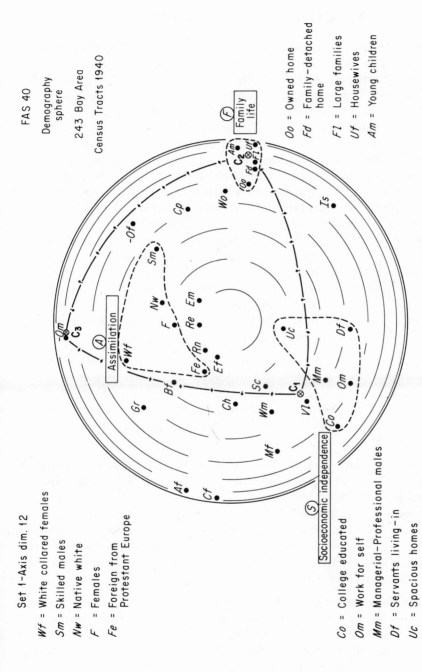

FIGURE 9.3 Three-dimensional subspace showing clusters of variables.

FAS 40

Demography
sphere

243 Bay Area
Census Tracts 1940

Set 1—Axis dim. 12

Wf = White collared females

Sm = Skilled males

Nw = Native white

F = Females

Fe = Foreign from
Protestant Europe

Co = College educated

Om = Work for self

Mm = Managerial–Professional males

Df = Servants living–in

Uc = Spacious homes

Oo = Owned home

Fd = Family–detached
home

Fl = Large families

Uf = Housewives

Am = Young children

Ⓕ Family
life

Ⓐ Assimilation

Ⓢ Socioeconomic independence

9.3   AN EXECUTIVE SYSTEM PROGRAM

Tryon [41] has conceptualized the various methods of multidimensional analysis as representing different arbitrary decisions at successive stages of a general program of analysis. The logic of his approach is illustrated in the schema [42] appearing in Figure 9.2. Any particular method of analysis, according to Tryon, is a variant of the general program, which has been programed for the IBM 704 computer. For example, Thurstone's *centroid factor analysis* is defined by the following decisions in regions A to G, representing V-analysis (i.e., variable analysis): A_2, B_3, C_n, C_4, E_4 or E_5, F_2, and G_2. All of these decisions are controlled by a parameter card which is read in ahead of the data cards. Such an integrated program allows a researcher to make many different comparisons on the same data. The several programs are so organized that new subroutines may be added to the executive routine (a program to select and monitor other programs). Tremendous latitude is available with such a flexible routine. There are more than 2,000 possible patterns of major decisions within V-analysis alone. Let it be noted that some kinds of analyses (in general those to the right of the schema) are highly abstracted variations, whereas those that deal with directly observed, finite, less constructed kinds of variation appear to the left.

As an example of the sorts of things such a program can do, consult Figure 9.3. Here is represented a graphic illustration of a three-dimensional subspace, where highly correlated clusters of variables are encircled by dashed lines. Such a printed output can be easily prepared for publication, thus saving a great deal of expense and time in preparing special charts.

In the preceding pages, we have outlined the most pressing methodological problems and some of the more extensive uses of computers by psychologists. We have also paid some attention to techniques which, although less used, are nonetheless adaptable to computers. Many methods and designs have not been mentioned, e.g., that of complex analysis of variance, discriminant function analysis in classification, and non-parametric statistics like chi-square, to name but a few. Nevertheless, such procedures as these have been programed.

A concluding word of caution seems appropriate. When trying to decide whether to use a computer (granting availability of both machines and programs), this is a good general rule: If the cost in time and/or money of clerical and computational assistance is greater than the cost involved in preparing data for machine analysis, then a computer is, of course, recommended; if the cost is equal, a computer is still preferable because of its greater reliability. Even at commercial rates of $300 to $500 an hour for large machines, substantial savings over desk calculations are possible because of the tremendous speed of analysis.

Some types of analyses are best handled by low-speed computers and/or ancilliary equipment, such as card-sorters, collators, etc. The value of such devices is not to be minimized.

Nevertheless, as Wrigley [47] has pointed out on several occasions, the increased availability of computers and the problems associated with program libraries often tempt some potential user to use statistical models which are either inappropriate or are little understood. Others may be tempted to correlate anything and everything just because the capacity of the program permits it. The computer is no substitute for good and long cerebration by its human user. This he can do best, despite the story of the computer, which when asked, "Is there a God?" allegedly printed out the reply, "There is now!"

REFERENCES

1 Allport, G. W., and Odbert, H. S., Trait Names, a Psycho-lexical Study, *Psychol. Monogr., 47,* 1936, 171; and Cattell, R. B., The Description of Personality: Basic Traits Resolved into Clusters, *Jour. Abnorm. Soc. Psychol., 38,* 1943, 476–506. Both of these works illustrate the steps and problems involved in this monumental task of condensation. With present computers, this area should perhaps be revisited.

2 Block, J., Levine, L., and McNemar, O., Testing for the Existence of Psychometric Patterns, *Jour. Abnorm. Soc. Psychol., 46,* 1951, 356–59.

3 Borko, H., A Factor Analytic Study of the MMPI, *VA Publ.,* 1952.

4 Cattell, R. B., *Factor Analysis.* New York: Harper, 1952; see also Guilford, J. P., Factorial Angles to Psychology, *Psychol. Rev., 68,* 1961, 1–20.

5 ———, *The Sixteen Personality Factor Questionnaire.* Champaign, Ill.: Inst. of Personality and Aptitude Testing, 1957.

6 ———, *Personality and Motivation Structure and Measurement.* Yonkers, N.Y.: World Book Co., 1957.

7 ———, and Cross, K., Comparison of the Ergic and Self-sentiment Structures Found in Dynamic Traits by the R- and P-Techniques, *Jour. Personality, 21,* 1952, 250–70.

8 ———, and Luborsky, L. B., P-Technique Demonstrated as a New Clinical Method for Determining Personality and Symptom Structures, *Jour. Gen. Psychol., 42,* 1955, 3–24.

9 Dennis, W., Infant Development under Conditions of Restricted Practices and Minimal Social Stimulation, *Genetic Psychol. Monogrs. 23,* 1941, 143–91. Of the many "experiments" that paraded under the guise of science in the Hitler era, not one is known that would merit serious consideration in a scientific journal. Despite the sadism of their execution, they lack even the single redeeming feature of yielding new knowledge. This article contains an interesting example of the role of ethics and the experimenter's emotional involvement in the objects of his interest.

10 Edwards, A. L., *Manual for the Edwards Personal Preference Schedule.* New York: Psychological Corp., 1954.

11 Gengerelli, J. A., and Butler, B. V., A Method for Comparing the Profiles of Several Population Samples, *Jour. Psychol., 40,* 1955, 247–68.

12 Guertin, W. H., An Inverted Factor-Analytic Study of Schizophrenics, *Jour. Consult. Psychol., 16,* 1952, 371–75.

13 Guilford, J. P., and Zimmerman, W. A., Fourteen Dimensions of Temperament, *Psychol. Monogr., 70* (No. 417), 1956.

14 Haggard, E. A., *Intraclass Correlation with the Analysis of Variance.* New York: Dryden Press, 1958.

15 Hathaway, S. R., and Monachesi, E. D., eds., *Analyzing and Predicting Juvenile Delinquency with the MMPI.* Minneapolis, Minn.: Univ. Minnesota Press, 1953. This work represents an ambitious attempt to predict delinquency using a clinical instrument (the MMPI) on several thousand Ss.

16 Hoffman, L. R., Homogeneity of Member Personality and its Effect on Group Problem Solving, *Jour. Abnorm. Soc. Psychol., 58,* 1959, 27–32.

17 Horst, P., Dvorak, A., and Wright, C., Computer Application to Psychological Problems. Paper read at a Symposium on Computer Applications, Seattle, Washington, Nov. 4, 1960.

18 Kelly, E. L., and Fiske, D. W., *The Prediction of Performance in Clinical Psychology.* Ann Arbor, Mich.: Univ. Michigan Press, 1951.

19 Lingoes, J. C., Multiple Scalogram Analysis: A Generalization of Guttman's Scale Analysis. Unpublished doctoral dissertation, Michigan State Univ., 1960.

20 Lorr, M., Jenkins, R. L., and Holsopple, J. Q., Multidimensional Scale for Rating Psychiatric Patients, Hospital Form, U.S. Vet. Admin. *Techn. Bull.* TB 10-507, Washington, D.C., 1953.

21 ———, Rubenstein, E. A., and Jenkins, R. L., A Factor Analysis of Neurotic Adults in Psychotherapy, *Jour. Consult. Psychol., 20,* 1956, 257–63.

22 Meehl, P. E., *Clinical Versus Statistical Prediction.* Minneapolis, Minn.: Univ. Minnesota Press, 1954. Actuarial versus clinical prediction is still a controversial area, with the present weight of evidence favoring the former.

23 ———, Configural Scoring, *Jour. Consult. Psychol., 14,* 1950, 165–71.

24 McQuitty, L. L., Isolating Predictor Patterns Associated with Major Criteria Patterns, *Educ. Psychol. Measmt., 17,* 1957, 3–42.

25 ———, Agreement Analysis: Classifying Persons by Predominant Patterns of Responses, *Brit. Jour. Statist. Psych., 9,* 1956, 5–16.

26 ———, A Method of Pattern Analysis for Isolating Typological and Dimensional Constructs. Lackland Air Force Base, San Antonio, Tex.: USAF Pers. and Trng. Res. Ctr. *Research Report,* AFPTRC-TN-55-62, Dec. 1955.

27 ———, Theories and Methods in Some Objective Assessments of Psychological Well-Being, *Psychol. Monogr., 68,* 1954 (Whole No. 385).

28 Moore, T. V., Stafford, J. W., and Hsu, E. H., Obverse Analysis of Personality, *Jour. Personality, 16,* 1947, 11–48.

29 Osgood, C. E., Suci, G. J., and Tannenbaum, P. H., *The Measurement of Meaning.* Urbana, Ill.: Univ. Illinois Press, 1957.

30 Overall, J. E., and Gorham, D. R., Factor Space D^2 Analysis Applied to the Study of Changes in Schizophrenic Symptomatology during Chemotherapy, *Jour. Clin. Exper. Psychopath., 21,* 1960, 187–95.

31 Rao, C. R., *Advanced Statistical Methods in Biometric Research.* New York: Wiley, 1952.

32 Rosenthal, R., Cognitive Complexity and the Implicit Personality Theory of the Judge. Unpublished doctoral dissertation, Univ. of Michigan, 1961.

33 Sarbin, T. R., Taft, R., and Bailey, D. E., *Clinical Inference and Cognitive Theory.* New York: Holt, Rinehart and Winston, 1960. This has an excellent discussion of the differences between physical and social objects.

34 Small, Edna, Age and Sex Differences in the Semantic Structure of Children, *Dissertation Abstracts, 19,* 1958, 872–73.

35 Smith, D. E. P., and Carrigan, P., *The Nature of Reading Disability.* New York: Harcourt, Brace, 1959.

36 Smith, Philip A., A Factor Analytic Study of the Self-Concept, *Jour. Consult. Psychol., 24,* 1960, 191.

37 Stouffer, S. A., ed., *Measurement and Prediction.* Prenceton, N.J.: Princeton University Press, 1950.

38 Talbott, R. D., The Multiple Predictive Efficiency of Ipsative and Normative Personality Measures. Seattle, Wash.: University of Washington, February, 1960. (Mimeographed manuscript.)

39 Thurstone, L. L., *Primary Mental Abilities.* Chicago: Univ. Chicago Press, 1938.

40 Tiedeman, D. V., On the Study of Types, *Symposium on Pattern Analysis,* S. B. Sells (chairman). Randolph Field, Tex.: Air University, USAF School of Aviation Medicine, 1955.

41 Tryon, R. C., Domain Sampling Formulation of Cluster and Factor Analysis, *Psychometrika, 24,* 1959, 113–35.

42 ———, Reliability of Individual Differences in Multidimensional Analysis, *Amer. Psychol., 15,* 1960, 499 (abstract).

43 Williams, H. V., A Determination of Psychosomatic Functional Unities in Personality by Means of P-Technique, *Jour. Soc. Psychol., 39,* 1954, 25–45.

44 Wittenborn, J. R., *Psychiatric Rating Scales.* New York: Psychological Corp., 1955; see also Wittenborn, J. R., and Holzberg, J. D., The Generality of Psychiatric Syndromes, *Jour. Consult. Psychol., 15,* 1951, 372–80.

45 Wright, C. E., Relations between Normative and Ipsative Measures of Personality. Unpublished doctoral dissertation, Univ. Washington, 1957.

46 Wrigley, C. F., Cluster Analysis or Factor Analysis? The Divisional Structure of the American Psychological Association, *Psychol. Reps., 3,* 1957, 497–506.

47 ———, Electronic Computers and Psychological Research, *Amer. Psychol., 12,* 1957, 501–508.

48 Zubin, J., The Determination of Response Patterns in Personality Adjustment Inventories, *Jour. Educ. Psychol., 28,* 1937, 401–13.

Joe H. Ward, Jr.
10/MULTIPLE LINEAR REGRESSION MODELS

Joe H. Ward, Jr., is Head of the Computer Analysis Section,
Personnel Laboratory, Lackland Air Force Base, Texas.
He received the B.A. degree in mathematics
and M.A. and Ph.D. degrees in
educational psychology from the University of Texas.
He has studied statistics at the University of Florida,
Virginia Polytechnic Institute, and North Carolina State College.
His major research interests are in the development of mathematical
and computer techniques for use in psychological research,
with particular interest in the simulation
of human intellectual functions by digital computers
and the development of effective prediction systems. He has
written articles concerning the use of
mathematical methods and electronic computers
in psychological research. He is a member of the
Association for Computing Machinery,
American Statistical Association, Institute of Mathematical
Statistics, American Psychological Association,
Psychometric Society, and Sigma Xi.

The early history of the behavioral sciences reveals that many fruitful hypotheses were derived from the application of simple correlational methods to scores paired on two variables. As the sciences advanced, interest shifted from descriptions of relationships to problems of prediction. Research hypotheses soon came to be too complex to be examined without the benefit of analytical techniques yielding information on the presence of common elements and interactions in a series of variables and on the influence of various combinations of variables. Before long, some of the requisite statistical tools were developed.

Scientists today identify these tools as factor analysis, partial and multiple correlation, and analysis of variance. These techniques have helped scientists to improve their approach to many different types of research problems, even when circumstances prevent experimental control over disturbing variables. Many questions now studied with these analytical techniques, however, are often better answered through the effective application of one general model—the multiple linear regression model.

The author is indebted to Marion E. Hook and Robert A. Bottenberg for many helpful suggestions in connection with the writing of this chapter.

In this connection, Mood [6] has commented on the assumptions that are made:

> In recent years it has come to be realized that most (though not all) correlation problems which arise in practice can be handled more appropriately by regression methods. The latter require only the assumption that deviations from the regression function be normal, whereas the correlation analysis requires that the variate and what we have called the observable parameters [identified in this chapter as the X vectors] all be jointly normally distributed [p. 312].

It is important to recognize that multiple regression analysis is quite unlike the multivariate correlational techniques. Although the computational procedures for the multiple linear regression model are the same as those for multivariate correlational analyses, the assumptions underlying the two approaches are different. In the multiple linear regression model, for example, predictor variables are not assumed to come from a multivariate normal distribution. The elements that define the predictor variables in an analysis may be of many complex functional forms whose distribution function may be quite unlike the multivariate normal distribution (see Section 10.3.1.2). In some problems, the elements may be simply binary-coded (1 or 0). It should be recognized that the analysis-of-variance procedure and pattern analysis are special cases of the multiple linear regression model in which binary-coded predictor elements are used (see Section 10.2.1).

Multiple linear regression analysis is not a completely new technique. In the past, the multiple regression model has been used primarily with very small groups of variables for the purpose of obtaining weights which, when applied to predictors, would yield optimal predictions of observed criteria. The computations required for even four- or five-variable problems are laborious and time-consuming when done by hand. Therefore, without access to high-speed computers to execute the numerical operations, investigators who did use the model were inclined to restrict their studies, securing only partial answers to their questions. Given computer facilities, however, scientists are free to work with large numbers of variables—expressed either in continuous or categorical form. They can even examine subordinate hypotheses at the same time that they secure meaningful answers to their major questions.

Utilization of high-speed computers with the multiple linear regression model not only reduces the dangers inherent in piecemeal research but also facilitates the investigation of broad problems never before considered "researchable." Scientific knowledge, therefore, can be advanced in ways not possible so long as experimental designs had to be tailored to less powerful modes of analysis. As Mood [6] has pointed out:

> Most experimental work today is based on the rule: "Keep all variables constant but one," an ancient and erroneous dictum which guarantees a high degree of inefficiency. One well-designed experiment taking account of all relevant factors, is worth dozens or even hundreds of experiments which study one factor at a time keeping the others constant [p. 358].

Behavioral scientists who understand the multiple regression model and master the appropriate modes of formulating problems for machine analyses have at their command a very useful statistical tool.

10.1 GENERAL MODEL FOR MULTIPLE LINEAR REGRESSION ANALYSIS

Scientists are familiar with the practical applications of multivariate correlational analysis in studies that require either (1) an evaluation of the extent to which each predictor variable or subset of variables contributes to the explanation of observed criterion scores for a sample, or (2) a prediction of criterion scores for a different sample for which information on the same group of predictor variables will be available. Some investigators, however, have not perceived the difference between multivariate correlational analysis and multiple linear regression analysis. For that reason, we include here detailed descriptions of the general regression model (Section 10.1.1) and the testing of hypotheses about parameters of interest to the investigator (Section 10.1.3). In addition, the rationale for the use of the least-squares method of estimating the values of unknown parameters is discussed (Section 10.1.2), and a computational procedure is given for obtaining least-squares solutions for regression problems and the simultaneous determination of an orthonormal basis (Section 10.3).

10.1.1 *Description of General Multiple Regression Model.* Details
of the classical theory underlying multiple linear regression analysis cannot be presented here.[1, 5, 6, 7, 8, 9] It seems desirable, however, to review the general regression model as well as the concepts and assumptions associated with it. The data required, assumptions made about the data, and the concepts and assumptions underlying the model are summarized in matrix notation.

10.1.1.1 *Data Required.*

a. Predictor data:*

$$\mathbf{X} = \begin{bmatrix} x_{11} & \cdots & x_{1r} \\ x_{21} & \cdots & x_{2r} \\ \cdot & & \cdot \\ \cdot & & \cdot \\ \cdot & & \cdot \\ x_{n1} & \cdots & x_{nr} \end{bmatrix}$$

X is a matrix of n complete sets of predictor information on r variables for the n sample members: each x value is assumed to be fixed; some or all x values may be constants chosen by investigator, e.g., on the sex variable, 1 if male and 0 if female.

b. Criterion scores (observed values):

$$\mathbf{Y} = \begin{bmatrix} y_1 \\ y_2 \\ \cdot \\ \cdot \\ \cdot \\ y_n \end{bmatrix}$$

Y is a column vector of criterion information, $y_1, y_2, \ldots, y_n$, for n sample members: the n criterion observations are assumed to be random observations from n different, normally and independently distributed variates which have the same variance, σ^2, with respect to this criterion; covariance of criterion scores is assumed to be zero.

10.1.1.2 *Assumptions about the Data.*

a. Weighting parameters:

$$\mathbf{B} = \begin{bmatrix} b_1 \\ b_2 \\ \cdot \\ \cdot \\ \cdot \\ b_r \end{bmatrix}$$

B is a column vector of r, as yet unknown, parameters which if known and applied to the n sets of values for the r predictors in **X**

---

* In general, $n \geq (r + 1)$. It is desirable to have a larger number of observations than predictor variables.

matrix would yield the expected criterion values, $m_1, m_2, \ldots, m_n$, respectively (see b, following).

b. Expected values of criterion scores:

$$\mathcal{E}(\mathbf{Y}) = \mathbf{M} = \begin{bmatrix} m_1 \\ m_2 \\ \cdot \\ \cdot \\ \cdot \\ m_n \end{bmatrix} = \mathbf{XB}$$

$\mathcal{E}(\mathbf{Y})$ is the expected value of the criterion score, which is equal to a column vector of n expected (predicted) criterion values, m_1, $m_2, \ldots, m_n$.

c. Difference between observed and expected values of criterion score:

$$\mathbf{E} = \mathbf{Y} - \mathbf{XB}$$

When observed values for criterion $\mathbf{Y}$ are compared with expected values of criterion scores [$\mathbf{XB}$, i.e., $\mathcal{E}(\mathbf{Y})$], there will be some discrepancy or error.

$$\mathbf{E} = \begin{bmatrix} e_1 \\ e_2 \\ \cdot \\ \cdot \\ \cdot \\ e_n \end{bmatrix}$$

$\mathbf{E}$, the error vector is a column vector of n residual values, $e_1, e_2,$ $\ldots, e_n$, assumed to be normally and independently distributed with mean equal to zero and variance of σ^2. That is to say,

$$\mathcal{E}(\mathbf{E}) = 0$$
$$\text{(null vector)}$$

The expected value of vector $\mathbf{E}$ is zero.

$$\mathcal{E}(e_i e_j) = 0$$

When i does not equal j ($i = 1, 2, \ldots, n; j = 1, 2, \ldots, n$), the covariance is zero.

$$\mathcal{E}(e_i e_j) = \sigma^2$$

When i equals j, the expected value of ($e_i e_j$) equal σ^2, the variance.

10.1.1.3 *Summary of Assumptions Underlying Multiple Linear Regression Model.* Two points about the data required for this model are noteworthy. First, predictor column vectors in the $\mathbf{X}$ matrix need not be linearly independent. Second, observed criterion scores are assumed to be random observations drawn from n different, normally and independently distributed variates having the same variance on this criterion; the covariance of criterion scores is assumed to be zero. The four assumptions underlying the multiple linear regression model may be summarized briefly.

a. The values in the $\mathbf{X}$ matrix are *fixed constants*, frequently selected by the investigator; the elements of the $\mathbf{Y}$ vector are *random* observations.

b. All n distributions from which the n criterion observations are drawn have the same variance, σ^2.

c. The covariance between y_i and y_j equals zero when i does not equal j $(i = 1, \ldots, n; j = 1, \ldots, n)$.

d. The y_i value associated with the ith row of the matrix $\mathbf{X}$, in which elements are designated

$$x_{i1}, \ldots, x_{ir}$$

is from a normal distribution with expected value, $\mathcal{E}(y_i)$, equal to

$$x_{i1}B_1 + \ldots + x_{ir}B_r.$$

10.1.2 Least-Squares Estimation of Unknown Parameters. In the multiple linear regression model, the prediction problem is formulated as an effort to derive, from a given sample of n observations, estimates of the r unknown parameters in vector $\mathbf{B}$ that will enable the investigator to make accurate predictions of the criterion observations he has made. Hence the predictor vector, $\mathbf{X}\hat{\mathbf{B}}$ (which is an estimate of $\mathbf{XB}$), should match $\mathbf{Y}$ as closely as possible. The estimator vector $\hat{\mathbf{B}}$, in which the elements $\hat{b}_1, \hat{b}_2, \ldots, \hat{b}_r$ are estimates of the r parameters in vector $\mathbf{B}$, is usually obtained by the least-squares method.

When the actual $\mathbf{Y}$ values are compared with $\mathbf{Y}$ values estimated from $\mathbf{X}\hat{\mathbf{B}}$, the residuals form a vector $\hat{\mathbf{E}}$ in which the elements are $\hat{e}_1, \hat{e}_2, \ldots, \hat{e}_n$. Therefore, if $\mathbf{X}\hat{\mathbf{B}}$ is to match $\mathbf{Y}$ closely, it is necessary to solve for $\hat{\mathbf{B}}$ in the matrix equation $\mathbf{Y} = \mathbf{X}\hat{\mathbf{B}} + \hat{\mathbf{E}}$ in a manner that insures that the sum of the squared residuals, $(\hat{\mathbf{E}})'(\hat{\mathbf{E}})$, is a minimum. This minimization can be accomplished by making the vector $\hat{\mathbf{E}}$ orthogonal to the space generated by the column vectors in $\mathbf{X}$ and solving the obtained simultaneous equations for the estimated values of the elements of $\hat{\mathbf{B}}$. (See also Section 10.3.3.3.)

10.1.3 *Testing of Hypotheses about Parameters.*

When an investigator conceives and plans a study, he usually considers many alternative hypotheses. Formerly, it was not feasible to test more than a few of these hypotheses within the context of a single study; hence investigations were often limited to a few, arbitrarily chosen predictor variables. When the general regression model is appropriate for the data analysis, it is no longer necessary to restrict so greatly either the number of variables or the number of hypotheses tested in a study. With high-speed computer equipment, the computational operations for multiple linear regression analysis are so quickly performed that no true economy results from the omission of essential variables from the predictor system. Furthermore, investigators can structure their analyses so as to use the machine outputs to test a series of related hypotheses in a systematic fashion. Care should be exercised, however, to include plans for testing *all* these hypotheses in the original experimental design and computational program. It is inefficient to test a few hypotheses, examine these findings, and then decide to test other hypotheses that will require additional machine outputs. Familiarity with computer programing will help investigators to secure machine outputs for testing a number of hypotheses in the most efficient manner.

In the general regression model, an hypothesis is considered to impose restrictions on the parameters of the full predictor system under study. Accordingly, the test of an hypothesis is made by comparing the efficiency with which observed criterion $\mathbf{Y}$ values can be estimated from a full, or unrestricted, model and from a restricted model. The full-model estimate is based on all predictor vectors in the $\mathbf{X}$ matrix; the restricted-model estimate is based on a matrix, $\mathbf{X}_H$, in which the predictor vectors reflect the restrictions placed on the full model in order to express the hypothesis.

The test of an hypothesis is readily accomplished by computing the appropriate F statistic, once the hypothesis has been formulated in a fashion that permits comparison of the sums of the squared residuals associated with the least-squares solutions for the two (unrestricted and restricted) models. When the hypothesis has been expressed in terms of $\mathbf{B}_H$, a subset of elements in vector $\mathbf{B}$ that results from the restrictions of the hypothesis, the residual vector $\hat{\mathbf{E}}_H$ is obtained in the usual fashion from a least-squares solution for $\hat{\mathbf{B}}_H$. The residual vector $\hat{\mathbf{E}}$ for the unrestricted model results from a least-squares solution for $\widehat{\mathbf{B}}$ from the full predictor-vector system. The two residuals to be compared are

$$Q = (\widehat{\mathbf{E}})'(\widehat{\mathbf{E}})$$

(sum of squared residuals for unrestricted model)

$$Q_H = (\widehat{\mathbf{E}}_H)'(\widehat{\mathbf{E}}_H)$$

(sum of squared residuals for model subject to restrictions of the hypothesis)

The F statistic takes the form

$$F = \frac{(Q_H - Q)/t}{Q/(n - p)}$$

where $n =$ number of observations
$p =$ rank of matrix $\mathbf{X}$ of unrestricted model
$t =$ the difference between p and rank of matrix $\mathbf{X}_H$, which results when restrictions are imposed.

The obtained F value is compared with tabled F values to determine if the hypothesized restrictions should be accepted or rejected.

When a predictor vector, in which all elements equal 1, is a subspace of the predictor vectors in both the unrestricted and restricted models, the F statistic can be calculated in terms of the squared multiple-correlation coefficients. Computation of the F statistic in this fashion is often convenient, for many computing programs have these values as their output.

$$F = \frac{(R^2 - R_H{}^2)/t}{(1 - R^2)/(n - p)}$$

where $R^2 =$ squared multiple-correlation coefficient for the unrestricted model

and $R_H{}^2 =$ squared multiple-correlation coefficient for the restricted model.

10.2   EXAMPLES OF MULTIPLE LINEAR REGRESSION MODELS USEFUL IN DATA ANALYSES

The six examples in this section illustrate the fundamentals of problem formulation in the regression model and the need for high-speed equipment to carry out the requisite numerical computations for large-scale regression analyses. These examples also show various ways in which the general multiple regression model may be adapted to meet the investigator's specific needs in analyzing different types of problems.

10.2.1 *Regression Models with Binary Predictor Variables for Use in Analysis of Variance Designs.* Behavioral scientists often desire to study phenomena of individual and group behavior which present special technical problems, e.g., sampling, identification of sources of variance, and measurement of operative variables. In the past few years, certain types of designs associated with analysis of variance have come to be extensively used. These designs enable the investigator to identify, assess, and compare the effects of separate variables and their interactions, even when they cannot be accurately quantified. At present, we lack sufficient knowledge about the constancy and hence the dependability of measurement units for many variables believed to be operative. Therefore, it is appropriate to consider the utility of binary variables, coded 0 or 1, to indicate membership in a category.

Data in the binary-variable form are readily analyzed by the multiple regression technique. Two examples are presented here. In Section 10.2.1.1, the general model is applied to a regression problem usually referred to as the completely randomized design of analysis of variance. In Section 10.2.1.2, the example leads to a regression equation that yields all the information that results from the traditional randomized complete block design of analysis of variance. Study of these models undoubtedly will suggest other adaptations of the general multiple linear regression model.*

Any analyses that can be accomplished by univariate analysis-of-variance or covariance techniques can be accomplished by solution of the general regression model. In fact, some of these techniques are special cases of the general model that involve binary-coded predictor vectors. It is important, however, to recognize that the regression model for the randomized complete block design (Section 10.2.1.2) imposes no constraints on the number of observations in the cells. That is to say, the simplifying assumptions of proportionality need not be made. Furthermore, the computations necessary to estimate the unknown coefficients for large numbers of descriptive categories in the regression model for this design can be performed economically if a general computing procedure is used to solve the normal equations by the least-squares method. Hence, use of the regression model has certain advantages for behavioral scientists, who often

---

* The use of binary predictor data and related topics are discussed in detail in Bottenberg, R. A., and Ward, J. H., Jr., *Applied Multiple Linear Regression Analysis* (in preparation).

must conduct their studies under circumstances that prevent strict adherence to the proportionality requirements. Indeed, in some situations, it may be almost impossible to obtain definitive results unless the investigator uses the more general regression model and takes advantage of the speed and flexibility of modern computers. Obviously, however, if the proportionality requirements are satisfied, the simplified computing routines for analysis of variance should be used even if high-speed computing facilities are available.

10.2.1.1 *Illustration of Binary Predictor Model I: Predictions Based on Categorical Data.* An investigator interested in the problem of developing students' typing proficiency designed a study to compare the effectiveness of three different methods of teaching typing, which he denoted as methods A, B, and C. He collected the following data:

> n_A observations of typing proficiency (scores) for students trained only with method A.
>
> n_B observations of typing proficiency (scores) for students trained only with method B.
>
> n_C observations of typing proficiency (scores) for students trained only with method C.

The criterion column vector, **Y**, for the regression analysis had as elements the typing-proficiency scores for the $n = n_A + n_B + n_C$ students who participated in the study. The investigator defined three predictor column vectors, $\mathbf{X}^{(1)}$, $\mathbf{X}^{(2)}$, and $\mathbf{X}^{(3)}$, so as to put in binary form the information on method of training. The following definitions were used:

> $\mathbf{X}^{(1)} =$ a vector of dimension n in which the element is 1 if the corresponding score in vector **Y** is associated with method A; and 0 otherwise.
>
> $\mathbf{X}^{(2)} =$ a vector of dimension n in which the element is 1 if the corresponding score in vector **Y** is associated with method B; and 0 otherwise.
>
> $\mathbf{X}^{(3)} =$ a vector of dimension n in which the element is 1 if the corresponding score in vector **Y** is associated with method C; and 0 otherwise.

For illustrative purposes only, the column vectors are shown here as if the data for individuals trained by methods A, B, and C came in that sequence. If the investigator had arranged the data in this fashion, the **Y** vector of dimension $n \times 1$ and the predictor matrix **X** which has dimension $n \times 3$, having been formed from the three **X** column vectors, would have this general appearance.

Criterion vector		*Predictor matrix* $\mathbf{X}$		
$\mathbf{Y}$		$\mathbf{X}^{(1)}$	$\mathbf{X}^{(2)}$	$\mathbf{X}^{(3)}$

$$
\mathbf{Y} = \quad
\begin{array}{c}
n_A \left\{ \begin{array}{c} \\ \\ \\ \\ \\ \end{array} \right. \\
n_B \left\{ \begin{array}{c} \\ \\ \\ \\ \\ \\ \end{array} \right. \\
n_C \left\{ \begin{array}{c} \\ \\ \\ \\ \end{array} \right.
\end{array}
\begin{bmatrix}
y_1 \\ y_2 \\ \cdot \\ \cdot \\ \cdot \\ \cdot \\ \cdot \\ \cdot \\ \cdot \\ \cdot \\ \cdot \\ \cdot \\ \cdot \\ \cdot \\ \cdot \\ y_n
\end{bmatrix}
\qquad
\mathbf{X} =
\begin{bmatrix}
1 & 0 & 0 \\
1 & 0 & 0 \\
\cdot & \cdot & \cdot \\
\cdot & \cdot & \cdot \\
1 & 0 & 0 \\
0 & 1 & 0 \\
0 & 1 & 0 \\
\cdot & \cdot & \cdot \\
\cdot & \cdot & \cdot \\
0 & 1 & 0 \\
0 & 0 & 1 \\
0 & 0 & 1 \\
\cdot & \cdot & \cdot \\
\cdot & \cdot & \cdot \\
0 & 0 & 1
\end{bmatrix}
$$

The regression problem is stated in the usual form:

$$\mathbf{Y} = \mathbf{XB} + \mathbf{E}$$

Then, with no restrictions on the predictors in the system, the $\mathbf{B}$-vector estimates, i.e.,

$$
\widehat{\mathbf{B}} =
\begin{bmatrix}
\widehat{b_1} \\ \widehat{b_2} \\ \widehat{b_3}
\end{bmatrix}
$$

are obtained by solving the matrix equation in the form $\mathbf{Y} = \mathbf{X}\widehat{\mathbf{B}} + \widehat{\mathbf{E}}$ for the vector $\widehat{\mathbf{B}}$ that minimizes $Q = (\widehat{\mathbf{E}})'(\widehat{\mathbf{E}})$.

The investigator has the hypothesis that methods A, B, and C have equally beneficial effects on typing-proficiency scores. This hypothesis may be simply expressed:

$$b_A = b_B = b_C = b_0, \quad \text{a common value.}$$

The regression model, $\mathbf{Y} = \mathbf{XB} + \mathbf{E}$, subject to this restriction, may be restated in this form:

$$\mathbf{Y} = b_0\mathbf{X}^{(1)} + b_0\mathbf{X}^{(2)} + b_0\mathbf{X}^{(3)} + \mathbf{E},$$

or

$$\mathbf{Y} = b_0(\mathbf{X}^{(1)} + \mathbf{X}^{(2)} + \mathbf{X}^{(3)}) + \mathbf{E}$$

However, if we let $\mathbf{X}^{(1)} + \mathbf{X}^{(2)} + \mathbf{X}^{(3)} = \mathbf{U}$, a column vector in which each element is 1, the equation may be stated more simply:

$$\mathbf{Y} = b_0\mathbf{U} + \mathbf{E}$$

Now the estimate for b_0, i.e., $\widehat{b}_0$, may be found by solving this equation in the form $\mathbf{Y} = \widehat{b}_0\mathbf{U} + \widehat{\mathbf{E}}_H$ for the value of $\widehat{b}_0$ that minimizes $Q_H = (\widehat{\mathbf{E}}_H)'(\widehat{\mathbf{E}}_H)$.

When the investigator has the **B**-vector estimates for the unrestricted model and the restricted model, he can compute the F statistic to use as a basis for accepting or rejecting the hypothesis that instructional methods A, B, and C produce equal levels of typing proficiency. The F statistic can be computed in the form:

$$F = \frac{(Q_H - Q)/2}{Q/(n-3)}$$

Since $R_H{}^2$, the squared multiple correlation for this restricted model, is equal to zero, the F statistic also can be computed in this form:

$$F = \frac{R^2/2}{(1 - R^2)/(n-3)}$$

This problem was presented primarily for the purpose of demonstrating the method of regression analysis. The results can be easily obtained by the standard analysis-of-variance computational procedure.

10.2.1.2 *Illustration of Binary Predictor Model II: Test for Interactions with No Restrictions on the Proportionality of Cell Frequencies.* The investigator interested in the effectiveness of the three methods of teaching typing (Section 10.2.1.1) wished to know whether the differences in the effects of instructional methods are the same for males and females. Thus he wished to test for "interaction" between the sex category and the teaching-method categories.

In addition to the criterion column vector, $\mathbf{Y}$, in which the elements were typing-proficiency scores, he defined six predictor column vectors:

$\mathbf{X}^{(1)} =$ a vector of dimension n in which the element is 1 if the corresponding score in vector $\mathbf{Y}$ is associated with method A and a male student; and 0 otherwise.

$\mathbf{X}^{(2)} =$ a vector of dimension n in which the element is 1 if the corresponding score in vector $\mathbf{Y}$ is associated with method B and a male student; and 0 otherwise.

$\mathbf{X}^{(3)} =$ a vector of dimension n in which the element is 1 if the corresponding score in vector $\mathbf{Y}$ is associated with method C and a male student; and 0 otherwise.

$\mathbf{X}^{(4)} =$ a vector of dimension n in which the element is 1 if the corresponding score in vector $\mathbf{Y}$ is associated with method A and a female student; and 0 otherwise.

$\mathbf{X}^{(5)} =$ a vector of dimension n in which the element is 1 if the corresponding score in vector $\mathbf{Y}$ is associated with method B and a female student; and 0 otherwise.

$\mathbf{X}^{(6)} =$ a vector of dimension n in which the element is 1 if the corresponding score in vector $\mathbf{Y}$ is associated with method C and a female student; and 0 otherwise.

The predictor matrix $\mathbf{X}$, then, is of dimension $n \times 6$, for it is composed of these six column vectors. It may be described in symbolic terms as follows:

$$\mathbf{X} = [\mathbf{X}^{(1)}, \mathbf{X}^{(2)}, \mathbf{X}^{(3)}, \mathbf{X}^{(4)}, \mathbf{X}^{(5)}, \mathbf{X}^{(6)}]$$

The regression problem takes the usual form:

$$\mathbf{Y} = \mathbf{XB} + \mathbf{E}$$

To solve the regression problem for the full (or unrestricted) model, the estimating equation is written:

$$\mathbf{Y} = \mathbf{X}\widehat{\mathbf{B}} + \widehat{\mathbf{E}}$$

where the estimates for the $\mathbf{B}$-vector parameters, i.e.,

$$\widehat{\mathbf{B}} = \begin{bmatrix} \widehat{b}_1 \\ \widehat{b}_2 \\ \widehat{b}_3 \\ \widehat{b}_4 \\ \widehat{b}_5 \\ \widehat{b}_6 \end{bmatrix}$$

are derived from a least-squares solution for vector $\widehat{\mathbf{B}}$,

and $\widehat{\mathbf{E}} =$ vector of residuals.

Owing to the orthogonal properties of the predictor vectors, the solutions for these parameters can be found easily by the usual analysis-of-variance procedure.

The hypothesis that the differences between the effects of instructional methods A, B, and C are the same for both sexes is expressed as:

$$b_1 - b_2 = b_4 - b_5$$
$$b_1 - b_3 = b_4 - b_6$$
$$b_2 - b_3 = b_5 - b_6$$

The last restriction is not actually necessary, since it follows as a consequence of the first two restrictions.

The solution to the regression problem with these restrictions imposed can be obtained by considering the following vectors:

$X^{(7)}$ = a vector of dimension n in which the element is 1 if the corresponding score in vector Y is associated with method A; and 0 otherwise.

$X^{(8)}$ = a vector of dimension n in which the element is 1 if the corresponding score in vector Y is associated with method B; and 0 otherwise.

$X^{(9)}$ = a vector of dimension n in which the element is 1 if the corresponding score in vector Y is associated with method C; and 0 otherwise.

$X^{(10)}$ = a vector of dimension n in which the element is 1 if the corresponding score in vector Y is associated with a male student; and 0 if associated with a female student.

$X^{(11)}$ = a vector of dimension n in which the element is 1 if the corresponding score in vector Y is associated with a female student; and 0 if associated with a male student.

The equation used to determine the parameter estimates then becomes

$$Y = X_H \hat{B}_H + \hat{E}_H$$

where the B-vector parameter estimates, i.e.,

$$\hat{B}_H = \begin{bmatrix} \hat{b}_7 \\ \hat{b}_8 \\ \hat{b}_9 \\ \hat{b}_{10} \\ \hat{b}_{11} \end{bmatrix}$$

minimize $Q_H = (\hat{E}_H)'(\hat{E}_H)$

and $X_H = [X^{(7)}, X^{(8)}, X^{(9)}, X^{(10)}, X^{(11)}]$.

These parameter estimates can be computed from a solution of the simultaneous equations resulting from the least-squares procedure. It should be recognized that the estimates of the restricted parameters are not unique. However the Q_H obtained from this solution is the same as that obtained from any set of vectors that results from an equivalent application of these restrictions to the full model.

The investigator can now compare the error sums of squares resulting from the unrestricted and restricted models to test his hypothesis that the differences between the effects of instructional methods A, B, and C are equal for both sexes. The F statistic can be computed in this form:

$$F = \frac{(Q_H - Q)/2}{Q/(n-6)}$$

where $\quad Q_H = (\widehat{\mathbf{E}}_H)'(\widehat{\mathbf{E}}_H)$

and $\quad Q = (\widehat{\mathbf{E}})'(\widehat{\mathbf{E}})$

The values for Q_H, Q, $\widehat{\mathbf{E}}_H$, and $\widehat{\mathbf{E}}$ are *not* the same as the values found in Section 10.2.1.1.

If preferred, the F test can be computed in terms of the squared multiple correlations:

$$F = \frac{(R^2 - R_H{}^2)/2}{(1 - R^2)/(n-6)}$$

where $\quad R^2 =$ squared multiple correlation in the unrestricted model

and $\quad R_H{}^2 =$ squared multiple correlation in the restricted model.

10.2.2 Regression Model for Evaluation of the Stability of Test Scores over Time. Studies in the behavioral sciences often require that a series of measurements be obtained for the same groups at intervals spaced over a period of time. It is virtually impossible to maintain precisely the same conditions for measurements taken at different points in time. Therefore, statistical techniques for taking account of such sources of variability are needed. The regression model described here is specifically adapted to situations in which the investigator seeks to test the stability of test scores over time, with controls for differences between individual subjects and between test administrators. It is assumed that no interactions occur between subjects and administrators.

The example shows clearly the need for a high-speed computer to solve the system of simultaneous equations required for the least-squares estimates for the unknown parameters of this regression model when the number of subjects is large. Use of this regression model for large problems involving nonorthogonal predictors was not practical before high-speed computers became available.

The investigator plans to evaluate the effectiveness of a new electronics training course on the basis of the stability of scores on a test covering the content of the course. This test will be given upon four different occasions equally spaced over the six-month period immediately following the n students' graduation from the course. Upon each occasion, three test administrators from the same group of five experienced men will be available; but the investigator cannot specify which three men will do the testing. Therefore he designs his analysis to control for individual differences both between students and between test administrators.[2] He is willing to assume that no interactions are involved and that the requirements for regression analysis are satisfied.

In formulating the regression problem, the investigator generates the following vectors:

$\mathbf{Y} =$ a vector of test scores of dimension $4n$, where $4n$ is the total number of scores obtained from the n subjects on the four administrations of the test.

$\mathbf{I}^{(i)}$ $(i = 1, \ldots, n) =$ a set of n vectors, each of dimension $4n$, each corresponding to one of the n students: the elements of $\mathbf{I}^{(i)}$ are 1 if the corresponding test score in $\mathbf{Y}$ came from the ith student; and 0 otherwise.

$\mathbf{A}^{(a)}$ $(a = 1, \ldots, 5) =$ a set of 5 vectors, each of dimension $4n$, each corresponding to one of the 5 test administrators: the elements of $\mathbf{A}^{(a)}$ are 1 if the corresponding test score in $\mathbf{Y}$ came from a test administered by the ath test administrator; and 0 otherwise.

$\mathbf{T}^{(t)}$ $(t = 1, \ldots, 4) =$ a set of 4 vectors, each of dimension $4n$, each corresponding to one of the time intervals: the elements of $\mathbf{T}^{(t)}$ are 1 if the corresponding test score in $\mathbf{Y}$ is associated with the tth time period; and 0 otherwise.

The predictor matrix $\mathbf{X}$, of dimension $4n \times (n + 9)$, is composed of the $n + 9$ vectors defined by the investigator. It may be described symbolically as follows:

$$\mathbf{X} = [\mathbf{I}^{(1)}, \ldots, \mathbf{I}^{(n)}, \mathbf{A}^{(1)}, \ldots, \mathbf{A}^{(5)}, \mathbf{T}^{(1)}, \ldots, \mathbf{T}^{(4)}]$$

With no restrictions on the predictors in the system, the $\mathbf{B}$-vector estimates are obtained by solving the matrix equation in the form $\mathbf{Y} = \mathbf{X}\hat{\mathbf{B}} + \hat{\mathbf{E}}$ for the vector $\hat{\mathbf{B}}$ that minimizes $Q = (\hat{\mathbf{E}})'(\hat{\mathbf{E}})$.

If the test scores are stable over the six-month period of the investigation, the four parameters associated with $\mathbf{T}^{(1)}, \ldots, \mathbf{T}^{(4)}$ may be hypothesized to be equal to zero. Accordingly, in the restricted model, a least-squares solution for $\hat{\mathbf{B}}_H$ is found by solving the matrix equation

$$\mathbf{Y} = \mathbf{X}_H \hat{\mathbf{B}}_H + \hat{\mathbf{E}}_H$$

where $\mathbf{X}_H$ is the matrix of dimension $4n \times (n + 5)$ formed by

$$\mathbf{X}_H = [\mathbf{I}^{(1)}, \ldots, \mathbf{I}^{(n)}, \mathbf{A}^{(1)}, \ldots, \mathbf{A}^{(5)}]$$

$\hat{\mathbf{B}}_H$ = vector of $n + 5$ estimators of the parameters in the restricted model

$\hat{\mathbf{E}}_H$ = residual vector for restricted model.

This least-squares solution minimizes $Q_H = (\hat{\mathbf{E}}_H)'(\hat{\mathbf{E}}_H)$.

The F statistic, which provides a basis for testing the hypothesis, can be computed in this form:

$$F = \frac{(Q_H - Q)/3}{Q/[4n - (n + 7)]}$$

10.2.3 *Regression Models for Investigations of Judgment.* In daily life, we often judge the extent to which some person or object possesses a given characteristic. Man's ability to make such evaluative judgments has contributed a great deal to the vigorous growth of the behavioral sciences. Judgments of one type or another have been widely used in the development of both predictors and criteria. In certain types of research, data in the form of judgments, or ratings, are indispensable.

In a sense, a judge serves as a kind of computer, receiving and synthesizing various types of data; he also determines which observations are to be given greatest weight in the system. Nonetheless, the human computer is easily overtaxed and rather unreliable; hence, large-scale studies are likely to present a number of methodological problems. Judges, for example, find it difficult to maintain a consistent "set," or policy, when a large number of evaluations are required; the same is true when the ratings must be made over an extended period of time. Such considerations have led to applications of multiple linear regression analysis in studies of samples of judgments that are designed to enable high-speed computers to simulate the judge. In effect, the computer ascertains the judge's complete policy and applies it, consistently and tirelessly. Judgment Model I, described in Section 10.2.3.1, is one such multiple regression model developed for large-scale studies in which the investigator desires to make optimal use of the opinions of experts. This regression model, as well as the one for testing the homogeneity of judgments (Section 10.2.3.2), has many applications in the behavioral sciences.

These two models had no practical value before the advent of high-speed computers. The reader will note the obvious contributions of high-speed equipment to all three phases of the problem in Judgment Model I: generation of the predictor vectors, computation of the regression equations, and making the desired predictions, or judgments. These three phases can be carried out in sequence by a computer, without interruption in passing from one set of operations to the next. The use of a high-speed computer is even more necessary for Judgment Model II, which involves more computations than Judgment Model I.

10.2.3.1 *Illustration of Judgment Model I: Predictions Based on Descriptive Data Used by Judge.* Conversion of plant A to the fabrication of items now produced in plant B is under consideration. The investigator has been asked to estimate how long it will take to crosstrain the men to the new jobs if the conversion is made. Since 500 old jobs and 500 new jobs are involved, crosstraining-time estimates for 250,000 possible job movements are required. No one judge, even if he knew all jobs equally well, could make so many estimates soon enough to help the decision makers; furthermore, it would be difficult for him to maintain a consistent "policy," i.e., a weighting of factors that affect his decisions, over the period required by the task. Therefore, the investigator decides to give standard items of information on jobs in both plants to a training expert who will use them as a basis for estimating the crosstraining-time requirements for a representative sample, of size n, selected from the 250,000 possible job movements. The investigator's plan is to develop a regression equation reflecting the judge's policy and to use it to make estimates for the other jobs from the same items of information given the judge. Let us see how this may be done.

The elements in the criterion vector, **Y**, of dimension n, are the estimates the judge provides for the crosstraining time needed to move from Old Job i to New Job j, to which a person may be crosstrained. The investigator must generate predictor vectors for use in estimating values in vector **Y**.

Among predictor sets often found useful are these two:

$\mathbf{X}^{(p)}$ = a column vector in which the element is the square of the difference between the amount of job characteristic p required by Old Job i (job which person is leaving) and the amount of job characteristic p required by New Job j (job to which person may be crosstrained) where the corresponding element in **Y** represents crosstraining time from i to j.

If there are k job characteristics, there will be k such predictor vectors.

$X^{(p')}$ = a column vector in which the element is 1 if Old Job i (job which person is leaving) requires an equal or greater amount of job characteristic p than is required by New Job j (job to which person may be crosstrained) where the corresponding element in Y represents crosstraining time from i to j; and 0 if Old Job i requires less of job characteristic p than New Job j.

If there are k job characteristics, there will be k such predictor vectors.

These two vector sets, $X^{(p)}$ and $X^{(p')}$, define a predictor matrix X, of dimension $n \times 2k$. This matrix may be described as follows:

$$X = [X^{(p)}, X^{(p')}]$$

where $p = 1, 2, \ldots, k$
and $p' = 1, 2, \ldots, k.$

The regression problem takes the usual form:

$$Y = XB + E$$

and the matrix equation is written:

$$Y = X\hat{B} + \hat{E}$$

where $\hat{B}$ = estimated regression weights, obtained from least-squares solution of equation, minimizing $Q = (\hat{E})'(\hat{E})$
and $\hat{E}$ = residual vector.

The resulting regression equation reflects the weighting given the k job characteristics by the judge when he evaluated the crosstraining times for the sample of n jobs. In the event that the accuracy of the regression equation is satisfactory, i.e., $Q = (\hat{E})'(\hat{E})$ is small, it would be appropriate to use the equation developed on this sample for predicting the remaining crosstraining-time values this judge would have given on the basis of a knowledge of the standard items of information on the jobs. In the event that the regression equation does not give satisfactory estimates of the criterion, two explanations are possible: (1) the judge is not consistent, i.e., he has no firm policy; (2) the regression equation has not adequately described his policy.

10.2.3.2 *Illustration of Judgment Model II: Testing of the Homogeneity of Judgments.* In the situation described in Section 10.2.3.1, let us suppose that the investigator did not want to depend on the crosstraining-time estimates of a single expert. Therefore he selected 10 different experts and asked them to make crosstraining-time estimates for the same sample of n of the 250,000 possible movements from old to new jobs. The investigator now wishes to know how well the 10 experts agreed; so he will test the homogeneity of their 10 regression equations.

In the full regression equation now, vector $\mathbf{Y}$ is of dimension $10n$, n estimates having been obtained from each of the 10 judges. The elements in the $\mathbf{Y}$ vector are the estimates of the crosstraining time that will be required for a person to move from Old Job i to New Job j, to which the person may be crosstrained.

Predictor vectors must be generated for the purpose of estimating vector $\mathbf{Y}$. If the 10 judges use the same job information as did the one judge (Section 10.2.3.1), the full regression equation will have 10 sets of $2k$ predictor vectors, one set for each judge. The vectors for the qth judge are defined in this fashion:

$\mathbf{X}_q{}^{(p)}$ = a column vector in which the element is the square of the difference between the amount of job characteristic p required by Old Job i (job which person is leaving) and the amount of job characteristic p required by New Job j (job to which person may be crosstrained) if the corresponding element in $\mathbf{Y}$ represents an estimate of crosstraining time to move from i to j furnished by the qth judge; and 0 otherwise.

There are k such predictors ($p = 1, \ldots, k$) for each q ($q = 1, \ldots, 10$).

$\mathbf{X}_q{}^{(p')}$ = a column vector in which the element is 1 if Old Job i (job which person is leaving) requires an equal or greater amount of job characteristic p than is required by New Job j (job to which person may be crosstrained) if the corresponding element in $\mathbf{Y}$ represents an estimate of crosstraining time to move from i to j furnished by the qth judge; and 0 otherwise.

There are k such predictors ($p' = 1, \ldots, k$) for each q ($q = 1, \ldots, 10$).

The predictor matrix $\mathbf{X}$ for the unrestricted model is of dimension $10n \times 20k$:

$$\mathbf{X} = [\mathbf{X}_1{}^{(p)}, \mathbf{X}_1{}^{(p')}, \ldots, \mathbf{X}_{10}{}^{(p)}, \mathbf{X}_{10}{}^{(p')}]$$

where $p = 1, 2, \ldots, k$
and $p' = 1, 2, \ldots, k$

With no restrictions on the predictors of the system, the matrix equation is expressed in the usual form:

$$\mathbf{Y} = \mathbf{X}\widehat{\mathbf{B}} + \widehat{\mathbf{E}}$$

Solution of this equation for $\widehat{\mathbf{B}}$ by the least-squares method minimizes the sum of the squared residuals, i.e., $Q = (\widehat{\mathbf{E}})'(\widehat{\mathbf{E}})$. Recognition of orthogonality among the vectors in this system of equations can lead to considerable computational savings.

Under the hypothesis that knowledge of the individual regression equations does not contribute to prediction of $\mathbf{Y}$, the 10 equations for the judges would be identical. Accordingly the restricted model's predictor matrix, $\mathbf{X}_H$, becomes:

$$\mathbf{X}_H = [\mathbf{X}_0{}^{(p)}\mathbf{X}_0{}^{(p')}]$$

where $p = 1, 2, \ldots, k$
and $p' = 1, 2, \ldots, k$

Here the $2k$ vectors resulting from the hypothesis are

$$\mathbf{X}_0{}^{(p)} = \sum_{q=1}^{10} \mathbf{X}_q{}^{(p)} \quad \text{for } p = 1, 2, \ldots, k$$

$$\mathbf{X}_0{}^{(p')} = \sum_{q=1}^{10} \mathbf{X}_q{}^{(p')} \quad \text{for } p' = 1, 2, \ldots, k$$

Estimates for the $2k$ parameters of the restricted model are found from the matrix equation, $\mathbf{Y} = \mathbf{X}_H\hat{\mathbf{B}}_H + \hat{\mathbf{E}}_H$, which is solved for the $\hat{\mathbf{B}}_H$ that minimizes $Q_H = (\hat{\mathbf{E}}_H)'(\hat{\mathbf{E}}_H)$.

Once the values of Q and Q_H have been obtained, the F statistic can be computed in the usual manner to test the hypothesis that the ten judges' estimates of crosstraining time are based on homogeneous regression equations; i.e., knowledge of the individual equations does not improve the prediction of the $\mathbf{Y}$ criterion values.

10.2.4 A Regression Model for Evaluating the Use of Equal Weights for Item Responses. In the behavioral sciences, much attention has been given to the development of measuring instruments and test batteries. Questions are often raised—and these must be answered on an empirical basis—about the relative merits of equivalent and differential weighting of item responses to serve various purposes. Almost all such questions require a comparison of the predictive efficiency resulting from the use of equal weights for all item responses with the predictive efficiency resulting from the use of a differential weighting system. Multiple regression analysis is well suited to this problem. Solutions to the predictor regression problems of the unrestricted model, which may involve large numbers of items, now can be obtained efficiently and economically with the aid of a high-speed computer.

Let us outline a case in which a test constructor has developed a set of 50 items to be used to predict a criterion of interest. It is proposed that these items be given differential weights to maximize the predictive efficiency of the test instrument. The test constructor, however, wishes first to investigate the possibility that adequate predictions of the criterion would result from the use of equal weights for all items. The full model would appear as

$$Y = XB + E$$

In this model the matrix X is composed of 50 column vectors, $X^{(i)}$ ($i = 1$, . . . , 50). Each element of $X^{(i)}$ is 1 when the corresponding element in vector Y is from an individual who has correctly answered item i; and 0 otherwise.

The hypothesis concerning the use of identical weights for all item responses is expressed as:

$$b_1 = b_2 = b_3 = . . . = b_{50}$$

The least-squares solutions for the estimators of the parameters in the unrestricted and restricted linear combinations provide the two error sums of squares of the residuals necessary for testing the hypothesis in the usual manner.

10.3 COMPUTATIONS ASSOCIATED WITH THE SOLUTION OF REGRESSION PROBLEMS

The effectiveness with which the general regression model is applied to research problems is closely linked with the efficiency with which computer capabilities are employed. In consequence, any investigator who plans to utilize the general regression model will desire to acquaint himself with the computational aspects of solving regression problems. Among those mentioned here are the ways in which computers may be utilized in preparing data for regression analysis (Section 10.3.1), desirable attributes of the computational procedures employed to obtain regression coefficients (Section 10.3.2), and techniques of communicating effectively with computers (Section 10.3.3).

10.3.1 *Data Preparation.* High-speed digital computers can perform a great variety of data-processing operations. Two such operations, essential to the preparation of data for use in the solution of regression problems, are involved in testing the source data (Section 10.3.1.1) and in generating new predictor variables (Section 10.3.1.2).

10.3.1.1 *Testing Source Data.* The first requirement in any numerical analysis is the testing of the source data. The speed and reliability of modern computers make it possible to test the legitimacy of each item in the data, i.e., to ascertain that it is within the expected range of values. This operation eliminates many errors from the basic information upon which the investigator will ultimately base his conclusions.

10.3.1.2 *Generating New Predictor Variables.* After as many errors as possible have been eliminated from the source data, the original information is often used as a basis for generating new predictor variables. In many instances, the variables that are to be represented in a regression analysis as predictor vectors have not been recorded in the required form (i.e., coded 1 or 0). Hence, a computer program is frequently needed to generate appropriate binary vectors from the source data.

In a similar fashion, when the investigator desires to use predictors that are complicated functions of the original variables, computer programs afford a convenient means of generating the requisite vectors. The usefulness of computer programs for this purpose becomes clear when it is recognized that just two of the original vectors, having elements denoted $x_i^{(1)}$ and $x_i^{(2)}$, might give rise, in a particular problem, to seven new vectors in which the elements are

$$(x_i^{(1)})^2, \quad (x_i^{(2)})^2, \quad (x_i^{(1)} x_i^{(2)}), \quad \left(\frac{x_i^{(1)}}{x_i^{(2)}}\right),$$

$$\sin \frac{2x_i^{(1)}}{12}, \quad e^{x_i^{(1)}}, \quad \text{and} \quad (x_i^{(1)} - x_i^{(2)}),$$

respectively.

10.3.2 *Desirable Solutions for Regression Coefficients.* In this chapter, we have frequently mentioned that investigators could not fully utilize the multiple linear regression model before high-speed computers became available. Such computers can perform, efficiently and economically, the numerical operations necessary to obtain regression coefficients for large-scale problems. It is advantageous, however, if the computational procedure used to estimate the unknown parameters possesses certain desirable attributes which are identified in Section 10.3.2.1. One computational procedure that has some of these desirable properties is described briefly in Section 10.3.2.2.

10.3.2.1 *Desirable Attributes of Computational Procedure Used in Solving Regression Problems.* After elimination of errors from the source data and generation of desired predictor variables, the problem is to secure estimates of the unknown parameters that minimize the sum of the squared residuals resulting from comparison of the actual criterion values with the estimated values. The coefficients themselves are obtained by solving the system of simultaneous equations resulting from the minimization of the residual sums of squares. It is often recommended that the solution of the equations be obtained by matrix inversion. In practical situations, however, when there is linear dependency among the predictor variables, the inverse solution may not exist; so some other procedure must be found.

It is clearly desirable to employ a computing procedure that will *always* provide a solution to the system of equations—whether or not a *unique* solution exists. It is also desirable to derive this solution economically. Since it is most unlikely that all of the large number of variables which may enter into any prediction system of interest to behavioral scientists will be linearly independent, an economical computational procedure that always yields a solution is especially needed in this area of research.

In addition to these two essential attributes of the computational procedure used to solve regression problems, it would be most advantageous to have a procedure that routinely tends to select, from the entire system of predictor variables, that subset of predictors which will produce the best estimates of criterion values. In practical situations, it is often either impossible or impracticable to secure information for the full array of predictors. Therefore most investigators seek to obtain as accurate predictions as possible from the smallest number of variables. Obviously, too, if some X-variables have no effect in determining the expected values of the criterion, i.e., make no independent contribution to the predictor system, the investigator may desire to substitute other variables for them in the system.

10.3.2.2 *A Computational Procedure for Solving Regression Problems.*
Recognition of the need for a computational procedure that guaranteed a solution and tended to select the most efficient subset of predictors in the system led to the development of the iterative procedure described by Kelley and Salisbury in 1926.[4] A variant of this procedure was developed and reported by Greenberger and Ward in 1956.[3] Since then, a more effective variation has been described by Bottenberg.*

---

* Certain aspects of this procedure were described in R. A. Bottenberg, "The Exploitation of Personnel Data by Means of a Multiple Linear Regression Model," a paper prepared for presentation to the Tri-Service Conference on Research Methods and Techniques in Personnel, sponsored by the Psychological Sciences Division, ONR, 25–27 May 1960. Bottenberg also discussed this variant procedure in an unpublished report, "An Iterative Multiple Regression Procedure Using the IBM 650," Technical Memorandum WCLL-TM-60-3, 1960.

The basic idea underlying the Kelley-Salisbury procedure and later variations is simple. At the outset, all regression weights are assumed to be equal to zero. The computer program, then, is designed to modify these zero regression weights, taking each variable in turn and one at a time, in a way that maximally decreases the residual sum of squares in the regression equation. This results in a maximal increase in the predictive efficiency of the system at each iteration.

This procedure not only has the properties described as essential attributes but also affords the advantages of certain computational savings not possible with other computational procedures. The details will not be discussed here; however, these savings occur in using this procedure, because it is frequently unnecessary to compute all the inner products of predictor vectors, as is ordinarily done. Consideration of both the details of the method and the operations of the computer to be used reveal the conditions that permit such computational savings to be effected.

10.3.3 Effective Communication with Computers. In this chapter, we have indicated that computers can assist in many aspects of regression computations. Nonetheless, it is still necessary to tell the computer how to do its task. Certain techniques for communicating with computers are particularly useful to persons who are not professional computer programers (and often useful to professional programers). These techniques consist of algebraic languages and compilers, which allow the problem formulator to "program" the machine indirectly. One such language system, known as FORTRAN, is usable on many different machines. The FORTRAN language adapted to the IBM 650 computer is called FORTRANSIT. Three examples of FORTRANSIT are given (Sections 10.3.3.1, 10.3.3.2, and 10.3.3.3) to illustrate how this language can be employed in regression problems. Detailed information can be obtained from FORTRAN-related manuals.* (See also Chapter 7.)

10.3.3.1 *Solution for Standardized Regression Weights for Two Predictors.* In order to gain familiarity with FORTRANSIT, let us suppose that the problem is to solve two simultaneous equations for the unknown, standardized regression coefficients, b_1 and b_2, corresponding to the two predictors, $\mathbf{X}^{(1)}$ and $\mathbf{X}^{(2)}$. Computation of the multiple-correlation coefficients is also required.

* These two publications will interest many readers: *IBM General Information Manual, Programmer's Primer for FORTRAN, Automatic Coding System for the IBM 704 Data Processing System,* New York: IBM Corp., 1957; *IBM Reference Manual, FORTRANSIT Automatic Coding System for the IBM 650 Data Processing System,* New York: IBM Corp., 1959.

230   Joe H. Ward, Jr.

If we assume there is a unique solution, we may state:

$$1\, b_1 + r_0 b_2 = r_1$$

$$r_0 b_1 + 1\, b_2 = r_2$$

where r_0, r_1 and r_2 are correlation coefficients.

The values of b_1 and b_2 are found by solving the following equations:

$$b_1 = \frac{r_1 - (r_2)(r_0)}{1 - (r_0)^2}$$

$$b_2 = \frac{r_2 - (r_1)(r_0)}{1 - (r_0)^2}$$

The multiple correlation coefficient, R, is given by

$$R = [(b_1)(r_1) + (b_2)(r_2)]^{\frac{1}{2}}$$

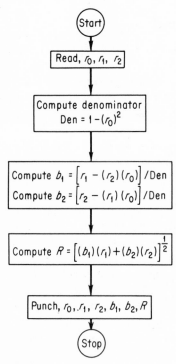

FIGURE 10.1   Example of flow chart for solution for standardized regression weights for two predictors.

The flow chart for this problem might be given in the form shown in Figure 10.1.

The FORTRANSIT program for the IBM 650 computer might employ the statements shown in Figure 10.2. These statements can be read into the computer and will be translated into an operating program. The same statements can be employed for other machines capable of translating the FORTRAN language.

10.3.3.2 *Prediction of an Independent Variable from the Regression Equation.* Frequently, after the regression coefficients have been computed, they are used to make predictions of an independent criterion. Let us assume, for example, that 20 regression coefficients have been obtained and that it is necessary to make actual predictions of a criterion. The regression equation, then, would take the form:

$$\mathbf{P} = b_0 + b_1\mathbf{X}^{(1)} + b_2\mathbf{X}^{(2)} + \ldots + b_{20}\mathbf{X}^{(20)}$$

The flow chart for this problem might be similar to that given in Figure 10.3.

Comment card	State-ment number	Statement	
C	1	MULTIPLE CORRELATION FOR TWO PREDICTORS	(Note: Comment cards are not processed.)
	2	READ, R0, R1, R2	
	3	DEN = 1 − (R0 * R0)	(Note: * means multiply.)
	4	B1 = (R1 − (R2 * R0))/DEN	
	5	B2 = (R2 − (R1 * R0))/DEN	
	6	R = [(B1 * R1) + (B2 * R2)]**.5	(Note: ** means exponentiation.)
	7	PUNCH, R0, R1, R2, B1, B2, R	
	8	END	

FIGURE 10.2 Example of FORTRANSIT program for solution for standardized regression weights for two predictors.

The FORTRANSIT program for the IBM 650 computer would be similar to that shown in Figure 10.4. FORTRAN language offers a number of statements that serve to abbreviate the description of the numerical procedure while producing the necessary computer operations for a whole series of computations. Statement No. 4, for example, insures that the machine will repeat the operations specified in statements 5 through 9 for all values, $i = 1, 2, \ldots, N$. Note also that, within the repeated series, statement No. 7 requires the repetition of the operations in statement 8 for all values $j = 1, 2, \ldots, 20$. In addition, the simple DO statements in statements 4 and 7 produce the machine operations required for the initializing, testing, and updating of the subscripts i and j in the flow chart. DO-type statements are particularly useful in describing such repetitive procedures.

10.3.3.3 *Least-square Solution of Regression Problems and the Determination of an Orthonormal Basis.* A widely used approach for solving for estimates of the unknown regression coefficients is sometimes referred to as the "elimination method." If certain results are properly recorded, this method will also yield an orthonormal basis of the space generated by the vectors involved in the regression problem. The final results of the procedure yield the desired regression coefficients and the coefficients required to express each vector as a linear combination of an orthonormal set of basis vectors. The flow chart for this procedure is shown in Figure 10.5; a FORTRANSIT program is given in Figure 10.6.

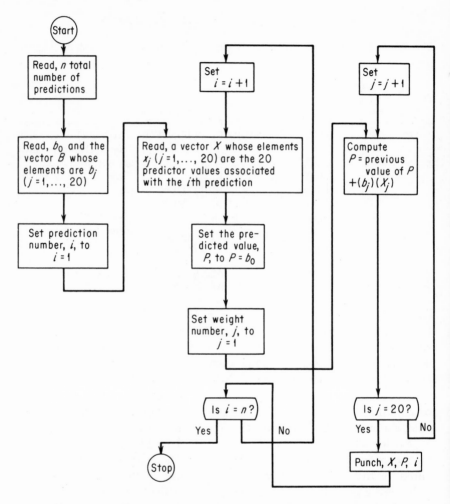

FIGURE 10.3 Example of flow chart for prediction of an independent variable from a regression equation.

Consider the set of n-dimension column vectors $\mathbf{X}^{(i)}$ $(i = 1, \ldots, m)$ arranged to form a matrix of dimension n by m:

$$\mathbf{X} = [\mathbf{X}^{(1)}, \mathbf{X}^{(2)}, \ldots, \mathbf{X}^{(m)}]$$

Then define

$$\mathbf{R} = \mathbf{X}'\mathbf{X}, \quad \text{with element } r_{jk}$$

which is a square symmetric matrix of dimension m. To predict $\mathbf{X}^{(m)}$ from a least-squares combination of $\mathbf{X}^{(1)}, \mathbf{X}^{(2)}, \ldots, \mathbf{X}^{(m-1)}$ and simul-

Comment card	State-ment number	Statement
C	1	PREDICTION FROM REGRESSION EQUATION
	2	DIMENSION B (20), X(20)
	3	READ, N, B0, B
	4	DO 9, I = 1, N
	5	READ, X
	6	P = B0
	7	DO 8 J = 1, 20
	8	P = P + (B(J) * X (J))
	9	PUNCH, X, P, I
	10	END

FIGURE 10.4 Example of FORTRANSIT program for prediction of an independent variable from a regression equation.

taneously to obtain an orthonormal basis of the space of $X^{(1)}$, $X^{(2)}$, . . . , $X^{(m-1)}$, we proceed as shown in Figure 10.5. The answers for a four-variable problem $X^{(1)}$, $X^{(2)}$, $X^{(3)}$, $X^{(4)}$ would appear as:

$$\begin{bmatrix} r_{11} & r_{12} & r_{13} & r_{14} \\ r_{21} & r_{22} & r_{23} & r_{24} \\ r_{31} & r_{32} & r_{33} & r_{34} \\ r_{41} & r_{42} & r_{43} & r_{44} \end{bmatrix}$$

Notice that these answers are not the same values as those in the original matrix R. The elements of R have been *replaced* by the desired answers.

If we designate the vectors a, b, c, and d as the orthonormal (i.e., the vectors are mutually orthogonal and are of unit length) basis of the vector space obtained from the computing procedure, the elements in and above the diagonal of the answer matrix provide the regression solutions for the prediction of $X^{(i)}$ as a linear combination of $X^{(1)}$, $X^{(2)}$, . . . , $X^{(i-1)}$ for all values of $i = 2, \ldots, 4$.

$$X^{(1)} = r_{11}a$$
$$X^{(2)} = r_{12}X^{(1)} + r_{22}b$$
$$X^{(3)} = r_{13}X^{(1)} + r_{23}X^{(2)} + r_{33}c$$
$$X^{(4)} = r_{14}X^{(1)} + r_{24}X^{(2)} + r_{34}X^{(3)} + r_{44}d$$

Punching each diagonal element before taking the square root provides the error sum of squares resulting from the prediction of $X^{(i)}$ from the least-squares combination of $X^{(1)}$, $X^{(2)}$, . . . , $X^{(i-1)}$.

Each of the orthonormal vectors $\mathbf{a}$, $\mathbf{b}$, $\mathbf{c}$, and $\mathbf{d}$ is easily obtained as a linear combination of $\mathbf{X}^{(1)}$, $\mathbf{X}^{(2)}$, $\mathbf{X}^{(3)}$, and $\mathbf{X}^{(4)}$. Furthermore, the elements in and below the diagonal of the answer matrix provide the expression of each vector $\mathbf{X}^{(1)}$, . . . , $\mathbf{X}^{(4)}$ as a linear combination of $\mathbf{a}$, $\mathbf{b}$, $\mathbf{c}$, and $\mathbf{d}$.

$$\mathbf{X}^{(1)} = r_{11}\mathbf{a}$$
$$\mathbf{X}^{(2)} = r_{21}\mathbf{a} + r_{22}\mathbf{b}$$
$$\mathbf{X}^{(3)} = r_{31}\mathbf{a} + r_{32}\mathbf{b} + r_{33}\mathbf{c}$$
$$\mathbf{X}^{(4)} = r_{41}\mathbf{a} + r_{42}\mathbf{b} + r_{43}\mathbf{c} + r_{44}\mathbf{d}$$

The orthonormal basis of the space generated by the set of predictor vectors, as shown here, is most useful when the same predictor matrix is to be used in conjunction with subsequent criteria.

10.4   SUMMARY

When high-speed computers are available to perform the computationally complex numerical operations, investigators can adapt the general multiple linear regression model for studies of a wide range of problems. The six illustrative examples in this chapter were chosen to show the formulation of different types of problems in the regression model and the contributions of computers to large-scale data analyses.

The multiple regression model has certain distinct advantages. These include the use of category-membership data, coded 0 or 1, as well as continuous variables in the prediction system. Since univariate analysis-of-variance and covariance techniques are special cases in which binary predictor variables are used, the regression model permits the investigator to perform such analyses, when necessary, without regard for proportionality requirements, or constraints on the number of observations for each category defined. Furthermore, the multiple linear regression model imposes no restrictions on the complexity of the functional form from which the elements of the predictor vectors are obtained. The multiple regression model, used in conjunction with high-speed equipment, enables investigators to study problems not considered "researchable" in the past. It seems desirable for those responsible for problem formulation to become familiar with the use of algebraic compilers, e.g., FORTRAN. An understanding of computer operations should help them not only to communicate with the machines to secure outputs for tests of hypotheses in an efficient and economical fashion but also to communicate their problems to professional programers.

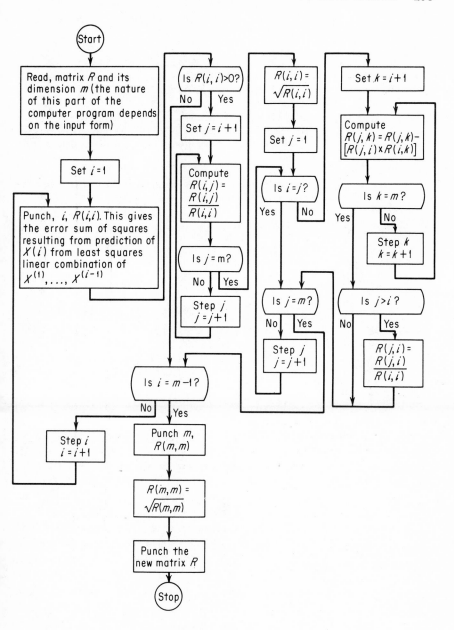

FIGURE 10.5 Flow chart for least-squares solution of regression problems and the determination of an orthonormal basis.

Comment card	Statement number	Statement
C	1	REGRESSION WEIGHTS AND ORTHONORMAL BASIS
	2	DIMENSION R (30, 30)
	3	READ IN THE MATRIX R (Note: The statements for reading the data depend on the form of input data and dimension of R.)

The following statements assume that the matrix R and the dimension M have been read.

	4	KSTOP = M − 1
	5	DO 19 I = 1, KSTOP
	6	PUNCH, I, R(I, I)
	7	IF (R(I, I)) 19, 19, 8
	8	IPL1 = I + 1
	9	DO 10 J = IPL1, M
	10	R(I, J) = R(I, J)/R(I, I)
	11	R(I, I) = R(I, I) ** .5
	12	DO 18 J = 1, M
	13	IF(I − J) 14, 18, 14
	14	DO 15 K = IPL1, M
	15	R(J, K) = R(J, K) − (R(J, I) * R(I, K))
	16	IF (I − J) 17, 18, 18
	17	R(J, I) = R(J, I)/R(I, I)
	18	CONTINUE
	19	CONTINUE
	20	PUNCH OUTPUT MATRIX R (Note: This matrix is replaced by the desired answers. The answers can be punched according to the desired output format.)
	99	END

FIGURE 10.6 A FORTRANSIT program for least-squares solution of regression problems and the determination of an orthonormal basis. (The matrix R is assumed to be read in according to the user's input format. The maximum dimension is assumed to be 30, as indicated by the DIMENSION statement.)

REFERENCES

1 Anderson, R. L., and Bancroft, T. A., *Statistical Theory in Research*. New York: McGraw-Hill, 1952, chaps. 13–21.

2 Danford, M. B., Hughes, H. M., and McNee, R. C., On the Analysis of Repeated-Measurements Experiments, *Biometrics, 16* (No. 4), December, 1960, 547–65.

3 Greenberger, M. H., and Ward, J. H., Jr., An Iterative Technique for Multiple Correlation Analysis, *IBM Tech. News Letter, 12,* 1956, 85–97.

4 Kelley, T. L., and Salisbury, F. S., An Iterative Method for Determining Multiple Correlation Constants, *Jour. Amer. Stat. Assoc., 21,* 1926, 282–92.

5 Mann, H. B., *Analysis and Design of Experiments*. New York: Dover, 1949.

6 Mood, A. M., *Introduction to the Theory of Statistics*. New York: McGraw-Hill, 1950.

7 Rao, C. R., *Advanced Statistical Methods in Biometric Research*. New York: Wiley, 1952, chap. 3.

8 Wilks, S. S., *Mathematical Statistics*. Princeton, N.J.: Princeton Univ. Press, 1950, chaps. 8, 9.

9 Williams, E. J., *Regression Analysis*. New York: Wiley, 1959.

Benjamin Fruchter & Earl Jennings
11/ FACTOR ANALYSIS

*Benjamin Fruchter is Professor of
Educational Psychology and Research Scientist
at the University of Texas. Previously,
he was Associate Director of Research for the USAF
Human Resources Research Center, Lecturer
at the University of Southern California, and
Aviation Psychologist in the AAF during World War II.
He obtained his Ph.D. and M.A. degrees
from the University of Southern California.
He is the author of* Introduction to Factor Analysis
*and has published over fifty articles in
professional journals in areas ranging from multivariable
research methods and the psychology of aptitudes to learning,
and to industrial and social psychology.*

*Earl Jennings is Research Associate
in the Department of Educational Psychology
and Executive Officer of the Human Talent Research
Project at the University of Texas.
He holds the B.S. and M.Ed.
degrees from the University of Texas, and he is
a candidate for the Ph.D. His current interests concern
the resolution of problems in the behavioral
sciences by automatic methods. He is particularly
interested in the simulation of intellectual functions.*

Factor analysis has found wide application in the behavioral sciences as a method of analysis and synthesis. Behavioral scientists often deal with large sets of variables (such as batteries of tests) whose nature and inter-relationships are not well established; hence they have frequent use for a method of analysis which helps to clarify the fundamental nature of the variables and the relationships between them.

11.1 QUESTIONS THAT CAN BE INVESTIGATED BY FACTOR ANALYSIS

Factor analysis starts with a matrix of the correlations among a set of n variables and seeks to investigate questions about it, such as the following:

a. Can the observed relationships be represented or reproduced, with little error or loss of information, from a set of r reference variables smaller in number than the n variables with which the analysis was begun?

b. Can the r $(< n)$ reference variables be interpreted to represent basic dimensions in the field of investigation of which the observed variables are linear weighted composites?

c. Are these basic variables completely independent in the population (represented on orthogonal reference axes), or related (represented on oblique reference axes)?

In order to investigate the first question, the test variables can be represented by vectors of length proportional to their common variability and separated by an angle so that the correlation between two variables, $r_{ij} = V_i V_j \cos \phi_{ij}$. A reference system of coordinate axes is then introduced into the test space and each test vector is expressed in terms of the r coordinate axes of the reference system. Estimating the length of the vectors representing variables, which has the effect of reducing the test space to the common factor space, and determining the dimensionality of the reference space are problems that must be dealt with in factoring the reduced correlation matrix. Various methods and computer programs, such as the centroid method, the principal axes method, and the multiple-group method, have been devised to deal with the factoring problems.

The second question involves the determination of a set of coordinate axes that is most useful and meaningful for the reference purposes of the investigator. Are there locations of the reference axes, determined by the structure of the interrelationships of the variables in r-space or by theory, or both, that are most useful for meaningful interpretation and reference? This is the problem of rotation, or translation of axes about the origin. A number of solutions, such as the two-factor, bifactor, and simple structure models, and a number of analytical methods, such as the varimax, quartimax, and oblimax programs, have been developed to deal with rotational problems.

With reference to the third question, it should be pointed out that the quartimax and varimax analytical rotation programs insert an orthogonal reference frame. The oblimax, biquartimin, and several other rotation programs insert an oblique frame of reference axes, the degree of obliquity being determined by the structure of the data being analyzed.

The investigator must select an orthogonal or oblique rotational solution. The mathematics of orthogonal solutions are simpler, and in many cases the structure is so nearly orthogonal that little is gained by introducing the complications of oblique factors. Also the theoretical framework used by some investigators requires orthogonal reference factors, regardless of the obliquity of the data.

In some areas of investigation there is considerable obliquity in the data. Where this is the case, a better simple structure fit can be obtained with oblique axes. A part of the information obtained from the analysis is the degree of obliquity or correlation among factors for a given set of data.

In addition to the questions and problems posed above, a number of other problems may be considered in connection with factor analysis. The general problem of matching factors from different studies will be considered in Section 11.5, and use of marker reference variables in Section 11.6. The generation of factor scores will be considered in Section 11.7, and some influences of computers on research in factor methods will be discussed in Section 11.8.

11.2 INTERCORRELATIONS

As applied in the behavioral sciences, the method of factor analysis generally starts with an intercorrelation matrix. From a mathematical point of view, the matrix to be factored need not be composed of correlation coefficients, but the examples in this chapter will be concerned with the factorization of a matrix composed of Pearson product-moment correlation coefficients.

Strictly speaking, the technique of obtaining correlations need not be treated in a chapter on factor analysis. The procedure is generally familiar, however, and it affords an excellent opportunity to mention some basic differences between solving problems on a hand calculator as opposed to solving them by means of an electronic computer. When one seeks to obtain a matrix of correlations by hand methods, one normally considers two variables at a time. The sums, sums of squares, and cross products for the two variables are laboriously collected, and eventually the correlation coefficients are computed. Then the process is repeated for two more variables and continued until all possible coefficients have been obtained. Because of time-consuming input-output considerations, as well as program logic, the technique just described would be a very inefficient way to utilize the capacity of an electronic computer.

A flow chart of a simple correlation routine which might be written for an electronic computer is presented in Figure 11.1. Within the boxes, k refers to the number of variables which are to be intercorrelated. In box 2, the term "record" refers to some type of input, such as punched cards, magnetic tape, paper tape, etc. The same consideration applies to box 15 regarding output. Notice that all summary information is collected before any of the correlation coefficients are computed. It may be inferred from the entry in box 6 that the sum of squares for a variable is regarded as being a special case of a cross product (i.e., the cross product of the variable with itself). Developing the program logic in this manner makes it unnecessary to write a separate loop for the sums of squares. Similarly, reference to box 14 indicates that the program would produce the correlation of each variable with itself along with all of the other correlations. A typical complete program would contain provisions for optional output of the summary data before box 9 and the variances after box 10.

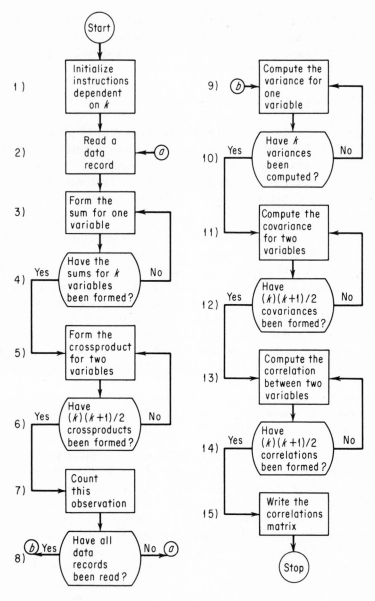

FIGURE 11.1 Flow chart for computing correlation matrix from score matrix.

Observe that $(k)(k + 1)/2$ storage locations are necessary to contain the cross products (box 5). As the covariances are formed (box 11), however, the cross products are no longer needed. Similarly, as the correlation between two variables is formed (box 13),* the covariance of the two variables is no longer needed and the correlation can be stored in the location which previously contained the covariance. Thus, the internal structure of memory can be visualized as a matrix which is replaced by succeeding ones at various stages in the process. This allows a maximum amount of memory to be used for computational storage purposes and a minimum number of memory locations to be devoted to storage of the end products. It is difficult to overemphasize the value of being able to visualize machine analysis problems in terms of matrices.

11.3 METHODS OF FACTORING

The basic equation for factoring the reduced correlation matrix,† $\mathbf{R}$, on orthogonal axes is

$$\mathbf{R} = \mathbf{F} \, \mathbf{F}'$$

where $\mathbf{F}$ represents the orthogonal factor matrix. The methods of factoring presented in this section all yield arbitrary orthogonal axes which must be rotated to orthogonal or oblique reference positions for meaningful factor interpretation. Before electronic computers, factor extraction done by pencil and paper arithmetic, or with the aid of a desk calculator, was a laborious process. Large-scale correlation matrices may be factored with relative ease on the modern electronic computer.

As previously mentioned, a number of analytical techniques are available for extracting factors from a matrix of intercorrelations. Examples are given in this chapter for two of the methods. The illustrative data are obtained from Fruchter.[4] All the sample analyses presented in this chapter were obtained by means of an IBM Type 650 Magnetic Drum Data Processing Machine, but the procedures may be generalized to other internally programed digital computers.

It is important to realize that computers are symbol manipulators. As such there is theoretically almost no limit to the magnitude of a problem which can be solved utilizing the computer. Practical limitations exist in abundance, however. Consider a correlation matrix consisting of fifty

---

* The formula which would be used for the program described is

$$r_{ij} = \frac{\sum x_i x_j}{N \sigma_i \sigma_j} \quad \text{or} \quad r_{ij} = \frac{(\sum x_i x_j)/N}{\sigma_i \sigma_j}$$

† The correlation matrix with estimates of the communality (h^2) of the variables inserted in the diagonals.

variables; 2500 storage locations would be required to store the entire square matrix. Theoretically, even if the machine contained only 2000 storage locations, the matrix could still be factored by cycling the data through the machine one column at a time. Operationally, such a solution rarely is used, particularly when the machine is input-output limited.* In this particular case, a compromise can be effected by entering only the triangular matrix; this procedure reduces the storage problem but increases the complexity of the programing.

Computers vary with regard to speed, capacity, accuracy, etc. It is important, therefore, to realize that in the discussion which follows, the comments are true, in general, for all general purpose stored program computers, but the task of implementing the procedures on a particular machine varies in complexity, depending upon the characteristics of the machine and the skill of the programer.

One of the decisions to be made in programing for factor analysis is whether to enter into the computer a square matrix of correlations or only the triangular matrix. A 5×5 square correlation matrix is represented in Figure 11.2(a). If all elements in the square matrix are stored in

	1	2	3	4	5
1	1	2	3	4	5
2	6	7	8	9	10
3	11	12	13	14	15
4	16	17	18	19	20
5	21	22	23	24	25

(a)

	1	2	3	4	5
1	1	2	3	4	5
2		6	7	8	9
3			10	11	12
4				13	14
5					15

(b)

FIGURE 11.2 (a) Memory locations required to store a complete 5×5 correlation matrix; (b) Memory locations required to store a 5×5 correlations matrix when redundant correlations are omitted.

memory, the numbers within the cells represent a possible memory location for each element. Notice Figure 11.2(b) contains the same amount of information, because of the redundant nature of correlation matrices since $r_{ij} = r_{ji}$, but utilizes ten fewer memory locations. Consecutive elements of the matrix in Figure 11.2(a) have consecutive memory locations when considered by row, and are displaced consistently by five when examined by column. Observe, however, in Figure 11.2(b) that the ele-

* Information within the computer is transmitted at electronic speed. Mechanical input-output devices do not presently have comparable speed. Some machines contain interlocking mechanisms to keep input and output functions from overlapping. We are using the term, input-output limited, to apply to such machines.

ments for column 3 are located in addresses 3, 7, 10, 11, and 12, which at first glance does not appear consistent. The mapping function for the displacement of consecutive elements in a triangular matrix is not difficult to calculate, but it does require additional programing. Additional programing usually requires more processing time, and the additional instructions themselves require memory locations. It is possible in a small problem for the additional programing to require more memory space than is saved; at the same time the processing time may be increased. In this example, only ten memory locations are saved, but in a 40-variable problem 780 locations would be saved. Frequently, it is difficult to achieve an optimum solution to a problem such as this. The solution depends upon what is expected from the program in the way of generality, on the characteristics of the machine for which the program is to be coded, and on the skill of the programer.

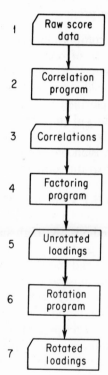

On a very large machine, it is relatively simple to enter raw data into the computer and receive rotated factor loadings as the final output, with optional provisions for intermediate output, such as correlations and centroid loadings. For smaller machines, and particularly for those without magnetic tape attachments, it is not feasible to link the steps together in a continuous process. Consider the situation schematized in Figure 11.3. The boxes with the "corner cuts" represent decks of punched cards containing the indicated information. The rectangular boxes represent the computer with the indicated program loaded in the memory. Frequently, the output format for one program will not match the input requirements of the next program in a process, even when the programs have been coded for the same machine. Suppose, for example, that the output in box 3 of Figure 11.3 represents a triangular matrix but the program in box 4 requires a square matrix.

FIGURE 11.3 Flow diagram representing the steps in going from the raw score data to the rotated factor loadings.

A number of solutions to this dilemma are possible. Probably the best procedure is revising the program at box 2 to produce the output in the proper format for box 4, or revising the program at box 4 to accept the format of box 3. There is a natural reluctance, however, to tamper with programs which have been checked out and are known to work well. Commonly, not enough storage remains in either program to make the necessary changes; and wading through pages of machine language coding (frequently necessary in program revision) can become tedious. Also on drum machines, where optimization is an important consideration, changing a number of instructions may increase processing time considerably.

Alternately, the data can be rearranged by a key punch operator. More important than the time taken is the possibility of keypunching errors. If the program at box 4 has a symmetry checking routine for the matrix and there are errors, it may take longer to debug the data than it took to debug the program.

A compromise procedure is writing a computer program that will accept cards of one format and rearrange the data for output in a different format. Routines of this nature are simple to write and they run very quickly. In this type of operation, however, the computer is being used as a glorified reproducer. In some situations, therefore, the expense or the ethics of employing valuable machine time for a task which does not properly utilize the full capacities of the computer should enter into the decision of whether to adopt this method of making the output of one program compatible with the input of a succeeding program.

11.3.1 *Centroid Method.* Where frequency of use is the criterion, the centroid method of factor analysis has been more popular than other methods. As high-speed computing facilities become more available and the problem of computational laboriousness becomes less important, the centroid method is likely to lose some of its appeal. Excellent theoretical and illustrative material pertaining to the centroid technique is available in several references. [21, 4, 7] The 11-variable example used for illustration is small and the advantages of solution on a computer are not as great as for larger problems. It was chosen because its size allowed using the same example many times for different procedures without obscuring major points, as might occur with larger tables. For additional details of the solution, see Fruchter. [4] The centroid factor loadings for the example are given in Figure 11.4. The values in the table were obtained using a program written for a *basic* 650; [16] i.e., none of the instructions in the program utilizes the floating point device, index registers, core storage, or magnetic tape. These values may be compared with those Fruchter obtained by desk calculator, if desired.

In general, the number of decisions which must be made by the operator at the console of a computer during a program run is inversely related to the economic efficiency of the program. Even though economic efficiency

TABLE OF CENTROID FACTORS *

				Factor			
Variable	I	II	III	IV	V	h²
1. Dial and table reading	7001	−2901	−0816	−1098	1512	6159
2. Spatial orientation I	5008	−2478	3771	−1532	−0927	4866
3. Reading comprehension	5749	1149	−2912	−1560	−1107	4652
4. Instrument comprehension	5731	1697	1079	−0645	1643	4001
5. Mechanical principles	5026	5141	0790	1625	−0199	5500
6. Speed of identification	4726	−1602	3931	−1251	−1509	4421
7. Numerical operations I	5008	−5090	−3278	1486	1592	6649
8. Numerical operations II	5661	−4588	−3521	2161	0217	7022
9. Mechanical information	2962	5213	0646	2155	−1275	4265
10. Practical judgment	4832	2526	−2192	−1498	−1859	4024
11. Complex coordination	4991	1039	2257	−0693	2199	3640
$\sum\sum a^2 / \sum r_{ii}$	.568	.812	.952	.999	1.040	

* Centroid factor loadings to four decimal places.

FIGURE 11.4

is not a major concern of the scientist, shortage of available machine time, or of money to pay for it may force him to accept procedures he might not consider best if he had an indefinite amount of time and facilities available. Often, therefore, decision functions which are the judgments of an informed operator are programed. In factor analysis, two of the major decisions which must be made concern the communality estimates and the point at which to cease extracting factors. In the program just mentioned, zeros are originally entered as the values in the principal diagonal of the correlation matrix, and the program is instructed to select and insert the highest correlation in the column in the principal diagonal of the correlation matrix, as the original communality estimate.

In the program used for computing the example, the criterion for the cessation of factoring is obtained as follows: The original communality estimates are summed. After each factor is extracted, the loadings are squared and summed. This value is added to all previous sums of squares of factor loadings, and the total sum is divided by the sum of the original communality estimates. When this ratio becomes larger than 1.00, the program ceases. If it should be decided that more centroid factors are needed after this criterion is reached, they can be obtained by resetting some of the control knobs on the console and starting the computer again. The ratio is reported below each column of the centroid factor matrix in Figure 11.4.

Since the value for the criterion is merely an estimate, this procedure is not the only one used in determining the dimensionality of the reduced correlation matrix. Basically, the number of meaningful, interpretable factors must be determined. This is done best during the rotation process.

11.3.2 Principal Axes Method. The principal axes method of factor analysis has long been regarded as superior to the centroid method from a mathematical point of view. Because of the computational difficulties involved, very few matrices of any size were factored by the principal axes method until computers became available. The chief advantage of the method is the fact that each factor extracted makes a maximum contribution to the remaining communality. The principal axes solution is obtained by computing the eigenvalues for the original correlation matrix. Associated with each eigenvalue is an eigenvector. The eigenvalues are also referred to as "characteristic roots," or "latent roots," of the matrix. The loadings in the table in Figure 11.5 were determined by taking the square root of the eigenvalue for a particular factor and multiplying it by the associated elements of the eigenvector. [26]

TABLE OF PRINCIPAL AXIS FACTORS *

			Factor			
Variable	I	II	III	IV	V	h^2
1. Dial and table reading	7301	−2076	0313	−0201	−0947	5864
2. Spatial orientation I	5096	−0387	4432	0676	0672	4667
3. Reading comprehension	5722	0887	−2441	1945	−0488	4350
4. Instrument comprehension	5544	2298	0627	−0782	−1158	3836
5. Mechanical principles	4417	5283	−1300	−1047	0354	5033
6. Speed of identification	4681	0500	4524	1050	1631	4639
7. Numerical operations I	5658	−5548	−1686	−1283	0299	6737
8. Numerical operations II	6219	−4700	−2371	−0556	1322	6844
9. Mechanical information	2239	5796	−1864	−1464	1946	4801
10. Practical judgment	4592	2493	−2391	2813	−0380	4107
11. Complex coordination	4828	2021	1992	−1653	−1863	3756
$\sum a^2$	3.0427	1.3545	.6987	.2183	.1495	

* All entries to four decimal places.

FIGURE 11.5

The program used to obtain the solution was written by Wright [23] and is based on Hotelling's iterative procedure. One of the important characteristics of the program is the fact that as each latent root and vector is found, the rank of the matrix is reduced, enabling subsequent roots to be determined with less computation. [8]

TABLE OF EIGENVALUES AND EIGENVECTORS *

Varirable	I	II	Eigenvectors III	IV	V
1. Dial and table reading	4186	−1784	0375	−0430	−2450
2. Spatial orientation I	2921	−0333	5302	1447	1739
3. Reading comprehension	3280	0762	−2920	4162	−1261
4. Instrument comprehension	3178	1974	0750	−1673	−2994
5. Mechanical principles	2532	4539	−1556	−2240	0916
6. Speed of identification	2683	0430	5411	2248	4218
7. Numerical operations I	3244	−4766	−2017	−2746	0773
8. Numerical operation II	3565	−4038	−2836	−1191	3418
9. Mechanical information	1284	4980	−2229	−3132	5032
10. Practical judgment	2632	2142	−2860	6019	−0983
11. Complex coordination	2767	1736	2383	−3536	−4816
Eigenvalues	3.0433	1.3548	.6990	.2185	.1496

* All entries to four decimal places.

FIGURE 11.6

11.4 ROTATION

Rotation of the frame of reference axes to a meaningful interpretable position is one of the valuable aspects of factor analysis as it is applied in the behavioral sciences. Although theoretical criteria (such as simple structure) for the location of the reference frame have been proposed, the determination of simple structure for a given set of variables has required a combination of skill and objectivity when done by graphical methods. Computers have not only reduced the laboriousness of the task but have made it feasible to apply objective analytical criteria, such as maximizing the variance of the squared factor loadings, to the determination of a unique set of reference axes for a given set of data.

The methods of factoring presented in the previous section yield arbitrary factor matrices. Each of the obtained factor matrices is merely one of the theoretically infinite number of orthogonal factor matrices from which the reduced correlation matrix can be reproduced by the basic formula $R = F F' + \rho$, where ρ represents the residual partial correlation matrix after removal of the portion of the correlations accounted for by the r common factors. The residual correlation may be due to errors of measurement (unreliability), computational errors such as rounding, or common factors if all of the common factors have not been removed.

For the rotational problem, it is desired to rotate or transform the arbitrary factor matrix into one more suitable for reference or interpretation.

Several models have been proposed for specifying the location of the reference axes; the most widely used of these is Thurstone's simple structure concept.[21] The rotated factor matrix may be on orthogonal reference axes, in which case it is represented by F_1; and the matrix which transforms it from its arbitrary to its rotated position is designated by Λ. If the arbitrary orthogonal factor matrix is designated by F_0, the orthogonal rotated matrix may be designated by

$$F_1 = F_0 \Lambda$$

The quartimax and varimax methods discussed later in this section are analytical methods which yield rotated solutions on orthogonal axes.

If orthogonal reference axes are not specified, the reference structure determined from the data may consist of oblique axes. The matrix of factor loadings on oblique simple reference axes is represented by the letter V, so that

$$V = F_0 \Lambda$$

The reduced correlation matrix is

$$R = V(\Lambda'\Lambda)^{-1} V'$$

and $\Lambda'\Lambda = C$ is the matrix of cosines of the angular separations among the oblique reference vectors or, in other words, the matrix of correlations among the oblique factors. The C matrix may be factored, rotated, and interpreted, if the factor structure at the second and higher orders is desired.

11.4.1 *Analytical Orthogonal Rotation.* Although attempts have been made over the years to reduce rotation procedures to analytical methods, little progress was made until computers became available. Several objective, analytic methods are now in use that transform an obtained arbitrary factor matrix to one useful for reference or interpretation. Various claims have been made for the different methods, but each aims at achieving a final solution which meets some or all of the criteria for Thurstone's simple structure concept. Basically, they depend on minimizing the sum of the cross products of squared factor loadings. Even though the behavioral scientist may not always be convinced that an obtained solution is best, in the sense that it is the most simple, at least he can report the analytical criterion he has used to reach the rotational solution. Either the analytical solution as obtained from the computer will be acceptable to the investigator or it will approach an acceptable solution. In the latter case, further rotations of the axes can be done by graphical methods.

Either an orthogonal or oblique frame of reference axes is specified by an investigator. If he wishes to use uncorrelated reference factors, an orthogonal method should be used. In orthogonal rotation, the reference axes maintain right-angle separations. If the investigator is willing to accept factors that are correlated, he should choose an oblique method which does not specify the angular separation of the axes. The degree of obliquity of the reference axes is determined from the data. Currently, two of the most popular techniques for orthogonal analytical rotation are the quartimax method and the varimax method. Examples of both are given in this section.

11.4.1.1 *The Quartimax Method.* Only limited information will be given concerning the analytical formulas. Those interested in programing specific routines require more detailed information than it would be feasible to include in this chapter. These details are available elsewhere.[7,17]

With regard to the quartimax method and, in general, for all the analytic rotational procedures, it is desired to obtain a matrix, generally called a "transformation matrix," which, when used to post-multiply the originally obtained factor matrix, yields a rotated factor matrix that meets the requirements for simple structure and meaningful interpretation. The programs that have been developed so far to obtain this transformation matrix are based on iterative procedures in which a given function is maximized or minimized. For the quartimax method, the function maximized is the sum of the fourth powers of factor loadings; hence the name "quartimax."

The centroid factor matrix reported in Figure 11.4 was rotated analytically by the quartimax method. The rotated loadings are shown in Figure 11.7. The solution reported in Figure 11.7 is called a "straight" or "non-normalized" quartimax solution.

When the original centroid loadings are used as the basic factor structure from which to begin the analytic procedure, the process is such that tests or variables that have high communalities influence the rotation more than variables with lower communalities. If the vectors representing the variables are extended to unit length before the analytic process is begun and then brought back to their original length after the process, the disproportionate weighting is eliminated.

The table in Figure 11.8 contains the loadings for the same example when rotated by the normalized quartimax method. In normalized quartimax, the vectors are extended to give equal weight to all variables in determining the rotational solution. A comparison of the values in Figures 11.7

TABLE OF NON-NORMALIZED QUARTIMAX ROTATED FACTOR SOLUTION *

Variable	I	II	Factor III	IV	V	h^2
1. Dial and table reading	6608	1572	3240	1052	1959	6159
2. Spatial orientation I	2574	0854	6425	0077	0101	4866
3. Reading comprehension	4003	3848	0693	3891	0247	4652
4. Instrument comprehension	2476	4474	2732	0333	2506	4001
5. Mechanical principles	0390	7344	0902	−0086	0296	5500
6. Speed of identification	1799	1458	6216	0123	−0426	4421
7. Numerical operations I	8107	−0676	0201	−0424	0288	6649
8. Numerical operations II	8296	0330	0219	−0113	−1104	7022
9. Mechanical information	−1003	6361	−0077	−0245	−1056	4265
10. Practical judgment	2214	4423	0613	3913	−0289	4024
11. Complex coordination	1898	3530	3393	0591	3910	3640
	N	M	P	V	S	

N = Numerical
M = Mechanical
P = Perceptual
V = Verbal
S = Spatial orientation

TRANSFORMATION MATRIX *

	I	II	III	IV	V
I	6602	5941	4330	−1281	0846
II	−5549	7585	−2684	−1548	1432
III	−4464	0300	7666	4583	0434
IV	1890	2611	−3327	7658	−4458
V	1449	−0499	−2047	4036	8784

* Entries to four decimal places.

FIGURE 11.7

and 11.8 indicates that they are structurally very similar; i.e., variables which have high loadings on certain factors in one solution tend to have high loadings on the same factors in the other solution. The magnitude of the loadings do differ somewhat. The values in the two figures can be compared with a solution obtained by a graphical method, if desired.[4]

Giving an extensive interpretation to the factors would serve little purpose here, but they are identified for reference. Factor I is labeled a numerical (N) factor, since its two highest loadings are for the two Numerical Operations scores. Because of the nature of the tests having high loadings on the factors, Factor II is labeled mechanical (M); Factor III, perceptual (P); Factor IV, verbal (V); and Factor V, spatial orientation (S).

TABLE OF NORMALIZED QUARTIMAX ROTATED FACTOR SOLUTION *

Variable	I	II	III	IV	V	h^2
			Factor			
1. Dial and table reading	6129	1692	4024	1182	1890	6159
2. Spatial orientation I	1829	0756	6686	0188	−0081	4860
3. Reading comprehension	3717	4023	1170	3884	0231	4652
4. Instrument comprehension	1988	4461	3165	0343	2454	4001
5. Mechanical principles	0044	7320	1128	−0211	0311	5500
6. Speed of identification	1064	1346	6392	0202	−0604	4421
7. Numerical operations I	8058	−0442	1087	−0286	0325	6649
8. Numerical operations II	8217	0583	1103	−0006	−1063	7022
9. Mechanical information	−1187	6327	−0058	−0397	−1021	4265
10. Practical judgment	1935	4548	0891	3862	−0309	4024
11. Complex coordination	1382	3461	3761	−0557	2837	3640
	N	M	P	V	S	

N = Numerical
M = Mechanical
P = Perceptual
V = Verbal
S = Spatial orientation

* Entries to four decimal places.

FIGURE 11.8

The quartimax solutions can be obtained very quickly on a computer, but they have limitations for some purposes. Since the quartimax procedure attempts to simplify the rows (variables) of the matrix, a tendency exists for a general factor to appear if the unrotated matrix had a strong general factor. Notice in Figure 11.7 that Reading Comprehension has a loading of .4003 on (N) and .3891 on (V). The normalized solution in Figure 11.8 changes the pattern only slightly. It does not have a great deal of meaning for a variable that purports to measure reading comprehension to have a higher loading on a numerical factor than on a verbal factor. In Fruchter's graphic solution, for example, the loadings on Reading Comprehension on (N) and (V) were .29 and .54 respectively, which makes more psychological sense. For some theories and sets of data, however, where a general factor is indicated, the quartimax solution may be the most appropriate.

11.4.1.2 *The Varimax Method.* The appearance of the general factor, which the quartimax method produces under some circumstances, is less common in rotated solutions obtained by the varimax method, because the varimax method simplifies the columns (factors) of the factor matrix as well as the rows (variables). The varimax method gives a rotational solution which is usually closer to the simple structure criterion of multiple factor analysis than does the quartimax method. Also, for some conditions, the loadings are less variant over a series of analyses, allowing for more valid generalization of the results.[11]

Procedurally, the varimax solution is very similar to the quartimax method. That is, an iterative procedure that maximizes a function is employed to determine a transformation matrix which, when used to post-multiply the original factor matrix, results in the rotated matrix. The function maximized in the varimax method is the variance of the squared loadings of the factor columns.

TABLE OF NON-NORMALIZED VARIMAX ROTATED FACTOR SOLUTION *

Variable	I	II	III	IV	V	h^2
1. Dial and table reading	6073	0880	3529	1970	2756	6159
2. Spatial orientation I	2058	0487	6573	0481	0865	4866
3. Reading comprehension	3488	2823	1022	4965	0824	4652
4. Instrument comprehension	1963	3816	2811	1545	3361	4001
5. Mechanical principles	0127	7051	1151	1534	1261	5500
6. Speed of identification	1318	1140	6381	0579	0345	4421
7. Numerical operations I	8060	−0643	0694	0152	0782	6649
8. Numerical operations II	8282	0435	0877	0662	−0474	7022
9. Mechanical information	−1062	6350	0172	1023	−0350	4265
10. Practical judgment	1738	3453	0889	4944	0235	4024
11. Complex coordination	1416	3020	3372	0399	3707	3640
	N	M	P	V	S	

N = Numerical
M = Mechanical
P = Perceptual
V = Verbal
S = Spatial orientation

* Entries to four decimal places.

FIGURE 11.9

Figures 11.9 and 11.10 present the straight varimax and normalized varimax solutions, respectively, for the example. Observe that the general factor is absent in both solutions. The normalized varimax solution reflects a relationship of Reading Comprehension to (N) and (V), which is more logically meaningful. The magnitudes of the two loadings are almost identical with those obtained by the graphical method, and the entire solution is very similar to the graphical solution. The solutions re-

TABLE OF NORMALIZED VARIMAX ROTATED FACTOR SOLUTION *

Variable	I	II	III	IV	V	h^2
			Factor			
1. Dial and table reading	5474	0029	3588	2732	3358	6159
2. Spatial orientation I	1591	0151	6576	0756	1513	4866
3. Reading comprehension	2834	2037	1112	5596	1332	4652
4. Instrument comprehension	1510	3036	2633	2156	4115	4001
5. Mechanical principles	−0060	6598	1071	2268	2274	5500
6. Speed of identification	0894	0884	6391	0835	1037	4421
7. Numerical operations I	7879	−1051	1027	0997	1123	6649
8. Numerical operations II	8110	0122	1323	1634	0046	7022
9. Mechanical information	−1057	6235	0165	1550	0468	4265
10. Practical judgment	1149	2804	0942	5441	0744	4024
11. Complex coordination	1039	2328	3139	0880	4389	3640
	N	M	P	V	S	

N = Numerical
M = Mechanical
P = Perceptual
V = Verbal
S = Spatial orientation

* Entries to four decimal places.

FIGURE 11.10

ported in Figures 11.7–11.10 were all obtained from a single program for the 650.[10] The different methods may be selected merely by specifying the one desired on a parameter card preceding the data into the computer. This parameter card also contains the tolerance value, which indicates to the computer to cease computing when the increase in the function to be maximized is less than the indicated amount. Obviously, different tolerance values produce slightly different results.

In some studies, the investigator has an hypothesis concerning the factors on which each test will have its major loadings. A computer program has been developed by Saunders to find the best-fitting orthogonal factors for a given hypothesis.[20]

11.4.2 *Analytical Oblique Methods.* In oblique rotation, the angles between the reference axes are determined by the structure of the data.[4] One might, therefore, infer that orthogonal rotation can be considered as a special case of an oblique solution. Once again, the attempt is made to maximize or minimize some function iteratively. The possibility exists that the solution which yields the maximum or minimum is an orthogonal one. In actual practice, such a result is rare, but it is theoretically possible. The oblique method is a more general method for this reason.

Currently, the oblimax method—of which this section gives an example—is the most widely used of the analytic oblique methods. Another analytic oblique method (for which an example is not shown) is the quartimin method. The quartimin criterion requires that the sum of cross products of squared factor loadings be minimized. Still another method, covarimin, requires that the covariances of the squared elements be a minimum. The quartimin criterion tends to yield axes that are too close; the covarimin yields axes that are too separated. Biquartimin [2] is an oblique solution which averages the tendencies of quartimin and covarimin by requiring that the sum of the two functions be a minimum.

The function to be maximized by the oblimax method is the ratio formed by the quotient of the sum of the fourth powers of all values in the matrix to the square of the sum of all the squared values in the matrix. The oblimax solution for the example is given in Figure 11.11.[18] The values in the table may be compared with those obtained by an oblique graphical method.[4] If .30 is taken as an arbitrary minimum value for presence on the factor, the structures of the two solutions are identical, with the exception that Variable 1 appears in the graphical solution with a loading of .32, but not in the analytical solution. It is interesting to note again the behavior of Variable 3, Reading Comprehension, on (N) and (V). The loadings are .01 and .40 in the oblimax solution. Also shown in Figure 11.11 are the transformation matrix and the C matrix of the cosines of the angular separations between the oblique axes.

11.5   FACTOR MATCHING

A recurring problem in factor analysis concerns the generalization of results over studies and the matching of factors from different studies. Several methods have been developed for this purpose,[3, 22] and the one proposed by Ahmavaara [1] will be illustrated here. A matrix is to be obtained with the elements representing the relationships between the factors across samples. The matrix (T) is computed by

$$T = (F'_1 F_1)^{-1} F'_1 F_2$$

where $F_1 = $ the rotated factor matrix from one study
            $F_2 = $ the rotated factor matrix from another study.

Notice how simple the computational logic of the problem becomes when conceived in terms of matrix operations. Follow the flow chart in Figure 11.12. Except for input-output functions, every step is a matrix operation.

TABLE OF OBLIMAX ROTATED FACTOR SOLUTION *

Variable	I	II	III	IV	V
1. Dial and table reading	0895	−1164	0504	1466	−1974
2. Spatial orientation I	−0112	−0307	4422	0046	−0269
3. Reading comprehension	3999	−0203	−0249	0149	0001
4. Instrument comprehension	0246	0664	−0196	−0568	−2956
5. Mechanical principles	0135	4032	−0162	0311	−1189
6. Speed of identification	−0006	0341	4623	−0036	0190
7. Numerical operations I	−0436	−0334	−0531	4611	−0336
8. Numerical operations II	0004	0869	0319	5422	0964
9. Mechanical information	0064	4435	0194	0540	0235
10. Practical judgment	4073	0435	0125	−0518	0474
11. Complex coordination	−0762	0339	0138	−0841	−3415
	V	M	P	N	S

N = Numerical
M = Mechanical
P = Perceptual
V = Verbal
S = Spatial orientation

TRANSFORMATION MATRIX

	I	II	III	IV	V
I	1321	−1754	−1690	2003	−1377
II	1799	−2977	3189	3839	−1942
III	−4877	−1697	−5641	2005	−1372
IV	−7180	−8791	−0209	−8604	2619
V	−4549	2806	7424	1784	−9251

CORRELATIONS AMONG OBLIQUE FACTORS

$$(\mathbf{C} = \Lambda'\Lambda)$$

	I	II	III	IV	V
I	1.0000	5034	−0127	5281	2468
II		1.0000	2571	6229	−3845
III			1.0000	1258	7200
IV				1.0000	−5200
V					1.0000

* Entries to four decimal places.

FIGURE 11.11

It is possible, therefore, to program a problem of this nature with standard coded matrix operations procedures. Normal precautions concerning numerical analysis may not be ignored, however. For example, some matrix inversion routines produce rounding errors of unacceptable magnitude as

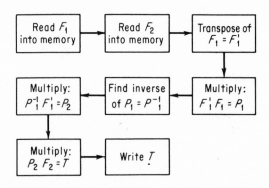

FIGURE 11.12 Flow chart of factor matching program.

the order of the matrix increases. A good subroutine description contains relevant information about its restrictions and capacities; within those limits, it can be used by the coder without detailed knowledge of the internal mechanics of the subroutine.

To demonstrate the factor matching technique, the factors obtained from the varimax rotation of the centroid solution (Figure 11.10) and the varimax rotation of the principal axis solution (Figure 11.13) were compared. Figure 11.14 illustrates the relationships between the factors from the two methods.[13] The near-unity diagonal elements indicate the high similarity of the corresponding factors and the off-diagonal near-zero values reveal the essential dissimilarity of the other factors. The method may be used to match factors from batteries having all or some of the same test variables. The variables common to the two batteries are used to compare the factors.

11.6   ESTIMATION OF FACTOR LOADINGS

In some situations an estimate is desired of the loadings of variables not included in the original factor analysis.[5] These loadings can be estimated by a regression procedure, if the correlations of the new variables with the variables in the factored battery are available.

The variables whose loadings are to be estimated may be new tests which were not available at the time of the original analysis, or they may be criterion measures which matured after the factor analysis was done. For some experimental studies, it is desirable to separate the variables into two categories: independent, or predictor, variables; and dependent, or criterion, variables. The independent variables may serve as a reference

TABLE OF NORMALIZED VARIMAX ROTATED FACTOR SOLUTION BASED ON PRINCIPAL AXIS FACTORS *

			Factor			
Variable	I	II	III	IV	V	h^2
1. Dial and table reading	5653	0585	3451	2240	3067	5864
2. Spatial orientation I	1745	0142	6338	0665	1727	4667
3. Reading comprehension	4495	1202	1098	4430	1005	4350
4. Instrument comprehension	1790	3210	2784	1930	3657	3836
5. Mechanical principles	0209	6254	1204	2141	2263	5033
6. Speed of identification	0954	0860	6599	0708	0824	4639
7. Numerical operations I	7992	−1079	1128	0444	0922	6737
8. Numerical operations II	8047	0082	1344	1364	0011	6844
9. Mechanical information	−0923	6799	0106	0887	0347	4801
10. Practical judgment	1456	3026	0886	5329	0779	4107
11. Complex coordination	1112	2376	3113	0637	4536	3756
	N	M	P	V	S	

N = Numerical
M = Mechanical
P = Perceptual
V = Verbal
S = Spatial orientation

* Entries to four decimal places.

FIGURE 11.13

TABLE OF FACTOR MATCHING FOR NORMALIZED VARIMAX ROTATION OF CENTROID AND PRINCIPAL AXIS METHOD *

		Varimax factors derived from centroid factors					
		I	II	III	IV	V	
	I	9986	0137	0090	−0464	0133	N
Varimax fac-	II	−0384	9986	0164	−0304	−0029	M
tors derived	III	−0099	0056	9998	0083	−0138	P
from principal	IV	2117	−0690	−0206	9742	0286	V
axis factors	V	−0158	−0310	−0039	0045	9993	S
		N	M	P	V	S	

N = Numerical
M = Mechanical
P = Perceptual
V = Verbal
S = Spatial orientation

* Entries to four decimal places.

FIGURE 11.14

battery for several sets of criterion variables. Only the independent reference battery is factor analyzed. The loadings of the dependent variables on the reference factors are then estimated by the regression technique. This procedure has the advantage that the structure of the reference factors is unaffected by the criterion variables; only the common factors in the reference space are used to make comparisons between the factor content of different sets of dependent variables. Variables with well-established factor content may be used as "marker" variables in the reference space.

By way of illustration, the validity correlations between the 11 tests used in the example, and pass-fail training criteria for three air crew positions are shown in Figure 11.15.[6] To estimate the loadings of these 3 criterion variables on the 5 factors derived from the analysis of the 11 tests, the formula provided by Mosier [15] is

$$\mathbf{V}_{tp} = \mathbf{R}'_{tj}\mathbf{F}'_{jm}(\mathbf{F}_{mj}\mathbf{F}'_{jm})^{-1}$$

where $\mathbf{V}_{tp}$ represents the matrix of factor loadings of the new variables on the rotated factors.

           $\mathbf{R}'_{tj}$ represents the transpose of the matrix of intercorrelations of the new tests (t) with the tests (j) in the original analysis.

           $\mathbf{F}_{mj}$ represents the matrix of factor loadings of analyzed tests on rotated factors.

The estimated loadings shown in Figure 11.16 were obtained with a program developed by King.[12] It may be observed that the pilot training criterion has its highest loadings on the spatial orientation and mechanical factors; the bombardier criterion has no appreciable variance on any of the factors; and the navigator criterion has its highest loadings on the verbal and numerical factors.

11.7   FACTOR SCORES

After the factors in a battery of test variables, or other measures, have been defined, it is frequently desired to represent the scores of individuals on the factors for further work, such as multiple regression. Before the advent of the computer, relatively little use was made of this procedure because of the amount of computational labor involved.

Consider the factor matrix in Figure 11.10. Variable 1 (Dial and Table Reading), Variable 7 (Numerical Operations I), and Variable 8 (Nu-

TABLE OF VALIDITY CORRELATIONS OF ELEVEN TESTS FOR
THREE PASS-FAIL TRAINING CRITERIA *

	Criteria		
Variable	*Pilot*	*Bombardier*	*Navigator*
1. Dial and table reading	28	18	55
2. Spatial orientation I	20	13	33
3. Reading comprehension	17	13	38
4. Instrument comprehension	32	23	28
5. Mechanical principles	37	10	25
6. Speed of identification	18	06	18
7. Numerical operations I	−01	12	38
8. Numerical operations II	03	12	41
9. Mechanical information	28	00	08
10. Practical judgment	13	14	35
11. Complex coordination	39	13	27

* Entries to two decimal places.

FIGURE 11.15

TABLE OF ESTIMATED LOADINGS OF THREE CRITERION
VARIABLES ON FIVE ROTATED FACTORS *

	Factor					
Criterion	I	II	III	IV	V	h^2
Pilot	−0128	3656	1740	−0087	5260	4409
Bombardier	0872	−0164	0511	1589	2879	1186
Navigator	3951	0696	2178	4070	2580	4406
	N	M	P	V	S	

N = Numerical
M = Mechanical
P = Perceptual
V = Verbal
S = Spatial orientation

* Entries to four decimal places.

FIGURE 11.16

merical Operations II) have loadings of appreciable magnitude on the factor we have labeled "numerical." In certain situations, it would be advantageous to have an estimate of an individual's numerical ability represented by one score rather than three. When such a score is developed from the factor matrix, it is called a "factor score." From the entire battery of 11 tests, 5 factor scores can be developed for each individual by the appropriate weighting of his scores on the original variables.

In computing a factor score, the goal is finding a weighted combination of the tests which best predict a factor.

The general formula is

$$X_f = \sum_{i=1}^{p} \beta_i X_i$$

$X_f =$ the factor score
$\beta_i =$ the weighting coefficient for the ith variable
$X_i =$ the raw score for an individual on the ith variable
$p =$ the number of tests which load on the factor

The weighting coefficients are obtained by multiple correlation. The matrix to be assembled is the correlation matrix composed of the p variables, with the factor loadings serving as validities. The regression weights obtained are used as the weighting coefficients in the formula. The determination of p is arbitrary. One possible procedure is to include all of the variables for each factor score. In practice, variables which load highest on a factor are used. Obviously, separate weighting coefficients must be derived for each factor score.

The use of factor scores as independent variables in multiple prediction work overcomes, to some extent, one of the liabilities of using electronic computers. Computers can generate nonsense at the same wondrous pace that they can generate sense. Where the labor of computation is no longer a paramount barrier in research, it may be tempting to add a few variables to a research battery to see what happens. Such a procedure may seem justified in factor analysis because of the experimental character of many tests. The content of a test is not established just because the originator of the test gave it a label. The sheer amount of data available for interpretation, however, can be quite discouraging in many cases. Reducing the number of variables by means of factor scores appears to be one useful method of reducing the number of predictor variables in multiple correlation or other analyses without losing the contributions of the individual tests.

11.8   EFFECT OF COMPUTERS ON FACTOR METHODS

The availability of the computational capacity of modern electronic computers has made it possible to apply desirable procedures which would be prohibitive without such powerful computational machines.

A program library for factor analysis studies should contain, as a minimum, routines for intercorrelation of large numbers of variables, matrix multiplication, and the inversion of real, symmetric, positive semidefinite matrices. A principal axes factor extraction program, and analytic rotation programs for orthogonal and oblique solutions are also desirable.

With the aid of a computer, it is possible to investigate many problems of theoretical interest that it would not be feasible to investigate without such aid. Some of these problems are the effect of reiterating the factoring with communality estimates derived from the previous factoring, to determine whether the communality estimates will stabilize, [24, 25] studying the effect of eliminating some of the variables in a battery on the factor structure, and trying out rotational solutions with varying numbers of factors to help determine the best estimate of the dimensionality of the correlation matrix.

There are a number of procedures which have desirable mathematical or statistical properties, but whose computational labor would be prohibitive without the use of a large-scale computer. These include Lawley's maximum-likelihood method of factor analysis, [14] in which a running chi-square test for the number of factors is provided, and Rao's canonical factor analysis, which also yields a test of significance. [19]

With the widespread availability of large-scale computers that can be expected in the future, much investigation of factor analysis methods will be possible, and great improvements in the objectivity and usefulness of the methods will occur. [9]

REFERENCES

1 Ahmavaara, Y., On the Unified Factor Theory of Mind, *Annales Akademie Scientarium Fennicae* (Helsinki), Ser. B, *106,* 1957.

2 Carroll, J. B., Biquartimin Criterion for Rotation to Oblique Simple Structure in Factor Analysis, *Science, 126,* 1957, 1114–15.

3 Cattell, R. B., and Baggaley, A. R., The Salient Variable Similarity Index for Factor Matching, *Brit. Jour. Stat. Psychology, 13,* 1960, 33–46.

4 Fruchter, B., *Introduction to Factor Analysis.* Princeton, N.J.: Van Nostrand, 1954.

5 ———, Review of Multivariate Studies Employing Independent-Dependent Variable Design and Some Problems of Generalization of Experimental Findings, *Handbook of Multivariate Experimental Design,* R. B. Cattell, ed., [tentative title; in preparation].

6 Guilford, J. P., ed., Printed Tests, *AAF Aviation Psychology Report,* No. 5, Washington, D.C.: U.S. Government Printing Office, 1947.

7 Harman, H. H., *Modern Factor Analysis.* Chicago: Univ. Chicago Press, 1960, pp. 192–211.

8 Horst, P., *Essential Characteristics and Special Cases of Multivariate Analysis Designs.* Seattle: Univ. Washington, December, 1960.

9 Kaiser, H. F., The Applications of Electronic Computers to Factor Analysis, *Educ. Psychol. Meas., 20,* 1960, 141–51.

10 ———, Computer Program for Varimax Rotation in Factor Analysis, *Educ. Psychol. Meas., 19,* 1959, 413–20.

11 ———, The Varimax Criterion for Analytic Rotation in Factor Analysis, *Psychometrika, 23,* 1958, 187–200.

12 King, F. J., An IBM 650 Program for Factor Estimation, Florida State Univ., School of Education, Dept. of Research and Testing, Tallahassee, Fla., 1960. (Mimeo.)

13 ———, An IBM 650 Program for Transformation Analysis, Florida State Univ., School of Education, Dept. of Research and Testing, Tallahassee, Fla., 1960. (Mimeo.)

14 Lawley, D. N., The Application of the Maximum Likelihood Method to Factor Analysis, *Brit. Jour. Psychology, 33,* 1943, 172–75.

15 Mosier, C. I., A Note on Dwyer: The Determination of the Factor Loadings of a Given Test, *Psychometrika, 3,* 1938, 297–99.

16 Navarro, S., Centroid Factor Analysis on the IBM 650, Texas A and M College, College Station, Tex.: Texas A and M College, 1957.

17 Neuhaus, J. O., and Wrigley, C., The Quartimax Method: An Analytical Approach to Orthogonal Simple Structure, *Brit. Jour. Stat. Psychol.*, *7*, 1954, 81–91.

18 Pinzka, C., and Saunders, D. R., Analytical Rotation to Simple Structure, II: Extension to an Oblique Solution, *Research Bulletin RB-54-31*, Princeton, N.J.: Educational Testing Service, 1954.

19 Rao, C. R., Estimation and Tests of Significance in Factor Analysis, *Psychometrika*, *20*, 1955, 93–111.

20 Saunders, D. R., A Computer Program to Find the Best-Fitting Orthogonal Factors for a Given Hypothesis, *Psychometrika*, *25*, 1960, 207–10.

21 Thurstone, L. L., *Multiple Factor Analysis*. Chicago: Univ. Chicago Press, 1947.

22 Tucker, L. R., A Method for Synthesis of Factor Analysis Studies, *PRS Report No. 984*, Personnel Research Section, Dept. of Army, Washington, D.C., 1957.

23 Wright, C., Principal Axes Factor Analysis for the IBM 650, *Tech. Report*, Office of Naval Research Contract Nonr-477(08), Univ. Washington, Division of Counseling and Testing Service, April, 1957.

24 Wrigley, C., The Effect Upon the Communalities of Changing the Estimate of the Number of Factors, *Brit. Jour. Stat. Psychol.*, 1959, *12*, 34–54.

25 ———, An Empirical Comparison of Various Methods of Estimating Communalities, *Educ. Psychol. Measmt.* (in press).

26 ———, and Neuhaus, J. O., The Use of an Electronic Computer in Principal Axes Factor Analysis, *Jour. Educ. Psychol.*, *46*, 1955, 31–41.

Paul B. Koons, Jr.

12/CANONICAL ANALYSIS

*Paul B. Koons, Jr.,
Assistant Professor of Psychology,
Ohio University, Athens, Ohio;
Ph.D., 1960, Michigan State University.
Currently, he is teaching
psychodiagnostic methods and
psychopathology, and working part time in
the university Psychological Service
Center. His major research
interests lie in the
application of multivariate
statistics to research problems
in clinical psychology
and personality dynamics.*

12.1 INTRODUCTION

Our attempts to chart the wilderness of behavior have resulted in an increasingly entangled geography of terms and boundaries. The surveyor's task is twofold: identifying clusters of related events to be included in the domain of a concept, and then developing refined procedures for analyzing the relationships among these complex, multivariate events. Concepts of aptitude, ability, or function have become collective terms representing many related, and often quite highly specific behaviors. In prediction problems, for example, we no longer are concerned with a simple single predictor–single criterion relationship. Rather, the increasing use of multiple regression analysis has suggested that many advantages are to be gained from the utilization of a battery of variables as predictors of our

I wish to express deep appreciation to Professor Charles F. Wrigley for his continuing help and stimulation and to acknowledge the major role he took in the development of the method of canonical analysis presented here. The "link" between U and V was his inspiration. I am grateful to Professor Amos Anderson for his critical reading of the manuscript.—Paul B. Koons, Jr.

267

criterion. In another case, we find it expedient to determine the relationships between a number of variables through correlational methods; subsequently, we reduce the correlations to their principal factors. We hope, of course, to be able to identify unifying principles and at the same time discard nonrelated phenomena. Note, however, that while we are happily conducting multivariate analyses on one side of the statement, predictor ↔ criterion, we are just as happily assuming the other side to be univariate for our analysis. This seems to be so whichever side of the statement we are examining. Obviously, our logic is faulty. Certainly, the milieu of data collecting and impatient theory building has perpetuated this fallacy, but the position taken in practice by many a behavioral scientist that method is secondary to theory building is hardly defensible. The numerous conflicting factor analytic studies of a single phenomenon clearly reflect the extent of this problem. A way out of this dilemma has been available for many years, but it has been largely ignored.

As early as 1935, Hotelling [6, 7] developed a method for determining what he designated "the most predictable criterion." His procedure makes it possible to determine the maximum correlation between a set of predictor variables and a *set* of (rather than a single) criterion variables. In other words, weights are found for the various parts of the criterion which, like the weights found for the predictors, will cause the combined sum of the criterion variables to correlate maximally with the combined sum of the predictor variables. These weights generally will be different for each battery. Although it is convenient to speak of "predictor" and "criterion" batteries, it should be obvious that with this procedure the distinction between them breaks down; we simply have two batteries that must be weighted in order to determine the maximum correlation between them. Hotelling [6] termed this method "canonical analysis."

The advantages of this procedure are several. Primarily, the burden of forming a composite criterion is reduced. The reseacher is no longer required either to pick and choose among criteria, in order to select that one which *seems* best to reflect the behavior being studied, or to assign arbitrary weights to the criterion variables. Secondarily, the sets of variables being studied do not have to conform to the predictor–criterion model. Indeed, the relationship between *any* two sets of variables may be studied by canonical analysis. Certain problems are attendant upon this application, however, and these will be discussed later.

12.2 HISTORY OF CANONICAL ANALYSIS

Canonical analysis has had a rather short history. Hotelling's original articles in 1935–36 [6] created something less than a stir when they originally appeared. Not until 1947, when the *British Journal of Psychology* added a Statistical Section devoted to the application of mathematical models to psychological problems, was canonical analysis brought to the attention of the psychological public. At that time three articles appeared simultaneously.[9, 2, 1] Of these, only one [9] attempted to illustrate the method as a working model for psychologists.

An examination of these articles shows one of the major difficulties of canonical analysis. The computations involved in even a simple problem, such as that presented by Thompson,[9] are complex and quite time-consuming, even when carried out by a mathematically sophisticated researcher. Further, the computational model requires several approximations by interpolation; this is seldom an accurate process. The advent of the high-speed electronic computer has all but eliminated the tedious and laborious mathematical computations required for canonical analysis. Complex computations have become routine; the related time element has become almost negligible, and computational errors all but vanish. With this advance in computation, the mechanical aspects of canonical analysis can be made routine and practical. It is to the presentation of such a routine that we now turn.

12.3   METHOD OF CANONICAL ANALYSIS

The procedure to be illustrated here was worked out on MISTIC,* a high-speed automatic digital computer, and is based on the method presented by Thompson.[9] For a discussion of the mathematical rationale of canonical analysis, the reader is referred to Hotelling.[6, 7]

The complete model for canonical analysis begins with the determination of the intercorrelations of the variables within each of two batteries, and the cross correlations between them. The first solution, utilizing one battery as "predictor" and the other battery as "criterion," then yields a matrix of correlations between the battery of predictors and the *composite* criterion as well as a matrix of regression weights for the battery of predictors. The second solution yields the reverse: the matrix of correlations between the battery of criteria and the composite predictor, and a matrix of regression weights for the criteria. These weights then may be substituted in regression equations for purposes of prediction. On the other hand, if the original variables represent independent tests or measures,

---

* MISTIC is the Michigan State University computer, modeled after ILLIAC. The author expresses his appreciation to the Computer Laboratory of Michigan State University and especially to the director, Dr. L. W. Von Tersch, for so generously making computer time and facilities available.

customary tests for the significance of a correlation coefficient may be employed.

The computation of the two sets of regression weights from raw data is relatively straightforward, involving only four standard programs on the average high-speed computer. Only one step will require special programing; this step could easily be accomplished by desk calculator if experienced programers are not available, even if analyses of several different sets of data are contemplated. The programs necessary for the complete canonical analysis are, in order of use :·

a. Computation of the Pearson product-moment coefficient of correlation (r), or its equivalent

b. Computation of the inverse of a matrix *

c. Postmultiplication of a matrix by another matrix †

d. Computation of λ: ‡ the matrix of latent roots (i.e., eigenvalues); and computation of U: the matrix of latent vectors (i.e., eigenvectors, or, more commonly factors loadings). This may be accom-

---

* The inverse of a matrix is that matrix which, when multiplied by the original matrix, yields a product matrix in which the diagonal elements are 1, and the off-diagonal elements are 0. This is the matrix equivalent of the reciprocal. In standard matrix notation: if $A^{-1} =$ the inverse of A, then; $AA^{-1} = 1$.

† Given two matrices: $_2A_2$ and $_2B_2$, where the subscripts stand for the number of rows and the number of columns in each matrix respectively, a product matrix $_2C_2$ may be found by postmultiplication using the *row by column* rule. By this rule,

$$C_{ij} = A_{i1}B_{j1} + A_{i2}B_{j2} + \cdots + A_{in}B_{jn}$$

Note that the number of columns of the first matrix must be equal to the number of rows of the second matrix.

EXAMPLE:

$$\begin{vmatrix} A_{11} & A_{12} \\ \\ A_{21} & A_{22} \end{vmatrix} \times \begin{vmatrix} B_{11} & B_{12} \\ \\ B_{21} & B_{22} \end{vmatrix} = \begin{vmatrix} C_{11} & C_{12} \\ \\ C_{21} & C_{22} \end{vmatrix}$$

$$C_{11} = A_{11}B_{11} + A_{12}B_{21}$$
$$C_{12} = A_{11}B_{12} + A_{12}B_{22}$$
$$C_{21} = A_{21}B_{11} + A_{22}B_{21}$$
$$C_{22} = A_{21}B_{12} + A_{22}B_{22}$$

‡ It will be shown later that λ is equal to the squared multiple correlation coefficient of the composite criterion on the battery of predictors.

plished by a program which solves a determinantal equation of the form:

$$|\mathbf{A} - \lambda\mathbf{B}|\mathbf{U} = 0$$

With the foregoing programs available, a high-speed computer * should permit the analysis of 10 predictors with 10 criteria in less than 30 hours. Only about three hours will be spent in actual computer running time; the remainder is consumed in casting the data into the proper format for computer input and checking the accuracy of the format (i.e., card or tape verification).

In the following presentation of the canonical analysis method, the outline of the steps in matrix manipulation will be paralleled by an arithmetic example. This example utilizes the set of hypothetical correlations employed by Thompson [9] in his reformulation of Hotelling's original method.

Consider the matrix:

$\mathbf{A}$	$\mathbf{C'}$
$\mathbf{C}$	$\mathbf{B}$

In this matrix, the letter symbols † represent the following quantities:

$\mathbf{A}$ = the matrix of intercorrelations of the "predictors"
$\mathbf{B}$ = the matrix of intercorrelations of the "criteria"
$\mathbf{C}$ = the matrix of cross correlations between "predictors" and "criteria"
$\mathbf{C'}$ = the matrix $\mathbf{C}$ with rows and columns interchanged (i.e., the transpose of $\mathbf{C}$)

Our procedure for extracting the maximum correlation between the batteries, and the regression weights of *each* battery on the other, is an extension of Thompson's [9] formulation. As he points out, in matrix terms, the maximum correlation between the batteries is found from the following equation:

$$\mathbf{R}^2{}_{max} = \frac{\mathbf{b'CA^{-1}C'b}}{\mathbf{b'Bb}} = \lambda$$

where $\mathbf{b}$ = the weights of the criterion that will maximize $\mathbf{R}^2$, or the multiple coefficient of correlation between battery and criterion.

---

* In this context a high-speed computer is defined as one which is capable of performing at least 50,000 multiplications per minute.

† Standard matrix notation is used throughout this section.

Solving for R^2 (i.e., λ) and **b**, and given the matrix

	P_1	P_2	P_3	C_1	C_2
P_1	1.00	.10	.60	.70	.20
P_2	.10	1.00	.40	.30	.80
P_3	.60	.40	1.00	.50	.30
C_1	.70	.30	.50	1.00	.40
C_2	.20	.80	.30	.40	1.00

1. Find A^{-1} (the inverse of **A**):

	1	2	3
1	1.622	.270	−1.081
2	.270	1.235	−.656
3	−1.081	−.656	1.911

2. By postmultiplication:
   CA^{-1}

	1	2	3
1	.676	.232	.002
2	.216	.846	−.168

3. By postmultiplication:
   $(CA^{-1})C'$

	1	2
1	.543	.321
2	.321	.669

4. Solve the detrimental equation for λ and **U**:

$$|A - \lambda B|U = 0$$

where $\quad A = CA^{-1}C'$

$\lambda 1 = .685$
$\lambda 2 = .453$

		1	2
$U =$	1	.316	−.840
	2	.949	.543

5. By postmultiplication:
   $U'B$

	1	2
1	.696	1.075
2	−.623	.207

6. By postmultiplication:
   $(U'B)U$

	1	2
1	1.240	.000
2	.000	.636

7. Determine the reciprocal of the square root of each element in the matrix:
   $U'BU \rightarrow (U'BU)^{-\frac{1}{2}}$

	1	2
1	.898	.000
2	.000	1.254

8. By postmultiplication:

		1	2
$\mathbf{C'U}$	1	.411	—.479
	2	.854	.182
	3	.443	—.257

9. By postmultiplication:
$(\mathbf{C'U})(\mathbf{U'BU})^{-\frac{1}{2}} = \mathbf{M}$
where $\mathbf{M}$ = the matrix of correlations between the predictors and the composite orthogonal criteria

	1	2
1	.369	—.601
2	.767	.228
3	.398	—.322

10. By postmultiplication:
$\mathbf{A^{-1}M} = \mathbf{P}$
where $\mathbf{P}$ = the matrix of absolute regression weights for the predictors. Column 1 represents the weights associated with $\lambda 1$; column 2, those associated with $\lambda 2$.

	1	2
1	.375	—.565
2	.786	.331
3	—.141	—.115

11. By postmultiplication:
$\mathbf{A^{-1}(C'U)}$

	1	2
1	.418	—.450
2	.875	.264
3	—.158	—.093

12. By postmultiplication:
$(\mathbf{A^{-1}C'U})(\mathbf{U'BU})^{-\frac{1}{2}} = \mathbf{b}_a$
$\mathbf{b}_a$ = the normalized regression weights for the predictors

	1	2
1	.466	—.359
2	.975	.211
3	.001	—.074

13. Check by postmultiplication:
$\mathbf{M'P} = \lambda$

	1	2
1	.685	.000
2	.001	.452

14. $R_1 = \sqrt{\lambda_1} = .828$
$R_2 = \sqrt{\lambda_2} = .672$

15. Determine $\mathbf{V}$ (the analog of $\mathbf{U}$), as follows:
a. Let $\mathbf{T} = \mathbf{A^{-1}C'U}$ (from Step 11); compute the sums of squares of $\mathbf{T}$, by columns.
b. Compute the square root of the sums of squares in a.

c. Compute the reciprocal of the square roots in b.
d. Multiply each element in *column* 1 of matrix **T** by its reciprocal root; each element of column 2 of matrix **T** by *its* reciprocal root, etc., yielding matrix **V**

	1	2
1	.426	—.850
2	.890	.498
3	—.162	—.174

16. By postmultiplication:
    V'A

	1	2	3
1	.418	.868	.450
2	—.905	.343	—.485

17. By postmultiplication:
    (**V'A**)**V**

	1	2
1	.878	.001
2	.002	1.024

18. Determine the reciprocal of the square root of each element in the matrix:
    $\mathbf{V'AV} \rightarrow (\mathbf{V'AV})^{-\frac{1}{2}}$

	1	2
1	1.067	.000
2	.000	.988

19. By postmultiplication:
    CV

	1	2
1	.484	—.533
2	.749	.176

20. By postmultiplication:
    $(\mathbf{CV})(\mathbf{V'AV})^{-\frac{1}{2}} = \mathbf{N}$
    where **N** = the matrix of correlations between the criteria and the composite orthogonal predictors

	1	2
1	.516	—.527
2	.801	.174

21. Find $\mathbf{B}^{-1}$ (the inverse of **B**) :

	1	2
1	1.191	—.476
2	—.476	1.191

22. By postmultiplication:
    $\mathbf{B}^{-1}\mathbf{N} = \mathbf{Q}$
    where **Q** = the matrix of regression weights for the criteria. Column 1 represents the weights associated with $\lambda1$; column 2, those associated with $\lambda2$.

	1	2
1	.233	—.710
2	.708	.458

23. By postmultiplication:

$\mathbf{B^{-1}(CV)}$		1	2
	1	.220	—.719
	2	.662	.463

24. By postmultiplication:

$(\mathbf{B^{-1}CV})(\mathbf{V'AV})^{-\frac{1}{2}} = \mathbf{b}_b$

$\mathbf{b}_b =$ the normalized regression weights for the criteria

		1	2
	1	.206	—.728
	2	.619	.469

25. Check

a. By postmultiplication:

$\mathbf{B^{-1}C}$

		1	2	3
	1	.739	—.024	.453
	2	—.095	.810	.119

b. By postmultiplication:

$\mathbf{C'(B^{-1}C)}$

		1	2	3
	1	.441	.145	.341
	2	.146	.641	.231
	3	.341	.231	.262

c. Solve the determinantal equation for λ and $\mathbf{V}$:

$$|\mathbf{B} - \lambda\mathbf{A}|\ \mathbf{V} = 0$$

where $\mathbf{B} = \mathbf{C'B^{-1}C}$

$\lambda1 = .453$
$\lambda2 = .684$
$\lambda3 = .000$

$\mathbf{V} =$		1	2	3
	1	—.849	.425	—.517
	2	.498	.890	—.184
	3	—.175	—.162	.835

d. Check by comparison of $\mathbf{V}$ above with $\mathbf{V}$ found in Step 15.*

e. By postmultiplication:

$\mathbf{N'Q} = \lambda$

		1	2
	1	.687	.000
	2	.000	.454

f. Check by comparison to the λ values computed in Step 13.

26. $R_1 = \sqrt{\lambda_1} = .829$

$R_2 = \sqrt{\lambda_2} = .674$

Check by comparison to the R_1 and R_2 values computed in Step 14.

As can be seen, our solution has yielded two sets of regression weights, one absolute and one normalized, for both batteries, as well as the set of squared multiple coefficients of correlation. The latter are, of course,

* If one begins the analysis of predictors on criteria with $|\mathbf{B} - \lambda\mathbf{A}|\ \mathbf{V} = 0$ as in Step 4, the $\mathbf{V}$ matrix so determined must be rearranged in decreasing order of magnitude of λ, i.e., column 2, column 1. Note that column 3 vanishes, since $\lambda3 = 0$.

identical for both parts of the solution. These computations may be summarized as follows:

1. $\mathbf{R}^2 = \lambda$ from $\begin{vmatrix} \mathbf{CA}^{-1}\mathbf{C}' - \lambda\mathbf{B} \end{vmatrix} \mathbf{U} = 0$
   and $\begin{vmatrix} \mathbf{C}'\mathbf{B}^{-1}\mathbf{C} - \lambda\mathbf{A} \end{vmatrix} \mathbf{V} = 0$

2. $\mathbf{P}$, the absolute regression weights of the predictors,
   $= (\mathbf{A}^{-1})(\mathbf{C}'\mathbf{U})(\mathbf{U}'\mathbf{BU})^{-\frac{1}{2}}$

and

   $\mathbf{Q}$, the absolute regression weights of the criteria,
   $= (\mathbf{B}^{-1})(\mathbf{CV})(\mathbf{V}'\mathbf{AV})^{-\frac{1}{2}}$

3. $\mathbf{b}^a$, the normalized regression weights of the predictors,
   $= (\mathbf{A}^{-1})(\mathbf{C}'\mathbf{U})(\mathbf{U}'\mathbf{BU})^{-\frac{1}{2}}$

and

   $\mathbf{b}^b$, the normalized regression weights of the criteria,
   $= (\mathbf{B}^{-1})(\mathbf{CV})(\mathbf{V}'\mathbf{AV})^{-\frac{1}{2}}$

4. $\mathbf{V}$, the matrix of vectors of predictors on criteria (analogous to $\mathbf{U}$), is given by the normalization of $\mathbf{A}^{-1}\mathbf{C}'\mathbf{U}$

5. A check on computational accuracy is given by
   $[(\mathbf{C}'\mathbf{U})(\mathbf{U}'\mathbf{BU})^{-\frac{1}{2}}]'[\mathbf{P}] = \lambda = [(\mathbf{CV})(\mathbf{V}'\mathbf{AV})^{-\frac{1}{2}}]'[\mathbf{Q}]$

It should be pointed out that we have computed $\mathbf{V}$ without solving the second determinantal equation. Instead, by using a link through $\mathbf{U}$ in the determination of $\mathbf{V}$, a major saving in computer running time has been provided. For example, in the analysis of a matrix of 17 predictors and 4 criteria,[8] *one* solution of the determinantal equation required 4¾ hours of actual computer operation before convergence was reached and the latent roots and vectors determined. The transformation of $\mathbf{U}$, replacing the second solution, required only 22 minutes on a desk calculator. It may be stated that as a general rule, when the size of the matrix increases, the time to reach convergence increases disproportionately.

12.4 DISCUSSION

The multiple correlation found by this method may be interpreted as is any *R*. The advantage peculiar to canonical analysis lies in the fact that the second set of variables has been weighted in terms of the amount of variance contributed by each single variable. This seems far superior either to arbitrary weighting by summation or to computing separate multiple correlation coefficients for each of the criterion variables. For example, imagine a situation where one is attempting to predict university achievement. The criterion usually employed is "grade-point average," representing the mean of grades earned in several areas of endeavor. Simple summation assumes that each area contributes equally to the total variances; in view of varying content, varying instructors, varying levels of difficulty, varying examinations and measures, etc., this assumption seems hardly reasonable. On the other hand, the computation of a set of multiple correlations between one's battery of predictors and the score for each separate criterion area may yield scanty information about the *over-all* adequacy of one's predictors. The canonical analysis R, combining all criteria with all predictors, should provide a much stronger index of association.

The weights for predictors and criteria offer a couple of possibilities for further experimentation. For instance, they may be plugged into a standard prediction formula; the predicted scores thus obtained may then be compared with actual scores from a fresh sample. Again, weights found by canonical analysis might be used in hypothesis testing. For example, the two batteries may represent sets of variables one is attempting to interrelate, such as indicators on psychodiagnostic tests and nosological categories in psychopathology. In such a situation, it would seem that the canonical analysis solution offers a far more rigorous criterion of association than does chi-square or than do statistical treatments involving a univariate model.

At this point, we should note that we do not yet know which method of multivariate analysis is most appropriate for a particular kind of data. The considerations for using canonical analysis can be identified only after further experience with the method. At the present time, selection of the appropriate multivariate method for a given problem can be determined only through empirical evaluation, though with sufficient experience we should eventually be able to establish adequate methodological criteria. For the present, we ought to utilize the results of several alternative procedures in a comparative fashion before we attempt to draw conclusions from the results of a canonical analysis method. In this connection, Burt,[2] Wrigley,[10, 11] and Horst [5, 4] have suggested several alternative approaches for evaluating the relations between two sets of variables:

a. The full canonical analysis model;

b. Reduction of the "criteria" to their independent dimensions by rotated factor analysis and the independent prediction of each "factor";

c. Combining the variables into one all-inclusive factor analysis, finding the independent predictor-with-criterion dimensions, and correlating these with the independent dimensions of predictors and the independent dimensions of criteria;

d. Making separate rotated factor analyses of "predictors" and "criteria," determining factor scores for both the predictors and criteria, and correlating these factor scores.

It would perhaps be wise for the experimenter to test at least several of these models on his own particular type of data before committing himself to a single approach.

Perhaps one additional issue should be mentioned. Although it appears obvious that one chooses variables that "seem" to belong together for manipulation—whether the choice is by hunch or hypothesis—the temptation of a data-engulfing computer is hard to resist. A shotgun approach certainly yields data: however, one is often hard pressed to interpret the results obtained. As an alternative to this indefensible procedure, I might suggest we meet temptation with rigorous self-discipline, since we can hardly defend our *model* if we cannot interpret the results it provides.

One last aspect of the canonical analysis model is worth noting. Horst [4] has recently developed a model extending the solution from the relations between two sets of variables to the relations between several sets of variables. This logical extension should also offer exciting possibilities for further study. For illustrating this technique, Hillmer,[3] a student of Horst's, developed the common factor structure of a set of personality items administered under three different conditions. He established several common factors, at the same time minimizing noncorresponding factor correlations. It would seem to be a promising technique, especially in the area of reliability of tests.

Like factor analysis, canonical analysis and the other multivariate techniques are on the frontier of psychological research. As with any method of experimentation, the researcher needs to expend fully as much energy exploring his model as he expends exploring his psychological domain. The search must be not only for methods of multivariate analysis that are mathematically defensible (which is an issue for psychological statistics generally), but also for methods that are readily interpretable psychologically.

REFERENCES

1 Bartlett, M. S., Internal and External Factor Analysis, *Brit. Jour. Psychol., Stat. Sect., 1,* 1948, 73–81.

2 Burt, C., Factor Analysis and Canonical Correlation, *Brit. Jour. Pyschol. Stat. Sect., 1,* 1948, 96–106.

3 Hillmer, M. L., Jr., Comparability of Factor Structure of Personality Items under Varied Instructions, *Tech. Report,* Office of Naval Research Contract Nonr-477(08) and Public Research Grant M-743(C5). Univ. Washington Division of Counseling and Testing Services, 1960.

4 Horst, P., Essential Characteristics and Special Cases of Multivariate Analysis Designs, *Tech. Report,* Office of Naval Research Cont. Nonr-477(08) and Public Health Research Grant M-743(C5). Univ. Washington Division of Counseling and Testing Services, December 1960.

5 ———, Relations Among *m* Sets of Variates, *Tech. Report,* Office of Naval Research Cont. Nonr-477(08) and Public Health Research Grant M-743(C4). Univ. Washington Division of Counseling and Testing Services, December 1959 (and *Psychometrika,* in press).

6 Hotelling, H., The Most Predictable Criterion, *Jour. Educ. Psychol., 26,* 1935, 139–42.

7 ———, Relations between Two Sets of Variates, *Biometrika, 28,* 1936, 321–77.

8 Koons, Paul B., Jr., Predicting Post-Hospital Adjustment: A Re-analysis. (Unpublished manuscript.)

9 Thompson, G. H., The Maximum Correlation of Two Weighted Batteries, *Brit. Jour. Psychol., Stat. Sect., 1,* 1947, 27–34.

10 Wrigley, C. F., The Prediction of a Complex Aptitude, *Brit. Jour. Psychol. Stat. Sect., 5,* 1952, 93–104.

11 ———, (Personal communication).

Benjamin W. White

13/STUDIES OF PERCEPTION

*Benjamin W. White is a
staff member in the Psychology Group
of Lincoln Laboratory,
Massachusetts Institute of Technology,
where, since 1955, he has been working on problems
of human pattern recognition. His interest
in perception began at an
undergraduate seminar with Hans Wallach
at Swarthmore College. Individual
differences in measures of perceptual
functioning formed a topic of his doctoral
dissertation in psychology at the University of
Michigan. While at Lincoln, he has
concentrated on studying the use of the
high-speed general purpose digital computer for
generating precisely specified and complex
visual and auditory stimuli.*

Rapid technological advances during the years following World War II have led to development of devices of unprecedented capability for handling visual and auditory material. There now exist sensitive microphones, film, and tape which can rapidly record sights and sounds with fidelity, and projectors, amplifiers, and speakers which can present this recorded information to our eyes and ears with such realism that it is sometimes difficult to distinguish the live from the canned. Such a technology allows the psychologist engaged in research on perception to exercise a degree of control over his stimulus material that would have been impossible 20 years ago—when the favored device for creating visual displays was a pen and India ink.

Much of the impetus behind these developments has stemmed from a need to provide human operators with reliable information to guide a vehicle or device traveling through space in real time toward a destination that might also be traveling through space in a path by no means perfectly predictable. In such a situation, the human engineer has the problem of presenting the necessary information so that the human operator can guide the vehicle to its destination with greatest accuracy. It is easy to specify completely the information necessary to carry out such a guidance task. It is by no means easy to discover how this information can be so presented that the operator can make best use of it. An operator has to know the present position, speed, and course of the vehicle he is guiding, and of the target, in order to solve the problem. But, displaying this information to him in the form of a compact table of numbers may not enable him to act upon it either promptly or accurately. Previous research in perception has remarkably little to offer toward the solution of such problems; hence, the psychologists faced with these display problems have had to rely on their own, often hastily conceived, research studies.

Problems relating to the display of information to human operators have cast a rather different light on the ancient and muddled question of veridicality in perception. Commonly, our ability to interact with and to manipulate our environment was assumed to be limited by the accuracy with which the perceptual world reflected the "real" world. Human engineering studies of displays have indicated that the accuracy of a display is only one of the factors involved in display effectiveness. In certain tracking tasks, large amounts of error are tolerable as long as data are presented in a proper form.

This need to present incoming information to the operator in a form he can readily assimilate has led to the introduction of special purpose computers linking the raw incoming data to the display system. Such devices may provide a number of links between the operator and the computer to enable the operator to insert or delete parts of the display, to alter its scale, and to interrogate the computer for additional information.[7]

As a result of these developments, those of us concerned with research in perception can take advantage of a technique of great flexibility for the generation and control of visual and auditory displays. Further, we now recognize that some of the most important and far-reaching problems in perception concern the kind of information processing that we perform on the waveforms and images impinging on our ears and eyes, in order to make rapid and accurate adjustments to events around us.

13.1 USING THE COMPUTER TO GENERATE VISUAL DISPLAYS

13.1.1 *Studies Using Computer-generated Visual Displays.* Comparatively few studies using computer-generated displays have as yet appeared in the psychological literature. One can account for this by the

small number of computers equipped with a video output and the small number of psychologists engaged in perceptual research. Green presented one of the first accounts of this use of the computer in 1957.[15] His presentation summarizes the programing involved in generating such displays and illustrates some of the displays generated. Several of these illustrations show patterns of vertical or horizontal bars composed of dots in a matrix, alternate bars having differing probabilities of a dot's occurring in this region. These patterns illustrate the use of a random number generator for such work. They were the stimuli employed in a study by Green, Wolf, and White.[14] In generating the film strips for this study, the random number generator was used to determine whether a dot should be painted in each matrix position, to determine whether, on a given frame, the orientation of the bars should be vertical or horizontal, and to determine the number of bars.

This work on the detection of bar patterns might also be described as a study in contour detection as a function of the distribution of elements in adjacent regions of the visual field. As such, it is similar to a different study of stereoscopic depth done by Julesz.[18] The displays in this study were dot matrices, in some respects similar to those used by Green et al. Instead of producing these displays on line, Julesz used the computer to produce a magnetic tape containing a list of brightness values so arranged that they could be read into a television transducer to produce the dot matrices on the cathode ray tube (CRT), where they were photographed. This method circumvents some of the annoying problems of generating displays on line with a computer. On the other hand, Julesz' technique makes it more difficult to change certain display characteristics. Complete control of the CRT display by digital tape would be convenient. Such a system for display generation would make more efficient use of computer time with no sacrifice in flexibility. The demand for such equipment has not yet been sufficient to make its commercial production feasible.

With these displays, Julesz has not only produced a novel and intriguing stereoscopic depth effect, but has given careful consideration to the kind of model which can account for the conditions under which this effect does and does not occur. The elimination of alternative explanations necessitated generating displays with particular characteristics such that one model would predict the occurrence of the effect and the alternative model would not. Without the computer, it would have been difficult to create some of these displays in order to sort out alternative hypotheses.

An exploration of the stimulus factors affecting the kinetic depth effect, has been undertaken by Green and by Braunstein.[13, 3] These studies

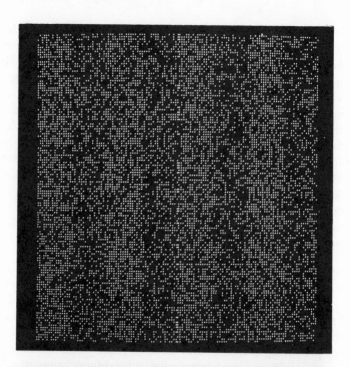

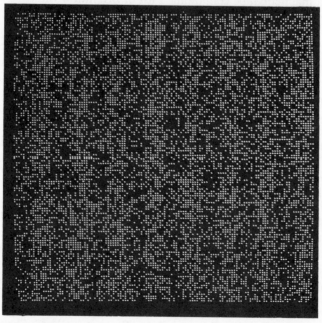

284

FIGURE 13.1 Computer generated bar patterns.

both used movies made with the computer. The displays consisted of sets of points or lines which were changed between each frame in such a way as to represent the rigid rotation of a three-dimensional constellation in space. A subject was asked to view a short movie of 250 frames showing the movements of such a constellation of points or lines and then to rate the coherence of the elements in the display. Parameters, such as the number of points or lines in the display, speed of rotation, axis of rotation, degree of linear perspective, and symmetry of element placement, were all varied to ascertain their effect on perceived coherence.

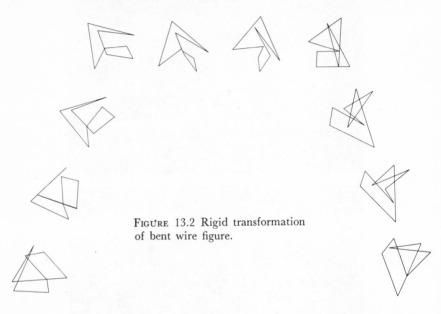

FIGURE 13.2 Rigid transformation of bent wire figure.

An unpublished study by the author involved the recognition of static, computer-generated displays of alphanumeric characters, the elements of which had undergone a number of two-dimensional random walks.[31] Subjects were shown these displays in scrambled order and asked to identify the character in each. The proportion of correct identifications declined regularly with the number of walks the points in a given figure had undergone, and the rate of this decline was markedly affected by the size of the step which a point could take on any given walk.

13.1.2 *Equipment*. Comparatively few high-speed, general purpose digital computers are equipped with a cathode ray tube output to enable the programer to generate pictures directly. However, the IBM 709 does have

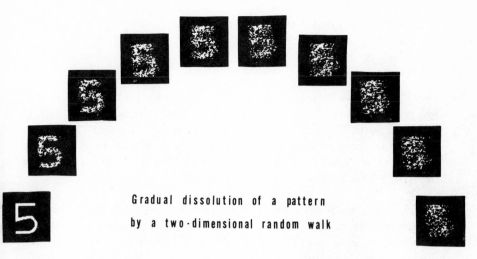

Gradual dissolution of a pattern
by a two-dimensional random walk

FIGURE 13.3 Elastic transformation by two-dimensional random walk.

such an output device as optional equipment, and the following description of the technique of generating visual patterns will be in terms of this equipment.[25] This machine has two cathode ray tubes as outputs, a 5-inch tube with fast decay phosphor, and a 21-inch tube with a slower phosphor. The latter is used only for monitoring; the former has mounted over it a 35mm camera whose shutter is normally open and whose film can be indexed by a pulse under program control. Three instructions are provided: one to select the unit and prepare it for data transmission, one to display a dot at one of two intensities and at some position within a raster 3.36 inches square, and a third to advance the film one frame in the camera. Dots may be written in this raster at maximum speeds in excess of 7100 dots per second. The square raster has 1024 positions on each (X and Y) axis.

Suppose, using this equipment, we wished to make a simple movie of a dot moving across the center of the frame at constant speed starting at the leftmost position and moving to the rightmost position. The display program would look something like this:

1. Put the integer 512 in "Y"
2. Put the integer 0 in "X"
3. Put a 1 in "Inc"
4. Display a point at X, Y
5. Add "Inc" to X
6. Advance film one frame

7. Is X now greater than 1024?
   No: go to 4
   Yes: go to next instruction
8. Stop

Should this movement be too rapid, the program could be altered to take two or more frames at each dot position. Should the programer wish to introduce some acceleration, a constant could be added to "Inc" after each frame. Exchanging X and Y will produce vertical motion; adding "Inc" both to X and Y will produce diagonal motion. What would be the effect of exchanging instructions 6 and 7?

13.1.3 *Representing Visual Patterns in the Computer.* In the moving dot program above, on any given frame the pattern was represented in the computer by a pair of numbers, the X, Y coordinates. When writing display programs in some languages, such as FORTRAN, this is the only straightforward way of representing a pattern. Should the pattern be large and intricate, such representation will involve two long lists for the X and Y coordinate values so that there is very little storage left over for the program designed to manipulate this pattern. Even with 32,000 available registers, this extravagant use of storage for representing a pattern may limit the programer severely if he wishes to perform any but the most simple transformations. Another method for representing patterns in memory is illustrated in Figure 13.4 below.

↑ 1	↑ 2	↑ 3	↑ 4	↑ 5
0 6	0 7	1 8	0 9	0 10
0 11	0 12	1 13	0 14	0 15
0 16	0 17	1 18	0 19	0 20
0 21	0 22	1 23	0 24	0 25
0 26	0 27	1 28	0 29	0 30
0 31	0 32	1 33	0 34	0 35

11111001000010000100001000010000100

FIGURE 13.4 T pattern in binary matrix and 35-bit storage register.

Here we see the letter T in a matrix consisting of five columns and seven rows. Each cell in this matrix has been given a number. The sequence of numbers from 1 to 35 traces an orderly path through the matrix. As we trace this path, let us write in a line a 0 for each empty cell we encounter, and a 1 for each filled cell which contains part of the T. This string of 35 0's and 1's is shown below the matrix. Such a string of binary digits can be directly represented in a single computer register (of sufficient length). In some sense, we have now represented the pattern T in one register. In our previous method, we would have required 22 registers, 11 for the X coordinate values and 11 more for the corresponding Y values. Actually, we could have done somewhat better than this by putting the paired X and Y values into one register, since only 10 bits are required to specify an integer between 0 and 1023. Even so, the method of storing the string of 1's and 0's in a single register saves a great deal of space. Some of this advantage must be sacrificed when the time comes actually to display this T pattern. If the X, Y coordinates are stored as paired numbers in 11 successive registers, we simply write a program to display 11 points whose coordinate values are to be found in these 11 registers. When the T is stored in a single register in the form of a string of 1's and 0's, however, we must write a subroutine which will enable the computer to convert this representation into an appropriate series of X, Y coordinate values. To do this, we need to furnish several things: a starting position for cell no. 1 of the 35-cell matrix, a dot separation value, and the information about the nature of the path through the matrix. With this, the subroutine can then simply consider each of the 35 bits in turn, painting a dot in the appropriate position if the bit is a 1, or skipping that locus if the bit is a 0. This method of pattern representation was used for the alphanumeric characters seen in Figure 13.5.

Patterns need not be reduced to a sequence of 1's and 0's. If the display equipment has the capability, and if the photographic equipment can deal with more depth of contrast, the number of brightness levels may be increased considerably above 2; in which case the pattern is stored as a sequence of numbers between 0 and the maximum dot intensity desired. In making the display, these numbers can be used either to control dot intensity on the cathode ray tube or to program the number of times a dot in a given position in the pattern will be painted on the scope. With each additional paint, up to some maximum, the photographed brightness in the region will increase.

13.1.4 *Input Techniques.* No matter how the pattern is represented in the computer the problem remains of how to put it there. If the display is regular and simple, such as a dot matrix, one can write a program to generate a matrix of a given size, grain, and location, and get around the problem of reading in the original pattern. Patterns composed of random sets of points may be similarly generated by the program. Aside from these special cases, however, one must face the problem of reducing some picture to a form which can be read into computer memory.

If the pattern is reduced to a list of X, Y coordinates, these may be put on cards or on magnetic tape for read-in. This can be a laborious process and

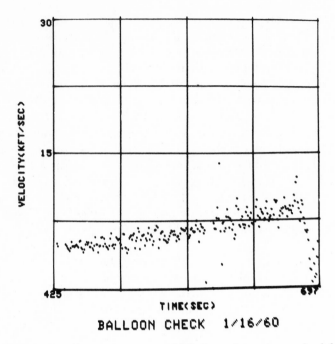

FIGURE 13.5 Computer generated display of pattern and alphanumeric characters.

one in which clerical errors are extremely difficult to correct. Manually reducing a pattern to a string of 1's and 0's is equally tedious. This whole problem could be by-passed with special equipment, such as a photoelectric device which could scan the pattern to be stored in the computer. Such a photoelectric device could scan the image and emit a pulse whenever the brightness of the area under scrutiny exceeded some threshold value. This pulse could either be used to activate some off-line device for preparing a tape or cards, or it could be used with a suitable input program and direct data entry provisions to store the train of pulses on line in successive registers as strings of 0's and 1's.[19]

Alternately, the CRT could be programed to display a raster of dots. If the pattern to be entered in memory were a transparency, this could be placed over the scope face. Over this, a suitable optical system and photomultiplier tube could be used to transmit the train of pulses to the computer in a form suitable for storage.[16]

13.1.5 *Pattern Transformations.* The whole point of going to all this trouble to get a pattern into a computer is to be able to operate on it in some way that will take advantage of the computer's unique capabilities: its speed and its enormous logical and computational facility. To put a pattern in storage only to display it unchanged would probably be the most expensive way of degrading an image yet devised. In what ways might a psychologist doing research in visual perception want to change the patterns which he had gone to such trouble to insert into computer memory?

To illustrate some of the more obvious transformations which the computer can perform on visual patterns, it will simplify the exposition to assume that the patterns are stored as lists of X, Y coordinates with integral values between 0 and 1023—in other words as lists of numbers. As far as the computer is concerned, these may be treated like any other numbers: they may be compared to ascertain whether two numbers are identical or not, they may be added, subtracted, multiplied, or divided. Rigid transformations of a two-dimensional figure are thus very simply computed. Horizontal or vertical movements are accomplished simply by adding a constant to all the coordinate values on the X and/or the Y axis, as was done in the sample program above. A program to generate one of Michotte's *lancement* displays would be simple to write and would require very little storage, since the figures and the movement patterns are so simple.[22]

Size transformations and rotations about the X, Y, or Z axes are computed with ease, especially if subroutines are available for the trigonometric functions. More interesting, perhaps, are elastic transformations which can be performed with ease on the computer, but which would be difficult to realize by any other means. The variety of these is limited only by the programer's ingenuity. Blurring of the pattern can be introduced by computing the brightness value of each point in the pattern on the basis of a local average of that point and its neighbors. Such averaging could be repeated several times until the pattern was unrecognizable. Shearing or stretching portions of the pattern are two more prosaic examples of non-rigid transformations which the computer can perform and which may be difficult to do by other means.

Among the useful capabilities of the computer is that of being able to generate a series of pseudo random numbers. Subroutines for this purpose exist which are surprisingly simple and rapid. With a random number generator in the display program, it is easy to introduce noise into the pattern, or to have the points in the pattern undergo a two-dimensional random walk. (See Figure 13.3.) A random number generator provides an extremely flexible method of producing textures in a wide variety of specifications.[15, 19]

13.2 AUDITORY PATTERNS GENERATED BY THE COMPUTER

13.2.1 Studies Employing Computer-generated Auditory Displays.
Computer-generated melodies, recorded on magnetic tape, have been used
in one experiment on the recognition of distorted melodies.[32] The first 24
notes of 10 familiar melodies were stored in the computer as paired numbers representing pitch and the duration of each note. No information
was stored about amplitude. One of the bits in the accumulator was
brought out to an amplifier and speaker which provided input to the tape
recorder. Actually, the distortions in the melodic patterns were computed
not in the machine, but by hand, and fed to the machine, a labor which
the author could have avoided had he been a more expert programer.
The distortions introduced were not of the usual kind encountered in
auditory research, but involved transformations such as doubling or halv-
ing the size of the musical intervals between each successive note in the
melody, eliminating all pitch or all duration information.

A research program recently begun on auditory discrimination training
dramatically illustrates the potentialities of the digital computer for psychological research.[30] Using a small (4000 words of core storage), high-
speed machine equipped with a digital-to-analog converter and special
output equipment and two electric typewriters for on-line input and output, a two-subject psychophysical experiment can be run entirely under
program control. The subjects are presented with a sound which can have
any of five values on five dimensions: frequency, amplitude, repetition
rate, duty cycle, and duration. The subject's task is to identify the sound.
This he may do by typing a series of numbers on the typewriter. The computer then informs him whether his response was correct, and if wrong,
in what respects it differed from the correct response. Having done this,
the computer then selects the next stimulus on the basis of the subject's
pattern of past responses. Two subjects may be run at once. The computer also keeps necessary records and computes summary statistics. The
stimuli here are simple waveforms, but this is by no means a necessary
limitation. In its present form, the computer generates the patterns by
producing a digitized signal corresponding to the desired sound and then
playing these time-quantized data through a digital-to-analog converter.
Here the computer is being used to generate the stimuli, compute the sequence of their presentation, feed back information to the subject, and
analyze results. Seemingly a tour de force, this novel application of a
computer only foreshadows widespread use in psychological research, as

the increasing availability of high-speed general purpose machines makes more practical their acquisition by laboratories and universities.

Perhaps the most common use of the computer as an auditory display generator has been in connection with the efforts to devise ways of transmitting speech using narrow bandwidth channels. This work is best summarized in the two-volume proceedings of a conference on this topic, which was held in 1959 at the Air Force Cambridge Research Center.[10] When a system has been devised for introducing the speech signal into a digital computer, has the signal been rendered unintelligible in the process? To ascertain this, the data are put out through a digital-to-analog converter to form a new auditory signal, which is presented to subjects whose accuracy in identifying the spoken words is evaluated.

13.2.2 Terminal Equipment. As with visual patterns, special terminal equipment is needed in order to get sounds into and out of a computer. Simple patterns, such as a sine wave of a certain frequency and amplitude, can be generated by the computer from a stored program.[30] An approximation to white noise might be produced in a similar manner.

To put a complex waveform such as human speech into the computer requires a different approach and special input equipment. A typical system designed to introduce a sample of speech into a digital computer is described by Forgie and Forgie.[9] A microphone picks up the speech and feeds it to a bank of 35 bandpass filters. Filter outputs are sampled at a rate of 180 times a second, the amplitude of each filter at each sampling period being converted to binary digital form and fed directly to the computer. Such a system can be used on line with a live speaker or in connection with a tape-recorded speech sample.

When the set of patterns to be generated is small and fixed, patterns may be stored on some device like a magnetic drum. The computer acts as a kind of switching device to select a given sequence of these messages.[24] Generating patterns from a larger set and placing various parameters of these patterns under computer control require equipment which is the reverse of the input equipment described above. A series of binary numbers corresponding to relative amplitudes of various frequencies is read out and changed in a digital-to-analog converter to a corresponding series of voltages. These may, in turn, be fed to a device such as a vocoder to generate the waveform.[29]

A simple way to produce noise from a computer is to connect one of the flip-flops in the accumulator to an amplifier and speaker. With such an arrangement, one can program this bit in the accumulator to change its state at a given rate for a given duration and in this way act as a square-wave generator. The pitch of the tone emitted from the speaker is determined by the rate at which the bit in the accumulator is changing its state. Some computers have such an arrangement as standard equipment to enable the operator to detect "loops" when a program is running. If the pitch of the tone is high, he knows that the loop is a small one; if it is low, he knows that the loop involves a number of instructions in the program. Such information is frequently useful in debugging a new program. This arrangement can easily be programed to play melodies.[32]

13.2.3 *Auditory Pattern Representation in the Computer.* From the foregoing description of the techniques for getting auditory patterns into and out of a computer, it is evident that the ways in which such patterns are represented in computer memory are parallel to those which were discussed for visual patterns. To generate melodies using the amplifier and speaker directly coupled to one bit in the accumulator, it is necessary merely to write a program which will put in memory a list of pitch and duration values for each note in the melody, a representation formally identical to the X, Y coordinate list method of representing a two-dimensional visual pattern.

The representation of speech which has been put in memory with the bandpass filter bank arrangement described above is formally identical with the matrix representation of a visual pattern shown in Figure 13.4 when only one bit of amplitude information is desired.

13.2.4 *Operating on Stored Auditory Patterns.* Just as visual patterns, once in the computer, can be subjected to a wide variety of transformations employing all the arithmetic and logical circuitry at the programer's disposal, so may auditory patterns be manipulated once they have been represented in computer memory. Actually, very little such manipulation of auditory patterns has been performed on computers—partly because many efficient special purpose analog devices exist for transforming such patterns. By using appropriate filters, amplifiers, choppers, and by changing tape speed at playback time, one can easily transform auditory patterns in many ways which are of interest to researchers in this area. These methods impose some distortion such as noise or periodic interruption on the pattern (which is uncorrelated with the pattern); or, such as bandpass filtering (which is correlated with the microstructure of the pattern and not with its macrostructure). For such operations, special purpose analog devices work admirably, but when auditory patterns must be manipulated at a more macroscopic level, a digital computer is useful.

Those, for example, who are manipulating speech at the level of the phoneme, are finding the high-speed general purpose digital computer a powerful tool.[10]

13.3   COMPUTER DISPLAYS FOR OTHER SENSE MODALITIES

As yet, the literature does not contain studies employing computer-generated displays designed for senses other than vision or audition. However, several research efforts are directed toward the use of the tactile modality as an information channel. Geldard's laboratory at the University of Virginia has for some years been doing basic psychophysical work in this area, and Geldard has described experiments successful in transmitting English text by means of vibrators attached to the skin.[11] The particular equipment used in Geldard's research transmitted text at such slow speeds that a computer was not required for generating and sequencing the signals. Were someone to modify this system to enable people to receive English text at speeds comparable to those achieved in ordinary visual scanning of printed text, or in auditory reception of spoken English, the speeds involved might make the use of the computer more attractive for such work.

Related to this area of reading machines for tactual input are the efforts to automate the production of Braille books. A program has been written for one of the large digital computers to enable it to turn clear English text punched on cards into grade 2 Braille, also punched on cards, which can be used with automatic equipment to set the plates for producing Braille books. Since grade 2 Braille involves a number of special characters and many contractions and abbreviations, the translation from clear English text is more complicated than a one-to-one mapping. Also under development are automatic devices to present the Braille code to the fingers of the human reader. These developments, together with the growing research interest in devices to aid those with sensory or motor deficits in navigation and communication, may well stimulate interest in the use of the computer for generating displays other than auditory or visual.

13.4   AUTOMATIC PATTERN RECOGNITION

Thus far we have outlined the use of the computer to generate patterns for perceptual research. Instead of programing the computer to generate stimuli for people to respond to, we may wish to study how the computer will respond to a pattern under various conditions. There are pressing demands for automatic pattern and character recognizers. An automatic handwriting recognizer would be of immense value to the Post Office Department. A machine to read handwritten numbers could expedite the processing of checks in clearing houses. Military agencies are interested in the development of automatic devices to aid in photo interpretation. There is a long-standing need for a device that can "read" a printed page and emit a train of signals which the blind can interpret.

The astonishing thing is that such pattern recognition is performed so readily by human beings. Postmen every day correctly sort mail addressed in handwriting which no machine now in existence could decipher. The need for automatic recognition devices has given rise to a considerable research and development effort, much of which is not relevant to this chapter, since it is concerned with engineering devices which will read a particular set of characters, rather than with the investigation of human pattern recognition.

13.4.1 *Template Matching.* Devices for character recognition now in commercial use depend upon a particular type font and a particular format in the document to be read. Every effort is made to eliminate sources of variation in the characters. In striking contrast, the human being is distinguished by his ability to recognize accurately characters of astonishing variety under conditions of severe pattern degradation.

As long as the variety of inputs which can be correctly classified is comparatively small, pattern recognition devices can be built which depend upon a matching of the input patterns with templates stored in memory. The template yielding the best match determines the response. Most of the automatic devices mentioned above operate on such a system. This system encounters difficulties when the class of permissible inputs is enlarged, a point clearly made in Selfridge and Neisser's discussion.[28] A theory of human pattern recognition based upon a process of template matching would have grave difficulty in coping with the realities of human recognition behavior.

13.4.2 *Neural Nets.* There is an alternative view of pattern recognition which has formed the basis for psychological models, which some workers have attempted to simulate on digital computers. Estes' earlier learning model conveys some flavor of this approach.[6] He hypothesizes that on successive learning trials some subset of stimulus elements is consistently associated with reinforcement. At the outset of learning, all the stimulus elements impinging on the organism are associated with the first success. After the second success, some of these stimulus elements will no longer be the same, while others will. The connections between the latter and the correct responses will be twice reinforced; the connections between stimulus elements unique to the first or second trial will have been reinforced but once. Thus, after a number of trials, a subset of stimulus elements emerges which has received more reinforcement than others. Thus is an S-R connection formed.

This fiction of a subset of stimulus elements common to all trials may be convenient in the context of the usual learning experiment where every effort is made to keep the physical environment of the organism constant from trial to trial; but it is hard to invoke it in the context of the recognition experiment where two patterns with no stimulus elements in common may be readily and correctly placed in the same category. Nevertheless the idea has been extended to a two-stage process in some attempts to simulate neural networks on a digital computer.[8, 4] Here the computer is programed to simulate a network of randomly connected nonlinear elements which are assigned parameters borrowed from neurophysiology: thresholds and refractory periods. The network is divided into four groups of elements: two fixed input groups and two output groups. An output is defined at any instant by the difference in the number of elements fired in the two subgroups during the instant. One input consists of firing all the elements in the first input group and none in the second. The alternative input is the reverse. An element that receives excitation above its threshold fires, and transmits excitation to all elements to which it is connected—the effectiveness of this excitation, known as its "weight," being a property of that particular connection.

The object of the program was to ascertain whether, by manipulating these weights following each input presentation, the network could be organized so that a given input would be reliably associated with one of the two outputs. Clark and Farley [5] found that such a network can be organized in this manner to classify the inputs in the desired manner with a probability significantly above chance. More interesting is their finding that such a network can do this even when the inputs are noisy; i.e., when they are not disjoint subsets of the input ensemble. That so disorderly a system could yield such orderly discriminations was suggested some years ago by Hebb in his discussion of the cell assembly and its role in recognition.[17] Further work with computer simulation of a randomly organized network has been done by Rosenblatt.[27] Roberts has investigated the effects of various methods of reinforcing the network, discovering that the kind of reinforcement scheme employed makes a significant difference in the rapidity with which the network can be taught to make a given discrimination.[26] In these random network pattern recognizers, learning is much more rapid if the characters are first centered on the "retina" and made the same size.

The random network experiments have been among the first attempts to use the computer to, simulate a psychological process. The model employed has been essentially neurological, in that the characteristics of the "elements" comprising the networks have borne an obvious relationship to neurophysiological concepts. The interesting properties of such networks and their possible relation to neural networks were first suggested by McCulloch and Pitts.[21]

13.4.3 *Parallel Processing.* Pointing out that the random net has severe limitations as a system which can be taught to make a number of discriminations under noisy conditions, Selfridge and Neisser propose a fundamentally different model for pattern recognition.[28] The model has been realized in the form of a digital computer program designed to recognize "sloppy hand-printed characters." [5] This program depends upon a number of tests being made of the pattern to be recognized. Is there a cross bar in the pattern? Is there an upward concavity? Is there a vertical line? During the training phase of the program, these tests are performed on a number of examples of each character in the set. After each example is presented, the correct "answer" is fed back to the computer so that eventually the machine builds up a number of probabilities linking the outcome of each test with each character. On the test trials, a pattern is again presented, the many tests are performed, and a "vote" is taken to determine, given the outcomes of these tests, which character has the highest probability of being associated with this set of outcomes. This strategy employed in a program to recognize "sloppy, hand-printed characters," made about 10 per cent fewer correct identifications than human readers made with the same material. Selfridge thinks that such a program can cope with much wider variability in the inputs than the random net approach without enlarging the size of the machine unduly. He points out that the training procedure could do more than alter the probabilities linking test outcomes with responses. Conceivably, the machine could be programed to abandon certain tests which failed to yield differential predictions and to alter the way in which probabilities are combined to make the final decision.

Notice that this model of recognition does not assume that there is some invariant in all instances of a pattern. The assumption is that there are features more or less characteristic of a given pattern, any of which may be present in a given instance.

A strategy of pattern recognition basically similar to the letter recognition program described above has been programed by Forgie and Forgie for the recognition of spoken English by a digital computer.[9] With special equipment for direct input of speech to the computer, the program examines the amplitude of the whole sound envelope sampled at the rate of 180 times per second. When the amplitude is above a fixed threshold, all subsequent samples are classified as belonging to one of the ten possible sounds being studied. These decisions are continued until the amplitude falls below the threshold, at which point a "vote" is taken of the decision for all samples and a final decision determined. The decision for each slice of speech is based upon a rough localization of the first two formants. The outcome of this processing determines which of a series of confusion-elimination operations will be performed before reaching a final decision for the sample. This program, which combines parallel and sequential processing, correctly classified 93 per cent of the utterances of 11 male and female speakers saying 10 English vowels.

When computers are equipped to deal directly with human outputs like the written and the spoken word, social scientists from many disciplines are going to find new and significant applications for them. There is already considerable interest in the use of a computer as a teaching machine. Were the computer capable of understanding the student's speech, its pedagogic possibilities would be significantly broadened. Social psychologists and sociologists, interested in studying communication practices of small groups or organizations, would have at their disposal a device which could greatly facilitate the tedious job of initial data reduction. Experimenters interested in psychophysics, discrimination learning, pattern recognition, rote learning, concept formation, or, in fact, any domain in which the subject is required to make a series of responses over a period of time, will find that the computer can be programed to make the next presentation, display, or trial, dependent in any desired degree upon the outcomes of previous trials. In short, automatic pattern recognition programs will make possible a much more intimate linking of man and computer than has been possible up to now.

13.4.4 *Existing Pattern Recognition Programs as Psychological Theories.* The relevance of this work for the psychology of perception is not easy to assess. Neurophysiologists today are less and less satisfied with the model of the neuron as something which fires or does not fire when its threshold is exceeded and hence are dubious about the value of continued computer simulation of neural nets based upon such a simplified model. There is no doubt about the finding that such nets can be trained to make discriminations of noisy inputs, provided the number of outputs is modest, but there is some uncertainty about the way in which such demonstrations can advance our understanding of human pattern recognition.

Similarly, Selfridge's parallel processing program is in some sense a model, though not a neurological model, of human pattern recognition. Selfridge rules out the random network as a reasonable model for pattern recognition, because the size of the network required to perform the discriminations we know the human has to make, and make reliably, is unreasonably large by current estimates. He regards the parallel processing strategy as more consistent with our present knowledge of human performance in this domain. It has indeed been shown to work with noisy human products like hand-sent Morse code and hand-printed letters, but much more needs to be done before such programs can be viewed as testable theories of human pattern recognition.

The fact remains, however, that a cleverly programed computer can learn to recognize patterns under conditions which are far from trivial. It is impossible to be involved in the construction of such a computer program without being forced to consider many facets of human pattern recognition and perception from a very different viewpoint. None of these computer recognition programs, for example, has tackled the problem of segmentation. In every case, it is assumed that there is but one letter, one vowel, one pattern in the computer to be recognized. No attempt is made to isolate the spoken vowel in a stream of connected speech nor, to isolate a single letter in cursive script. The Morse code program described by Selfridge is almost the only recognition program which deals with such segmentation problems, and it is significant that a large part of the processing done in this program is devoted to segmentation—isolating the sequence of dots and dashes to be recognized.[28] Work is being done on this problem in spoken English, but the problem is far from solved. These difficulties focused renewed attention on the whole problem of unit formation in perception—a problem which has received little or no attention from psychologists since the heyday of the Gestalt school.

It is only natural that there should be a rush to prove that the powerful new high-speed general purpose digital computers can perform many tasks previously thought to be uniquely human. Can computers think? Can they be original? Can they solve problems? Can they recognize patterns? Non-trivial affirmative answers have now been given to all these questions. Programs to do all these things have been written, and they work, so the existence proofs are in. Now it is time to go on to other things.

Since the computer has been shown to be capable of pattern recognition, it becomes a possible tool to use for testing psychological models of this process. As yet almost no studies have had this orientation. The study of the detection of bar patterns in statistically defined dot matrices is one of the first perceptual studies using the computer as a stimulus generator which examines the empirical data from the standpoint of a particular theoretical model—statistical detection theory.[14] This model influenced the choice of independent variables, certain aspects of the analysis, and served as a focus for the interpretation of the results, which in some instances were at variance with the model.

Julesz' work with stereoscopic depth is another instance of a fruitful use of a computer in a series of studies designed to test a first approximation to a model for stereoscopic depth perception.[18] The model predicts certain conditions under which the effect will and will not occur. These are put into the computer as parameters and displays generated to these specifications in order to see whether observers report the effect under these conditions.

13.5 AREAS FOR FUTURE APPLICATION OF COMPUTER TECHNIQUES TO PERCEPTUAL RESEARCH

The computer has thus far been used in the field of perception *either* as a recognizer or as a generator of patterns. There is no reason it can't do *both* and, in so doing, act as a powerful tester of hypotheses about human pattern recognition. The computer could, for example, generate a series of patterns which varied along some parameter known to make recognition increasingly difficult for human beings. These same displays could be fed back to the computer programed as a pattern recognizer to study the degree its recognition performance matched that of human observers. To the extent that it did, the program on that machine could be said to be an adequate theory of human pattern recognition.

This approach looks promising, but a word of caution is perhaps in order. Those who have labored to introduce multidimensional arrays like pictures and complex time-varying waveforms into a digital computer for processing are uneasy about the awkwardness of the procedure. They contend that the speed and reliability with which people handle the same information indicate that the representation of patterns in human memory must be significantly different from the techniques used thus far in storing pictures in digital computers. Because of the stepped-up program of research in outer space, rapid advances in the technology of optical image processing are being made. Such devices may ultimately be more appropriate tools than digital computers for perceptual research. Lettvin's recordings from the optic nerve of the frog suggest that before the information arrives at the cortex considerable image processing may be done by a multiply-connected system which could be simulated by a network of resistors and diodes.[20] Initial processing of visual images might best be done by such an analog device before attempting to read them into a digital computer for further processing. The current enthusiasm for digital computers should not blind us to the possibilities of analog devices in this area. Certainly the neurophysiological data available on end organ and central nervous system behavior make it obvious that there is room for both models.

The computer could be of immediate use in generating stimulus materials for certain perceptual studies. The extremely important research being done by Gibson and his colleagues at Cornell on the perception of slanted surfaces requires the use of stimulus materials which are complex and difficult to manufacture so that the statistical properties of the textures are known.[12] The generation of such material on a computer with a video output would be rapid and would give the experimenter the chance to get a number of independent samples of a given texture, as well as a number of different textures whose parameters could be stated exactly. Gradients of texture within one display are easily programed.

Attneave and his associates have published a number of studies using nonsense two-dimensional forms constructed according to certain well-defined rules so that all forms so generated can properly be said to be members of this family of figures.[1] A recent study employed such a technique to generate a set of stimuli for a discrimination experiment.[2] The cells of a 300 × 300 matrix were filled or not filled according to a rather elaborate set of rules. Out of this matrix, the shapes used in the experiment were cut. Such a procedure must have required hundreds of man-hours. The same displays could have been generated with a computer program in a matter of seconds, with considerably less opportunity for error. The very fact that the rules for generating such figures are so explicit makes their computer generation simple to program.

The most far-reaching development is foreshadowed by the recently initiated research of Swets.[30] Here the computer is serving a number of functions which an experimenter cannot usually encompass with such precision. It has stored within it a set of rules for generating a finite set of stimulus patterns, a set of rules for determining which member of the set will be presented next, a method of matching the subject's response with the stimulus and displaying the discrepancy between the two, and provision for giving the subject control over a number of stimulus parameters. With audio and video outputs, and on-line communication with the computer by the electric typewriter, this system comes about as close to being the all-purpose automatic experimenter as one could hope.

Interestingly, some will see this arrangement as a machine for studying human learning, thinking, or problem solving, whereas others viewing the same elephant will be inclined to see it as the perfect machine for studying perception. Both are correct, of course, and those who are doing this work are well aware that they are studying discrimination learning. With rare exceptions such as Lashley and Harlow, workers in the field of learning have been content to leave the stimulus alone or to vary it in only one dimension; and workers in perception have been cavalier about the response. Use of the computer in psychological experiments may offer a unique opportunity to the many disciplines of experimental psychology to recognize and correct former limitations.

13.6   CONCLUSIONS

It is certainly premature to say what the effect of the computer has been on the psychology of perception. There have been too few studies. Computer simulation of a perceptual process like pattern recognition does force one to reconsider some long-held assumptions. Although they would deny it vigorously, many psychologists still have as their implicit model of perception a cable of insulated wires running from the retina to the cortex, where the image of the world is reconstructed. Such a model merely postpones important questions. To have the image in the cortex as well as the retina does not solve the problem of how we are able to make use of it to guide our decisions and our actions. How is information extracted from the optical array or from the time-varying complex waveform impinging upon the auditory apparatus? Today, this question is being asked most insistently not by psychologists, but by logicians, electrical engineers, and others who have been directly concerned with the problem of developing machines to perform perceptual tasks like recognition. The list of references at the end of this chapter contains many names of people and of journals strange to social scientists. The "automatic pattern recognition" people look at human perceptual behavior in a rather different way from the traditional American psychologist.

The introductory psychology text is apt to emphasize that about the only thing a neonate can do with his eyes is to track a bright moving object. The engineer who has just finished building a guidance system is apt to think that such a capability is no mean achievement, indicative of a wiring diagram of considerable complexity. When he is told that there is a psychophysical correspondence between certain perspective transformations and the perception of motion of a rigid body, he is apt to reply that that is all very well, but what sort of processing of the input could yield such a response? Some psychologists will find such questions irritating, meaningless, or beyond the scope of psychology as they conceive it. Others, who believe that more should lie between S and R than a hyphen or even an "O," will find themselves quite at home with these people from other disciplines.

Those who have been engrossed in programing a computer to recognize patterns are likely to believe that the heart of perceptual theory should lie in the nature of the processing done on the sensory input. Correlations between measures of stimulus parameters and identifying responses are important data, but they beg to be explained. Computers have been programed to perform certain perceptual functions. For this reason, they offer promise as devices on which to test theories of perception. Now someone needs to get to work to tailor these models to the data of human perception.

What sort of data might such computer models of perceptual processes require? If the work in the simulation of human thinking and problem solving is any indication, the data required to test the fit of the model will be much finer grained than most data previously published in this field.[23] Recognition data, for example, have consisted almost entirely of statistics summarizing error rate in some manner (either a threshold or a probability of correct identification) reflecting the psychologist's almost exclusive concern with veridicality. These data will almost certainly not be adequate for testing the kind of models which have so far been proposed for pattern recognition. We shall need to know not only the error rate but the entire confusion matrix. Models concerned with recognition learning will require not only data on confusions, but on the order in which they occur. With rare exceptions, such data are just not available in the psychological literature.

Computers may in part be responsible for the increased emphasis in many areas of psychology on fine-grain data. Increasingly in learning research, experimenters examine not just summary statistics of trials to criterion, but actual sequences of responses. The advent of the teaching machine is having a similar effect on human learning research. The work on simulation of problem solving already mentioned attempts replication not merely of measures such as time to solution or number of incorrect initial hypotheses, but also of the actual sequence of steps to solutions. Fine-grain and sequential analysis have been infrequent in psychological work. They are laborious, expensive, and time-consuming. The peculiar economics of the computer are such, however, that once the data are entered, very little extra cost is incurred in detailed processing and analysis. This should have a salutory effect in the field of perceptual research. Studies of pattern recognition by computers have hinted at how intricate a device must be in order to cope with the noisy inputs from the world around us. A model for human pattern recognition can be no less intricate. Intricate it may be, but the computer has also proved that such models of cognitive and perceptual processes are feasible.

REFERENCES

1 Attneave, F., Some Informational Aspects of Visual Perception, *Psychol. Rev., 61* (No. 3), May 1954, 183–93.

2 Baker, C. A., Morris, D. F., and Steedman, W. C., Target Recognition of Complex Displays, *Human Factors, 2* (No. 2), May 1960, 51–61.

3 Braunstein, M. L., Rotation of Dot Patterns as Stimuli for the Perception of Motion in Three Dimensions: The Effects of Numerosity and Perspective. Unpublished doctoral dissertation, Univ. Michigan, 1960.

4 Clark, W. A., and Farley, B. G., Generalization of Pattern Recognition in a Self-organizing System, *Proc. Western Joint Computer Conf.,* March 1955, 86–91.

5 Doyle, W., Recognition of Sloppy, Hand-Printed Characters, *Proc. Western Joint Computer Conf.,* May 1960, 133–42.

6 Estes, W. K., and Burke, C. J., A Theory of Stimulus Variability in Learning, *Psychol. Rev., 60* (No. 4), July 1953, 276–86.

7 Everett, R. R., Zraket, C. A., and Benington, H. D., SAGE—A Data-Processing System for Air Defense, *Proc. Eastern Joint Computer Conf.,* December 1957, 148–53.

8 Farley, B. G., and Clark, W. A., Simulation of Self-organizing Systems by Digital Computer, *Trans. I.R.E. Professional Group on Information Theory,* September 1954, 76–84.

9 Forgie, J. W., and Forgie, C. D., Results Obtained from a Vowel Recognition Computer Program, *Jour. Acoust. Soc. Amer., 31* (No. 11), November 1959, 1480–89.

10 Frick, F. C., Research on Speech Recognition at Lincoln Laboratory, *Speech Compression and Processing, 2,* AFCRC-TR-59-198, September 1959.

11 Geldard, F. A., Adventures in Tactile Literacy, *Amer. Psychologist,* March 1957, *21,* 115–24.

12 Gibson, J. J., The Perception of Slanted Surfaces, *Amer. Jour. Psychol., 63,* 1950, 367–84.

13 Green, B. F., Jr., Figure Coherence in the Kinetic Depth Effect, *Jour. Exper. Psychol., 62* (No. 3), September 1961, 272–82.

14 ———, Wolf, A. K., and White, B. W., The Detection of Statistically Defined Patterns in a Matrix of Dots, *Amer. Jour. Psychol., 72* (No. 4), 1959, 503–20.

15 ———, The Use of High-Speed Digital Computers in Studies of Form Perception, *Form Discrimination,* Wulfeck, J. W., and Taylor, J. H., eds., National Academy of Sciences–National Research Council Publication *561,* 1957, 65–75.

16 Gurley, B. M., and Woodward, C. E., Light Pen Links Computer to Operator, *Electronics, 30* (No. 47), November 1959, 85–87.

17 Hebb, D. O., *The Organization of Behavior.* New York: Wiley, 1949.

18 Julesz, B., Binocular Depth Perception of Computer-generated Patterns, *Bell System Tech. Jour., 39* (No. 5), September 1960, 1125–62.

19 Kirsch, R. A., Cahn, L., Ray, C., and Urban, G. H., Experiments in Processing Pictorial Information with a Digital Computer, *Proc. Eastern Joint Computer Conf.,* December 1957, 221–29.

20 Lettvin, J. Y., *et al.,* What the Frog's Eye Tells the Frog's Brain, *Proc. Inst. Radio Engineers, 47* (No. 11), November 1959, 1940–51.

21 McCulloch, W. S., and Pitts, W., A Logical Calculus of the Ideas Immanent in Nervous Activity, *Bull. Mathemat. Biophysics, 5,* 1943, 115–33.

22 Michotte, A., *La Perception de la Causalité.* Louvain: Publ. Univ. Louvain, 1954.

23 Newell, A., Shaw, J. C., and Simon, H. A., Elements of a Theory of Problem Solving, *Psychol. Rev., 65* (No. 3), May 1958, 151–66.

24 Poppe, C. W., and Suhr, P. J., An Automatic Voice Readout System, *Proc. Eastern Joint Computer Conf.,* December 1957, 219–21.

25 *Reference Manual, 709-7090 Data Processing System.* New York: IBM Corp., 1959, 127–30.

26 Roberts, L. G., Pattern Recognition with an Adaptive Network, *Inst. Radio Engineers Convention Record,* Part 2, March 1960, 66–70.

27 Rosenblatt, F., The Perceptron: A Probabilistic Model for Information Storage and Organization in Man, *Psychol. Rev., 65* (No. 6), November 1958, 386–408.

28 Selfridge, O. G., and Neisser, U., Pattern Recognition by Machine, *Scientific American, 203* (No. 2), August 1960, 60–68.

29 Smith, C. P., An Approach to Speech Bandwidth Compression, *Speech Compression and Processing, 2,* AFCRC-TR-59-198, September 1959.

30 Swets, J. A., Green, D. M., and Winter, E. F., Learning to Identify Non-Verbal Sounds, *Jour. Acoust. Soc. Amer., 33,* June 1961, 855 (A).

31 White, B. W., The Computer as a Pattern Generator for Perceptual Research, *Behavioral Science, 6* (No. 3), July 1961, 252–59.

32 ———, Recognition of Distorted Melodies, *Amer. Jour. Psychol., 73,* 1960, 100–107.

Harry F. Silberman & John E. Coulson

14 /AUTOMATED TEACHING

*Dr. Harry F. Silberman holds
the Ed.D. in Educational Psychology from the
University of California at Los Angeles,
and is a certified psychologist in the
state of California. Dr. Silberman's professional
affiliations are membership in the American
Psychological Association (Division of Educational
Psychology), American Educational Research Association,
National Council on Measurements Used
in Education, and Mathematical Association
of America. Dr. Silberman is primarily interested
in the application of computers in educational research and
is currently Associate Director of the Automated Teaching Project
conducted by the System Development Corporation.*

*Dr. John E. Coulson is Director of the
Automated Teaching Project conducted by the System
Development Corporation. His academic achievements include
the Ph.D. and M.A. degrees in psychology, awarded
by Columbia University, and a B.S. in physics
and a B.A. in psychology granted by
the University of Arizona. At Columbia University,
Dr. Coulson specialized in learning theory, experimental
design, and sensory and perceptual research. Dr. Coulson
is a certified psychologist in the state of California,
a member of the American Psychological Association and of the
National Council on Measurements Used in Education.*

14.1 THE "TEACHING MACHINE" AS AN EDUCATIONAL TECHNIQUE

"Automated teaching" is an educational technique having the following characteristics:

a. A series of instructional materials, or "items," is presented to the student. An item may contain a statement of information, a question, or both.

b. The student attempts to answer each question contained in the instructional items, usually by some overt action, e.g., choosing a correct alternative or writing one or more missing words in a sentence.

c. The student is generally given knowledge of results immediately after he responds to each question; i.e., he is given information from which he can determine whether his answer was right or wrong.

The device by which automated teaching is conducted or controlled is called a "teaching machine." Teaching machines range in complexity from textbooks with special page format and instructions, to elaborate electromechanical devices costing thousands of dollars.[5, 6] The functional components of a teaching machine are shown in Figure 14.1.

Teaching machines bring to education a means by which teachers may be relieved of certain routine, repetitive instructional tasks and thus be given time to perform the more creative activities for which the human is uniquely qualified. In this way, the teacher can, for the most part, avoid the role of drillmaster or record keeper and concern himself more with the motivational, social, and inspirational aspects of the instructional process.

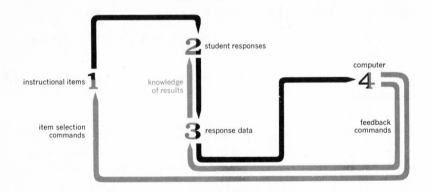

FIGURE 14.1 Functional components of a teaching machine.

Automated teaching offers further advantages as an effective educational technique in its own right. First, the overt responses required of students by most machines, for example, help to insure active participation and thus help to maintain interest on the part of the student. Secondly, the teaching machine allows each student to proceed systematically and independently through the instructional materials. He is required to answer questions on one topic or concept before he can advance into new concepts. This differs greatly from many conventional classrooms in which a teacher lectures at a rate that is too fast for some students, and too slow for others. Thirdly, teaching machines provide immediate reinforcement for desired response behavior, whereas in many conventional classrooms, students receive reinforcement only through test papers returned days or weeks after the administration of the test.

Teaching machines are also useful as research tools for investigating basic variables in human learning. They make possible precise control and replication of experimental conditions. Spurious effects caused by the personality of the experimenters and similar uncontrolled factors can be held to a minimum.

14.1.1 *Adaptability in Teaching Machines.* Although the design of the machine is important, no teaching machine can provide effective instruction without a well-prepared, well-tested set of items. The machine may present the instructional materials either in a fixed, predetermined sequence, or in a sequence that varies with the student's specific responses to each item.

A teaching machine that presents materials in a predetermined sequence can be extremely simple in design. With minor embellishments, it can also keep error records and help prevent student cheating. Such a machine, however, cannot be responsive to individual student differences; i.e., it cannot give each student a particular sequence of materials and type of reinforcement suited to his individual needs, as these needs are progressively revealed by the adequacy of his responses. For this reason, the further development of teaching machines appears to lie in the direction of making them flexible and adaptive to the student's responses.

To show concretely what is involved in developing such flexibility and to illustrate the means by which it can be achieved, we shall later describe a particular experimental teaching machine that has been developed by the System Development Corporation's (SDC) Automated Teaching Project. This machine uses a small general purpose digital computer, the Bendix G-15, and its control unit. The computer is programed to adapt its teaching behavior to the needs of the student. During an instructional session, it can determine what sequence of items to present and what feedback messages to provide the student, so as to make learning relatively efficient.

Incorporation of a computer in the teaching machine provides a second type of flexibility, one of great importance when the machine is used as a research tool. The machine's operation can readily be altered between instructional sessions. This is done by changing the computer program, a change more readily effected than would be an equipment modification.

Many changes can be made in the operation of the machine by minor changes of a few numbers in the program. Such alterations permit different teaching procedures and machine characteristics to be investigated. The teaching machine used at SDC is sufficiently adaptable to allow a wide range of automated teaching research. Investigators can manipulate many types of experimental variables without major restrictions arising from machine limitations. Thus the computer-based teaching machine is, in effect, not just one machine but many different machines.

14.1.2 *Computer-controlled Teaching Machines.* A brief account of some explorations of the uses of computers to control teaching machines will illustrate the technique and its application. The feasibility of using a computer as a teaching machine was probably first established by a research group of the International Business Machines Corporation. Rath, Anderson, and Brainerd at IBM demonstrated the use of an IBM 650 to teach binary arithmetic.[8] The lesson taught the student to count in the binary system, then to add, subtract, multiply, divide, and finally to convert from decimal numbers to binary and from binary to decimal. In this application, the machine typed out the questions for the student, who then responded by pressing the appropriate keys of a typewriter. The answer was scored by the computer, one key stroke at a time. The instant an error occurred, the computer stopped the student, typed out "wrong," and presented another problem. If the student was making few errors, he was asked whether or not he wanted to skip some items. When the student typed his choice, the computer complied either by presenting additional items or by skipping. When the program advanced to a new problem in response to an error, the new problem chosen was a function of the number of errors made in that section of the lesson. Thus the new problem could be equally or less difficult. The average student completed the lesson in binary arithmetic in approximately one hour. Upon completion, the student was tested by the machine on each of the six topics taught. The test was individualized and contained more items relating to those topics on which the student had made the most training errors.

Alan Perlis at the Carnegie Institute of Technology has written a special program of feedback messages designed to provide computer programers with knowledge of where they made errors in their programs.[7] During the testing phase, when an error is encountered, an appropriate message is printed out supplying the student programer with information designed to help him avoid that type of error on future occasions. Although this is not strictly a teaching machine application, it does have some educational value and represents an interesting method of teaching computer programing.

Bolt, Beranak and Newman, Incorporated,* of Cambridge, Massachusetts is using a computer called the Programed Data Processor, manufactured by the Digital Equipment Corporation, as a teaching machine for vocabulary, spelling and foreign language instruction. The computer presents a word from a set A of words of language X. The student then tries to type a corresponding word in language Y. If the student's response is correct, the computer confirms its correctness, posts a score, offers a compliment, eliminates the presented item from A, and presents a new item from A. If the student's response is incorrect, the computer says so, moves the item to a "missed" set B and offers him the choice of trying again or seeing the correct answer. When the student has replied correctly, or has seen the answer, the computer posts a score, makes a suitable remark, and presents a new item from A or a missed item from B. Another program for automatic instruction in sound recognition was developed to investigate techniques for improving the methods of teaching people to differentiate between similar sounds. The program presents tones for the student to identify which differ in frequency, amplitude, duty cycle, repetition cycle, and length of total signal. It grades the student's answers as right or wrong, providing immediate playback of right and wrong answers for comparison and continually modifying itself to keep pace with the student, stressing sounds which trouble him and discarding those he seems to know well.

At the Coordinated Science Laboratory,† an engineering department at the University of Illinois, a teaching machine system has been developed which is named PLATO (Programed Logic for Automatic Teaching Operations). The system uses the ILLIAC computer as a control unit, a slide reservoir, a storage tube which will permit material given by the student or by the computer to be displayed along with the slides, the screen of a closed-circuit television system, and the student's control panel. PLATO will adjust to individual ability of the student; it will allow the exceptional student to progress at high speed, while a less capable one proceeds at a slower rate.

An educational application of computers, somewhat related to teaching

* *News from Digital Equipment Corporation,* Maynard, Massachusetts, March 1961.

† *Engineering Outlook at the University of Illinois,* Vol. 2, No. 4, April 1961.

machines, uses simulation procedures.[3] An IBM 650 has been used by the American Management Association for training top management personnel, through simulation procedures. Trainees make judgments concerning production, sales, advertising, etc., in connection with competitive business situations. These decisions are entered into the computer, which then processes the information, interrogates the trainee further, and supplies him with knowledge of results indicating probable consequences of his actions. In this way, the student learns to estimate the probability of various consequences that are contingent on his decisions. (See Chapter 23, "Business Simulation.")

At SDC,[1] a computer is used in training exercises to simulate an air defense environment which includes hostile attacks by "enemy" missiles and aircraft. During the training exercise, Air Force personnel man their normal positions in an air defense center. They see and respond to the simulated air defense problem and take whatever actions are necessary to cope with the simulated situation. Each crewman in the system receives information which reflects the consequences of his own actions, as well as the actions of other members of the system. In addition, computer programs provide both individual and subsystem scores on a number of problem-solving situations in the simulated exercise.

14.2   THE AUTOMATED TEACHING PROJECT OF THE SYSTEM DEVELOPMENT CORPORATION

By way of a concrete example, we shall describe the Automated Teaching Project sponsored by SDC.

14.2.1 *Description of the Experimental Teaching Machine.* The experimental teaching machine at SDC (Figure 14.2) consists of three major units: (a) a Bendix G-15 computer; (b) a random access slide projector; and (c) an electric typewriter.

   a. *Bendix G-15 computer.* The Bendix G-15 is a relatively small, general purpose computer. It has a photoelectric unit with which it can read information from punched paper tapes. A bell mounted in the computer frame can be rung under computer control, thus permitting programed auditory signals. This computer serves as the central control unit for the teaching machine. It determines, at all times during a training session, the materials that are to be presented to the student. The computer analyzes student responses to the instructional items and compares these responses with stored data.

FIGURE 14.2 SDC experimental teaching machine.

b. *Random access slide projector.* This projector, developed by the engineering staff at SDC, is used to display instructional materials to the student. It holds up to six hundred 35mm slides, arranged in 15 magazines of 40 slides each. Each slide contains one item. The projector receives instructions from the G-15, selecting and projecting slides in the sequence indicated by the computer. The use of an external random access slide projector contrasts with the methods of Anderson and Rath, and of Perlis, who used internal computer storage for problem materials.

c. *Electric typewriter.* This typewriter, which is linked to the computer, serves two important functions. First, the student uses the keyboard to insert his answers to the instructional materials, normally in multiple-choice form. Second, the computer program takes control of the typewriter to print messages telling the student how successful he has been in answering the questions.

One additional piece of equipment is used in the automated teaching project, although it is not actually part of the experimental teaching machine. It consists of a direct punched card input to the G-15 computer. Information about the instructional items can be manually punched on IBM cards; these cards can then be read into the computer, where the information can be transcribed directly onto punched paper tape.

14.2.2 *Operation of the Machine.* In its application as the control unit for a teaching machine, the computer has two somewhat unusual characteristics. First, in automated teaching the student can be regarded as "on line" with the computer. That is, the computer and the student interact during the entire lesson; for much of the time the computer is simply waiting for the student to take some switch action, i.e., answer a question. This contrasts with the more common computer usage in which a large mass of data is fed to the computer and is then processed at a rapid rate until the required solution is reached. In a low duty cycle application such as automated teaching, costly equipment can be justified only by time-sharing the central computer among other users.

A second unusual characteristic of the computer's performance in automated instruction involves the small amount of arithmetic calculation. Most of the computer's work in a teaching machine involves storing data, transferring data, and making "logical decisions" based on these data. Only rarely does it perform the mathematical operations usually regarded as the primary role of computers.

14.2.3 *Presentation of the Lesson.* A lesson begins with the student seated in front of the typewriter. The slide projector displays a question or a multiple-choice item for the student to answer. The student reads the item and, if an answer is required, inserts his choice of answer by pressing the typewriter key corresponding to the number of his choice, e.g., 1, 2, 3, 4, or 5. The student may change his answer by inserting another choice before requesting an evaluation of his answer. When the student presses the "Enter" key on the typewriter keyboard, the machine evaluates the last answer inserted. Once the "Enter" key is activated, the answer cannot be changed. The typewriter, then under computer control, informs the student whether his choice was correct. The "Enter" key is pressed again and a new slide is presented. This cycle is repeated for each item until the end of the lesson.

Instructional slides are selected by the computer on the basis of four aspects of the student's behavior: (1) errors in answering questions; (2) speed of the student's responses; (3) the student's evaluation of his own performance; and (4) pre-inserted information about the student, for example, aptitude, personality, and achievement indices. When a student is in trouble, the computer recognizes this fact and supplies extra remedial material. When the student is doing well, some materials are omitted.

The procedures appear to be simple and logical, yet a vast amount of effort must precede the presentation if the lesson is to be effective. To provide the reader with a realistic example of the preparation involved in using a computer as a research tool in an auto-instructional experiment, the steps required for preparing a short lesson are described in some detail.

14.2.4 *Preparation of the Lesson.* The first step is the preparation of instructional material. The items to be presented must be written, tested, revised, and prepared in the form of slides. Branching procedures have to be designed, and the information about the items and the branching decisions must be specified on special manuscript forms. The manuscripted material must then be coded onto punched paper tapes for interpretation by the computer program. The entire process is checked, using the slides, the paper tapes, the typewriter, and the internally stored computer program. Only after these tasks are completed is the lesson ready for presentation. Preparation of a two-hour lesson may take several months.

STEP 1: *Instructional items.* In developing a set of items one must decide what is to be taught by the machine and then prepare a set of questions covering the material.

This provides a skeleton of the teaching sequence. The gaps are then filled in with new items that provide information prerequisite to answering the original questions. Cues or prompts are added to help the student give the correct answer. The material is pretested. Gross oversights, including items which can be answered correctly without reading explanatory information, items with ambiguities, and other faults are detected and removed in the next revision.

The preparation of instructional items is the very heart of effective machine teaching. In fact, many workers in the auto-instructional field view the machine as nothing more than the "binding of the book." [4] This is an extreme view, for the computer may or may not make full use of the materials. If students are permitted to skip items which they do not need in order to learn the material, considerable time can be saved, allowing the student to go on to more advanced topics. If students have difficulty in certain areas, they can be given extra remedial work on those topics

1. In ordinary English we use words like "and," "but," "or" to combine simple statements into compound statements. The sentence, "The sun is very bright and I will take a walk," is a _____ statement.
   1. simple
   2. compound
   3. complex

2. In logic, for convenience we use letters to stand for statements. A different letter is used for each simple statement. Thus we can represent the statement, "The house is white," by _____.
   1. p
   2. 5
   3. +

3. If we use the letter p to represent one simple statement, and the letter q for another simple statement, p and q can be combined to make a _____ statement.
   1. literal
   2. simple
   3. compound

4. The connective "or," called the disjunction, is represented by the symbol "V." The statement, "The boy is tall or he is short," can be translated into the symbolic form of _____.
   1. p V q
   2. p ∧ q
   3. p ⟶ q

5. You have completed some material on simple and compound statements, using symbols to represent statements, and the connective "or." Before starting on the next topic do you think you would benefit from another look at some of these materials?

FIGURE 14.3 Sample of items written to teach logic.

which are troublesome. The machine may be programed to select different materials for different kinds of students. This process of tailoring the instruction to fit the individual student makes it possible to obtain the maximum value from the material in a minimum time.

Figure 14.3 shows a sample of items written to teach logic. These items and their flow chart are only illustrative and do not represent an actual teaching program. They serve to show how items are written, flow charted, and manuscripted for experiments with the computer. The preparation of items is not a computer programing project, but a job

1. Yes. I could use some more practice.
2. No. I'm pretty confident that I'm ready to try the next topic.

6. Which one of the following is a statement?
    1. Count Basie plays the piano.
    2. Did the Dodgers lose the game last night?

7. Congratulations. You got that answer completely wrong. The sentence, "Did the Dodgers lose the game last night?" is a question. A question cannot be a statement. Try that last one again.

8. If "The weather is nice" is replaced with p and "It is very hot" is replaced by q, which of the following is a compound statement.
    1. p
    2. q
    3. p and q
    4. pq

9. Suppose t represents the statement, "Elvis is an admiral," and u represents "Elvis is a hound dog." The meaning of t V u is _____.
    1. Elvis is an admiral and Elvis is a hound dog.
    2. Elvis is an admiral or Elvis is a hound dog.
    3. Elvis is an admiral but not a hound dog.

10. Which of the following sentences is a compound statement?
    1. Twelve of the cars were painted black.
    2. Roses are red or they are yellow.

11. You probably noticed that the disjunction, "V," is simply the conjunction, "∧," turned upside down. An easy way to keep them straight is to remember that "∧" stands for "And." What does "V" stand for?
    1. or
    2. and

FIGURE 14.3 (Cont.)

for the subject matter specialist who understands the students to be taught and knows what he wants to teach and how to write items to teach these concepts.

STEP 2: *Branching*. The branching program permits the computer to select a variable sequence of slides from the projector in response to different aspects of each student's behavior. For example, if the student makes too many errors, takes too much time on a particular topic, or in reply to an item asking him how well he thinks he is doing, indicates that he is having trouble, then he will receive the extra remedial items.

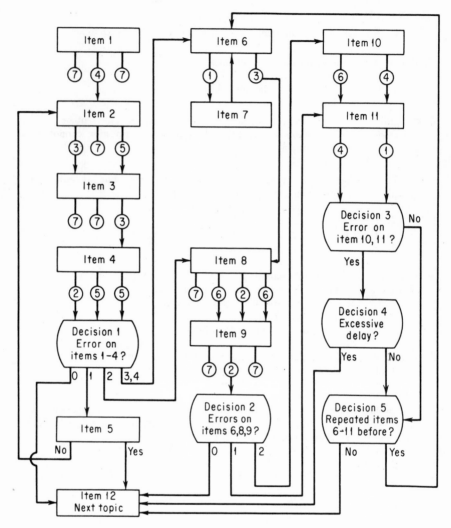

FIGURE 14.4 Flow chart for item branching.

Code Number	Message
1	(No message—go immediately to next slide.)
2	"Very good"
3	"You are correct; the answer is _____"
4	(No printed message—a bell is sounded instead.)
5	"The correct answer is _____"
6	"Wrong!"
7	"No! No! Try again"

If the student is making no errors, responding rapidly, and confident about his progress, then items will be skipped, and he will be permitted to cover the material more rapidly.

Some of the multiple-choice items contain distractors—a common type of misunderstanding. If one of these distractors is chosen, the student is immediately branched to remedial items designed to clarify that particular point.

At the end of each topic, or at the end of the lesson, the student may be given the option to repeat items for review. If the student has performed very poorly he may have no choice but to accept the review items. Branching decisions are made by the computer during the lesson, but the criteria for each branch are prespecified by the educator preparing the materials. The branching structure for the items shown in Figure 14.3 is presented in the form of a flow chart in Figure 14.4. In this flow chart, there are 12 items and 5 decision points. Each circle beneath an item represents a possible answer to the question. The first circle to the left would be the computer response to choice No. 1; the second to choice No. 2, etc. The numbers in these circles designate feedback codes. The student selecting a particular choice of answer will receive the message on his typewriter corresponding to the feedback code shown in Figure 14.4.

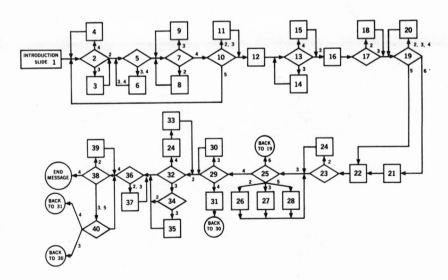

FIGURE 14.5 Flow chart: introduction to the binary number system.

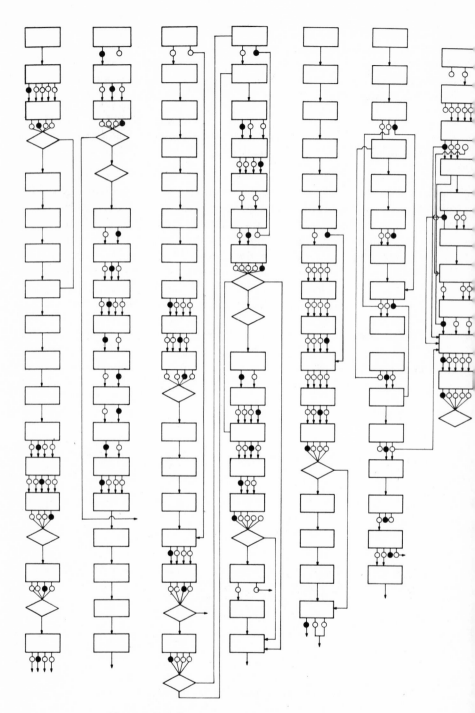

FIGURE 14.6 Computer decisions governing item sequence.

By comparing the code above with Figure 14.3 and Figure 14.4, one can see that if the student chooses the wrong option on the first item, he must answer again until he hears the sound of the bell. He proceeds in a similar manner from item to item until he completes Item 4. If he has made no errors on Items 1–4, he is skipped to the next topic which begins with Item 12. One error sends him to Item 5, which will ask him whether he would like to review Items 2–4 before going to Item 12. Three or four errors branch him to Item 6; only two errors branch him to Item 8. Similarly, the remainder of the program can be followed by reference to the flow chart. (Additional examples of flow charts, prepared for other sets of items, are shown in Figure 14.5 and Figure 14.6.)

STEP 3: *Manuscripting. Item manuscripting.* After the items have been written and the flow chart completed, all the information contained therein must be converted to a form that can be interpreted by the computer. The first stage of this conversion consists of coding or "manuscripting." The data are prepared on forms such as those shown in Figure 14.7 and Figure 14.8. For each item, the following descriptive information is required: an item number uniquely assigned to each item, the number of the correct multiple-choice answer (option), transfers, feedback messages, and concept counters. These last three terms, perhaps, require a little more explanation. A "transfer" is used if it is desired to branch the student on the basis of his answer to a single multiple-choice item. The number of the item to which he will be transferred is entered in the column corresponding to the choice of option on which the transfer will be executed. (See columns 46–68 in Figure 14.7.)

After the student responds to an item he will receive information, or "feedback," regarding the correctness of his answer. This feedback message may be printed out on the typewriter or presented as part of the next slide. If the messages are to be typed out, they must be prestored in the computer and an identification number assigned to each. The coded identification numbers on the item manuscript form insure that the proper feedback will occur after the appropriate response to a given item. (See columns 31–43 in Figure 14.7.) The student's errors on any set of items covering a particular topic or concept may be tallied by using "concept counters." A counter is a register located in the internal storage of the computer where a record may be accumulated. The number of a particular counter is entered opposite each item of the set, and a count is kept of student errors. (See columns 12–25 in Figure 14.7.)

Command manuscripting. Commands are special computer instructions, which may also be used to implement the branching decisions. The com-

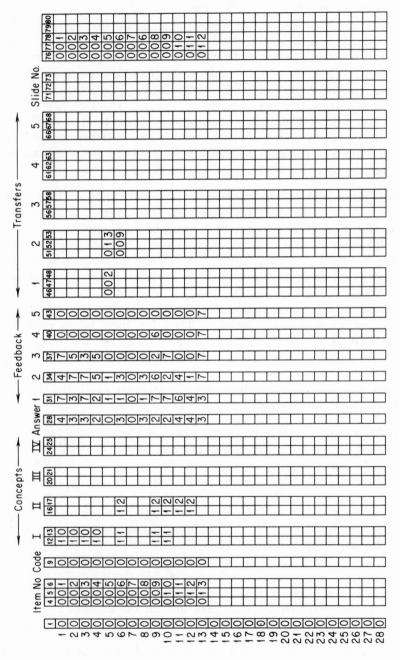

FIGURE 14.7 Item manuscript form.

324

mands are manuscripted along with the items and refer to the items by number. The command manuscript form is shown in Figure 14.8. As an example of the use of commands consider the first decision which appears

Item No.	Code	Command No.	±		OP I	OP II	ID No.
4 5 6	9	37	40	43	46 47 48	51 52 53	76 77 78 79 80
0 0 1	0	2			0 1 0	0 0 2	1
0 0 1	0	2			0 1 1	0 0 2	2
0 0 1	0	2			0 1 2	0 0 0	3
							4
							5
0 0 2	0	4			0 1 0	0 0 0	1
0 0 2	0	6			0 0 1	0 0 6	2
0 0 2	0	6			0 0 0	0 0 9	3
0 0 2	0	5			0 1 0	0 0 2	4
0 0 2	0	6			0 0 2	0 1 3	5
							1
							2
							3
							4
							5

FIGURE 14.8 Command manuscript form.

after the fourth item in the flow chart (Figure 14.4). The decision is to branch to one of four new items, depending upon how many errors are made on Items 1–4. If no errors are made, branch to Item 12; if two errors, branch to Item 8; if three or four errors, branch to Item 6. Item 5 asks the student whether he wants to review or would rather go on to the next topic. Item 2 will be indicated as a transfer on option 2 so that the student will be returned to Item 2 if he chooses to repeat a few items before continuing to the next topic. If he does not want a review, he will be transferred to the next topic.

14.2.5 *Preparation of Punched Paper Tapes.* After the item and branching information has been manuscripted, it is punched onto cards. By using a special tape preparation computer program, the information on the cards is converted to punched tape. The computer program records the information on a five-channel paper tape in the form of punched holes. This tape is called the "item tape." The punched holes on the item tape represent two classes of information: item data and commands for branching.

Note that the item tape is entirely separate from another tape containing the computer program, which selects the slides to be presented to the student. This second tape is called the "slide selection program" and is stored inside the computer on the magnetic drum. The slide selection program requires certain input data in order to perform its function of selecting slides for presentation. These input data are contained on the item tape. Several blocks of data from the item tape are read into the computer at a time. After the slide selection program has used these data, it may call for more data from the item tape. This process continues at a rate depending on the speed with which the student responds to the items.

14.2.6 *Lesson Checkout.* After the tapes have been prepared, they must be checked for errors. The internally stored slide selection program is read into the computer. After the slide selection program has been entered, the tape containing information on the items and on the branching is mounted on the computer and the lesson is started. As the internally stored slide selection program interprets the answers received via the typewriter, it reads the item tape. Using the information contained on the item tape and the information from the typewriter responses, the slide selection program records and evaluates the inserted responses. The program also prints feedback messages and selects appropriate slides for subsequent presentation, dependent on the branching decisions which have been executed. Every possible branch must be tried and found to occur under the conditions originally specified in the flow chart. The information on the slides must also be consistent with the flow chart. A student must not be reinforced for answering items incorrectly. Neither should the student be incorrectly branched to wrong items at inappropriate times. Once the programs are checked, the lesson may be presented whenever desired without further preparation; the program tapes have merely to be read into the computer. The instructions on the tape will cause the machine to perform the teaching operations in proper sequence.

14.3 THE COMPUTER-CONTROLLED TEACHING MACHINE AS A RESEARCH TOOL

Computer-controlled automated instruction does not stand divorced from existing knowledge about education and the learning process; rather, it is a new tool through which this knowledge can be applied and extended. Traditional research variables, such as the mode of presentation of materials, whole versus part learning, student aptitude and personality characteristics, etc., are still relevant. However, since one of the main advantages of using a computer as a control element for a teaching machine is its capacity to modify the sequence of instructional items during the tutoring session, the problem of determining the nature of a good sequence of items has been a central issue for research by workers in this field.

Different research workers have contrasting points of view about the nature of an optimal sequence of instructional items (often called a "program"). Various opinions prevail on questions such as, "What is an optimal sequence of items on a topic?" and "To what extent should items be tailored to individual students?" [5, 6]

The computer-based teaching machine developed at SDC represents one tool by which such problems may be explored. One question currently being studied at SDC is, "What decision criteria should be used in determining when to branch a student to less difficult remedial items?" For example, in theory it may be desirable to minimize errors for optimal learning on a program, but at the same time it may be necessary to use errors as a criterion for branching. Studies may consequently be directed toward the evaluation of methods of reducing the number of items needed to determine branching (i.e., the number of test items). This approach assumes a distinction between test items and teaching items. The function of the test item is to yield a maximally valid and reliable measure of individual differences, whereas the teaching item attempts to reduce individual differences with respect to the content of the item.

One possible method of reducing the number of test items required is the sequential test, by which the selection of each test item to be presented to a student depends upon his previous responses to other test items. Instead of keeping a test score on each individual by the number of correct answers to a long series of test items, the score is determined by the path traversed by the student through a branching tree of test items. Hence, a given student will never see more than a few of the test items. The resulting measure may provide validity and reliability equivalent to measures obtained by having each student traverse, in order, each test item in a long series.

Other examples of studies that may have relevance to the branching criterion problem involve a comparison of post-test scores and training time for alternative branching criteria. For example, a criterion based largely on type of error may be superior to one based on error rate. Branching in one experimental program may be entirely contingent upon the selections of particular multiple-choice options on single items which transfer the student immediately to remedial items. In another program, using the same teaching items, the student will be branched to alternative remedial items contingent upon how many errors were committed on a series of test items. Still further comparisons may be made using a combination of criteria for branching. This approach is illustrated in Figure 14.4, which is a flow chart containing branching decisions based on the response latency, the type of error, the student's self-evaluation, and the number of errors accumulated over several items. During the course of the lesson, weights may be assigned to non-error criteria, such as response latency and self-evaluation, depending upon how accurately these criteria reflect the student's performance.

Other questions relating to branching concern the interaction effects between individual difference variables, content variables, and the effectiveness of different branching criteria. For example, from some rationale one may deduce that highly motivated over-achievers would benefit more from response latency branching criteria than from error rate criteria on conceptual material, but the two methods may be predicted to be effective in the reverse order on rote material. Such a study might lead to a procedure whereby the branching criteria are weighted differentially on the basis of measured student characteristics, and the appropriate technique is selected by inserting the weighted scores into the computer as part of the initial conditions. In an alternate procedure, the decision might be made during the teaching sequence to branch to a different weighting system determined by the results of the ongoing testing.

An important consideration in any study is the development of a criterion, or set of dependent variables, which is sufficiently sensitive to variations among independent variables to detect their effect in small-scale pilot explorations using relatively few subjects and items. One approach to this problem is establishing different levels of criteria for evaluating the effect of different decision schemes. For example, one level of criteria may use the stimulus characteristics of the branching structure as rational or face-validity evidence of its effectiveness. A program which contained all branching decision points in the same location would be clearly suspect, since certain decisions are contingent on the outcomes of previous decisions in the program. A second criterion level may use response data on the training items. Ideally, an optimal branching structure should minimize errors on training items as well as total number of training items presented. At yet a third level, a post-training objective or performance test may be used as a criterion. The nature of this criterion may vary with respect to its similarity to the training task. Ultimately, we are primarily interested in the student's ability to transfer this learning to new situations.

The results of research studies, such as those described above, not only provide information on the effectiveness of decision criteria for branching, but also furnish data for the revision and improvement of the instructional items that were used in the experiment. With each revision, the items become more useful in promoting student learning. Items are organized into topics, each topic being covered at several difficulty levels. If a student is doing exceptionally well at one level of a topic, he may be branched to more advanced material. If he is not doing well, he will be branched down to a lower level of difficulty.

14.4 FUTURE DEVELOPMENTS

With the completion of the computer-based teaching machine, a number of studies were undertaken to determine its operational feasibility and the teaching effectiveness of the adaptive "branching" mode of instruction. Preliminary findings from current experiments indicate that computer-based teaching machines are indeed feasible and that such machines can function very effectively by adapting the materials to the individual student. The program described in the previous section represents only one of many possible designs which can be programed for the teaching machine.

At present, SDC is developing an expanded educational facility, using a more powerful digital computer, the Philco 2000. With this computer, large numbers of students can simultaneously receive individualized automated instruction. The computer will have in storage detailed information about the instructional material and about each of the students being taught. It will receive input information from each student, perform logical decisions concerning the next item or feedback message to be shown to the student, and send necessary output messages to the display devices. Because of its high speed, it will be able to process the information for each student so rapidly and so frequently that no student need wait any appreciable time for the computer to respond to his insertions. At any given time, different students might be working on a different portion of the lesson, or even on different subject areas. Ten or fifteen students might be receiving instruction in algebra, for example, while others are learning English composition. Thus it will be possible, when using the Philco

2000, to obtain experimental data on many students concurrently, rather than working with one at a time as is the case with the present machine.

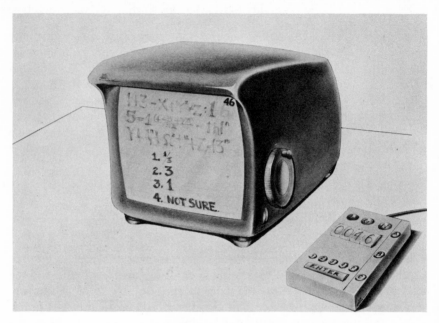

Figure 14.9 Student display unit and response.

The new facility, designated CLASS (Computer-based Laboratory for Automated School Systems), will provide an individualized item display panel and a response device for each of many students. Simple displays will also be provided for teachers, so that the teacher can monitor individual student or group progress and can intervene when a particular student is having unusual difficulty. Figure 14.9 shows one student's display unit and the response device for multiple-choice insertions. Figure 14.10 illustrates the functional design of the CLASS facility.

Separate rooms will be provided in CLASS for school administration and counseling functions normally associated with the operation of an educational system. The computer will receive and process many types of data, such as registration, class attendance, tests, and previous educational background. These data will be made available in digested forms as requested by teachers, administrators, and counselors.

The CLASS facility will permit investigation not only of the individual learning process, but of an entire integrated educational system. Interactions among students, and between students and teachers, might be studied. Conventional methods of instruction would be used in addition to automated teaching. The effectiveness of different combinations of techniques, including textbooks, instruction by human teachers, film and television presentations, as well as teaching machines, would be evaluated. Hopefully, the results of these studies will provide information on the direction that should be taken by future educational systems.

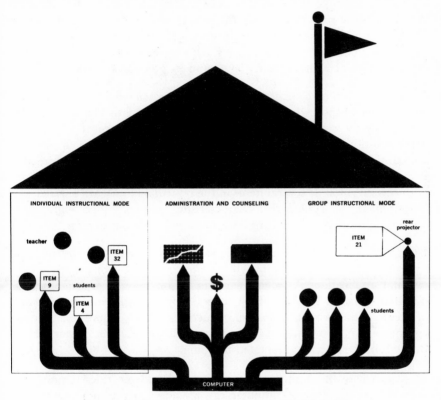

FIGURE 14.10 Functional diagram of CLASS facility.

One area in which future progress might be expected is in the generation of a set of items on some basis other than a completely prespecified branching structure. The earlier description showed that the instructional sequence was specified by the items and branching decisions as described in the flow chart. The exact sequence of items in any branch of the sequence is completely specified before the lesson begins. An alternative to this procedure is programing certain general rules to be used by the computer in selecting slides. To illustrate the operation of such a program, a design similar to the following might be used.

The program will contain a large store of items with a description of each. Instead of the lesson planner's having to go through all of the items in order to select the members of each remedial branch, the computer will be programed to select items according to certain constraints or legality rules. For example, one rule might specify the order in which different types of items should be selected; first the lead-in, or orientation items; then items stating the principle; next practice examples, review items; and finally, test items. Another rule may specify the proportions of each type of item to be used for each topic; 5 per cent lead-in, 10 per cent review, 15 per cent examples, 5 per cent test items, etc. Each item would have to be classified by topic, type of item, difficulty level, and its prerequisite topics.

Items might also be classified as belonging to a remedial series or a basic series, depending on whether they are prespecified by the experimenter or selected by the computer. A *basic series* is any sequence of prespecified items constituting a central stream of interlocking items which are presented in sequence to the student. In contrast, the items in the remedial detour are selected from a library of items by the computer in accordance with certain rules. If several items in the remedial library are parallel, i.e., if they have the same coded characteristics, the computer might select an item at random by resorting to a random number generator.

Using a computer to assist in preparation of sequences of instructional items is particularly important when items are written for extensive educational application. A single two-hour lesson may incorporate several hundred items. A four-year high school program will require thousands of items. The task of organizing such extensive sequences becomes enormous, and computer assistance would constitute a major breakthrough in the area of automated teaching.

In cases where the number of items is small and the rules required for selection are simple, the computer can already generate practice or drill exercises for the student. For instance, in a multiplication lesson where the student is required to practice multiplying single-digit numbers, the machine can randomly compose exercises by assigning digits to be multiplied. Rather soon, the computer should be capable of selecting, from a large pool of items, a series that will uniquely meet the needs of any given student.

Another area in which future progress might be expected is the programing of a "learning" feature in the machine itself. One of the remarkable characteristics of the master teacher is ability to modify his teaching with experience and thus progressively increase his skill in helping others to learn. One might assume that this process of improvement stems from trying different teaching approaches, retaining those which work well, and abandoning the methods which are not effective. The teaching machine of the future may also contain this property. The computer would have stored information on aptitude, personality, and previous achievement of each student. It would then select the teaching method which had been found to work best with this type of student. Performance on test items in the program would provide a standard against which different methods would be compared. Methods that are highly correlated with performance on the test questions would be assigned weights for their teaching effectiveness. In subsequent teaching sessions, methods with the highest weights would be tried first. If none of the machine methods were helpful, the experimenter would have to add new approaches to the program. But it is also possible that the computer may derive new methods from the existing available techniques. The emerging methods, obtained by combining the existing methods with the highest weights, would then be added to the list of available methods and assigned weights on the basis of their effectiveness. As the teaching machine gained in experience, those unique combinations of methods which were found to be most effective would gain priority in the hierarchy of techniques and less effective procedures would drop out.

Finally, in future auto-instructional systems, a student may be given much more freedom in the kinds of information he can insert and receive from the teaching machine. He may be allowed to answer questions posed by the machine, or even ask questions of his own, using conventional English. The enormous storage capabilities of computers may be used to allow the student to call up reference materials needed in the solution of problems. In general, efforts are being made to eliminate arbitrary restraints imposed by machine design and to allow the student a wide variety of modes of expression, as well as alternative methods of solution to different problems. Of course, the scope of applications of computers to education will grow. Computers are already being used in processing test scores, in registration and scheduling, attendance and grade reporting, etc. Computers are also used for predicting school population, for estimating future school costs, salary bill projections, capital outlay for school plant, and other management forecasting and optimization problems. In the future, it is not unreasonable to expect such applications to be integrated with the instructional function and processed in a central, general purpose, high-speed digital computer. School administrators, teachers, counselors, supervisors, and curriculum specialists will have instant access to information heretofore available only at great cost to assist them in making educational decisions for an entire school district, whether at the local, county, state, or national level. Certainly, the computer will play a paramount role in the school of the future.

REFERENCES

1 Carter, L. F., Exercising the Air Defense System. Paper presented at the Joint Meeting of the Human Factors Society of San Diego and the San Diego Chapter, Institute of Aeronautical Sciences, January 1959.

2 Coulson, J., and Silberman, H. F., Automated Teaching and Individual Differences, *Audio-Visual Com. Rev.*, 9, January–February 1961 (in press).

3 Craft, C. J., and Steward, L. A., Competitive Management Simulation, *Jour. Ind. Engineering, 10*, September–October 1959, 355–63.

4 Eigen, L. D., and Komoski, K., The Constructive Use of Teachers' Talent, *Calif. Jour. Sec. Educ., 35* (No. 4), April 1960.

5 Galanter, E. H., ed., *Automatic Teaching: The State of the Art.* New York: Wiley, 1959, 63–68.

6 Lumsdaine, A. A., and Glaser, R., eds., *Teaching Machines and Programmed Learning: A Source Book.* Washington, D.C.: Department of Audio Visual Instruction, National Education Association, 1960.

7 Perlis, A. G., Research and Development in Programing Study Assignments, *Progress Report,* Carnegie Institute of Technology, Computer Center, July 1959.

8 Rath, G. J., Andersen, N. S., and Brainerd, R. C., The IBM Research Center Teaching Machine Project, *Automatic Teaching: The State of the Art.* Galanter, E. H., ed., New York: Wiley, 1959, chap. 11, 117–30.

Julian Feldman

15/COMPUTER SIMULATION OF
COGNITIVE PROCESSES

*Julian Feldman is an
Assistant Professor in the Schools
of Business Administration, University
of California, Berkeley. He
received his M.A. in political science
from the University of Chicago in 1954 and
his Ph.D. in industrial administration
from Carnegie Institute of Technology in 1959.
He has published in the* American
Journal of Psychology *and in*
Psychometrika. *His major research interest
is in the computer simulation
of cognitive processes.*

15.1 INTRODUCTION

The study of cognitive processes—the higher mental processes involved in activities generally referred to as "thinking" and "problem solving"—has attracted considerable attention in recent years. A major reason for this attention has been the development of a method for studying human cognitive processes by simulating these processes on a large, high-speed digital computer.[15, 21, 27, 29] The behavior of the computer is determined by a program; hence the major effort in this method centers around writing a program that will cause the computer to perform a task the same way that people do. The statements of such a program form a theory or model of human behavior in the task situation. The implications of the model are determined by running the program on the computer and observing the resulting behavior.

Although the method of studying human cognitive processes by computer simulation is only a few years old, a number of important results have already been achieved. The first major contribution was made by Newell,

This chapter was prepared while the author was a member of the Center for Social Science Theory, University of California, Berkeley. The author is indebted to A. Newell, E. A. Feigenbaum, H. Kanter, A. C. Hoggatt, and his colleagues at the Center for their comments on an earlier draft of this chapter.

Shaw, and Simon,[25, 27] who programed a computer to simulate the behavior of subjects solving problems in symbolic logic. Solution of a logic problem requires that a given logic expression be converted into a desired formulation by the application of certain rules to the given expression. The problem-solving program is an explicit model of problem-solving behavior in this task. The program proceeds to solve these problems by finding differences between the two expressions and selecting rules which, when applied to the given expression, will lead to a reduction of those differences. The application of a single rule to the given expression usually yields an expression intermediate between the original expression and the one desired. This intermediate expression is then compared to the desired expression, the differences detected, and once again the appropriate rule is applied. This procedure is repeated until the desired expression is obtained. The behavior of this program is quite similar in procedure to human problem-solving behavior.

A second contribution to our understanding of cognitive processes has resulted from the computer model of verbal learning behavior developed by Feigenbaum.[10] This program is designed to simulate the behavior of humans learning lists of nonsense syllables. The program learns these syllables by constructing a series of tests based on the differences between the syllables. These tests form a discrimination mechanism for a list of syllables. The performance of this program in learning lists of nonsense syllables reveals marked similarities to the activity of human subjects engaged in the same task.

Our understanding of cognitive processes will be further increased by the computer models that have been or are being developed to simulate human behavior in portfolio selection,[4] concept formation,[16] and music composition.[30] (See also Chapter 18.)

The purpose of this report is to introduce the method of studying cognitive processes by computer simulation. The method will be presented by describing the author's work on computer simulation of behavior in the binary choice experiment.[11] This form of presentation has the advantage of discussing techniques and problems in specific contexts rather than in the abstract. The reader is cautioned, however, that the material presented here is descriptive rather than prescriptive.

15.2   SIMULATION OF BINARY CHOICE BEHAVIOR—An example of simulation of cognitive processes

15.2.1 *The Binary Choice Experiment.* In the binary choice experiment, the subject is asked to predict which of two events, E_1 or E_2, will occur on each of a series of trials. After the subject makes each prediction, he is told which event actually occurred. The order of the events is determined by a random process, but the subject is not given this information. The subject is instructed to make as many correct predictions as he can.

15.2.2 A Statistical Learning Theory Explanation of Binary Choice Behavior. One model of behavior in this experiment has been offered by the statistical learning theorists.[2, 9] In its simplest form, this model says that the probability that the subject will predict that event E_1 will occur on trial t is increased if event E_1 occurred on trial $t - 1$. Conversely, the probability that the subject will predict that event E_1 will occur on trial t is decreased if event E_2 occurred on trial $t - 1$. The more often one event occurs, the greater the probability that the subject will predict that event.

The simple statistical learning model is consistent with some characteristics of the behavior observed in the binary choice experiment, notably that subjects usually predict each event about as often as it occurs. But the simple statistical learning model is not consistent with other characteristics of behavior observed in the experiment. For example, after several successive occurrences of one event, subjects tend to predict the occurrence of the other event.[18] This behavior is quite frequently observed in non-experimental situations and is referred to as "gambler's fallacy" or "negative recency." This behavior is, of course, not consistent with a model that predicts that successive occurrences of one event increase the probability that the subject will predict that event. Evidence has also been presented that the statistical learning model does not adequately predict the subject's responses when the subject is predicting an event series that contains conditional probability relationships; e.g., the probability that E_1 will follow E_1 is not the same as the probability that E_1 will follow E_2.[1, 8]

15.2.3 A Computer Model of Binary Choice Behavior. The difficulties of the simple statistical learning model and the comments of investigators of binary choice behavior would seem to indicate that binary choice behavior is much more complex than the statistical learning model would indicate. The subject's response is not determined simply by the frequency and recency with which an event has occurred, as the statistical learning model implies. Post-experimental interviews and analysis of trial-by-trial responses suggest that subjects entertain hypotheses about patterns in the event series. The subject is apparently not a passive mechanism being conditioned to make responses with a certain probability. He is more adequately depicted as an active information-processing mechanism that views the binary choice task as the problem of finding the structure of the event series. Such a complex information-processing model can be stated in the form of a computer program, and the model can be studied by running the program on the computer.

Before the computer model can be written, information must be obtained about the cognitive processes involved in binary choice behavior. The data available from previous experimentation did not provide sufficient information, and a new set of experiments was run in which the subject was asked to "think aloud" while making his choices.

15.2.3.1 *"Thinking Aloud."* The "thinking aloud" procedure is not new. Woodworth [38] says it was advocated by Claparéde in 1917. Heidbreder [14] used the "thinking aloud" procedure in her work on concept formation, and Duncker [7] also made very effective use of the same procedure in his work on problem solving. The procedure has been used in several computer simulation studies of thought processes [4, 27, 30] in addition to the study of binary choice behavior.

The "thinking aloud" procedure consists simply of asking the subject to verbalize while performing a task. The statements of the subject and the experimenter are recorded. This record is called a "protocol." The "thinking aloud" procedure is not to be confused with introspection. The distinction made by Duncker [7] is worth repeating:

> This instruction, *"Think aloud,"* is not identical with the instruction to introspect which has been common in experiments on thought-processes. While the introspecter makes himself as thinking the object of his attention, the subject who is thinking aloud remains immediately directed to the problem, so to speak, allowing his activity to become verbal. When someone, while thinking, says to himself, "One ought to see if this isn't . . . ," or, "It would be nice if one could show that . . . ," one would hardly call this introspection; yet in such remarks something is revealed. . . [p. 2].

The following excerpts from the protocol of subject DH predicting a series of "$+$" symbols and "$\sqrt{}$" symbols in a 200-trial binary choice experiment give some indication of the information obtained with this technique:

> The ninth one will be a $\sqrt{}$. I think that you just gave me the $+$ to throw me off, and you'll continue the progression.
>
> $\cdot$ $\cdot$ $\cdot$
>
> The fourteenth one will be a $+$. You're beginning a new progression with $+$'s.
>
> $\cdot$ $\cdot$ $\cdot$
>
> The sixteenth one will be a $\sqrt{}$. . . . to throw me off now.
>
> $\cdot$ $\cdot$ $\cdot$

Ninety-nine is a $\sqrt{}$. You've begun a progression of three $+$'s and three $\sqrt{}$'s. You've already had the three $+$'s. Ninety-eight (sic) will be a $\sqrt{}$.

. . .

One-twenty-nine will be a $\sqrt{}$. You've begun a progression of two $+$'s and two $\sqrt{}$'s.

. . .

One-thirty-two will be a $+$. You're alternating the signs now.

The "thinking aloud" protocols not only furnished additional information on the cognitive processes of the subject, but also transformed the goal of the research. The goal became the explanation of the behavior indicated by the protocol. The strategy followed in the study of binary choice behavior was construction for each subject of a model that would make the same predictions as the subject for the same reasons that the subject gave. In the next section, the development of a model for one of the subjects, DH, will be retraced, and in the following section the model for DH will be described.*

15.2.3.2 *Analysis of the Protocol.* The protocol obtained with the "thinking aloud" technique was the raw data for the construction of the computer program. Cursory examination of the protocol provided some understanding of the processes the subject used in the formulation of his responses. The protocol of DH in the binary choice experiment seemed to corroborate the conjecture about hypothesis behavior in the experiment, i.e., that the subject entertained hypotheses about patterns in the event series. But a casual examination of the protocol did not provide detailed information about which hypotheses the subject entertained and under what conditions these hypotheses were evoked and selected.

This detailed information was obtained from a careful analysis of the protocol. The first step in this analysis was to code the subject's statements on the basis of their apparent meaning. For example, DH's comment, "You're following with a $\sqrt{}$ and two $+$'s," was coded as the pattern-hypothesis $\sqrt{} + +$. The comment, "You've begun a progression of two $+$'s and two $\sqrt{}$'s," was coded as the pattern-hypothesis $+ + \sqrt{} \sqrt{}$. The second step was to investigate the seemingly plausible conjecture that a relationship existed between the subject's hypotheses and the sequences of events and predictions preceding the statement of those hypotheses. Some regularities were uncovered. For example, after several $\sqrt{}$'s occurred, DH would say that a progression of $\sqrt{}$'s was beginning. After the

---

* The strategy of constructing models to match individual protocols has been used in several other computer simulations of cognitive processes.[4, 27, 29] Feigenbaum, in his study of verbal learning behavior,[10] has constructed a computer model of a generalized subject rather than separate models for individual subjects.

event sequence $+ \checkmark + \checkmark$, the subject would say that the signs were beginning to alternate. The analysis also revealed that DH usually changed hypotheses after incorrect predictions and retained hypotheses after correct predictions. The hypotheses were also consistent with the subject's symbol predictions.

15.2.3.3 *The Model for DH.* On the basis of the information obtained from the analysis of the protocol, together with some conjectures where this analysis could not supply the necessary information, a rough outline of a model of DH's behavior in the binary choice experiment was obtained:

> A hypothesis is generated about the structure of the event series on the basis of the preceding events. This hypothesis is used to obtain a prediction of the next event. The prediction performs the role of a test of the hypothesis. If the prediction is correct, the hypothesis is retained unless a decision is made that the pattern of events will be interrupted ("negative recency"). If the prediction is incorrect, either the event is explained as an interruption of the pattern ("you just gave me the $+$ to throw me off") or a new hypothesis is generated.

The completion of the model was a lengthy task involving the iterative procedure of proposing a detailed model, testing the model against the data, modifying the model, testing again, and so on. During this procedure, almost every part of the model originally proposed was modified or replaced. In addition, modifications of the model led to new interpretations of the data, and these interpretations led to further modifications of the model.

The completion of the model for DH's behavior in the binary choice experiment began with attempts to specify the mechanism for pattern selection. Several mechanisms were considered, only to be rejected. Similarly, several negative recency mechanisms were tried. The representations of certain basic elements of the model, e.g., the patterns and hypotheses, were also the subject of experimentation. After much experimentation, the model for DH described below was completed.

The basic element of this model is the hypothesis. Every hypothesis has a pattern component, e.g., progression of $\checkmark$'s, simple alternation $(+ \checkmark)$, double alternation, etc. Some hypotheses have a second component which is a negative or "guess-opposite" component. If the guess-opposite component is not present, the prediction of the hypothesis is the prediction of the pattern component; e.g., the prediction of the hypothesis which has a pattern component "progression of $\checkmark$'s" and no guess-opposite component is a $\checkmark$. If the guess-opposite component is present, the prediction of the hypothesis is the "opposite" of the prediction of the pattern component;

e.g., the prediction of the hypothesis which has a pattern component "progression of $\sqrt{}$'s" and a guess-opposite component is a +.

The model itself is divided into two phases. Phase 1 is concerned with the processing for the pattern component of the model. The output of this phase may also be interpreted as the subject's explanation of the preceding event (the explanation hypothesis). Phase 2 is concerned with the processing of the guess-opposite component of the model. The output of this phase becomes the subject's hypothesis for predicting the event of the next trial (the prediction hypothesis).

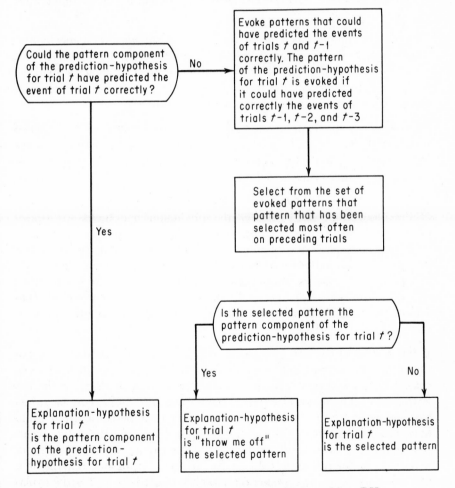

FIGURE 15.1 Phase 1 of binary choice model for subject DH.

Phase 1 of the model for DH is presented in Figure 15.1. The model sharply distinguishes between patterns that predict an event correctly and those that do not. Indeed, this simple idea of retaining hypotheses that predict correctly and changing, or at least considering the possibility of changing, hypotheses that predict incorrectly is a basic premise of the model. The distinction is made between the ability of the hypothesis to predict an event and the ability of the pattern to predict the event. If the hypothesis contains a guess-opposite component and it predicts an event *correctly*, the pattern will not be able to predict correctly and will be considered for change. If the hypothesis is negative and it predicts *incorrectly*, the pattern will be able to predict correctly and will not be considered for change.

The pattern-change mechanism, composed of the evocation mechanism and the selection mechanism, is really a device for choosing a pattern from the basic list of nine patterns that the subject uses. The choice is made in two stages. In the evocation stage, a subset of the patterns is nominated. In the selection stage, a single pattern is selected.

The model says the experimenter tried to "throw me off" on trial t when a pattern failed to predict the event of trial t, but the pattern-change mechanism does not select another pattern. Otherwise, the explanation-hypothesis contains only a pattern.

Phase 2 of the model for DH is represented in Figure 15.2. This phase of the model first tests whether the prediction hypothesis for trial t contained a guess-opposite component. If the guess-opposite component is present, it is processed in much the same fashion that the pattern is processed in the pattern-selection phase. If the negative hypothesis predicted correctly, the guess-opposite component is saved. If the negative hypothesis did not predict correctly, the guess-opposite component is considered for retention in a fashion analogous to the throw-me-off consideration in the pattern phase.

If the guess-opposite component was not present in the prediction hypothesis for trial t, the model considers whether or not the guess-opposite component should be introduced. This consideration is made in the following way: The model determines the number (N_1) of events including and preceding trial t in which the explanation hypothesis for trial t could have predicted correctly. Then the number (N_2) of contiguous events that could have been predicted by the last occurrence of the explanation-hypothesis is determined. If $N_2 > N_1$, the guess-opposite component is not introduced; and the prediction hypothesis for trial $t + 1$ is the explanation-hypothesis for trial t. If $N_2 = N_1$, the prediction hypothesis for

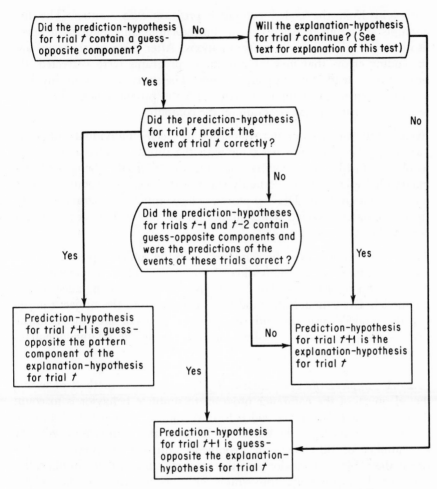

FIGURE 15.2 Phase 2 of binary choice model for subject DH.

trial $t + 1$ is guess-opposite the explanation hypothesis for trial t. If $N_2 < N_1$, the model concludes that the previous occurrence of the explanation hypothesis as represented by N_2 is not really pertinent. The model then searches for an occurrence of the explanation hypothesis preceding the occurrence represented by N_2 and repeats the process. If no occurrence is found, the guess-opposite component is not introduced, and the prediction hypothesis for trial $t + 1$ is the explanation hypothesis for trial t.

15.2.4 The Study and Testing of the Computer Model. After the model was specified in a form such as that of the flow charts in Figures

15.1 and 15.2, the coded computer program was written. The first attempts at coding revealed logical contradictions and inadequate specifications in earlier flow chart formulations. After these inaccuracies and the coding errors that inevitably occur in programs were corrected, the program was ready for study and testing. The study and testing involved a comparison of the human behavior and the program behavior as determined by running the program on the computer.

Even in the case of computer simulation of specific individuals, the comparison of the program's behavior with the subject's behavior does not involve a word-for-word comparison. The model of DH's behavior in the binary choice experiment certainly was not designed to produce a word-for-word facsimile of DH's protocol. The computer program was designed to match a coded representation of the protocol, such as was discussed above.

The model's protocol can be compared with the subject's protocol which served as a basis for the derivation of the model. This comparison is, of course, not a rigorous test, but it does give some idea of the adequacy of the model. Even though the model was derived from the subject's protocol, the model's protocol and the subject's protocol are not identical. Thus, some procedure is required for determining the relative adequacy of the model.

15.2.4.1 *Simple Difference Count.* The most obvious method of testing the adequacy of the computer program to simulate behavior is to count the differences between the coded form of the subject's protocol and the machine's protocol. In the binary choice case, this comparison will give the number of differences in hypotheses and symbol predictions between the subject's behavior and the machine's attempt to simulate this behavior. Unfortunately, this simple error count can be misleading. Human behavior and models of this behavior generally contain a large number of interdependencies. The model's decision at any given point in time t depends quite heavily on its prior decisions, and if one of these prior decisions is different from the subject's decision, the model is quite likely to make a decision different from that of the subject at t. The ability of the model of DH's behavior to select the same hypothesis as the subject does at trial t depends on the ability of the model to select the same hypothesis that the subject did at trial $t - 1$. If the model's hypothesis at trial $t - 1$ was different from the subject's, the model's hypothesis at trial t is most likely to be different, too. Because of the interdependencies in the behavior and the model, two differences would result. The second difference, however, may have resulted from the first and not from any inadequacy in the model. Thus the difference count would be exaggerated. By similar reasoning, the difference count might be reduced.*

15.2.4.2 *Turing's Test.* One solution to the problems involved in comparing the behavior of complex models and the behavior of the subjects that the models are simulating is to use a version of the "blindfold" test. We are all familiar with the advertisements that challenge the reader to distinguish between oleomargarine and the "high-priced spread." This same type of test might be used to see whether an expert could distinguish between the subject's protocol and the machine's protocol. Such a test was suggested by Turing[37] as a pragmatic solution to the debate over whether machines could think. Turing proposed that an interrogator question a machine and a person on a variety of topics via a teletype. If the interrogator could not distinguish the machine's responses from the human's, Turing was willing to conclude that machines could think. Such a test has been applied in at least one case. McGovern[20] has programed a computer to answer questions about the weather. These questions were also asked of nine people. McGovern then listed the questions and the answers given by the computer program and the humans. Another group of 10 people was asked to pick out the program's response to each question out of the 10 responses listed for each of the 25 questions. These 10 people made 42 correct choices out of 250 opportunities, which is not better than would be expected if these judges were choosing randomly. Newell and Simon [27] have proposed that a version of Turing's test, such as the one used by McGovern, might be used to determine the adequacy of computer simulations of human cognitive processes. Thus, judges might be handed the protocol obtained by computer simulation and coded versions of nine human protocols and be asked to pick out the machine's protocol.

Turing's test lacks the rigor that the computer simulation of cognitive processes promises to restore to the study of cognitive processes. It is certainly true that the use of judges is a respectable test, and statistical techniques are available for determining the ability of judges to discriminate beyond mere guessing. The use of Turing's test, however, implies that no good operational criteria exist for comparing human protocols and machine protocols. Furthermore, the ability of the computer simulation of cognitive processes to achieve its goal—the creation of a model that will produce a reasonable facsimile of the subject's behavior—is probably not very well tested by Turing's test. Turing's test is adequate for telling the

---

* For a different view of the usefulness of the simple difference-count procedure, see reference 5.

researcher whether or not he has achieved a program that will produce behavior that is indistinguishable from human behavior. But Turing's test is not adequate for matching the protocol of the machine's behavior and the subject's behavior; since even though these protocols may be quite different, judges cannot determine which is the machine's protocol. In statistical terminology, Turing's test is not very powerful for testing simulation models. The probability of an error of the second kind, i.e., accepting the model when it is in fact wrong, is quite high.

15.2.4.3 *Conditional Prediction.* Another method for obviating the difficulties that arise in the simple difference-counting method of comparing the machine's protocol and the subject's protocol involves an attempt to eliminate the interdependencies that vitiate the difference-counting method. Every time the program makes a decision different from that of the subject, the program can be set back on the track, i.e., the subject's decisions imposed on the model, so that the differences between the subject's behavior and the program's behavior at any point in time will not be caused by the differences that occurred earlier. Thus the decisions of the model at any point in time are conditional on the preceding decisions of the model's being the same as those of the subject.*

This system of conditional prediction was applied to the binary choice model of DH that has been presented above. The program of DH's behavior was subdivided into segments, each of which was capable of making a decision that could be compared to a decision of the subject, e.g., pattern evocation, pattern selection, pattern prediction, etc. After each segment was executed, the decision of the segment was compared to that of the subject by a test; e.g., "Did the pattern-evocation mechanism evoke the subject's pattern?" If a difference between the program's decision and the subject's decision was detected by any of these tests, the program's decision was replaced by the subject's decision. The program itself was not modified. Thus, if the pattern-evocation mechanism failed to evoke the subject's pattern, the subject's pattern was added to the list of evoked patterns. This corrected list of evoked patterns was then used as the input to the pattern-selection mechanism. Thus, the inputs to the pattern-

---

* The terminology is due to Theil.[34] A conditional prediction technique similar to the one described here has been used by Newell, Shaw, and Simon in requiring their chess-playing program to play a book game [26] and by Samuel [31] in requiring his checker machine to play a book game. In both these cases, if the machine made a move other than the book move, the move was withdrawn and the book move was imposed. Setting the chess and checker program back on the track, however, was considerably more difficult than was the case in the binary choice program for DH.

selection mechanism and each of the other program segments were correct or at least contained the information required by the segments to make a correct decision.

The results of using the program of DH to predict in this conditional fashion are given in Figures 15.3 and 15.4. Figure 15.3 is a restatement of the flow chart of Figure 15.1, with the addition of the tests and control statements required for conditional prediction. Figure 15.4 is the corresponding restatement of Figure 15.2. Thus in Figure 15.3, after the program decided not to select the pattern-change mechanism (on 120 trials), control was transferred to the error test. This test checks to see whether the subject actually kept his pattern. He did on 117 trials.

If he did not, an error was tallied (three trials) and control was transferred back to the simulation program beginning with the pattern-evocation mechanism. The conditional prediction system performed similar functions after the program made any decision that could be checked against the protocol. Thus the input to each segment of the program was eliminated as a source of error. Examination of Figures 15.3 and 15.4 indicates that, except for the guess-opposite mechanism, most segments of the program performed reasonably well under these conditions.*

This type of conditional prediction offers several advantages as a device for comparing machine protocols and subject protocols. The first advantage—the elimination of the interdependencies in the model as a cause of spurious differences between the model's behavior and the subject's behavior—has already been mentioned. A second advantage derives from the ability to test each segment of the model separately. For example, the number of times the pattern-evocation mechanism fails to evoke the subject's pattern and the number of times the pattern-selection mechanism fails to select the subject's pattern are determined independently of each other. This separation allows easy identification of those segments of the model that make large numbers of errors. A third advantage derives from the greater number of tests given each component of the model by the use of the conditional prediction technique. If the pattern-evocation mechanism fails to evoke the subject's pattern, the subsequent operation of the pattern-selection mechanism cannot be considered a valid test for reasons that have been previously discussed. If the mistake of the pattern-evocation mechanism is corrected before the pattern-selection mechanism is used, however, the pattern-selection routine will be given a valid test.

* The program predicts for 195 trials (it begins at trial 6 of the 200-trial sequence).

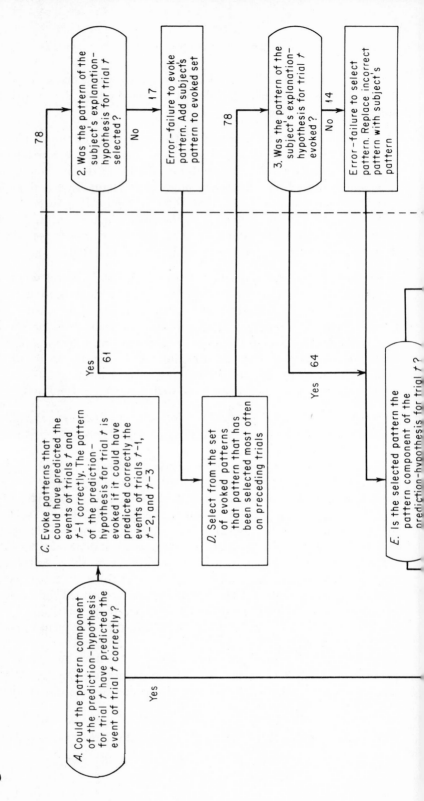

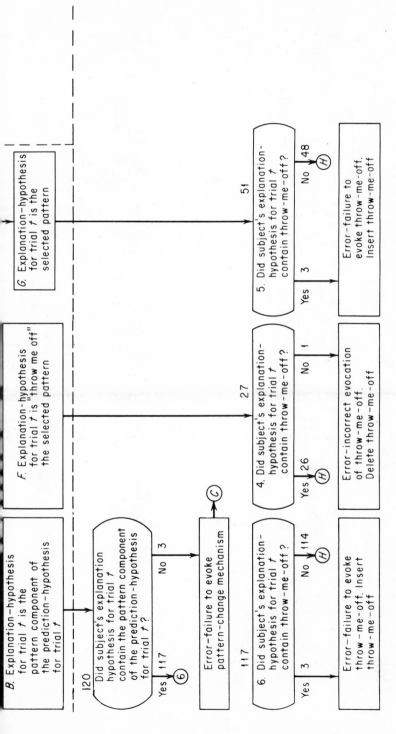

FIGURE 15.3 Phase 1 of binary choice model for DH with conditional prediction controls.

351

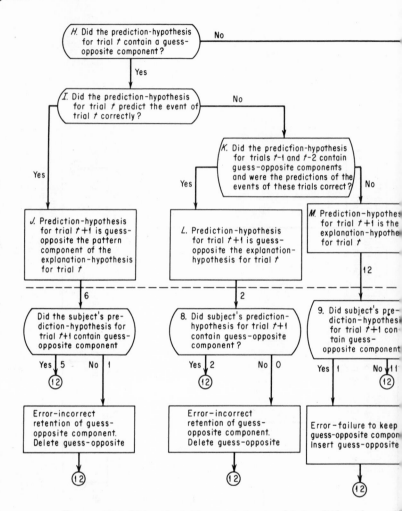

FIGURE 15.4 Phase 2 of binary choice model for DH with conditional prediction controls.

The problem of comparing the program's behavior and the subject's behavior can be summarized as follows: The errors made by a model in predicting the subject's behavior result from either erroneous inputs to the model or incorrect specification of the model. The difficulty with the simple difference count is that it confuses these two sources of error. Turing's test is not sharp enough to determine specific inadequacies of the model. The major virtue of the conditional prediction technique is its separation of the two types of errors; thus, it permits identification of the components of the model that are inadequately specified.

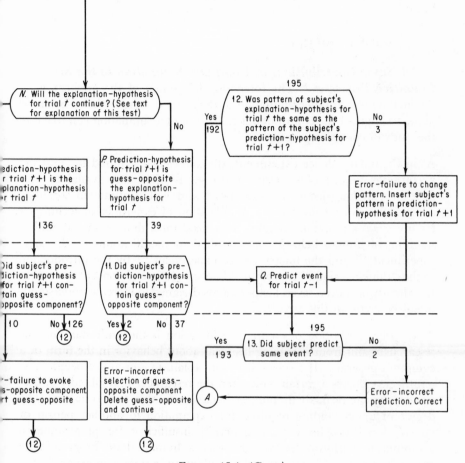

FIGURE 15.4 (Cont.)

15.2.4.4 *Testing Models of Generalized Individuals.* In the cases where the computer program represents a generalized individual rather than a specific individual, [10] the simple difference-count comparison of behavior is certainly not appropriate. The conditional prediction technique is of less value than in the case of simulation of specific individuals. Turing's test suffers from the same inadequacies in this case as in the case of specific individuals. Perhaps the traditional statistical comparisons are the most useful tests in this situation. For example, the serial position curve generated by a verbal learning program simulating behavior in a nonsense syllable learning experiment can be compared to the curve obtained from human behavior in the same experiment. Other summary statistics of the program's behavior can also be compared with those of the subjects' behavior.

15.3   CONCLUSIONS

15.3.1 *Some Contributions of Computer Simulation to the Study of Cognitive Processes.** The foregoing description of the application of the method of computer simulation to the study of binary choice behavior indicates some of the contributions that computer simulation can make to the study of cognitive processes.

As in the binary choice experiment, the knowledge required to construct a computer model of cognitive processes is often not available. This deficiency of knowledge has stimulated and will continue to stimulate additional experimentation and modification of experimental techniques for investigating human thought. This need for a more complete understanding of human behavior has resulted in modifications of the logic experiment[27] and the binary choice experiment[11] by the introduction of the "thinking aloud" procedure. The simulation of concept formation has already produced several experiments designed to increase understanding of behavior in this area.[3, 17]

A second contribution of computer simulation is the understanding the researcher gains from specifying his ideas about behavior in the form of a computer program. If a researcher can explain to a group of people how a subject performs a certain task, then the researcher undoubtedly understands a great deal about human behavior in this task situation. The degree of understanding required for explanation to another person or group of persons, however, is generally insufficient for programing a computer to perform the task the way a human does. Programing a computer requires a precision and unambiguity in statement generally not required or provided in ordinary discussion or writing. Hence the method of computer simulation contributes to the study of cognitive processes by forcing the investigator to make a complete and precise statement of the cognitive processes required to perform a task.†

A third contribution of computer simulation to the study of cognitive processes results from the fact that complex models have become more tractable with the aid of the large, high-speed digital computer. Thus,

---

* For an early but still relevant discussion of this topic, see reference 33.
† Perhaps the time has come to add a phrase about the benefits of writing a computer program to Francis Bacon's aphorism "Reading maketh a full man, conference a ready man, and writing an exact man."

we are encouraged to study and construct rigorous models of those aspects of behavior, e.g., thinking and problem solving, that were heretofore often considered too complex for analysis. The presence of the computer not only makes possible the study of large, complex models but also encourages their construction, because the means for studying them is now at hand. Thus, we are encouraged, as in the binary choice case, to consider more complex cognitive models for behavior inadequately explained by previously offered simple models of conditioning and learning.

15.3.2 Some Problems of Computer Simulation. Although computer simulation has contributed to the study of cognitive processes, it also raises problems of its own. The problem of testing computer models, especially for the simulation of specific individuals, has already been discussed at some length. The problem of making inferences about cognitive processes from protocols has also been discussed but hardly solved. Duncker has warned us that protocols are generally not complete and that "[a] protocol is relatively reliable only for what it positively contains, but not for that which it omits." [7] Duncker has also provided us with some excellent examples of inferences drawn from protocols. The study of protocols is certainly not a simple process, however, and merits further investigation. The effect of the "thinking aloud" procedure on behavior is another problem that needs investigation. Colby [6] has recently shown that the mere presence of an experimenter affects the behavior of the subjects who are free-associating. How much more does the probing of the experimenter affect the problem-solving processes? Problems encountered in coding complex models for computers are numerous and difficult. List-processing languages have been widely used in simulations of cognitive processes, and these languages solve some of these problems. [12, 19, 28] Currently, work is going on to improve these languages and build computers that are more suitable for the simulation of cognitive processes than the currently available general purpose digital computers. [32] The present emphasis on the behavior of individuals in the simulation of cognitive processes has eliminated problems involved in the aggregation of behavior. Yet the behavior of specific individuals is of less interest than the general characteristics of behavior. The problem of finding these general characteristics from the programs for individuals also needs study. Thus, although computer simulation in its present form can contribute much to the advancement of our knowledge about cognitive processes, much work needs to be done in the development of the method.

15.3.3 Artificial Intelligence Programs. The work in the field of artificial intelligence, especially heuristic problem solving—in which researchers are programing computers to solve difficult problems without exhaustive searches, e.g., playing checkers,[31] playing chess,[23] balancing assembly lines,[36] and proving geometry theorems,[13]—also has some relevance to the study of cognitive processes. The artificial intelligence work differs from the work in computer simulation of cognitive processes in that the goal of artificial intelligence programs is only to solve the problem. There is no requirement that the artificial intelligence programs solve the problem in the same way that humans solve it. People, however, still probably constitute the best device for solving complex problems, and many artificial intelligence researchers have used their own problem-solving techniques as guides in the construction of their programs. Thus, some aspects of artificial intelligence programs are implicitly simulations of the programer's cognitive processes. Artificial intelligence programs also suggest hypotheses about problem-solving behavior. For an introduction to artificial intelligence programs, the reader is referred to the review articles by F. M. Tonge[35] and M. Minsky.[22] For an analysis of the relevance of an artificial intelligence program to the theory of human problem-solving behavior, see Newell, Shaw, and Simon.[24]

15.4   SUMMARY

The development of the modern high-speed digital computer has made possible the study of human cognitive processes by simulating these processes on the computer. This simulation requires the specification in the form of a computer program of the cognitive processes required to perform a task. The processes are then simulated by running the program on the computer. A computer model for the behavior of a subject in the binary choice experiment has been used as an example to illustrate (1) some of the consequences of computer simulation for the study of human cognitive processes and (2) some of the techniques that have been used in the construction and testing of computer models of cognitive processes.

REFERENCES

1 Anderson, N. H., and Grant, D. A., A Test of a Statistical Learning Theory Model for Two-Choice Behavior with Double Stimulus Events, *Jour. Exper. Psychol., 54,* 1957, 305–17.

2 Bush, R. R., and Mosteller, F., *Stochastic Models for Learning.* New York: Wiley, 1955.

3 Cahill, H., and Hovland, C. I., The Role of Memory in the Acquisition of Concepts, *Jour. Exper. Psychol., 59,* 1960, 137–44.

4 Clarkson, G. P. E., and Simon, H. A., Simulation of Individual and Group Behavior, *Amer. Economic Rev., 50,* 1960, 920–32.

5 Cohen, K. J., *Computer Models of the Shoe, Leather, Hide Sequence.* Englewood Cliffs, N.J.: Prentice-Hall, 1960.

6 Colby, K. M., Experiments on the Effects of an Observer's Presence on the Imago System during Psychoanalytic Free-Association, *Behavioral Science, 5,* 1960, 216–32.

7 Duncker, K., On Problem-solving, *Psychol. Monographs, 58* (No. 270), 1945.

8 Engler, J., Marginal and Conditional Stimulus and Response Probabilities in Verbal Conditioning, *Jour. Exper. Psychol., 55,* 1958, 303–17.

9 Estes, W. K., and Straughan, J. H., Analysis of a Verbal Conditioning Situation in Terms of Statistical Learning Theory, *Jour. Exper. Psychol., 47,* 1954, 225–34.

10 Feigenbaum, E. A., An Information Processing Theory of Verbal Learning, *P-1817.* The RAND Corp., 1959, and The Simulation of Verbal Learning Behavior, *Proc. of Western Joint Comp. Conf., 19,* 1961, 121–32.

11 Feldman, J., An Analysis of Predictive Behavior in a Two-Choice Situation. (Unpublished doctoral dissertation.) Carnegie Institute of Technology, 1959, and Simulation of Behavior in the Binary Choice Experiment, *Proc. of Western Joint Comp. Conf., 19,* 1961, 133–44.

21 Gelernter, H., Hansen, J. R., and Gerberich, C. L., A. Fortran-compiled List-processing Language, *Jour. Assoc. Computing Machinery, 7,* 1960, 87–101.

13 ———, and Rochester, N., Intelligent Behavior in Problem-Solving Machines, *IBM Jour. Research and Development, 2,* 1958, 336–45.

14 Heidbreder, E., An Experimental Study of Thinking, *Arch. Psychol., 11* (No. 73), 1924.

357

15 Hovland, C. I., Computer Simulation of Thinking, *Amer. Psychologist, 15,* 1960, 687–94.

16 ———, and Hunt, E. B., Computer Simulation of Concept Attainment, *Behavioral Science, 5,* 1960, 265–68.

17 Hunt, E. B., and Hovland, C. I., Order of Consideration of Different Types of Concepts, *Jour. Exper. Psychol., 59,* 1960, 220–25.

18 Jarvik, M. E., Probability Learning and a Negative Recency Effect in the Serial Anticipation of Alternative Symbols, *Jour. Exper. Psychol., 41,* 1951, 291–97.

19 McCarthy, J., Recursive Functions of Symbolic Expressions and Their Computation by Machine, Part I, *Comm. of ACM,* 1960, 184–95.

20 McGovern, P. J., Computer Conversation Compared with Human Conversation, *Computers and Automation, 9,* September 1960, 6–11.

21 Miller, G. A., Galanter, E., and Pribam, K. H., *Plans and the Structure of Behavior.* New York: Holt, 1960.

22 Minsky, M., Steps Toward Artificial Intelligence, *Proc. I.R.E., 49,* 1961, 8–30.

23 Newell, A., Shaw, J. C., and Simon, H. A., Chess-Playing Programs and the Problem of Complexity, *IBM Jour. Research and Development, 2,* 1958, 320–35.

24 ———, Elements of a Theory of Human Problem Solving, *Psychol. Rev., 65,* 1958, 151–66.

25 ———, Report on a General Problem-solving Program, *Information Processing,* Paris, UNESCO, 1959. Reprinted as A General Problem-solving Program for a Computer, in *Computers and Automation, 8,* July 1959, 10–17.

26 ———, Report on the Play of Chess Player I-5 of a Book Game of Morphy *vs.* Duke Karl of Brunswick and Count Isouard, *CIP Working Paper No. 21.* Carnegie Institute of Technology, Graduate School of Industrial Administration, 1959.

27 ———, and Simon, H. A., The Simulation of Human Thought, *Current Trends in Psychological Theory,* Pittsburgh: University of Pittsburgh Press, 1961, 152–79.

28 ———, *et al., Information Processing Language-V Manual,* Englewood Cliffs, N.J.: Prentice-Hall, Inc., 1961.

29 Reitman, W. R., Heuristic Programs, Computer Simulation, and Higher Mental Processes, *Behavioral Science, 4,* 1959, 330–35.

30 ——, Information Processing Languages and Heuristic Programs: A New Stage in the Bead Game, *Bionics Symposium* (WADD TR 60-600). Wright Air Development Division, Directorate of Advanced Systems Technology, Wright-Patterson Air Force Base, Ohio, 1960, 409–17.

31 Samuel, A. L., Some Studies in Machine Learning, Using the Game of Checkers, *IBM Jour. Research and Development*, 1959, *3*, 210–30.

32 Shaw, J. C., *et al.*, Command Structure for Complex Information Processing, *Proc. 1958 Western Joint Comp. Conf.*, 1959, 119–28.

33 Simon, H. A., and Newell, A., Models, their Uses and Limitations, *The State of the Social Sciences*, L. D. White, ed., Chicago: Univ. Chicago Press, 1956, 66–83.

34 Theil, H., *Economic Forecasts and Policy*. Amsterdam: North-Holland, 1958, 57, 162.

35 Tonge, F. M., The Use of Heuristic Programing in Management Science, *Management Science, 7*, 1961, 231–37.

36 ——, *A Heuristic Program for Assembly Line Balancing*. Englewood Cliffs, N.J.: Prentice-Hall, 1961, and, Summary of a Heuristic Line-Balancing Procedure, *Management Science, 7*, 1960, 21–42.

37 Turing, A. M., Can a Machine Think? *The World of Mathematics*, J. R. Newman, ed., New York: Simon and Schuster, *4*, 1956, 2099–2123.

38 Woodworth, R. S., *Experimental Psychology*. New York: Holt, 1938, 772.

Robert F. Simmons

16/SYNTHEX: TOWARD COMPUTER SYNTHESIS OF HUMAN LANGUAGE BEHAVIOR

*Robert F. Simmons was born
May 14, 1925, in Massachusetts. He
received his Ph.D. in industrial psychology
from the University of Southern California
in 1954. He worked for three years at
Psychological Services, Inc.,
in Los Angeles, primarily in research on flying
safety with USAF pilots and aircraft. The
subsequent two years were spent at Douglas Aircraft
developing computerized methods for
predicting man-hour costs of building
newly designed airplanes. For the past five years,
he has been employed at The RAND Corporation and
System Development
Corporation, where he is
currently doing research toward the development
of Synthex, a computerized system to
synthesize human language behavior.*

16.1 INTRODUCTION

Synthex is the name of a research project at the System Development Corporation. The project has as goals the development of research methodologies and vehicles for the eventual creation of a computerized system which will synthesize human cognitive functions, particularly in the area of human language behavior.

This chapter attempts to summarize the results of a wide body of research pertinent to the development of such a language synthesizer. It also outlines the major problems and methods of research involved in the construction of machine systems that will ultimately be successful in synthesizing language behavior.

16.1.1 *Language and Cognition.* The processes used by humans in their thinking, learning, and perceptual behaviors are a matter of never-failing interest to the psychologist. "How does a man know?" has remained a central question in psychology from the time of the Greek

361

similacra, through the associationists, introspectionists, behaviorists, even to this mid-twentieth century age of computer technology.

The questions "What does a man know?" and "How does a man learn?" have more frequently been studied by means of language in verbal types of testing instruments and in learning experiments with language materials than by any other methods. In rebelling against introspectionism, the early behaviorists threw out the subjective verbal report only to have it reintroduced as a class of behavior as much deserving of study as any other; and many of today's studies of thinking, of human perception, and of learning are equally interpretable as studies of the human use of language. Obviously not all of psychology can be encompassed by studying man's use of language, but to the extent that man uses his language to symbolize, to communicate, perhaps to remember, even to perceive much of his world, the study of human language behavior is the study of human cognition.

16.1.2 *Language and Action.* One great portion of the study of man not obviously related to his use of language is the whole area of motor skills, muscular behavior toward a particular end. But the release of a sequence of complex laryngeal behavior in phonation or the careful control of the myriad tiny responses required in writing or typing are examples of perhaps the most complex of all human motor skills. Most other motor skills can also be mediated by the use of language. Thus, to a significant extent, the study of language even includes the study of how particular words and sentences can be related to motor behavior.

It soon becomes apparent in the study of language behavior that if a psychologist could understand all aspects of man's use of language, he probably would in the process have developed a complete functional blueprint of the relations holding in the vast area between the stimulus input and the response. This functional understanding would be independent of the particular symbology or coding used by any given sense modality.

Such is the thesis of this study of language behavior. In the discovery of the functional relations necessary for transforming a language input to a language output for any given purpose, it is believed that, in symbolic form, the functions necessary for the transformation of any other behavioral input to output are being studied also. For example, if in hearing and answering a question, a subject must encode a sequence of sounds, correlate certain aspects of this string with stored information, evaluate the result, then recode it into an appropriate motor output, is it not reasonable to conclude that these procedures are typical of the functions used in reacting to a visually perceived situation?

16.1.3 *Synthesis and Simulation.* In synthesizing a complex molecule, the chemist builds it by combining elements or simpler molecules. If he is copying an existing material, the ideal result is a molecule alike in every particular to the one copied. If, as often is the case, he is attempting to construct a molecule that he calculates can exist, his success is measured by comparing his results with his computations (or even by the discovery of unexpected by-products).

Computer studies of human behavior fall untidily into both classes: the copying or simulation of human processes and the creation of other procedures not necessarily used by man to achieve a comparable output. Usually the term "simulation" loosely embraces both approaches (as well as a much broader area of mathematical modeling, war-gaming, etc.). This section draws a distinction believed to be important in furthering the progress of computer research on cognitive behavior. *Simulation* is used for work that explicitly attempts to copy or model the processes used by humans in their cognitive behavior. *Synthesis* is used for research aimed at the construction of systems which, given the same inputs as a human, produce outputs comparable in kind and amount. The synthetic system, in contrast to the simulated one, may use any convenient means to go from input to output and is not necessarily limited to modeling what is known or observable in human behavior. The method of synthesis has this advantage: the researcher is not limited by prevailing notions as to his procedures for attaining a behavior comparable to that of a human.

As in the Newell-Simon [25] simulation approach, it is argued here that a computer program, which accepts a human type of inputs and generates a product comparable to that of a human, using gross stages that are apparently similar to those of humans, will in itself be a testable theory of that human behavior. But since the resulting programs are based on a computer whose internal switching logic may be vastly different from that of the brain, a language synthesizer may turn out to be a functional analog of human language behavior only in the sense that a wheeled vehicle performs the function of locomotion. If this type of functional relationship is found, the synthesized system may have furnished a testable hypothesis about human behavior, but one later found to be invalid. Considering the success of the wheel and the airplane wing from a practical viewpoint, perhaps more is to be gained in the long run if computer-synthesized behaviors eventuate in ersatz rather than truly simulated human behaviors.

16.1.4 *Practical Usefulness for Language Machines.* One other sense of the word *synthesis* is important in the discussion of language-processing machines. Philosophers have long used the word to communicate the idea of combining separate elements of thought or sensation into a whole, of simple into complex conceptions. Such an idea is basic to any conceivable purpose to which a language machine might be oriented. The essence of any use of language appears to be the selection and recombination of ideas or objects symbolized now by one set of words and later by another. In practical application, a language-processing system faces the exceedingly difficult task of extracting and recombining concepts or meanings from widely varying sources, and synthesizing these into a reasonably concise response to a question or command.

The social value of language synthesizers lies in the potential creation of "thinking" systems of much greater memory capability than that of a single person. An ultimate language processor could be expected to store vast quantities of information, which might have been extracted from whole libraries of human endeavor. Depending on the degree to which these machines have a logic for creative synthesis of widely separated facts, they could routinely apply interdisciplinary discoveries from the entire breadth of science and scholarship to the answering of a question or the solving of a problem.

More immediately, many large bureaucracies are faced by ever-increasing communications problems in which the volume of written communications simply exceeds the capacity of the human executives. Scientific reports, market reports, progress reports, business summaries, etc., all flood the control arm of any large corporation. Even the daily business activities of cataloging, inventory control, and purchasing are to a large extent simple examples of language-processing tasks in which a vocabulary of numbers and a syntax of permitted combinations evolve into a new natural language of our age.

Recently Kellogg [18] outlined a fact retrieval machine which showed clearly how a language synthesizer could serve a factory executive by accepting written or graphic material and maintaining a capability of showing the entire picture, big or small, of the current operation, in response to questions in a special simplified language. Such machines obviously become of increasing importance as the complexity of an already vastly complicated economy continues to grow.

But perhaps the most important aspect of the eventual importance of language-processing machines lies in the capability of language to serve as a model, precise or rough as required, of any given set of experiences or actions. Just as the digital computer is a general purpose machine that can be connected between any input-output devices, so will the language synthesizer probably become a much more easily programed mediator between a human society and the work it wishes to accomplish at any given time. Already the current generation of compilers translates from problem-oriented languages close to natural English into the bits and operations of the computer. In some tomorrow, perhaps not so distant, the logic of the compiler-translator and the research in language processing will be merged into a computer with the wired-in capability of computing with natural language.

16.2   RESEARCH TRENDS

In the fifteen years that have seen computers become widely available, there has been a corresponding growth in attempts to use them to simulate or synthesize various aspects of human behavior. One is tempted to believe that almost every programer or computer engineer immediately senses a rough analogy between logic switching and thinking; the least sophisticated have been known to rush into print with remarkably inadequate descriptions of "mechanical brains" or "thinking machines." The literature, however, bears witness to an ever-growing number of computer-associated researchers who have paused long enough to formulate hypotheses about a particular behavior and who have then programed a computer in the attempt to duplicate that behavior and test their hypotheses.

16.2.1 *Simulation of Cognitive Processes.* A recent survey of attempts to simulate human cognitive processes on computers [35] found more than four hundred published articles. As many as half of these were theoretical formulations, verbal or mathematical; but almost as many described an already constructed system which in some manner appeared to duplicate complex human processes. It is both interesting and significant that more than half of these documents were written since 1958. (Figure 16.1 shows the exponential growth curve of this rapidly increasing literature.)

Although many of the techniques and findings developed by these researchers in the synthesis of cognitive processes are pertinent to the study of language behavior, lack of space must limit discussion of their findings to a few general statements. Gelernter,[12] Newell, Shaw, and Simon,[25] and Wang [39] have all been concerned from varying points of view with the development of program systems which can use heuristic methods or specially designed algorithms to prove geometric or logical theorems.

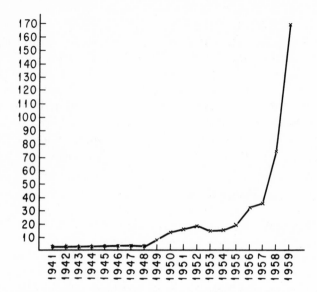

FIGURE 16.1 The growth of literature in the simulation of cognitive processes for 1941–1959.

Newell and Simon have generalized from their work to the development of GPS (*General Problem Solver*) which shows considerable promise as an approach to computerized problem solving. Also as an outgrowth of this work, Shaw and Simon [26] have built several versions of IPL (*Information Processing Language*) a list-structured programing system. This program serves to allow a general purpose computer to simulate a computer whose wiring makes easy many of the operations required in studying human cognitive behaviors.

The Rosenblatt Perceptron [33] and a large family of more practical pattern-recognition devices have demonstrated means by which computer-synthesized learning can be accomplished, particularly in a perceptual context. In regard to learning of the conditioned response type, a whole genus of machines exists. Interestingly enough, the earliest models of these predate computers and are to be found in the psychological journals of the 1930's. One historical curiosity is a hydraulic model of a nerve net system which had a limited capability to retain experience. S. B. Russell, an engineer, published this model, with careful drawings and explanation, in 1913 in the *Journal of Animal Behavior*.[34] (For more recent examples of learning machines the reader is referred to work by Ashby,[2] Walter,[38] Farley and Clark,[8] Friedberg,[10] Pask,[29] Uttley,[37] and Andrew.[1])

Since the main theme of this section is recent computer research in the area of language behavior, we must reluctantly ignore the highly instructive work in the development of chess, checker, bridge, and other game-playing systems and the whole area of the development of hardware to translate from printed or spoken patterns of language into bit patterns of use to the computer. For surveys of this work, see Fatehchand,[9] and for a definitive summary in the field of artificial intelligence, see Minsky.[23]

The remainder of this section will focus on current work in mechanical translation, information retrieval, recent linguistic and psychological research pertinent to language, and on a discussion of a few prototypes of general purpose language-processing machines.

16.2.2 *Mechanical Translation and Information Retrieval.* These two topics, each of which has its own fairly large literature, can be considered together as simply differing emphases in research on the computer processing of natural language. Researchers in each area are usually acquainted with work in the other and, in fact, often contribute to both. Together, the two fields include the bulk of present research in natural language processing and are a rich mine of hypotheses, programing techniques, and methods of approach to the synthesis of human language behavior.

The problems of mechanical translation have recently been described in detail by Oettinger [27] and by Reifler [32] and are further discussed by Hays in Chapter 17 of this book. In the information retrieval area, Bar-Hillel [3] has made a highly critical review of progress toward a theoretical understanding, with particular emphasis on the pitfalls into which he believes most researchers have already stumbled. For a general survey of current research in computer processing of language information, the National Science Foundation, *Current Research and Development in Scientific Documentation*,[24] periodically lists the work in progress in this and other countries.

The mechanical translation work began with the oversimplified hypothesis that, given a large enough bilingual dictionary, a computer could successfully substitute words from one language for words from the other and that the result would be a translation useful for some purposes. In fact, the early result turned out to be largely gibberish. It is still possible, however, to argue that, if the dictionary were so arranged that any word, phrase, or sentence in the one language had an appropriate correspondent in the other, mechanical translation would indeed be easy. But the completion of such a dictionary is an impossible task (because languages are open sets of words and sentences in which theoretically a new item may always be added to the existing set). Even the approximation of such a dictionary would be a task so vast as to be unfeasible. Moreover, every human translator knows that a vocabulary of words and a set of syntactical rules are a much more efficient approach to translation; but although every competent speaker of the language is proficient in the use of its grammatical or syntactic rules, not even the linguists or the grammarians have completely stated them.

The inadequate knowledge of these syntactic rules may be considered as the current major obstacle to successful machine translation of languages. As this barrier of syntactic ignorance yields to the attack of linguists and other researchers, an equally inadequate knowledge of the rules for forming semantic categories will probably become apparent. To date, it is generally believed that a thorough syntactic analysis will resolve problems of translating from a word with multiple meanings in one language to one of the many words which sometimes carry similar meanings in the target language. At least, today, the problem of selecting from multiple meanings is less bothersome than that of translating word sequences from one language to another.

The importance of mechanical translation to the synthesis of language behavior is threefold. One, the work itself is the first major example of computers processing language data in a way previously possible only to humans. Second, the work has generated a renewed interest in the detailed development of means for syntactically analyzing language and has been a major motivating force in the recent linguistic developments to be reviewed below. Finally, the language translation work has developed specialized research methods by which one may attack and eventually solve language problems with the aid of computers.

In the area of information retrieval, in contrast to mechanical translation, it appears that the major logical difficulty for computers is one of semantic or meaning analysis. Here the primary problem is to accept a request for a fact or a document, to search mechanized files for the terms stated in the request, and to deliver all, and only, those documents which the requestor considers pertinent. Unfortunately, many pitfalls lie between the requestor's desire and the retrieval system's response. Most of these difficulties are in the use of language.

For example, the requestor may be searching for literature on machines or systems that simulate human cognitive processes. Assume that the mechanized library contains all such documents that have been written.

Very obviously, the words, "simulated cognitive processes," have been used only infrequently in the titles (or for that matter, in the contents). Titles such as "A Machine that Learns," or "Teaching the Computer to Play Chess," or "A Theorem Proving System," will be far more frequent representatives of the genre desired. If a machine is programed to find synonyms, it will not only miss what the ingenious author has devised as a unique and attention-commanding title, but it will also begin to gather many kinds of irrelevant documents. And of course, to top off the difficulties, what the requestor really wanted might have been a group of mathematical articles on conditional probability machines. At any rate, discovering what the request is actually aimed at is a critical problem.

In response to these difficulties, information retrieval (henceforth, IR) researchers have developed several ingenious schemes for categorizing documents according to content words which some requestor might eventually use in calling for them. Luhn,[21] Edmundson,[7] Maron,[22] and Doyle [6] have all investigated properties of the automatic indexing and abstracting techniques originally developed by Luhn. In regard to automatic indexing, the findings appear fairly encouraging; by selecting those words which appear in the document more frequently than normal usage would predict, a set of content words useful for indexing can be obtained. Luhn's KWIC (*Keyword in Context*) Index [20] is an example of one simple but useful system for automatic indexing. Ohlman's permutation index is another. Both of these systems rely on cross-referencing titles by all possible content words in the title; thus "Teaching a Machine to Learn" would be found under, "Machine to Learn, Teaching," "Learn, Teaching a Machine," as well as under the author's title.

Further developments of automated indexing are currently being investigated. Doyle is studying the usefulness of indexing associative paths between words as discovered by computer analysis of their bivariate frequency in a set of documents. Maron is studying means of weighting index words according to empirical probabilities of their being used to call forth a particular document. Methods for evaluating the effectiveness of various indexing procedures have been studied and applied on small samples of literature by Cleverdon and by Swanson.[36] However, the comparative evaluation of various IR methods is still a matter for future resolution.

This chapter, however, is less concerned with the practical utility of various computerized IR approaches than with their implications for the synthesis of language behavior. These implications appear significant.

Automated indexing techniques hint at a direction of research that may allow computer processing of quantities of text toward the development of a fairly inclusive set of the semantic categories found in natural language. (This point will be developed further in Section 16.3.2.) Automatic abstracting techniques, which score each sentence in proportion to the number of a particular set of content words it contains, may be significant in the development of methods for evaluation of text as the computer selects an answer to a natural language question.

The particular emphasis of this section on automatic indexing and abstracting in IR research should not be interpreted to mean that these problems are at the heart of the IR problem. Nor should the preoccupation with semantic categories be understood to imply that IR does not have syntactic problems as well. To the contrary, the important work of Perry and Kent [30] at Western Reserve owes much of its success to their use of a limited syntactic analysis carried in "role indicators," which distinguish such terms as "ballistic missile" from the similar appearing but considerably different "missile ballistics." Probably, as appears the opposite of the situation in mechanical translation, the most important current problem in IR is semantic categorization and organization. As this problem approaches solution, one may expect the syntactic organization of language to assume ever-increasing importance.

16.2.3 Linguistic and Psychological Research.* In the field of linguistics, some important developments have occurred in the past few years. Most important of these appears the truly significant work of Zellig Harris [14] and his students at the University of Pennsylvania. Harris and Chomsky [5] have developed a means of syntactic analysis which on the one hand promises eventually to become a system and a mathematical model for the generation of many or all grammatical English sentence forms. On the other hand, the approach is being developed at Pennsylvania as a method of analyzing sentences in text into constituent grammatical structures and into "subsentences" and transformations. Harris's project is computer-oriented and he has so far succeeded in programing the UNIVAC to make a syntactic analysis ". . . adequate for the writing that appears in scientific articles. . . ." [24] Harris' work can be expected to yield methods useful to any language synthesizing system

---

* Although the important pioneering work of Thorndike and Zipf is not discussed here, the reader should be aware that their studies of language often underlie the researches cited.

both for analysis of input text and for the generation of output in grammatical English sentences.

At Indiana University, Householder and Lyons [17] are working on a systematic syntactic and semantic analysis of English with the aid of an electronic computer. They, too, report some success in the automation of methods of syntactic analysis, particularly in the area of computer determination of the syntactic function of words in the text. Other linguists, like Garvin and Oettinger, are working with the specific problem of mechanical translation and making significant progress toward computerized treatment of the structure of languages.

Osgood, [28] studying linguistic behavior from a psychological point of view, has developed a measuring instrument called the "semantic differential." By factor analyzing subjects' scaled evaluation of words, he measures the placement of each test word in a semantic space whose dimensions are the evaluation factors so extracted. Osgood's work has given rise to a significant number of psychological studies of various aspects of language usage by means of the semantic differential. A fairly remarkable consistency in factors underlying the evaluation of words has been found. Seemingly, factors named "Evaluation," "Potency," and "Activity" underlie most subject's ratings. To the synthesis of language behavior, the semantic differential suggests similar procedures as a possible means for finding other types of semantic categories.

Bruner, Goodnow, and Austin in their already classic *Study of Thinking* [4] suggest other important semantic categories. They are willing to argue that all cognitive activity depends on the formation of categories of events and the subsequent treatment of such categories. They distinguish carefully between concept formation, or the development of categories, and concept attainment, or the achievement of distinguishing features which separate categories from each other. Although the work of these psychologists is not directed precisely at the human use of language, it does show that one can hardly study human cognitive activity without learning more about the human's use of language in the process. The concept categories of Bruner serve equally well as concept or meaning categories for the use of language. And interestingly enough, one subclass of meaning categories includes those that deal with the structure of syntactic meanings or uses of words. Techniques of Bruner and of Osgood, useful in studying cognitive activity from their own particular emphasis, transfer easily to means profitable for the development of a language synthesizer.

Thus, from current linguistic research it becomes apparent that means for computer processing of syntax are almost developed to a practical state. Means for the formation and processing of semantic categories are suggested by some of the current studies in IR and in the psychology of thinking, but many key concepts are yet lacking for the computer synthesis of language behavior.

16.2.4 *Pseudo-cognitive Language Systems.* In the last two years, at least three programs have been started toward the development of general purpose language processing systems. Lindsay,[19] using one of the RAND Information Processing Language systems, has developed a computer program which analyzes English syntax and constructs a semantic model that makes explicit the implicit meanings of some words. His program is concerned with sentences about family relationships, such as father, mother, brother, etc. His syntactic analyzer, however, is designed to work with a very large class of sentences composed of Basic English words. His process, essentially, is to make a detailed syntactic analysis of sentences in such a manner as to clarify nouns, subjects, objects, and the particular grammatical relations existing among them. The semantic section of the program has routines which can work with the words, "mother, father, brother, sister, and offspring," using the results of the syntactic analysis to relate them to names that have been mentioned in the text. The program then "annexes" these names to appropriate branches of a hierarchical family tree. By the nature of the family tree structure, it is possible to infer that if John is the brother of Mary, and Mary, the daughter of Meg, Meg is the mother of Mary, Meg is the mother of John, etc.

The generality of Lindsay's reading machine can be seen to derive from the use of syntactic analysis as a means for developing semantic maps or models. Because these models represent in their structure a broad frame of relationships between the objects (or words) modeled, it becomes possible to deduce from the model more information than is actually given in any sentence that the system reads.

Another system based on a hierarchical classification of data is that of Green and Selfridge [13] which is now being programed to answer questions expressed in English about baseball scores. Their programs break into four parts; syntactic analysis, content analysis, data finding, and data processing of the answer. Their approach puts a heavy emphasis on the analysis of the question into a set of terms that call forth an appropriate sequence of routines which can extract pertinent data from the well-organized computer storage.

A third language processing system still in early stages of development is the author's Synthex system. The Synthex approach will attempt to develop a completely general data organization for the material read in a way such that the machine's store of information can grow as a function of the commands and questions given it and of the quantity of reading it does. Methods aimed'toward these hopeful goals and an example of the author's approach are to be found in the following sections.

The three systems outlined here and a few others, either less general or in earlier stages of progress, begin to show how the research findings from mechanical translation, information retrieval, linguistics, and psychological research can be integrated into general purpose language synthesizers. In passing, it is probably significant to note that both Green and Lindsay are psychologists and that Lindsay develops at considerable length the relationship of his work to the study of human cognitive processes with rather cogent suggestions for additional research on human subjects.

16.3 PROBLEMS IN COMPUTER LANGUAGE SYNTHESIS

In this section, problems associated with computer synthesis of the human ability to read, remember, organize information, and write statements in response to questions are examined in detail. For convenience, these problems are categorized into the three broad areas of syntactic analysis, logical analysis, and semantic analysis. Unfortunately, the problems are not so clearly distinct as the categories would imply, and it will often become apparent that there are complex interrelationships among each of the three areas. As means generally available for computer processing of language data are discussed, the distinction made earlier between computer synthesis and computer simulation of human behavior will be clarified. Methods found to be convenient and apparently necessary for computer solution of language problems will not always be those used or required by humans.

One important problem, the development of optical scanning devices for reading printed pages into the computer, is not considered in this section since it is adequately covered in Chapters 5 and 17. Print-reading devices reflecting several years of research in pattern recognition are already in advanced states of development and are likely to be readily available long before any language synthesizer is in use.

16.3.1 *Syntactic Analysis.* Why need a language be analyzed syntactically? People seem to read, write, and talk very adequately without necessarily being able to diagram a sentence or even to recognize parts of speech. In fact, the whole business of grammatical analysis is often to be summarized in an adult by some negative feelings toward a particular grammar teacher who insisted that a number of apparently arbitrary lines and subdivisions be superimposed on a sentence obviously much more meaningful without them.

In computer uses of language, the extent and type of syntactic analysis appears to be a function of the task. In information retrieval work of some types, the only use of syntax to be observed is the sequence of topic words in a request. If this sequence is preserved in the search, the use of syntax remains implicit. In mechanical translation where two languages differ significantly in grammatical structure, the syntactic relations in one must be translated to grammatical relationships in the other. The syntax of one language is related to that of another by analyzing both in terms of the sequence rules for combining categories that may be common to both, such as nouns, verbs, prepositions, subjects, objects, tenses, etc. For a reading and question-answering machine, syntactic analysis of questions is required at the very least to translate them into information retrieval commands. If the system is to do even such simple things as to find the noun to which a pronoun refers or determine major topics of a sentence, a fairly complete syntactic analysis is essential.

Syntactic analysis may be looked upon as the derivation of a structural interlingua between sentence organization and storage organization, or between question structure and the structure of information in memory, or between grammatical sequences in two languages. So from this viewpoint, unless the input-output language sequences are built into the storage and program organization, any language processing machine must undertake such syntactic analysis as is required to make a common linguistic structure for input, storage, and output.

16.3.1.1 *Syntactic Analysis—Word Class.* Underlying any grammatical analysis of sentences or larger units is the requirement that each word in the sentence be categorized into such word classes as noun, verb, pronoun, etc., or into some comparable categorization, such as Fries' [11] form-classes and function words. The practical value of word class is minimizing the number of grammatical rules needed for analyzing sentences. By dealing with all words that have certain grammatical functions in common as a single category, e.g., "nouns," it is often possible to ignore their differences in structure and meaning. This economy is particularly worthwhile in customary analyses of sentences where eight or nine word classes are generally found sufficient for most grammatical operations. Depending on the depth of analysis, however, some researchers in mechanical translation find it desirable to distinguish twenty or thirty different parts of speech. The new word classes account for certain, not too frequent, anomalies that grammarians have typically been willing to list as exceptions to their rules of analysis.

Computer assignment of word class to each word in a sentence is most frequently accomplished by dictionary look-up procedures. The dictionary used includes not only equivalent verbal meanings of each word, but also its part of speech, its possible inflections, and a host of other grammatical codes as well. Since a very large number of words in any natural language may be used as more than one part of speech, determining word class from a dictionary is not simply a matter of table look-up. Depending on position and sequence, or on tense and number, a very complex logic is required to make an adequate syntactic classification of the particular use of a word. Sometimes, too, the word cannot be classified until the context phrase or sentence has been partially analyzed at a higher level.

A second possible approach to identifying parts of speech without using a complete dictionary has some evidence in its favor. Some preliminary experiments by the author have given support to the hypothesis that human subjects can recognize parts of speech from grammatical context without the aid of cues from the word to be identified. The procedure in these experiments was that of blanking out the content words in a sample of text while leaving unchanged such grammar-loaded forms as prepositions, conjunctions, articles, and certain bound morphemes. For example, "These ____s also ____ the ____ to ____ ____ly along." *
The subject is required to identify the part of speech of each word that has been blanked out. Scores from a sample of five subjects on a fairly simple 500-word text ranged from 90 per cent to 99 per cent correct classifications. In addition, no error was common to all subjects. Finally, the subjects reported that the bound morphemes (such as ____ly or ____al) were often misleading and usually helpful only as secondary cues to confirm a hypothesis based on word sequences.

The direction of this evidence is toward the idea that if human subjects can indeed identify parts of speech with a high degree of accuracy without knowing the actual word involved, then it should be possible to determine the cues of sequence and sentence structure that they use and formulate them into a computer program to accomplish the same task. Such

* bristles, enable, worm, crawl, slowly

a program would work with a small dictionary of function words and sequence rules and allow the language processer to accept words it had never before encountered, without failing in its task of syntactic analysis.

16.3.1.2 *Syntactic Analysis—Sentences.* After the parts of speech or word classes have been recognized, it is possible and customary to break the sentence into such larger functional units as clauses, phrases, subjects, predicates, objects, and complements. Or for a particular purpose, the sentence may be transformed into a hierarchical tree structure of dependencies or of constituents. In general, the analysis at this functional level reveals what units of the sentence include what other subunits. Thus, in "The old man sat down," the subject is not *man,* but *old man,* and the predicate includes both the verb and its adverb. In most types of analysis found useful with computers, the tree structure would list *old* beneath *man,* and *down* beneath *sat,* to show these relations.

A general way of looking at English sentences is to conceive of them as sequences made up as follows:

SENTENCE
   Nominative (or noun phrase)
      Modifiers
      Complements
   Verbal (or verb phrase)
      Modifiers
      Complements

The *nominative* is a word or phrase acting as a noun. It may include other words, phrases, or clauses, which limit or add breadth to its meaning, in the form of modifiers or complements. The nominative may be the subject of a sentence, or the complement or the object of a verb, or the complement or modifier of another nominative. In a similar manner, verbs may be complemented or modified by other words or phrases. The modifiers and complements may each be made up of nominative-verbal units, etc., so that, theoretically at least, a sentence need never end. The task of syntactic analysis is separating out and making clear these and other types of relationships which hold among the words in a sentence.

A number of procedures for the analysis of sentences have been developed into fairly practical form by researchers in the language processing area. Among these, the *predictive analysis* methods of Ida Rhodes which have been further developed by Oettinger and the Harvard Mechanical Translation Group, [27] Zellig Harris' *kernel analysis* approach and David Hays' *dependency analysis* [16] all appear to be the quite general type of technique which can prove adaptable to many language processing uses. Each of these approaches exists in more or less usable form as a computer program system, and of course, none is so well developed as to handle anything approaching all possible structures of English.

16.3.2 Logical Problems. Logical aspects of language thoroughly permeate both the syntactic and semantic areas. On the syntactic level, Reichenbach devoted a long chapter of his *Symbolic Logic* [31] to the analysis of conversational language. He suggested that traditional grammatical analysis simply ignored many of the logical relations inhering in the structure of sentences. He proposed the beginnings of a grammar based on the calculus of functions. In such a grammar, a sentence like "The sky is blue," would be analyzed Blue (sky), where the parentheses indicate the simple following relationship: sky belongs to a category of blue objects. Another example is more to the point. "John gave the book to Jack"; is converted to Gave (John, book, Jack) to indicate the complex directional relationship of *John, book,* and *Jack* as determined by *gave.* Reichenbach believed that his approach could be generalized to give a grammar far more useful than those available from the usual formulas of grammarians.

Clearly, with a grammar in terms of logical functions, the propositional calculus would become more easily applicable to the determination of truth values of statements. The calculus of propositions can be considered in this light as a syntax of argument which studies the connective relationships between statements and furnishes principles for recognizing and testing the validity of deductions.

The word classes used by such a logical grammar would be quite different from the usual parts of speech. For example, the brother of, the father of, or the employer of, might all belong to different structural categories because they each predicate different relationships between subject and object. Such terms as *and, or, not,* the blanks between sentences, and a host of other connectives would occupy special categories in the grammar. And perhaps most important of all, the line between syntactic and semantic categories would obviously become a meaningless division.

This last point calls attention to two facts of importance in natural language and their grammars. Usually syntax is taken to include the rules for the categorization of parts of speech and the rules for the sequencing of parts of speech in sentences. But there appears to be a continuation of categorization and sequencing rules throughout the area of language usually considered as semantic. The rules are apparently implicit in natural languages for the formation of such semantic categories as synonymity, oppositeness, family relationship, and hierarchical relationship. Equally implicit are the rules by which semantic categories are combined into meaningful statements. So the first fact appears to be that in natural languages the difference between rules of grammar and rules of meaningful usage is simply that the former syntax has been made more explicit than the latter.

This principle explains the second fact mentioned earlier in this section that the indicators of logical conjunction and logical deduction are to be found both in the "grammar" and the "semantics" of a natural language.

As a consequence, from the customary linguistic viewpoint, the logician, for all his care in distinguishing function and content of words, seems to be dealing with a hodgepodge mixture of syntax and semantics. And from the logician's view, the natural languages are imprecise and undisciplined.

Thus, looking at language from Reichenbach's vantage point leads to a better understanding of the problems of syntax and semantics. A most important problem in semantics is the determination of the categories of meaningfulness and the rules for arranging meaning categories into meaningful statements. A second important problem is the discovery and inventory of the cues of language that serve as logical connectives and as signs of equivalence, subordination and superordination between words. Defining the language problem in these terms helps to guide the research effort through a largely unmapped semantic territory.

16.3.3 *Semantic Problems.* Semantic problems may be classified as either problems of word meanings or problems of the meanings of questions and sentences.

16.3.3.1 *Word Meaning.* To deal at all with semantics, it is necessary first, to find a referent or an operational definition of the term "meaning." For working with computers, the word has a number of convenient referents. In mechanical translation, the meaning of a Russian word is one of the English entries in a bilingual dictionary. In a question-answering system, the meaning of a word would be the subroutine it calls forth for a particular type of answering operation. In a general language-processing system, the meaning of a word might be a set of coordinates relating it to a hierarchical structure or meaning space. Generally, at least for computer operations, the meaning of a word is taken as a definition of what the computer does with it or because of it.

Words may have many meanings even when treated in the simplified sense described above. For example, in mechanical translation, there may be several entries in the dictionary. Which one is to be chosen? In the question-answering machine, the word *which* in a question may call forth a routine to find, evaluate, and rearrange data, whereas in a statement, *which* calls forth a subordinating conjunction routine to operate on the oncoming clause. How is a computer to select the appropriate meaning or action?

The answer tends to define *context*. The meaning of a word depends on its context, and dictionaries frequently give examples of the context in which a particular meaning applies. For the computer, a set of rules is required; e.g., "if the word is a Russian verb, select the second English equivalent, if a noun, select the third," or "if *which* is in a statement followed by a question mark, take routine 74; otherwise, routine 22."

In this manner, context will mean to the computer that it must determine to what categories a word belongs in order that it may select a particular meaning or action. Thus, the function and need for extended syntactic and semantic categories conjoined with appropriate action routines becomes apparent in any language synthesizer. And some of the most important of all problems in constructing such a system center on defining increasingly precise categories for operations on words.

16.3.3.2 *The Meaning of Questions and Sentences.* If the meaning of a word can be understood as the selection of a particular routine for storage or for action, what of the meaning of sentences and questions? Once again it must depend on the purpose of the machine. To a computer translator, the only meaning of a string of Russian words is to transform it into an English string according to its program. To such a computer, the meaning of a Russian string of words is the activation of an *appropriate sequence* of analysis and transformation routines. In the general purpose language synthesizer, a sentence may call forth several different sequences, depending on whether the machine is in a reading, writing, or question-answering mode. But the idea of meaning as an *appropriate sequence* of operations applies in every case, and the statement or question must be so analyzed as to reveal appropriate syntactic and semantic cues for the selection of operations to be performed.

With this view of meaning, a language synthesizer can be considered a system in which a string of input words is a set of events that map onto a meaning space whose coordinates might be the various modes of operation and whose metric might be in terms of categories which could call forth particular subroutines to operate on the input. Regardless of the model through which the system may be conceptualized, however, the significant problem remains of designing and programing a sufficient set of routines to do the various particular tasks which in their totality form the Gestalt of language behavior synthesis.

16.4   METHODOLOGY FOR SOLVING LANGUAGE PROBLEMS ON THE COMPUTER

A problem can generally be measured as easy or difficult not so much in terms of the number of operations required, but by completeness of the description available for those operations. Thus the building of an automobile or ten thousand of them is a complex but well-understood task which can be accomplished by unskilled labor following detailed instructions. On the other hand, the design of an automobile is a very difficult task insomuch as it requires a set of procedures which are not completely defined or completely describable. Both research in general and the designing of a language synthesizer obviously fall in the category of work whose operations are poorly defined.

Yet the basic principles of scientific method apply as much to computer research as to any other type and go far toward simplifying the task of the language researcher. In the language of systems science, the principles of scientific method form a feedback loop of hypothesis formation, hypothesis testing, hypothesis revision, retesting, and successive revision until deviations of reality from the hypothesized reality fall within tolerable limits. In the area of computer research on languages, workers have developed their own special variations of scientific method to make feasible the exceedingly difficult tasks in which they are engaged. These methods are more often used than formally discussed by researchers in the field,* but they are nonetheless basic to the successful accomplishment of their work.

16.4.1 *The Method of Simulation.* Underlying all the research on simulated or synthesized cognitive functions is the existence theorem of an organism which can accomplish the task in question. If an animal can solve a problem by a series of observable or semiobservable operations, why not also a machine? In conjunction with some understanding of how the neural control of organic behavior may be reduced to the action

---

* But see Hays [15] and Newell, Shaw, and Simon. [25]

of switching circuits, and the extent to which a general purpose digital computer can simulate any finite switching network, the simple, often poorly defined existence theorem rapidly comes to generate research hypotheses testable by building a computer program.

The Newell and Simon [25] protocol approach shows most clearly how this method works. Given a complex human behavior, such as problem solving, describe the behavior as precisely as possible by giving human subjects samples of the type of problem to be solved by the computer. Observe their behavior and obtain from them protocols describing in as much detail as possible the steps the subjects went through in coming to a solution. Reduce these descriptions to a sequence of binary decisions and the data which determined the direction of each, and the behavior is then described in terms amenable to computer programing. In the attempt to write the program, it often becomes apparent that the behavior has not been described adequately, so it then is necessary to observe more closely and to describe more thoroughly any neglected aspects of the behavior.

The simulation method, in an informal sense, appears basic to the writing of any computer program. What does a programer do except find an approach that he as a human can use to solve a particular problem and then translate it into a machine program? The technique must be completely described if a program is to be written, and it is validated by a program that accomplishes the task. The advantage of formulating the simulation approach via protocols as a formal method, and thus the significant contribution of Newell and Simon, lies in the researcher's being directed to a set of operations which eventually converge to a solution of his problem.

16.4.2 *The Method of Iteration.* Mechanical translation researchers have developed their own version of scientific method in application to their language problems. Although just as dependent on the procedures of humans, their method is not explicitly or necessarily the simulation of human behavior (except in the sense that any program records the programer's solution to a problem). This methodology can be seen clearly in the mechanical translation program of Hays (Chapter 17). The general approach could begin with a specialized Russian-English dictionary on magnetic tapes, a simple set of rules for assigning English prepositions to substitute for Russian case endings, and a program which examined each word in succession, looked it up in the dictionary, and printed the dictionary output on the translation tape. The output of such a translation system would be a hash of English in the sequence of Russian, and with all English equivalents listed for each Russian word.

By setting up a parallel system in which a human translator translates the same text, a criterion is obtained against which the machine output can be compared. Where the machine output falls short, the human editor attempts to write a rule to improve the system. This rule is then programed as an additional condition for words that fall in its category. Over a long enough period of time and a large enough sample of text, eventually a set of programs will be obtained that can translate the kind of text that the editor-computer system has experienced.

This iterative approach can set up a man-machine system that routinely improves itself as a function of experience. Although the computer does not learn, the editor continually modifies the program to minimize its errors. The computer serves as a high-speed hypothesis tester which continually tests the programs against an ever-increasing sample of situations. With the computer-editor learning system, it is usually desirable also to have special analysis routines which can make statistical summaries of all the translations of a particular word, or all the uses of a given rule or procedure, in such a manner as to simplify the editor's task of discovering under what circumstances the program failed and so to lead him in profitable directions toward correcting it.

16.4.3 *Methodology for Language Behavior Synthesis.* The protocol method of simulation and the iterative method of the language translator reduce to similar forms emphasizing slightly different aspects of a basic computer-researcher methodology. The simulation method emphasizes the formalization of means for developing hypotheses; the iterative approach is more concerned with the testing and improving of hypotheses. Together or singly, each method defines a research task in such a manner as to minimize wasted effort and almost to insure success if enough time and effort are expended. This section will attempt to demonstrate how the methods in combination apply to the problems of language behavior synthesis.

At the syntactic level of word class analysis, the approach presents human subjects with the problem of determining parts of speech for content words that have been blanked out of a sample of text.* Protocols with particular emphasis on the cues for word class recognition are then collected. These cues are translated into a program system which reads a

---

* See Section 16.3.1.1.

sample of text until it comes to a content word, then transfers to a table of routines associated with the preceding and following function words. On the basis of these routines or rules, the system tentatively assigns a part of speech, and reads until it reaches the next content word, at which it repeats its basic procedure. At the end of a sentence, the system tests for consistency (presence of noun and verb, absence of illegal construction, etc.). If inconsistencies are found, it applies alternate permissible rules until the sentence is consistent or until it runs out of rules. At the end of a run through a set of text, the program's diagnostic routines would compare the results with the editor-supplied criterion which showed the correct word-class assignments and would summarize and print out the errors made and the rules used in each case. The human editor is then in a position to analyze the errors and revise the program system.

A similar approach is obviously applicable to the more complex aspects of syntactic analysis. Fortunately, in the area of analysis of sentences, the language researcher can begin with a fairly well-tested computer logic and thus, by building on the shoulders of the considerable work already accomplished, shorten the number of iterations necessary to achieve a system that meets his requirements.

The methods apply equally well in the semantic areas, particularly in a question-answering system. The semantic problem, as discussed previously, is largely one of developing and organizing myriads of subroutines at both word, phrase, and sentence levels; inference routines (for example: "The king's name is George" = "King George," or "The eel is a fish" = "*eel* is a subcategory under *fish*"); routines for translating questions into retrieval requests; routines for scoring and evaluating data produced in response to a request; routines for making words into meaningful sequences; routines for casting sequences of words into grammatical statements; and hosts of special rules for varying basic systems in accordance with the categories to which the words belong.

But complex as the resulting system will undoubtedly be, it can be constructed program by program with the aid of an error feedback loop and editors to infuse the system with additional intelligence. As the example in Section 16.5 shows, a question-answering system can begin with a very simple logic and a small set of rules. As the system of editor and program gains experience, the rules become increasingly adequate and the failures less frequent. The output of the program, compared against the editor's criterion of what the answers should be, continually focuses effort on those portions of the system which are inadequate. By such means, eventually a large enough sample of question types can be answered adequately by the machine so that it gradually achieves the status of a useful language processer.

16.5   A SIMPLE QUESTION-ANSWERING MACHINE

As an illustration of how the methods described in the preceding section work, a simple question-answering machine that the reader can build with a card file is described below. Simple as the system is, it nevertheless shows how a computer can be simulated in a card file in the early stages of developing the logic of what may eventually become a very complex program system. By limiting the operations possible in the system to computations, comparisons, and transfers, the card file allows a researcher to develop the logic for programs needed to answer questions submitted in ordinary English.

First, a sample of English text is selected; for example, a one-page article about electric fishes. Each content word in the text is assigned a sequence number. The lowest sequence number is the first content word in the first article "read" to the machine; the highest sequence number is the last content word that has so far been "read" to the system. (It will later become apparent that certain advantages accrue from assigning the sequence numbers to sentences or paragraphs rather than to words.)

The card file is then constructed so that a card exists for each different content word that the system has experienced. On each card is a record (or index) of all the different sequence numbers in which the word occurred in the sequenced text. Additional cards are placed in the file for question-making words, such as *how, what, why, which,* etc. Under each such word is a list of rules for recognizing an answer to a question that it signifies.

Also on the card file in conjunction with each word is a growing list of cross references to other words in the file. These cross references are developed empirically as a result of discovering that if the question had used a different word, it could have found an answer.

To use the system the researcher (henceforth, the editor) takes a question that he (or preferably, someone else) has written, and converts it by simple syntactic rules into the form of a declarative statement that ends with the question words. For an example, "How powerful is the shock of an electric eel?" is transformed to, "The shock of an electric eel is how powerful." The means of the transformation in this case is a simple reversal of subject and predicate.

Shock	Electric	Eel	Powerful	How (Adj.)
4	4	20	63	_____ is _____ enough to
13	11	26	163	
11	19	34		_____ so _____ as to
56	22	42		
64	33	55		_____ as _____ as
80	41	112		
117	49	169		_____ is the most _____
132	67	174		
164	94			_____ is the least _____
167	104			
170	111			_____ is more _____ than
184	113			
188	131			_____ is less _____ than
	151			
	168			

FIGURE 16.2 Table of index records of content words.

The content words and the question word are then extracted as the key words for an information request. The index records for *shock, electric, eel,* and *powerful* are reproduced in Figure 16.2. This table also shows the rules that have so far been developed for distinguishing the answer to a "How (adj.)" question from other statements containing the key words. Figure 16.3 selects those sequence numbers that occur within 25 words of the occurrences of the critical word *powerful*, which was chosen as a reference point because it modified the question word and because it had the fewest number of references.

Shock	Electric	Eel	Powerful
51	41	42	63
56	49	55	
64	67		
80			
164	151	169	163
167	168	174	
170			

FIGURE 16.3 Intersection of content words in the question.

Figure 16.3 thus shows two ranges of text in which all four words of the question intersect. These are then extracted from the text in such a manner as to complete the paragraph at the beginning and the end and to find a referent for every pronoun. This procedure results in the statements in Figure 16.4.

1. The electric eel [19] [20] is a well-known electric fish. This fish is not really an eel. It gets its name because it is slender like an eel. Many electric eels grow to a length of eight feet and weight of 50 pounds. Electric eels are found in the Amazon and Orinoco rivers in South America.

The electric batteries, or shocking organs, are along both sides of the eel. The shock they give is said to be strong enough to stun a horse. It is the most powerful shock found among the electric fishes. Each battery is made up of tiny six-sided sections. Nerves run from these sections to the brain. If these nerves are cut, no shock [80] is given [81].

2. The electric catfish [151] [152], which grows to be about three feet long, is found in fresh water in Africa. This fish gives a powerful shock, almost as strong as the shock of the electric eel. But its shocking organs are quite different from those of the eel. They form a kind of greasy layer just under the skin. The fish can give off a number of very short shocks. Then it must eat and rest before it can continue its shocking habit. This fish has been found in Egyptian pictures that are more than 4,000 [196] [197] years old.

** The superscripted numbers are the content word sequences; the underlined words are the content words in the example question.

FIGURE 16.4 Response to information request in question. (Reprinted from the Golden Book Encyclopedia, Volume 5, by Bertha Morris Parker and Staff. Copyright 1959 by Golden Press, Inc.)

The human reader easily sees that the first of the two statements contains an answer. This answer is: "The shock of an electric eel is strong enough to stun a horse. It is the most powerful shock found among the electric fishes."

By finding those paragraphs which contained an intersection of all the question terms, the simulated computer provided two statements which might contain answers to the question. Unfortunately, the logic for determining which statement, if either, contains an answer is very complex. Notice that what the first statement actually contains is, "The shock they give is said to be strong enough to stun a horse. It is the most powerful shock found among the electric fishes"; *they* refers back to, "electric batteries give the shock said to be strong enough to stun a horse, etc." In the second statement, *this fish* refers back to the electric catfish which gives a powerful shock. Thus there is no simple statement that tells how powerful the shock of an electric eel is, and the rules under "How (adj.)" do not apply.

Any simple rule for selecting the statement in which shock of the electric eel is the subject predicating *powerful* immediately fails by rejecting both statements. A rule is needed that will allow the system to synthesize the information that (1) the shocking organs found along both sides of the eel give shocks; (2) the shocking organs give shocks strong enough to stun a horse; (3) *strong enough* is a measure of *how powerful*.

The preposition *of* in *shocking organs of the eel* allows the editor to formulate a rule that "if a subject term is in an 'of' relationship to a term in the question, the latter term may be substituted for the former." The editor also cross-references *strong* and *powerful*.

As a result of applying the newly formulated rules and of having substituted antecedents for pronouns, the first statement is computed to read, ". . . the *shock* (*electric* batteries or *shocking* organs $=$ they $=$ *eel*) give is said to be *strong enough to* stun a horse. [It $=$ the *shock* (*electric* batteries or *shocking* organs $=$ *eel*) give] *is the most powerful shock* found among the *electric* fishes. . . ." The first statement now contains two sentences in which not only do all four terms intersect, but in which the predicates include *enough to* and *is the most,* both of which have previously been determined as conditions for answering a "How (adj.)" question (see Figure 16.2). The system can now select the first statement, or the particular sentences in it, as answering the question. A validation test of the editor-devised rules occurs every succeeding time one of the rules is used for answering a question.

Thus by failing a question, the system focused on a worthwhile problem for the editor's attention and forced him to write a rule of inference for use by the program. As the set of rules grows, some validated by additional questions, some found wanting and eventually rejected, the computer-in-a-box accumulates the design for a true computerized question-answering system. Eventually a point is reached at which the original sequence-organized memory system may become too cumbersome, but by that time the difficulties which define cumbersome will probably also have indicated the direction for improvements.

Some readers may have wondered whether there may not be simpler methods for selecting the statement which contains the answer to the question. For example, an application of Luhn's logic for weighting content words comes quickly to mind. Although a simple count shows that the content words of the question are more frequently represented in the second statement (which does not contain an answer) than in the first (which does), it appears that an iterative method could equally well be applied to the development of statistical criteria for distinguishing the two. Sooner or later, however, a statistical weighting approach not based on the syntax and semantic rules of language would almost certainly reach a limit far short of the precision of word meaning and grammatical cues for signaling the answers to questions.

Even more important, the research goal in this work is a system that synthesizes human language behavior. To achieve an eventual synthesis at a level at all comparable to the level of humans, it will unquestionably be necessary to use as many as possible of the cues to meaning that language provides. Thus, even at the beginning, it is important that a language synthesizer take the most general approach possible.

16.6 SUMMARY

From the wealth of ideas and research findings in the area of simulated cognitive processes and research on language, this chapter has attempted to present a detailed picture of the procedures and progress toward the goal of a computer system synthesizing human language behavior. From work on the computer simulation and synthesis of learning, pattern recognition, problem solving, theorem proving, etc., it can be concluded that these types of cognition are possible, although not necessarily efficient, on computers. They have furnished numerous ideas and programing methods for use in a language synthesizer.

Mechanical translation and information retrieval researchers have already come to grips with the problem of computer processing of natural languages. Their methods and their solutions for some language problems are directly applicable. The recent work of linguists in developing new methods of syntactic analysis and of psychologists in studying meaning categories has many implications for the present purpose. A few researchers have already set their goals toward a prototype of a language-synthesizing machine and have made some progress toward it.

But the problems associated with the actual construction of such a machine are more apparent than are their solutions. There exist problems of recognizing parts of speech, of making syntactic analyses, of logical inference on the basis of syntactic and semantic structures, and a myriad of problems concerned with the meaning of words and sentences.

Yet the plentitude of problems is no insuperable obstacle. The existing computer research on languages and on the synthesis of cognitive processes has developed specialized methodologies whose use goes far toward insuring eventual success. These methods are offshoots of the basic scientific methodology and, like it, are characterized by the recursive process of formulation, testing, reformulation, and retesting of hypotheses until the hypothesis is well supported by the reality. These methods use the computer as a hypothesis tester and as a data-summarizing tool to direct a human researcher toward profitable revisions of his ideas by showing him just where his program fell short. A combination of the Simon-Newell protocol method of simulation and the iterative method of the mechanical translators is seen to provide a basic approach to the synthesis of language behavior.

The question-answering machine on index cards provides a simulated computer which can serve not only to demonstrate the methodological approach, but also to accumulate the design features necessary in actually programing a system to synthesize language behavior. As it stands, the question answerer can be represented in a computer very simply in the form of an index tape of content words and a memory tape which records seriatim the text that has been so far read. The procedures for tape look-up and for detailed processing of the recovered text according to a table of rules would constitute the program. By iterative modification of the table of rules and of the cross referencing of the index tape, the system would, over a period of time, achieve practical value in answering questions difficult enough to challenge humans.

How long a time will elapse until these research efforts do result in practical language-processing machines is still a matter of guesswork. But interest in the problem continues to increase, and even relatively small research efforts are almost daily uncovering important new findings. Since the potential value of the resulting systems is obviously very great, the trend toward increasing amounts of work aimed at the problem will probably continue to grow over the years. If the frequently observed exponential curve of scientific progress applies to this field, perhaps practical and useful examples of machines that synthesize language behavior are much closer than we think.

Quite apart from the ultimate development of useful language synthesizers is the psychological importance their construction implies for an increased understanding of human thinking processes. Each time a question is transformed into a set of rules for computing a response, each time the pattern of inference in a sequence of words is translated into a program for drawing a conclusion, something will have been learned about the functional processes of thinking. Whether the knowledge so gained is about human thinking or about machine thinking, it will unquestionably generate hypotheses whose testing on human subjects will advance our understanding of human cognitive processes. Thus it is believed that

Synthex, and other research projects devoted to the synthesis of human language behavior on computers, are important avenues down which psychologists are progressing toward answers for the ancient question, "How does a man know?"

REFERENCES

1 Andrew, A. M., Learning Machines, *Symposium Mech. Thought Proc.*, London: Her Majesty's Stationery Office, 1958, *1*, 475–505.

2 Ashby, W. R., The Mechanization of Habituation, *Symposium Mech. Thought Proc.*, London: Her Majesty's Stationery Office, 1958, *1*, 95–113.

3 Bar-Hillel, Y., Some Theoretical Aspects of the Mechanization of Literature Searching, *Tech. Report No. 3*, Jerusalem: Hebrew University.

4 Bruner, J. A., Goodnow, J. J., and Austin, G. A., *A Study of Thinking.* New York: Wiley, 1956.

5 Chomsky, N., *Syntactic Structures.* The Hague: Mouton and Company, 1957.

6 Doyle, L. B., *Semantic Road Maps for Literature Searchers, SP-199.* System Development Corp., 1961.

7 Edmundson, H. P., Oswald, V. A., Jr., and Wyllys, R. E., *Automatic Indexing and Abstracting of the Contents of Documents, PRC R-126,* ASTIA AD No. 231606. Los Angeles: Planning Research Corporation, 1959.

8 Farley, B. G., and Clark, W. A., Simulation of a Self-organizing System by a Digital Computer, *I.R.E. Trans. Inf. Theory, 4,* September 1954, 76–84.

9 Fatehchand, R., Machine Recognition of Spoken Words, *Advances in Computers,* F. L. Alt, ed., New York: Academic Press, Inc., *1,* 1960, 193–229.

10 Friedberg, R. M., A Learning Machine, I, II, *IBM Jour. Research and Development, 2,* January 1958, 2–13; *3,* July 1959, 282–87.

11 Fries, C. C., *The Structure of English.* New York: Harcourt Brace, 1952.

12 Gelernter, H., and Rochester, N., Intelligent Behavior in Problem-solving Machines, *IBM Jour. Research and Development, 2,* October 1958, 336–45.

13 Green, B. F., Jr., and Selfridge, O. G., in Nat'l Science Foundation, *Current Research and Development in Scientific Documentation* (No. 7). Washington, D.C.: U.S. Government Printing Office, 1960.

14 Harris, Z. S., Linguistic Transformations for Information Retrieval, *Proc. Int. Conf. on Sci. Inf.,* Washington, D.C.: Natl Acad. Sciences–Natl Research Council, 1959, 937–50.

15 Hays, D. G., with Edmundson, H. P., Studies in Machine Translation —2: Research Methodology, *RM-2060*. The RAND Corp., 1957.

16 ———, Studies in Machine Translation —10: Russian Sentence-Structrue Determination, *RM-2538*. The RAND Corp., 1960.

17 Householder, F. W., Jr., and Lyons, J., Third Quarterly Report on the Automation of General Semantics, Indiana Univ., 1960. (Mimeo.)

18 Kellogg, C., The Fact Compiler: A System for the Extraction, Storage, and Retrieval of Information, *Proc. Western Joint Computer Conf.*, 1960, 73–82.

19 Lindsay, R. K., The Reading Machine Problem. Unpublished doctoral dissertation, Carnegie Institute of Technology, 1960.

20 Luhn, H. P., Keyword in Context Index for Technical Literature (KWIC Index), *ASDD Report, R. C-127*. IBM Corp., 1959.

21 ———, Auto-encoding of Documents for Information Retrieval Systems, *Modern Trends in Documentation*. (Proceedings of a Symposium held at the University of Southern California, April 1958.) New York: Pergamon Press, Ltd., 45–48.

22 Maron, M. E., and Kuhns, J. L., On Relevance, Probabilistic Indexing, and Information Retrieval, *Jour. Assoc. Computer Machines, 7* (No. 3), July 1960, 216–44.

23 Minsky, M., Steps toward Artificial Intelligence, *Proc. I.R.E., 49* (No. 1), January 1961, 8–30.

24 National Science Foundation, *Current Research and Development in Scientific Documentation* (No. 7), NSF 60–65. Washington, D.C.: U.S. Government Printing Office, 1960.

25 Newell, A., Shaw, J., and Simon, H., Elements of a Theory of Human Problem Solving, *Psychol. Rev., 65,* May 1958, 151–66.

26 ———, *et al.* and Tonge, F. M., An Introduction to Information Processing Language V, *Jour. Assoc. Computer Machines, 3,* April 1960, 205–11.

27 Oettinger, A. G., *Automatic Language Translation.* Cambridge, Mass.: Harvard Univ. Press, 1960.

28 Osgood, C. E., Suci, G. J., and Tannenbaum, P. H., *The Measurement of Meaning.* Urbana, Ill.: Univ. of Illinois Press, 1957.

29 Pask, G., Physical Analogues to the Growth of a Concept, *Symposium Mech. Thought Proc.* London: Her Majesty's Stationery Office, *2,* 1958, 879–922.

30 Perry, J. W., and Kent, A., *Documentation and Information Retrieval.* New York: Western Reserve Univ. Press and Interscience Publishers, Inc., 1957.

31 Reichenbach, H., *Elements of Symbolic Logic.* New York: Macmillan, 1947.

32 Reifler, E. R., *et al., Linguistic and Engineering Studies in Automatic Language Translation of Scientific Russian into English, Phase II.* Seattle, Wash.: Univ. Washington Press, 1960.

33 Rosenblatt, F., The Perceptron: A Probabilistic Model for Information Storage and Organization in the Brain, *Psychol. Rev., 65,* March 1958, 386–407.

34 Russell, S. B., A Practical Model to Simulate the Working of Nervous Discharges, *Jour. Animal Behav., 3,* 1913, 15–35.

35 Simmons, P., and Simmons, R., The Simulation of Cognitive Processes: An Annotated Bibliography, *I.R.E. Trans. Electronic Computers,* September 1961.

36 Swanson, D. R., Searching Natural Language Text by Computer, *Science, 132* (No. 3434), Oct. 21, 1960, 1099–1104.

37 Uttley, A. M., The Design of Conditional Probability Computers, *Information and Control, 2,* April 1959, 1–24.

38 Walter, W. Grey, *The Living Brain.* London: Gerald Drechworth & Co., 1953.

39 Wang, H., Toward Mechanical Mathematics, *IBM Jour. of Research and Development, 4,* January 1960, 28–35.

David G. Hays

17/AUTOMATIC LANGUAGE-DATA PROCESSING

*David G. Hays received his doctorate in sociology
from Harvard in 1956. His field of special interest was
small group research (e.g., the study of families,
conference groups, teams); his thesis concerned the development
of a mathematical model for social interaction. He spent
the year 1954–55 as a Fellow at the Center for Advanced Study
in the Behavioral Sciences, an independent organization
endowed by the Ford Foundation in Stanford, California.
He has been with The RAND Corporation since September 1955
and was initially involved in interaction research,
attitude measurement, etc. Since 1957, he has been leader of
the project on machine translation and linguistic research and is
helping to prepare a series of RAND research memoranda on
machine translation—six papers have already been released.*

Automatic Language-Data Processing (ALDP), as Bar-Hillel has re-marked,[1] should be discussed in hypothetical sentences: "A machine-translation (MT) system, if one existed, would probably consist of input and output devices, a dictionary, a grammatic-analysis program, a se-mantic-analysis program, and corresponding synthesis programs." But hypothetical language is unwieldy; I shall use direct statements for sim-plicity, despite their unrealistically vivid tone. At the close of 1960, there did in fact exist—as reels of magnetic tape—several MT programs ca-pable of translating from one natural language to another.* Whether those programs yielded adequate products was a matter of sometimes

---

* Produced, for example, at Harvard University, Georgetown University, The RAND Corporation, Ramo-Wooldridge Division of Thompson-Ramo-Wooldridge, Inc., and IBM. Cf. *Current Research and Development in Scientific Documenta-tion*, National Science Foundation.

vitriolic dispute.* The word *translation* has in fact been used to cover
the best and the worst; let us admit that the 1960 systems did translate,
but realize that they did not translate very well. The hypothetical systems
that concern us here will (or would) do better.

MT is not the whole, of ALDP. It is, however, the earliest species to develop and probably the simplest. Reasonably good translations seem to
require little or nothing more than knowledge of grammar, whereas indexing and abstracting seem to require much more, and the increment
must be drawn from the terra incognita of semantics (nor is this the
only metaphor that has been used to emphasize the degree of difficulty in
semantic exploration; the subject was once described as "a monster sitting
on a blank wall"). Other subfields of ALDP intersect more crucially
with psychology: automatic content analysis of novels and editorials, of
discussion-group transcripts, of field and clinical interviews lies just ahead,
although grammar and semantics would have to be supplemented by
analysis of the psychological functions of language before automatic content analysis could be put into practice.[7]

17.1 MACHINE TRANSLATION

The input is a document in a natural language, such as English, Russian,
French, or German. The output is a document in another natural language. Between input and output, the system is initially unspecified; it
may, but it need not, imitate the successive steps by which a human translator would do the same job. This freedom, incidentally, is fortunate,
since no one knows how translation is performed in the brain. In an
MT system, the first step is to "read" the input document, i.e., to put it
into computer-accessible form. The second step is dictionary look-up; the
third, syntactic analysis; the fourth, syntactic synthesis; and the last is
printout. More steps may prove to be needed for better quality. Between the third and fourth, for example, semantic analysis and synthesis
may be needed.

17.1.1 *Input and Output*. The classical input device is a keypunch
machine, which has a keyboard like that of an ordinary typewriter. In-

* For example, at a National Symposium on Machine Translation, held at the University of California, Los Angeles, in February 1960. The *Proceedings* are being
published by Prentice-Hall, Inc., under the editorship of Harold P. Edmundson.
Also see House Committee on Science and Astronautics, *Research on Mechanical
Translation*, 86th Cong., 2d sess., 1960.

stead of printing characters on a page—or in addition to printing them— it punches holes in a card or tape, or records spots on magnetic tape. Machines now in commercial use automatically scan printed characters and punch cards or tape without human intervention.[25] These machines, unfortunately, are restricted to special characters, such as those on many oil-company credit cards (see Figure 17.1). These characters are designed for easy automatic reading, and only ten of them have to be distinguished. To identify characters designed for easy human reading, and to distinguish each of several hundred characters, is more complicated and bound to be more expensive. Nevertheless, automatic full-scale print readers are being developed.[22] Their coming will reduce the cost of MT and all ALDP applications, perhaps to a level that many commercial and research organizations can afford.

FIGURE 17.1 Scanning special characters—oil company credit card. (Courtesy of Farrington Electronics, Inc.)

For some purposes, print reading is unnecessary. If a book or journal was set in type with a Monotype machine, or if a newspaper or magazine was transmitted by teletype, a punched paper tape was created in the process. The ALDP operator need only obtain the tape and convert it to a form that his computer can accept. Obtaining tapes is easy or difficult, depending on the attitude of the publisher; converting them is conceptually simple, but requires a special-purpose device.[23]

One other difficulty lies in the number of characters and formats available in a computer. Alphanumeric machines usually represent each character with six bits, and they are therefore limited to 64 characters ($2^6 = 64$). Any printer's font has more characters—even a typewriter has 84—and a book or journal is printed in several fonts. Furthermore, although linear order of the individual characters is a good first approximation to the way characters are printed, linear order is not an absolute restriction to a good printer. Many a displayed equation (see Figure 17.2), or even a sequence such as X_{min}, can cause trouble in a computer

Согласно (7), E_N, $|\mathbf{p}_N|$, E_l, E_v выражаются через X и J по формулам

$$E_N = m_N + \frac{m_Y - m_N}{1 + \xi}\, \xi\,(1 - J),$$

$$|\mathbf{p}_N| = \frac{m_Y - m_N}{1 + \xi}\, X_m\,(J) = \frac{m_Y - m_N}{1 + \xi}\, \sqrt{(1 - J)(1 - \xi^2 J)},$$

$$E_l = \frac{m_Y - m_N}{2\,(1 + \xi)}\left[(1 + \xi J)\left(1 + \frac{\eta}{J}\right) + X\left(1 - \frac{\eta}{J}\right)\right],$$

$$E_v = \frac{m_Y - m_N}{2\,(1 + \xi)}\,[1 + \xi J - X]\left(1 - \frac{\eta}{J}\right).$$

FIGURE 17.2 Scanning mathematical equations.

that can take characters only one by one. (Linguistically, the subscript "min" does not follow the character to which it is attached, but in computer storage it must follow.)

Output devices have been automatic since the 1930's. They use bars, wheels, drums, or chains filled with precast characters, printed with hammer strokes from behind the paper. They use cathode ray tubes and photosensitive paper or film. They use matrices of wires, whose tips can be energized in various patterns to print characters electrochemically. But they are customarily limited to the same range of characters that can be stored. Two problems, therefore, need special attention in ALDP. First, more characters are required in a standard font than are supplied for numerical calculation. Second, since printers can cast new type for special purposes, an end-run technique—going directly from input to output with a *picture* of the printed character—is needed. The special character presumably need not be translated, abstracted, or otherwise analyzed; only its shape is wanted. With these two features, the output device is prepared for ALDP.

One other input problem deserves mention. The automatic system of the future should have an input hopper, served by the postman. A machine is needed to open the mail, spread and turn the pages, and present them to the print reader. Such a machine will not be cheap to design or construct, but its details have little relevance to psychology. Neither, for

that matter, do the other aspects of input and output, which can therefore be dropped at this point. It is worth knowing, however, that practical ALDP in the psychological laboratory depends on more than sound
linguistic research.

17.1.2 *Dictionary Look-up.* ALDP systems use dictionaries because
there is no cheaper way to compute the meaning of a word from its alphabetic composition than by table look-up. If the meanings of sentences
cannot be computed in the same way, it is only because there are too many
sentences for convenient tabulation. But the number of words in a language at any given time is not too large for computer storage (provided
that the programer is clever, or that the largest available storage devices
are used), and the rate of growth of the vocabulary of Russian, say, is
not too large for a reasonable lexicographic staff to handle.

As text reaches the computer, it consists of a simple sequence of characters. Let us divide the characters arbitrarily into *letters,* marks of *punctuation,* and *spaces.* There may also be numerals and special symbols, such
as *equal signs,* etc., but these can be neglected for the present purposes.[18]
Dividing the text into sub-sequences at all spaces and marks of punctuation converts it into a sequence of *occurrences* of *forms.* An *occurrence* is
a sequence of letters preceded and followed by spaces or marks of punctuation. A *form* is a kind of occurrence distinguished by spelling from all
other forms. Thus occurrences have definite locations in texts; forms
occur in texts, and they are listed in dictionaries.

A dictionary that lists forms is unusual, however. The typical published
dictionary lists a representative form of each word. A *word* is, roughly
speaking, a set of inflected forms having a common base. For example,
the word *take* is listed only once and represented by its form *take.* But
the word *take* includes several forms: *take, takes, taking, took,* and *taken.*
With a regular English word like *walk,* the base is more obvious than with
take:

walk–	take–
walk–s	take–s
walk–ing	take–ing = taking
walk–ed	take–ed = took
walk–ed	take–en = taken

The present tense form is identical with the base (*walk, take*), having a
zero ending. The third person singular present tense form adds –*s* to the
base (or –*es* to a base like *wish*). The present participle adds –*ing,* drop-

ping final –*e* from stems like *take,* but not from stems like *see.* The past tense form adds –*ed,* sometimes dropping an –*e* from the base or doubling a final consonant (*flitted, averred*). The past participle form is sometimes distinct from the past tense form, as with *took* versus *taken,* but with some verbs the same ending is used for both forms, as with *walked, walked.* There are some irregularities in the conjugation of English verbs, but not very many.[10] And when new verbs are coined, unless they are compounds of irregular verbs or show strong analogy to an irregular verb, they are regular; i.e., they follow the pattern of *walk.*

The study of form-word relations is a branch of grammar called "morphology." Linguists, who have converted the study of grammar from art to science, would reject this definition for technical reasons that are quite valid but not germane to the present discussion. We can at least say that the usefulness of morphology in ALDP is primarily in dictionary look-up, and whether it is required for that purpose hinges on the format of the dictionary. Are *words* or *forms* to be stored?

Every human being (pathological cases excepted) has a practical knowledge of the morphology of his native language and of any foreign language than he can speak with a minimum of fluency. He uses that knowledge whenever he turns to a dictionary, since he must shift internally from whatever *form* he has in mind to the *word* to which it belongs before he can find the appropriate entry. In his native language, the human dictionary user applies morphological operations unconsciously, but the native speaker of English who has only an elementary knowledge of German may be painfully conscious of the operations by which a form can be associated with a word. If the entries in an ALDP dictionary are to be words or bases rather than forms, those operations must be painstakingly programed.[19]

The programing and operating costs of automatic morphology must be recouped in less expensive programing and operation, thanks to the smaller size of a word dictionary. In English, the word-form ratio is perhaps 3:1 or 4:1. In Russian, 10:1 is possible.[16] Such a reduction cannot be gainsaid when a million bases may have to be stored. Several Russian deinflection programs were in operation at the end of 1960, with others planned; * one of them could be adopted by the designer of a new system.

---

* For examples, see the National Science Foundation *Current Research and De-velopment in Scientific Documentation.*

One simple technique stores bases with cross references to ending sets. With the base *walk,* for example, the ending set $(-\theta, -s, -ing, -ed, -ed)$ would be referenced. (Here θ denotes the zero ending of the present-tense form.) An occurrence of the form *walked* would be identified in two operations. The left-hand portion is matched against the base list to find the longest available base first.* When *walk* is found, a reference to an ending set is picked up. The remainder of the occurrence is matched against the endings in the referenced set. If a match is obtained, the base and ending are taken as components of the form that occurred, and the information about them both is read out of the dictionary. If no ending is matched, the search for a base is resumed. If another, shorter base is matched, another set of endings must be searched. If no base-ending combination is matched, the form is not represented in the dictionary.

As described here, the base-and-ending-set method is only economical on a machine that can store the whole base list in high-speed random access memory. A variation makes the plan economically feasible on any machine with reasonable memory size and high-speed buffered tapes.[11] This plan is logically simple and therefore easier to program than some others. Like the others, it requires that irregular forms (e.g., *took*) be listed among the bases.

When an occurrence in text has been correlated with an entry in the dictionary, information is read out. Everything depends on the completeness and accuracy of that information, since all further programs in the ALDP system rely on it. For our hypothetical MT system, the stored information must include a grammatical description of the input-language form, one or more output-language equivalents, and grammatical descriptions of the equivalents. What kinds of information are needed, and how the information should be stored, will be more obvious after the next programs have been described.

17.1.3 Syntactic Analysis. Almost every high school graduate has parsed sentences in his native language. Thus everyone should know that sentences have structures. Grammar consists of morphology, dealing with the internal structures of forms, and *syntax,* which treats of their occurrence relations in sentences. Syntax is taught as a set of rules, but the rules that can be covered in high school are not exhaustive. Many more rules are learned implicitly, by reading and listening. The scientific study of syntax consists of the discovery and codification of those implicit rules,

* Running from top to bottom in an ordinary dictionary, the shortest base would be found first, but running from bottom to top gives the desired result.

much as scientific sociology consists largely of the discovery and codification of implicit rules of behavior.

To recognize a form occurrence, it is necessary to identify it as a sequence of certain letters in a certain order and to match it with a similar, stored form. Previously, of course, the existence of certain forms must have been ascertained and a list constructed. To recognize the occurrence of a syntactic relation, the computer must carry out similar steps. Whatever *meaning* the form may have is irrelevant to the problem of recognizing its occurrence, and the same is true of syntactic relations. The explicit and implicit rules of syntax establish the syntactic relations that can occur.

Using them in reverse, as morphological rules are used in a deinflection routine, enables the listener or the (properly programed) computer to recognize relation occurrences.

For example, English authors compound nouns by placing the modifying noun in front of the modified: *task force, probability vector, President Roosevelt,* etc., are all formed this way. Reversing the rule, the occurrence of a sequence of two nouns would be identified as an occurrence of *modification.*

Word order is used as an *indicator* of syntactic relationships (just as letter order is used within forms) in English and in many if not all other natural languages. English has other devices, including punctuation, agreement, and function words. *Punctuation* divides a text into sentences. The same device separates clauses, sets off parenthetic expressions (with commas, dashes, or parentheses), and so on.

Agreement is exemplified by the rule that almost every present-tense subject-verb combination in English contains an *s:* "The book lie*s,*" but "The book*s* lie." Collective nouns prove that the rule is more complicated: "Fish swim"; "The jury are eating lunch." In English, word order is more pervasive an indicator than agreement, whereas in a highly inflected language, in which agreement can carry more of the load, word order is somewhat more free. Only sophisticated, near-formal languages (such as classical Latin) go very far in this respect: *De Rerum Natura* is *mistranslated* "Of Things the Nature," since it actually means "Of the Nature of Things." Many of the implicit rules that are not taught in school are agreement rules that control, for example, the selection of prepositions.

Prepositions, conjunctions, auxiliary verbs, etc., are *function* words; i.e., words that serve primarily to indicate syntactic relations. These words are not meaningless—but neither are other relation indicators. Syntactic relations do or do not have meaning in the same sense that forms do or do not. Function words, however, differ from other words in the vocabulary and are similar to other syntactic indicators, in several respects. They are few in number; new ones are rarely invented; they are interchangeable (to some extent, in some languages) with other indicators; and they have a strong influence on recognition of sentence structure. Changing one noun for another usually does not change the structure of a sentence, but changing one preposition for another often does.

Using these indicators in an efficient manner is a problem that vexed MT programers for several years. Between 1958 and 1960, several programs were written for sentence-structure determination (SSD); two of them are discussed below. Each has as its output a version of the input text in which syntactic relationships are shown explicitly and unambiguously rather than implicitly and ambiguously as in natural-language text.

17.1.4 Synthesis. Skipping from SSD to syntactic synthesis is tantamount to making one of three assumptions about what is commonly called the "multiple-meaning problem." The problem arises because a word in the input language can have, in different contexts, different output-language equivalents. The assumptions are (1) that the multiple equivalents must be printed out each time, since choosing among them is impossible; (2) that all multiple-equivalent situations can be resolved grammatically; or (3) that grammatically irresoluble multiple equivalences can all be solved by using different dictionaries for different fields, the so-called *topical* dictionaries in which each word has only the equivalents needed to translate it in contexts of one branch of knowledge. For the moment, let us take up assumption 3 and proceed; in Section 17.4, we shall examine the idea of semantics more closely and see what relationship it bears to the multiple-meaning problem.

With input-language sentence structures all determined, so that all syntactic relationships are known by explicit and unambiguous indicators, the only task of the syntactic synthesis program is finding output-language indicators for those relations. Since its operations are relatively simple, let us examine them forthwith and have done.

Function words must be inserted to show some relationships. But the relationships are known—i.e., what occurrences are related and in what fashion. The syntactic synthesizer need only pass once through the sentence structure, looking up each relation in a table that shows what function word, if any, is needed to indicate it.

Agreements are sometimes a matter of base choice and sometimes a matter of ending. In Russian, an adjective that premodifies a noun must agree with it in number, gender, and case, but all those properties can be indicated by choice of the right ending. In English, the same "meaning" that is carried by the word *large* in "large volume" must be carried by *high* in "high voltage"; which of these two words to use is a question of agreement. The same pass through the sentence, and the same table that shows the need for function words, can be used to discover the necessity for agreement and the specific choices that must be made to indicate agreement in a particular relation.

Word order would seem to be a tricky and delicate matter; its simplicity cannot properly be explained until the notion of sentence structure has been developed more fully. Punctuation cannot be discussed until word order is treated, since the need for punctuation is partially a matter of word order. As it will turn out, both word order and punctuation can be added to the table in which function-word requirements and agreement rules are listed.

The whole of syntactic synthesis therefore reduces to a single pass through each sentence, in which decisions based on explicit indicia of syntactic relations are converted, by means of a table, into natural-language indicators of the four major types: word order, punctuation, function words, and agreement rules.

17.1.5 Summary of MT. A document is tossed into the hopper and automatically unwrapped, unfolded, and scanned. The printed characters are converted into computer-accessible form, e.g., spots on magnetic tape. The character sequence is divided into sub-sequences wherever spaces or marks of punctuation occur. Each sub-sequence is identified as the occurrence of some *form* by matching with the entries in a dictionary; the matching process can be direct and simple, or it can be more complicated if programing the morphology of the input language is justified by the reduction in storage requirements gained by listing bases rather than forms. The dictionary yields syntactic information about each form and also tells what its output-language equivalents are (perhaps only the equivalents needed in a single field of knowledge). An SSD program, using word order, agreement rules, function words, and punctuation, finds and makes explicit the syntactic relations in each sentence. A syntactic synthesis program, operating on the explicit structural description of each sentence, shows the syntactic relations within it by finding, in a table, the natural-language indicators required. The result is put out in reproducible form, fed to automatic multicopying machines, addressed, and delivered to the Post Office. (But let us remember that all of the sentences in this paragraph belong in the hypothetical mode.)

As an illustration, let us take a Russian preposition. From the dictionary, the computer learns that it is a function word. The SSD program uses it up by finding that it expresses a certain relationship between two other occurrences. Thenceforth it might as well not exist, since the synthesis program does, or does not, insert an English preposition on the basis of structural indications. The preposition is translated, if that term is appropriate, only in an indirect sense. Many nouns, verbs, adjectives, and adverbs are, of course, translated much more directly (but see Section 17.4).

17.2   SENTENCE STRUCTURE

At this point we must make a wider detour through linguistic theory than we have done heretofore. Before attempting to determine the structures of given sentences, we must have more than high school understanding of what structures are. In brief, we need a formalism.

Two formalisms are extant in linguistics. One is often called "phrase-structure theory," the other "dependency theory." Both are well known, both are known to be inadequate. For a fuller treatment of either, and for a discussion of transformation theory (which builds on either), the reader should examine the linguistic literature.[2, 4]

17.2.1 Phrase-structure Theory. In its simplest form, this theory asserts that any sentence can be segmented into two or more parts, each continuous; that each part can be segmented in the same way; and so on, until the parts that remain unsegmented match dictionary entries. For example, "The man with dark hair was wearing a trench coat" has the structure shown in Figure 17.3. This sentence divides into subject and predicate. The subject consists of an article ("The") and a noun phrase. The noun phrase consists of a noun and a prepositional phrase. The prepositional phrase consists of a preposition and a noun phrase. The noun phrase consists of an adjective and a noun. The predicate consists of a verb phrase ("was wearing") and a noun phrase, the object of the verb. The verb phrase consists of an auxiliary verb and a present participle. The noun phrase (object) consists of an article and a noun phrase. The noun phrase ("trench coat") consists of two nouns.

A more formal version of phrase-structure theory can be established. The formal system consists of a unique element, S, a finite set of other symbols, N, V, etc., and a finite set of rules of the form X ⟶ YZ. The unique symbol S, mnemonic for *sentence,* is the universal starting point. The other symbols are phrase categories. The rules, which can be read "X is rewritten YZ," build sequences of phrase symbols. Another set of rules, of the form X ⟶ *a,* carries phrases into forms; here *a* is any form in the vocabulary, and the vocabulary, a finite set of forms, completes the system.

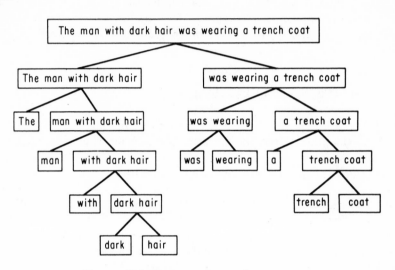

FIGURE 17.3 Phrase structure of a sentence.

We can build the sentence diagramed in Figure 17.3 with the following model of the phrase-structure system:

The unique symbol is S.

The phrase-category symbols are NP, VP, T, NP′, PP, P, A, N, V, V_{was}, V_{ing}.

The phrase-structure rules are S ⟶ NP VP, NP ⟶ T NP′, NP′ ⟶ N PP, PP ⟶ P NP′, NP′ ⟶ A N, VP ⟶ V NP, V ⟶ V_{was} V_{ing}, NP′ ⟶ N N.

The vocabulary consists of the forms that occur in the sentence.

The rules that assign forms to phrase categories are T ⟶ *The,* T ⟶ *a,* N ⟶ *man,* N ⟶ *hair,* N ⟶ *trench,* N ⟶ *coat,* V_{was} ⟶ *was,* V_{ing} ⟶ *wearing,* P ⟶ *with,* A ⟶ *dark.*

The development of the sentence diagramed in Figure 17.3 is plotted in Figure 17.4. Note that the two diagrams are identical except for the

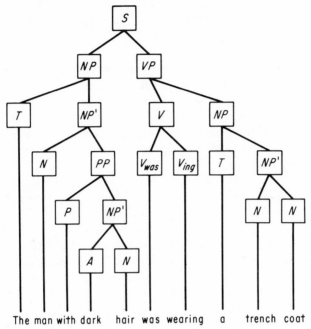

FIGURE 17.4 Phrase structure generation of a sentence.

contents of the boxes. Writing equations connecting the contents of corresponding boxes assigns a phrase type to each of the phrases in Figure 17.3. Thus, "a trench coat" = NP.

The same model is capable of generating other sentences. For example, "The trench with dark coat was wearing a hair man." According to some linguists,[4] an English grammar is a model that generates "all and only the sentences of English." Is "A hair with dark coat was wearing the man trench" a sentence of English, or is it not?

Unfortunately, some students of language believe that it is, others that it is not. I belong to the latter school. But the point of the dispute is to set a boundary between syntax and semantics. Syntax is part of grammar; do the rules that prevent authors from writing phrases like "A hair with dark coat" belong to syntax, and thus to grammar, or to semantics, and thus to terra incognita? Phrase categories as broad as *noun* or *verb* are much too broad, and every linguist is willing to subdivide them. The ALDP research project at The RAND Corporation probably goes further than any other in making these subdivisions. The dispute, if it is ever settled, may well be settled along the lines suggested in Section 17.4 below.

Phrase-structure theory' (also called "immediate-constituent analysis") has many advantages; for example, it reveals, with unimprovable clarity, the fact that the nature of any phrase is a function of all its constituents. The phrase "was wearing" is, for example, the past tense, third singular, progressive form of the verb *wear*. Tense and person are inherited from "was," the connection with *wear* from "wearing," and progressiveness from the combination.

Phrase-structure theory is not perfect, however. The requirement that phrases be continuous is essential to the simplicity of the theory and its applications, yet the requirement runs against preformal conceptions of sentence structure. In an English sentence like "He gave it up," the obvious constituents of the verb phrase are "gave up" and "it." The apparatus of grammatical transformations has been developed to buttress the weak points of the theory, but it cannot alter the fundamental fact that direct connections between pairs of form occurrences are *lost*. Since the loss is the result of deliberate policy, perhaps "discarded" would be a more accurate term.

17.2.2 Dependency Theory. An alternative formalism, dependency theory, does not have all the inherent advantages of phrase-structure theory, but it does retain the concept of direct relations between pairs of occurrences. In fact, those relations, called "dependencies," are the central feature of the theory. In Figure 17.4, the relation between "man" and "wearing" can be traced, but only along the chain N-NP'-NP-S-VP-V-V_{ing}. In contrast, their relation in the dependency structure of the same sentence, Figure 17.5, is immediate.

Dependency is a generalized syntactic relation, linking pairs of occurrences within a sentence. It is antisymmetric; i.e., if occurrence X depends on occurrence Y (written XdY), then occurrence Y does not depend on X. For convenience, let us use *government* to mean the inverse of dependency; thus, "X depends on Y" and "Y governs X" are equivalent statements. According to Figure 17.5, "man" depends on "wearing" (as its subject), "was" depends on "wearing" (as auxiliary), and "coat" depends on "wearing" (as object). Obviously, the connections alone are not

enough—just as phrase divisions are insufficient in phrase-structure theory
—and *dependency types* must be added.

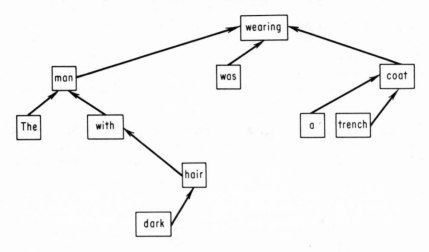

FIGURE 17.5 Dependency-structure of a sentence. $X \longrightarrow Y$ means
that X depends on Y.

Remember that syntactic relations have the same status as forms; they can
be listed independently of any text, for a given natural language, and then
they can be said to occur in particular locations in particular texts. The
indicators of *relation* occurrences are not as easy to describe as the indicators of form occurrences, but they can be made equally definite. How
do we know that "coat" is the object of "wearing" in our example? By
word order, by the grammatical categories of the occurrences (i.e., by their
"agreement," in a sense), and so on.

A remarkable property of many sentences in many languages, similar in
force to the *continuity* of phrases in phrase-structure theory, is illustrated
in Figure 17.5. This property, which has been called "projectivity," [12]
can be seen best by a simple construction. In Figure 17.5, draw a
projection line downward from each node (that is, from each box in
which an occurrence appears) to the bottom of the figure, and copy the
form of the occurrence at the lower end of the line. Reading from left
to right, the forms occur in their original order—the sentence has been
reconstructed from the dependency diagram.

Now, if the construction has been made accurately, the definition of
projectivity is clear: there are no intersections among projection lines and

connection lines. Since all the projection lines are parallel, they cannot intersect, but connection lines could cross one another, or projection and connection lines could meet. They do not in this figure, and they do not in similar figures constructed for many sentences in many languages.

Projectivity is a remarkably strong property; violate it, and the "meaning" of the sentence usually changes. For example, move "dark" in such a way that projectivity fails, perhaps by putting it ahead of "with": "The man dark with hair was wearing a trench coat." The connection between "dark" and "hair" is no longer indicated; the man, rather than the hair, is now dark.

Projectivity is *not,* however, a universal property of English, say, or of Russian, etc. Certain combinations of words indicate certain syntactic relations that violate projectivity. One of these is the English combination

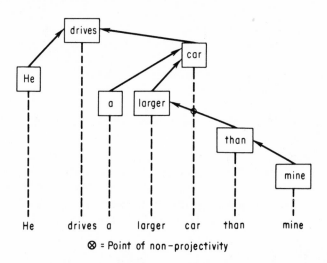

⊗ = Point of non-projectivity

FIGURE 17.6. A non-projective sentence.

of comparative adjectives with *than* (Figure 17.6). The same construction is used in Russian with the same word order.

Whether projectivity in dependency structures is more or less common than continuity of phrases in phrase structures (in natural-language text) is unknown. A large body of text must be processed in accordance with both theories before comparisons can be made. Transformation theory is added to either phrase-structure or dependency theory to account for discontinuity or non-projectivity, but if it is needed too often it only proves the weakness of the basic theory.

To *construct* sentences in dependency theory requires a formal system much like that of phrase-structure theory. There is, first of all, a finite set of symbols, N, V, etc., the *grammatical* categories. Second, there is a finite set of rules of the form $I(X)$, where $I(\ )$ means that the symbol in parentheses can be independent in a sentence and X is any category symbol. Third, there is a finite set of rules of the form $X^i(Y^j, \ldots, Z^k)$; here X, Y, etc., are category symbols, $X(\ )$ means that an occurrence of category X can govern occurrences of the types within parentheses, and the superscripts i, j, k, etc., order the governor and its dependents. These superscripts and the rule of projectivity are enough to determine the order of all the occurrences in the final sentence, as we shall see. Fourth, there is a finite set of rules of the form $X(\phi)$, meaning that symbol X need not have any dependents. Finally, there is a set of category assignments, by which category symbols can be converted into forms.

To build a sentence, choose any symbol that can be independent. Then choose any possible set of dependents for the original symbol. Choose any possible set of dependents for each dependent of the original symbol, and so continue until every symbol has had a null set of dependents chosen for it. Then choose a form to replace each category symbol and take them in the order required by the rule superscripts and the principle of projectivity. Suppose that we choose $I(V)$, $V^2(N^1, N^3)$, and then, for the first noun, $N^2(A^1)$, for the second $N^2(A^1)$, and for each adjective $A(\phi)$. One noun must precede the verb; one, follow it. The adjective dependents must precede their noun governors, and one stands at the head of the sentence. But one adjective could stand in several different positions; to satisfy the rule of projectivity, it must follow the verb, and the sentence can only be A N V A N.

17.3   SENTENCE-STRUCTURE DETERMINATION

Syntactic analysis, better called parsing or sentence-structure determination (SSD), is one of the keys to ALDP, including MT. Although several plans have been programed, we have space to consider just two: a phrase-structure determination program written (but not yet published) by John Cocke of IBM Research, and a dependency-structure determination program written at The RAND Corporation.[9] Cocke's program is designed to yield as many structures as possible for each sentence, revealing ambiguities if any exist. The RAND program cannot yield more than one structure for a sentence, but it is intended to find the most plausible.

17.3.1 A Phrase-structure Determination Program. The basic plan is to build all possible two-occurrence phrases, then all possible three-occurrence phrases, etc. The (several) structures of an n-occurrence sentence are the n-occurrence phrases.

Some occurrences have alternative grammatical types—they are *homographic*. Perhaps a sentence can be parsed if one grammatical type is chosen for a given homographic occurrence, and not if another is chosen; perhaps different structures are obtained. In any event, choice of grammatical type for a homograph influences SSD, so each type must be noted. Cocke's routine assumes that glossary look-up has assigned one or more grammar-code symbols to each occurrence. It takes these symbols as input (Figure 17.7).

Item number	Form	Grammar-code symbol
1	The	T
2	man	N
3	with	P
4	dark	A
5	hair	N
6	was	V_{was}
7	wearing	V_{ing}
8	a	T
9	trench	N
10	coat	N

FIGURE 17.7 Input to Cocke's SSD routine.

Next, all consecutive pairs of occurrences are examined, with all possible grammatical interpretations. In the example, the first two occurrences must be examined as T–N and as T–V. Each pair is tested for agreement. Although there are many ways to make such tests, table look-up is simplest and as powerful as any (though perhaps less economical in operation than some). The table that Cocke requires is a list of ordered triples, X–Y = Z. These entries are, of course, just phrase-structure rules written in reverse.

Any pair that shows agreement (by matching the left-hand side of a table entry) is a phrase. The grammatical type of the phrase is the symbol on the right in the entry. A phrase is adequately described by its length, the sequence number of its first occurrence, and its grammatical type.

To form a phrase of length 3, it is necessary to use a 1-occurrence phrase and a 2-occurrence phrase in combination. The program now proceeds to look over all such pairs, but taking only those in which the 1-occurrence phrase starts at location n, and the 2-occurrence phrase at location $n + 1$, and those in which the 2-occurrence phrase starts at n and the single occurrence at $n + 2$.

The program iterates on the length of the phrases to be constructed, continuing until phrases as long as the sentence have been attempted. At each phrase length, say p, it looks at all phrases of length r, $r = 1, 2, \ldots,$ $p - 1$, immediately followed by phrases of length $p - r$.

The output of the program is a list of all the phrases formed, at all lengths. Tracing backward through the listing (Figure 17.8), it is clear that the program produced, for the illustrative sentence and using only the phrase-structure rules in Section 17.2.1, exactly the structure shown in Figures 17.3 and 17.4.

Item	Starting location	Length	Form	Grammar-code symbol	Constituent items
1	1	1	The	T	
2	2	1	man	N	
3	3	1	with	P	
4	4	1	dark	A	
5	5	1	hair	N	
6	6	1	was	V_{was}	
7	7	1	wearing	V_{ing}	
8	8	1	a	T	
9	9	1	trench	N	
10	10	1	coat	N	
11	4	2	dark hair	NP'	4, 5
12	6	2	was wearing	V	6, 7
13	9	2	trench coat	NP'	9, 10
14	3	3	with dark hair	PP	3, 11
15	8	3	a trench coat	NP	8, 13
16	2	4	man with dark hair	NP'	2, 14
17	1	5	The man with dark hair	NP	1, 16
18	6	5	was wearing a trench coat	VP	12, 15
19	1	10	The man . . . a trench coat	S	17, 18

FIGURE 17.8 Output of Cocke's SSD routine.

Cocke's routine has been extended to deal with phrase-structure rules of the form X $\longrightarrow$ YZW and with grammars in which pairs of rules, such

as X —→ YZ, W —→ YZ, are used. If two kinds of phrases can be rewritten in the same way, it is impossible to know (until longer phrases are
formed), which kind of phrase gave rise to a certain sequence. Cocke's
table entries are therefore of the form

$$W-X- \ldots Y-Z = R \text{ or } S \text{ or } \ldots \text{ or } T$$

Matching the sequence on the left yields (tentative) phrases of all the
types shown on the right.

If discontinuous phrases have to be handled, Cocke's routine must be extended still further in order to look at noncontiguous pairs or sequences
of phrases. The logic that would be involved would lead us too far afield,
however.

17.3.2 A Dependency-structure Determination Program. The
RAND program relies on projectivity. An occurrence X is said to "precede" an occurrence Y if the two occurrences can be connected in a pro-
jective sentence. The general plan is to find occurrences that stand in the
precedence relation, test them for agreement, connect them if they agree,
and iterate. As more and more connections are made, new precedences
are established. Let us see how the plan works out in some detail.

A *stage* in SSD ends when a dependency connection is made. At any stage,
X precedes Y (written XpY) if and only if (1) X is to the left of Y; (2)
X does not derive from (depend, directly or indirectly, on) Y, and Y does
not derive from X; (3) either X is still independent, or Y is, or both are;
and (4) every occurrence between X and Y derives from one or the other
of them.

Condition 1 differentiates XpY from YpX, keeping word order in the
notion of precedence. Condition 2 prevents multiple connections between any two occurrences. Condition 3 prevents further testing of a
pair of occurrences, each of which already has a governor—no occurrence
can have two governors in a dependency structure. Condition 4 guarantees projectivity in any structure formed. Graphically, every new connection line is *above* any intervening nodes (cf. Figure 17.5).

A dependency connection is established, i.e., XdY is formed, when (1)
XpY or YpX; (2) X is independent; and (3) X and Y agree, in the sense
that X belongs to a grammatical type that can depend on an occurrence
of type Y.

Condition 1 ties together precedence and dependence. Condition 2 guarantees that no occurrence shall have two governors. Condition 3 is the obvious agreement requirement. Agreement can be tested here, as in Cocke's routine, with a table, but the entries have a different form. Each entry contains the grammar-code symbol of a governor, the grammar-code symbol of a dependent, and a *resultant* grammar-code symbol for each. The order of the two occurrences in text is reflected in the precedence relation and tested against the order of the two grammar-code symbols in the tabular entry to prevent, for example, connecting a noun to a following preposition that it could serve as object if their order were reversed. One more bit in each entry indicates which of the two occurrences is governor in the combination.

The need for resultant-code symbols is partially similar to the need for output symbols in a phrase-structure table. A noun governing an article is not equivalent to a noun with no dependents and can depend on different governors. In short, the resultant grammar-code symbol of the governor describes the whole *phrase* consisting of the governor and all its direct and indirect dependents as far as they have been attached.

But resultant symbols have another purpose. Since the sentence-building form of a dependency grammar attaches all its dependents to a governor by a single rule, whereas the SSD form connects them one by one, the resultant symbol must show what dependents have been attached and what can still be added. For example, after a verb and its object have been connected, a subject can still be made to depend on the verb, but not another object.

The RAND program works from left to right through a sentence, going back as many times as necessary. In our illustrative sentence, however, this order would cause some trouble since the pair "a–trench" is tested before the pair "trench–coat." One more trick is needed, namely, a system of values. [8] At any stage of SSD, more than one precedence pair is likely to be available. Each entry in the table of agreements has a value number assigned to it; the dependency connection with highest value is made first, and the one earliest in the sentence if several tie for highest value.

Dependency SSD is illustrated, stage by stage, in Figure 17.9. The values that have been assumed are arbitrary to some extent, but not entirely. Modifiers of nouns must be handled early, and prepositional phrases must be assembled before subjects and verbs can be coupled—lest a preposition's object be regarded as a verb's subject, as might have happened here.

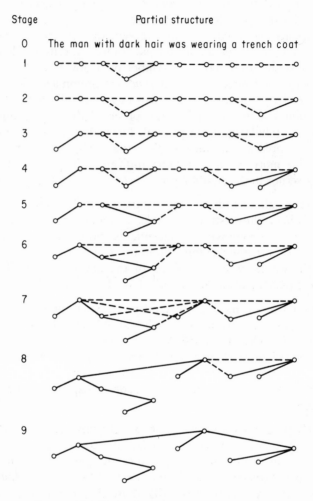

FIGURE 17.9 Dependency-structure determination.

17.3.3 A Note of Caution. If the logic of SSD programs is so simple, how can there be any doubt about their soundness and effectiveness? The answer is appallingly clear: by the end of 1960, no SSD routine had been tested on a large enough text, with a good enough agreement table, to prove its empirical validity. The principles of several systems are charmingly simple, and those systems are certainly economical. None of them work with near-perfect accuracy, but their errors can usually be blamed on the dictionary or the agreement table. The table—or its surrogate—is the "grammar" of a natural language. When work on ALDP programs began, there were no complete grammars or dictionaries, and no one was interested in constructing them. The exigencies of linguistic computation proved that complete descriptions of natural languages had to be constructed, and by empirical research: analysis of actual texts. But such research takes time, and it had not been completed by the end of 1960.

Only when empirical work has produced almost complete grammars will it be possible to judge current theories of syntactic structure and the SSD programs they have inspired. If most sentences prove to have ambiguous structures, or if high accuracy can only be attained by far more complicated logic than is now envisaged, ALDP may be forgotten.

Encouragingly, the RAND program is about 75 per cent accurate, and four errors out of five *seem* to be due to inadequacies in the agreement table or the grammar-code symbols stored in the dictionary. But the RAND program has only been tested on Russian physics text, selected from well-edited journals.

17.4 SEMANTICS

The meaning of a word is either (1) the part of the world that it represents, (2) the response that it evokes from a hearer, or (3) what you will. According to Morris, semantics is concerned with the relationship between language and reality, whereas syntax has to do with the structure of the language itself.[17] Many linguists restrict the definition of syntax even more strictly, referring (vaguely, I think) to the native speaker's belief that one "can" or "cannot" say certain things in his language as delimiting syntax. The limited view is that *absolute* rules are syntactic, *probabilistic* rules semantic. One broader view of syntax, based on Morris' position, considers any findings based on analysis of text syntactic, and any finding that uses other criteria non-syntactic.

17.4.1 *Semantics and MT*. Semantics and meaning, whatever they are, serve MT only by (1) helping with sentence-structure determination, or (2) helping to choose among multiple output-language equivalents of an input-language word. "Analysis of proteins in the liver" and "analysis of proteins in the laboratory" may convince some students—including Ida Rhodes *—that semantics can contribute to SSD, but others, such as

* Personal communication: see also her contributions to the *Proceedings of the National Symposium on Machine Translation,* 1960 (in press).

Chomsky,[3] are convinced that it cannot. If pairs of phrases, like those quoted above, do have different structures, then *liver* and *laboratory* belong to different word classes. It is not yet certain that purely textual analysis can demonstrate the two structures, but it is certain that once the word classes have been established SSD procedures can be made to differentiate the phrases given the class memberships of the words involved.[5]

Some multiple-equivalent words are said to be resolvable if the field of discourse is known.[21] A Russian word has one English equivalent in physics, another in chemistry, etc. In the RAND physics glossary, which contains only the English equivalents needed to translate Russian words as they occur in physics text, most words have only one equivalent apiece. Now, if these words have no other equivalents in other fields, the multiple-meaning problem is slight for Russian-English MT. If they do have other equivalents in other fields, then field of discourse is a powerful aid in reducing the problem. Of course, a human reader must decide what field a document falls into, but there is reason to believe that that decision can be made automatically. The clues might include the words in the title of the book or journal (*Journal of Experimental and Theoretical Physics,* for example), or the words in the text that appear more often in one field than another.[15]

Even in the RAND glossary, some words have multiple English equivalents. Many of those are grammatical function words, such as prepositions, and are not translated—instead, the relations that they express are translated and put into English function words, word-order rules, etc. Then there are verbs that govern either infinitives or *that* clauses, and have different equivalents: "One should [plus infinitive]" or "It follows that. . . ." And there are adjectives that mean one thing (*light*) with concrete nouns, and another with verbal nouns (*easy*).

Words like the adjective that is translated *light* or *easy* pose a delicate problem for the semantic-syntactic theoretician. If the distinction is syntactic, then *light* and *easy* are semantically identical: *easy* is to actions as *light* is to objects. Then the Russians are clever to use just one word, and our required word choice is redundant. On the other hand, if we speak of both colors and objects as *light*, whereas the Russians must use two different words, then we are the clever ones. We can decide how to translate one of these adjectives by looking at its governor and choosing the equivalent of the modifier according to the word class of the governor, but we are not learning very much about semantics in the process.

In short, decision procedures for most multiple-equivalence problems apparently can be found by examining translations and comparing the translation wanted with the syntactically related occurrences. The governors of adjectives, the subjects and objects of verbs, the governors and modifiers of nouns, and so on, can frequently be classified in such a way that the translation of the adjective, verb, or noun depends only on the classes to which related words belong. But all of this amounts to a simple-minded kind of semantics.

17.4.2 *Semantics and Information Retrieval.* Another kind of ALDP application is the retrieval from a library, or a file, of answers to questions or documents containing answers to questions. Some studies, such as Maron's [15] (cited above) or Luhn's,[13] have concentrated on vocabulary disregarding syntax. Their general position is as follows: knowing what words are in a document generally provides sufficient information to determine what questions the document can answer. Some positive results have been obtained, but it might be claimed that the questions used to test these methods have all been too easy. Little has been done about using syntax in information retrieval.

The main idea behind retrieval by vocabulary is the same as the use of subject-field glossaries in MT: different scientific subjects use slightly different words. Therefore, having compiled a list of words that are used in a certain field more often than in others, documents that contain words on the list are likely to belong in the given field. A question also belongs in a field—the answer to the question is to be found by looking through documents with the right vocabulary.[26] Another plan is to omit the field classification and go from a question to a list of words that should appear in any document containing its answer to documents containing all or most of those words.[14]

Still another plan—as yet untried—would be to perform SSD on a proposed question, regarding it as an incomplete sentence. Then its answer would be located by comparing it with the complete structures of sentences in stored text. Unfortunately, a question like "What is the boiling point of hydrogen?" is not likely to be answered by a system that can only find the answer in a sentence that reads (literally), "The boiling point of hydrogen is. . . ." The answer is more likely to be in a table, mentioned in text only by a sentence such as "The liquid-vapor phase-change temperatures of the elements are given in Table . . ." (See Chapter 16.)

This plan would require, therefore, a truly sophisticated syntactic theory, capable of recognizing similarities among quite varied sentences—as transformation theory hopes to do. Furthermore, if it did not require real semantics, it would at least require recognition of the fact that the *boiling point* of a substance is the *liquid-vapor phase-change temperature,* and that *hydrogen* is an *element.*

17.4.3 Semantics and Psychological Data Processing. Much of the raw material of social science consists of natural-language data obtained from interviews, interaction sessions, and the like. Osgood's work[20] provides the key to automatic content analysis, at least in the rudimentary style appropriate to pioneers, and I have written on the subject.[6] (Sebeok is working on automatic methods in analysis of folklore texts, but that branch of social science would lead us too far afield.) [24]

Osgood's method of evaluative assertion analysis is designed to estimate a speaker or writer's attitude toward an object—as overtly expressed—by summating or averaging the evaluative references that he makes to it. An evaluative assertion is a construction that links the object of unknown value with a word or phrase of widely known value, a common-meaning term.

SSD is required to make the detection of linkages automatic, and it probably has to be followed by transformational analysis, at least for convenience. Furthermore, in many cases, information about linking words must be stored in the dictionary. "He employs criminals" and "He pursues criminals" both link *him* with *criminality,* syntactically, but one sentence makes the connection positively, the other negatively. The evaluations of common-meaning terms also must be in the dictionary, where *criminal* is identified as *bad.* The goodness or badness of a word is certainly part of its meaning and therefore belongs in a semantic theory.

To detect expressions of affect, respect, or other attitudes in face-to-face conversation, to detect moods, needs, etc., in any utterance, or to find signs of neurosis or response to treatment in clinical interviews will presumably require more elaborate analysis than Osgood has contemplated. These applications—which have not yet been tried, or even thought through in a serious way—will probably require sentence-structure determination, as MT does. They will also require semantic, or near-semantic, analysis of the relationships among words and phrases in the vocabulary, as sophisticated information retrieval does (cf. "Hydrogen is an element"). And they will no doubt require still more, including goodness-badness measurements on words, etc.

The psychologist who is anxious to see ALDP in his laboratory cannot claim that it will save him labor (Does the cyclotron save labor for the physicist?), but only that it will give him the power to analyze more material more thoroughly than he can do otherwise. He can expect MT, information retrieval, commercial applications, and the scientific interests of linguists to provide him, eventually, with much of what he needs, even including much of the semantic analysis. But finally social scientists themselves must investigate the use of language for psychological and social ends.

REFERENCES

1 Bar-Hillel, Y., Report on the State of Machine Translation in the United States and Great Britain. Jerusalem: Hebrew Univ., 1959.

2 Bloomfield, L., *Language*. New York: Holt, 1933.

3 Chomsky, N., Semantic Considerations in Grammar, *Linguistics and Language Teaching* (Monograph No. 8 on Languages and Linguistics.) Weinstein, R. H., ed. Washington, D.C.: Georgetown Univ. Press, 1955, 141–54.

4 ———, *Syntactic Structures*. (Janua Linguarum No. 4.) 'S-Gravenhage, The Netherlands: Mouton, 1957.

5 Harper, K. E., Machine Translation of Russian Prepositions, *P-1941*. The RAND Corp., 1960.

6 Hays, D. G., Automatic Content Analysis: Some Entries for a Transformation Catalog, *P-1962*. The RAND Corp., 1960.

7 ———, Automatic Language-Data Processing in Sociology, *P-1866*. The RAND Corp., 1959.

8 ———, On the Value of a Dependency Connection, *RM-2712-AFOSR*. The RAND Corp., 1961.

9 ———, and Ziehe, T. W., Studies in Machine Translation—10: Russian Sentence-Structure Determination, *RM-2538*. The RAND Corp., 1960.

10 Jespersen, O., *Morphology,* Part VI of *A Modern English Grammar on Historical Principles*. London: George Allen, Unwin, Ltd., 1911. The other six parts of this work are also useful to the student who wants to learn how much detail a complete grammar must contain, although Jespersen's grammar is by no means complete for English.

11 Kelly, H. S., and Ziehe, T. W., Glossary Lookup Made Easy, *Proc. 1960 Los Angeles Symposium on Machine Translation* (in press).

12 Lecerf, Y., Programme des Conflits, Modèle des Conflits, *La Traduction Automatique,* October 1960, *1* (No. 4), 11–20. See also Harper, K. E. and Hays, D. G., The Use of Machines in the Construction of a Grammar and Computer Program for Structural Analysis, *Information Processing*. Paris: UNESCO, 1960, 188–94.

13 Luhn, H. P., Auto-encoding of Documents for Information Retrieval Systems, *IBM Jour. Research and Development,* 1958.

14 ————, Keyword-in-Context Index for Technical Literature, KWIC Index, *RC 127*. Yorktown Heights, N.Y.: IBM Advanced Systems Development Division, 1959.

15 Maron, M. E., Automatic Indexing: An Experimental Inquiry, *RM-2601*. The RAND Corp., 1960.

16 Micklesen, L. R., Russian-English MT, *Linguistic and Engineering Studies in Automatic Language Translation of Scientific Russian into English*, Reiffler, E., ed. Seattle, Wash.: Univ. Washington Press, 1958, 5.

17 Morris, C. W., Foundations of the Theory of Signs, *International Encyclopedia of Unified Science*, Neurath, O., Carnap, R., Morris, C., eds. Chicago: Univ. Chicago Press, *1*, part 1, 1955, 84–85.

18 Newman, S. M., *et al.*, A Notation System for Transliterating Technical and Scientific Texts for Use in Data-processing Systems, *Information Retrieval and Machine Translation, Advances in Documentation and Library Science*, Kent, A., ed. New York: Interscience Publishers, Inc., 1960, *3*, part I, 345–76.

19 Oettinger, A. G., *Automatic Language Translation*. Cambridge, Mass.: Harvard Univ. Press, 1960. Refer to this for a thorough treatment of dictionary operation, based on work with Russian.

20 Osgood, C. E., Saporta, S., and Nunnally, J. C., Evaluative Assertation Analysis, *Litera, 3*, 1956, 47–102.

21 Oswald, V. A., Jr., The Rationale of the Idioglossary Technique, *Research in Machine Translation*, Dostert, L., ed. (Monograph No. 10 on Languages and Linguistics.) Washington, D.C.: Georgetown Univ. Press, 1957, 63–69.

22 Samson, R. F., The Role of USAF Research and Development in Information Retrieval and Machine Translation, *Proc. Western Joint Computer Conf.*, Mar. 3–5, 1959, 66–69.

23 Savage, T. R., The Preparation of Auto-Abstracts on the IBM 704 Data-processing System, *Report*. Yorktown Heights, N.Y.: IBM Corp., 1958, 2.

24 Sebeok, T. A., and Zeps, V. J., On Non-Random Distribution of Initial Phonemes in Cheremis Verse, *Lingua, 8*, 1959, 370–84.

25 Shepard, D. H., and Heasley, C. C., Jr., Photoelectric Reader Speeds Business Machines, *Electronics, 28* (No. 5), May 1955, 134–38.

26 Swanson, Don R., Searching Natural Language Text by Computer, *Science, 132*, Oct. 21, 1960, 1099–1104.

Lejaren A. Hiller, Jr. & Robert Baker

18/COMPUTER MUSIC

*Lejaren A. Hiller, Jr. earned his Ph.D. in chemistry in 1944
from Princeton University, where he also took extensive course work
in music, primarily composition and theory with Roger Sessions,
as well as considerable course work in electrical engineering.
He has since also obtained a M. Music from
the University of Illinois. After several years of research work with
E. I. duPont de Nemours, Inc., primarily in the fields of
high polymer chemistry and reaction kinetics, he became a faculty
member in the Department of Chemistry of the University of Illinois.
Since 1958, he has worked in the School of Music,
where he now directs research and teaching in experimental
composition and acoustics. While in the chemistry department,
he did research on applications of computers to theoretical problems,
particularly those of a statistical nature. He is the author of
some twenty-five technical papers and books and has composed
about thirty musical works—conventional as well as
experimental compositions, such as those described in this article.*

*Robert Baker was born in Leavenworth, Kansas,
in 1933. He received his B.A. degree
from Washington University, St. Louis, in 1957,
and the M.A. degree from there the following year.
Since 1958, he has attended the University of Illinois
to fulfill the requirements leading to the D.M.A. degree
in composition. He has held teaching assistantships
at both Washington University and the University of Illinois;
at present, he holds a research associateship to pursue
studies of computer applications to musical problems.
His compositions include both orchestral and chamber works,
as well as smaller vocal and choral pieces.*

18.1 INTRODUCTION

Music is recognized to be an important communication medium because both composing and listening to music seem to have significance as components of a process for transmitting qualities of subjective human experience. Music, however, demands fewer referential meanings than other communication systems, notably language. In fact, it is possible, as every music listener knows, to achieve "musical sense" purely in terms of the elements of music itself. For this reason, the properties of music as communication attract the interest of investigators of language structure and decision making as well as of artists directly concerned with music as a means of artistic expression. Especially today, with the recent development of high-speed electronic digital computers, the opportunity exists for precise and quantitative systematic studies of various musical structures on a scale that was not previously possible. It is the purpose of the present paper to demonstrate this point by describing an investigation performed late in 1960 with the aid of the ILLIAC, the electronic digital computer at the University of Illinois. We expect the results of this investigation to throw light on the nature of the compositional procedure and, perhaps, ultimately to yield some understanding of the way in which the logic of music may reflect the logic of thought in general. We present the material even though some of it is still provisional and may be affected by anticipated results, because it illustrates the technique that permits one to interpret the procedures of one form of communication, music, in terms of another type of formal structure, machine programing. Let us also note that, for composers, perhaps an even more important objective is the development of compositional procedures which yield musical structures that specifically exploit the logic of digital computer processes and exhibit forms unique to the method.

18.2   PREVIOUS EXPERIMENTS IN COMPUTER COMPOSITION

The use of an electronic digital computer for musical composition had its inception in 1955–56 in a series of experiments carried out by one of the present authors in collaboration with Leonard M. Isaacson, at that time a research associate at the University of Illinois. Since the idea of using computers for musical composition was then new, the primary objective was simply to evaluate as efficiently as possible a reasonably broad spectrum of various compositional techniques in terms of their suitability for computer programing. No particular process was examined in detail; rather the objective was to achieve at least some semblance of a number of simple but characteristic musical structures. By the end of 1956, enough results were accumulated to form a twenty-minute composition which we named the *Illiac Suite for String Quartet,* after the University of Illinois' digital computer. The score of this composition was subsequently published[6] with statements that "the musical materials . . . were taken from a much larger body of material by unbiased sampling procedures so that a representative rather than a selectively chosen musically superior group of results would be included in the *Suite* . . . our primary aim is *not* the presentation of an aesthetic unity—a work of art. This music is meant to be a research record—a laboratory notebook." A more recent publication that presented a full account of this work, including all programing details,[5] also gave references to other less extensive but nonetheless important experiments in computer analysis and synthesis of music carried out by other investigators through 1958. Since that time, two other applications of computers to musical composition have come to our attention,[7, 8] though at the time of writing we have not been able to obtain the details of these experiments. Finally, we might mention two briefer recent articles written by one of the present authors, which review aspects of this earlier work.[2, 3] Because the studies contained in the *Illiac Suite* have already been so fully discussed, we propose now to review this work solely to introduce the new experiments we plan to outline here.

The process of generating computer music for the *Illiac Suite* was rationalized into a series of simple steps as follows: Initially, the computer was instructed to propagate random integers equated to notes of the musical scale, and later to other musical elements, such as rhythm and dynamics. These random integers were rapidly produced in the ILLIAC by a conventional random integer generating process. They were then subjected to various arithmetic tests derived from the particular "rules of composition" being employed in the various experiments. These arithmetic tests were compiled into the testing program which effected the acceptance or rejection of the sequence of random integers such that the "accepted" integers were employed to build up in the computer memory a short musical "composition" that did not violate the rules in effect. Further, it was necessary to include in the computing program, a "try-again" subroutine which we entered whenever a random integer was rejected, so that a new integer might be propagated and tested. An "erase" procedure was also provided so that if an untenable situation developed in the process of composition such that no further composition was possible, i.e., that all subsequent notes were unacceptable, we could erase part or all of the composition thus far composed and start over again from some previous point. This total procedure leads to a cyclic program having a general form like that shown in Figure 18.1. Since this block diagram does not presuppose any particular musical form or style, to obtain a particular style we must specify, if we can, the particular rules which lead to that style. Once we do that, we produce a more specific block diagram for programing. An example is shown in Figure 18.2, where the block diagram is given for producing first-species strict counterpoint, an

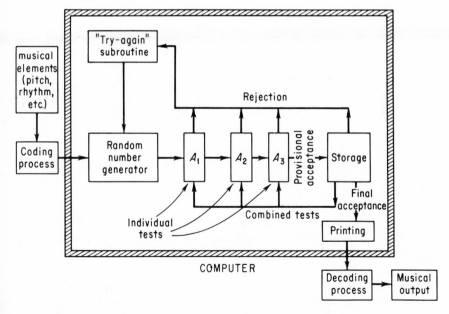

FIGURE 18.1 Steps in generating computer music for the *Illiac Suite*.

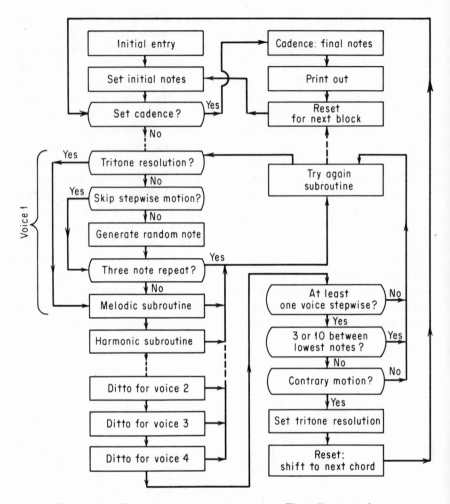

FIGURE 18.2 Experiment two: main routine. Flow diagram of program for producing first-species strict counterpoint. (Courtesy of McGraw-Hill Book Co., Inc.)

academic form of composition based on sixteenth-century style. The detailed programing of this and similar block diagrams for composition is discussed fully elsewhere.[5]

The *Illiac Suite* is made up of four *Experiments,* four movements that represent different research objectives. In *Experiment One,* the primary purpose was simply to work out basic procedures that would enable the

ILLIAC to produce four-part writing suitable for string quartet performance. As a means of testing the various technical procedures, a limited
number of first-species strict counterpoint rules were employed to produce
a loose resemblance to sixteenth-century style. *Experiment Two* was produced to demonstrate that an accurate reproduction of this well-recog-
nized compositional style could be achieved, because in this instance rules
for producing that style were available in a form specific enough for translation into computer instructions. In *Experiment Three,* attention was
shifted to the problems of generating rhythms, dynamics, and dynamic
changes, playing instructions, certain procedures for producing dissonant
chromatic music and for producing twelve-tone rows. Finally, in *Experiment Four,* examples of "Markoff chain music" were generated in which
successive note selection was made to depend on probability functions
computed from tables of values arbitrarily derived from the overtone
series and from a consideration of vertical interval lengths. In certain
sections of *Experiment Four,* these probability functions were also made
to depend on previous notes chosen and on their relation to the tonal
center of the movement, chosen arbitrarily to be C. The "coda" of this
movement was developed to demonstrate how a simple complete closed
musical structure might be produced in a computer. This coda is an extended generalized cadential structure which resolves on the tonic note, C.

All four movements of the *Illiac Suite* represent procedures which find
formalization in the mathematical theory of communication, also called
"information theory," developed by R. V. L. Hartley, C. E. Shannon,
and numerous other investigators concerned with defining a quantitative
rationale of the communication process. This theory has as its basis a
definition of the word *information* that relates to the measure of randomness in a message. The more random is the choice of symbols making up
a message, the higher the "information content" of a message is said to
be. This statement finds quantitative expression in Shannon's equation:

$$H_n = \sum_{}^{n} p_i \log_2 p_i \qquad (18.1)$$

in which, H_n is the information content measured in bits per symbol (a
bit is the basic unit of information) and p_i are the probabilities associated with each of the symbols that might be employed in the message.*
One great value of Equation (18.1)—and equations related to it—in
musical studies is its provision of a quantitative measure of aspects of
musical style that have not been precisely defined by other means. In

* Some of the general ramifications of this theory as applied to musical problems
have been discussed elsewhere.[2, 5]

studies recently completed at the University of Illinois,[1] it was shown that even the simplest application of this theory to the analysis of complex musical structures, specifically four sonata expositions by Mozart, Beethoven, Berg, and Hindemith, discloses wide divergences among these composers in terms of their respective styles; divergences that, in terms of information, appear to correlate well with the qualitative results of traditional musical analysis.

Because information theory says that maximum information occurs in a message when the message is made up of symbols chosen at random and that the information content can be reduced by reducing this randomness, it follows that the process for producing music in the *Illiac Suite* directly works on the principle of information content reduction. We start with random integers that, used as generated, produce random music. In such random music, all elements of the musical structure under processing, such as pitch values, occur with statistically equal frequency in a sample of sufficient size. However, rules were inserted to make the choices unequal, often by forbidding certain choices, which is equivalent to setting certain $p_i = 0$. In other instances, particularly in *Experiment Four*, certain choices were made more probable than others, thus also providing non-random selection of elements, but based on more complex sets of statistics. Actually, an interesting study would be the computation of the reduction in information afforded by the rules applied in the four movements of the *Illiac Suite*. Perhaps this will be the subject of a future reexamination of this music.

18.3 A GENERALIZED MODEL FOR MUSICAL COMPOSITION

After the *Illiac Suite* was completed, the most pressing problem became the formulation of a method for computer realization of more complete and varied musical structures that would begin to exhibit at least some real degree of aesthetic coherence. Obviously, a more generalized attack on the problem of describing the process of musical composition was required.

As a point of departure, we organized this new study partly in terms of analysis and partly in terms of synthesis, because if we postulate some model of the compositional process, we must test its validity and effectiveness in terms of how well it yields recognizably musical results. In other words, we must devise a method of musical analysis that provides data for the compositional process so that it, in turn, provides the requisite musical output.

We next proposed that compositional procedure be regarded as an exercise in decision making in which, for convenience, we distinguish between two basically different types of decisions that confront the composer: (1) procedural decisions, and (2) elemental decisions. The first of these are decisions concerning the *order* in which the various elements of a composition are to be chosen, regardless of what the specific choice of each successive element is to be. This order we call "procedural logic." By the second process, then, we mean the decisions concerning the specific choices of elements from among the many possible values these elements may take on.

Our general problem then may be stated as follows: (1) to determine whether or not a general procedural logic exists, and if so, to formulate this procedural logic, and (2) to determine which factors, on the elemental level, influence the choice of other factors and to attempt a quantitative description of the extent of this influence in terms of probability.

Our hypothesis is that a procedural logic does exist, at least for specific historical styles, and that this procedural logic *may even be independent of the specific historical style.* If this hypothesis seems to yield promising results in historical styles, it will also find application in *a priori* methods of composition and, more importantly, as the basis for self-generating processes of musical composition (see below). Moreover, we can then set up a "dummy model" for the composer in which the procedure is independent of the elements to be chosen. Graphically, this can be represented by a scheme like that shown in Figure 18.3. This model represents only one point in the music, so it would recycle for every such point until the composition under production is completed. Our present problem then is to find what to call E_1, E_2, . . . , etc. A not unreasonable conjecture as to what these might be is depicted in Figure 18.4 for eighteenth-century homophonic music *not including* such things as thematic components and thematic form.

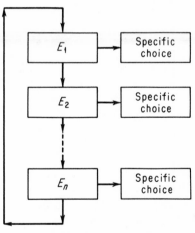

(E_i = "elements" such as harmony, melody, rhythm)

FIGURE 18.3 Flow diagram showing musical elements and specific choices.

To see how this compositional model is being treated, we shall first consider how it can be used to set up an

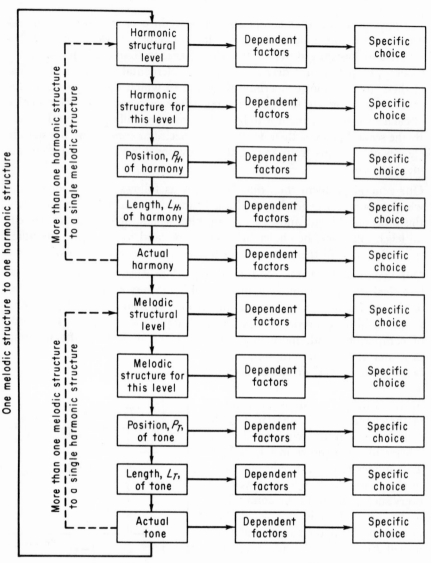

FIGURE 18.4 Flow diagram of program for producing melodic and harmonic structure.

analytical method and, later, how it provides a basis for music synthesis. In this context, let us note that quantitative data concerning musical styles (which can be expressed, if one so desires, in terms of information contents) thus permit an alternative approach to the insertion of what amounts to *a priori* probabilities into computer programs for musical composition. When the *Illiac Suite* was composed, such data were not available, so the only reasonable procedure was the use of *a priori* restrictions on randomness. There is nothing wrong with this, but the other alternative now also becomes possible. In fact, one might now suggest three basic sources of "style" available to the programer of computer music, namely:

a. *A priori* conditions chosen by the programer, on any basis that seems justified to him, including the use of completely arbitrary restrictions.

b. Statistical conditions developed from the statistical analysis of styles or procedures; this is the primary basis of the present method.

c. Self-generated styles developed by the computer itself as a logical consequence of a set of initial specifications that permit this freedom of development.

The last procedure is, of course, the most sophisticated form of computer programing of musical composition because it also incorporates techniques of coding learning processes. It would seem at present the logical goal toward which present experimentation should progress. Obviously, it is also inclusive of the first two sets of conditions.

18.4   THE STATISTICAL ANALYSIS OF STYLE

If we assume that the process of musical composition comprises a series of choices involving almost every aspect of music as we know it, we observe first that the choices are not normally random, but depend on (1) preceding elements for which choices have already been made; (2) what occurs simultaneously, neither choice having yet been made; and (3) what is to follow, if that choice has already been made. If we expect a computer to choose objectively, the computer must be programed to make two basic types of choices: (1) choose factor A independent of all other factors, and (2) given another factor, B, choose A dependent on B. (B may include several factors instead of only one.) To carry out this experiment we first must determine two things: (1) What is the most logical sequence in which to make the choices? (2) Which elements are influential in the choice of one another?

The answer to (2) would seem to provide the answer to (1), for if we regard all elements as possible variables and if at any point we can classify these variables as either independent or dependent, the "logical" sequence would be to choose the independent variables first in each case. But once having ascertained which elements influence others, and even assuming that some outcomes are ruled out because of a preceding choice, one is still left with a multitude of possible choices. Which of these then is the most "logical" to make? Or rather, which is the most "stylistic" to make? How can we define the term "stylistic" in a useful way? At this point we propose the following answer: If, after all influencing factors are taken into account, there are still a number of possible outcomes, then that outcome is most "stylistic" which is most statistically probable.

We adopt this statistical viewpoint because the methods of traditional musical analysis have been largely confined to an objective description of certain explicit aspects of music—its form, structure, vocabulary, effect, and so on. Little attempt has been made to describe music from the composer's point of view—the compositional process itself and the reasons for having chosen a specific "outcome" from among the large number of possible "outcomes." The difficulties in making such a study are indeed enormous. We are, after all, only presented with the *fait accompli,* the finished piece of music, a series of musical facts having form, structure, relationship to one another, and providing no explicit clues as to their motivational origin in the composer's mind.

At the very simplest level of composition, the composer is conscious of a *style* and chooses elements consistent with that style. The explanation for the style itself cannot be an entirely logical argument. Style is a historically evolving and constantly mutating collective conception of the propriety or impropriety of certain musical relationships. The composer consciously or unconsciously assimilates this style and makes use of it. For example, we cannot positively account for the reasons a harmonic progression, such as dominant to tonic, is so consistently used during certain historical periods, although many acoustical reasons may be advanced. Since much speculation has already been done at this level, we propose instead merely to accept style as an established fact and to look for the reasons behind the relationships of elements at a higher level, just as the composer himself accepts style, yet must fashion out of this basic material a composition having a higher form and structure.

Such a decision, however, does not relieve one of the responsibility of describing the style, for it is certainly possible and probable that the conception of style is responsible for many of the decisions at higher structural levels.

We are aware that many musicians may take exception to the probabilistic view of style proposed here, for the term "probability" seems to imply a certain amount of randomness inconsistent with the dialectical thought processes generally ascribed to the composer. That this need not be true is not always realized. Even the most logical of systems may be described in terms of probabilities, the probabilities so assigned being either 1 or 0, complete certainty of an event's occurring, or complete certainty of an event's not occurring. No randomness is necessarily implied. If musical composition were such a system of determinate logic ruled by certain laws of combination, then it would be the purpose of this inquiry to discover these "laws." Most musicians, ourselves included, would rather take the view that music is not such a completely rigid system of logic, and that few, if any, such general and always consistent laws exist. Indeterminacy is a common and probably vital aspect of music and, as such, suggests the need for further exploration of the relation between indeterminacy and subjective response.

As an analytical tool, therefore, the computer is being programed to compute two types of probability corresponding to the two choice types mentioned previously, namely:

$$
\begin{aligned}
&(1) \ \ p(A), \quad \text{simple} \\
&(2) \ \ p(A|B), \quad \text{conditional}
\end{aligned}
\tag{18.2}
$$

Then, for two such elements, A and B, one can compute

$$
\begin{aligned}
&p(A) \\
&p(A|B) \\
&p(B) \\
&p(B|A)
\end{aligned}
\tag{18.3}
$$

such that, if

$$
p(A|B) = p(A)
\tag{18.4}
$$

then also

$$
p(B|A) = p(B)
\tag{18.5}
$$

and A and B are independent. If this is true, the sequence of choices is immaterial. If this is not true, however, we are still faced with the decision of defining the dependent and independent variables in a functional relationship.

$$A = f(B), \quad \text{or} \quad B = f(A) \qquad (18.6)$$

Either way will do mathematically, but for purposes of computation, it is easier to regard the one with the fewest possible outcomes as the independent variable and to make the choices in that order. We believe the composer also takes this path of reasoning.

If, however, more elements are involved, say eight, many more computations would have to be made. Specifically, for each element, we would have to compute the probability of that element, given all possible combinations of the other seven elements. This would yield

$$1 + 7 + 21 + 35 + 35 + 21 + 7 + 1 = 2^7 = 128$$

computations for each element, and altogether, $2^7 \times 2^3 = 1024$ computations for all elements. Each one of these combinations would, in turn, have to be tested against each of the others for equivalent probabilities. Not only would the sample have to be enormously large to include a significant number of all of these possibilities, but the number of computations and the amount of storage space required in the memory for these data would require a program so long that the prospect looks hopeless. And there are far more than only eight elements of music which might be taken into account. For this reason, we have selected certain elements from among the many for a study of their own interrelations, disregarding the others.

Since our study is largely a probability study, we shall endeavor to pick a sample to be analyzed that is large enough such that each of the possible choices for the other ignored elements will occur with a frequency proportional to its frequency of occurrence within the total population from which our sample is drawn. If so, we shall be calculating marginal probabilities. Indeed we should be doing this, even if we were to attempt a single complete study, for it is certainly doubtful if one could even formulate *all* factors which might influence the choice of an element. One would have to take into account each composer, his age, musical background, temperament, disposition that day, the weather, and so on, *ad absurdum*. In all events, such a study would be essentially useless, for theorists are primarily interested in a generalization based on a limited number of specific conditions which seem to recur often.

The value of our study lies then, not in the extent to which we shall have described all factors influencing a choice, but rather in the extent to which we shall have generalized a large set of specific circumstances into a smaller set of cases, each with a certain probable structure. For this reason, our present approach to the problem is one of marginal probabilities. We are limiting ourselves to a study of the marginal relationships between the following three aspects of musical structure: harmony, harmonic rhythm, and tonal structure. The samples of music chosen for analysis are from the so-called classic period of the late eighteenth and early nineteenth centuries, a style that is representative of common practice in compositional procedures. Specifically, we are analyzing a set of string quartet movements chosen from the compositions of Haydn, Mozart, and Beethoven. Again, as in the earlier studies contained in the *Illiac Suite,* in which sixteenth-century style was employed as a check procedure, we have picked a well-known style as the first basis of testing the programing. It is our intention, as we did before, later to extend these studies to more novel styles and procedures once we have basic computer processes in operation. In this way, we expect to provide the link from the traditional and recognizable through currently employed techniques to the speculative and experimental.

18.5 THE ANALYTICAL METHOD

Let us now consider a particular example of the analytical method applied to specific musical structures. Let us note also that some of its logic bears considerable formal resemblance to certain modern methods of structural analysis of tonal music, notably processes first worked out by the analyst Heinrich Schenker. In the report of the earlier experiments incorporated in the *Illiac Suite*,[4] it was observed that Schenker's ideas of structural layers in music might provide "a working technique for structural assembly . . . that permits the assigning of a greater or lesser value to significant musical elements, particularly in relation to the time scale of the musical structure." Our present analytical scheme may yield *quantitative* data supporting the *qualitative* results of such earlier studies. So, for purposes of analysis, let us define three significant structural levels in music as follows:

a. The detailed structure as it develops from measure to measure.

b. The larger sectional structures.

c. The over-all tonal structure.

Let us now briefly investigate the methods applied at each level.

18.5.1 *The Detailed Structure.* We first seek to classify the variables as either independent or dependent. In order to isolate factors of harmony and harmonic rhythm, we delete from our sample of works all passages of a modulatory nature and transpose the remaining passages into a single key. We make the assumption that transposition of a passage into another key in no way affects the probabilities involved; i.e., that the relation of one element to another remains functionally the same regardless of key. We then separate passages in the major mode from those in the minor mode and run the experiment for both modes independently. We are left, then, with essentially three variables to investigate: (1) the harmony at any point in the passage, (2) the duration of the harmony, and (3) the position within the bar at which the harmony begins.

To determine which of these factors is dependent on one or more of the others, we then compute probabilities as follows:

First, we define the symbol, $\overrightarrow{H_{i-j}H_{i-j+1}H_{i-j+2}\ldots H_{i-1}H_i}$, to mean the sequence of harmonies occurring in time in the direction of the arrow. We also define the symbol, $p(\overrightarrow{H_{i-j}H_{i-j+1}\ldots H_{i-1}H_i})$, to mean the probability of H_i following the sequence, $\overrightarrow{H_{i-j}H_{i-j+1}\ldots H_{i-1}}$.

We compute, then,

1. $p(H_i)$

2. $p(\overrightarrow{H_{i-1}H_i})$

3. $p(\overrightarrow{H_{i-2}H_{i-1}H_i})$

   . . .

n. $p(\overrightarrow{H_{i-j}H_{i-j+1}\ldots H_{i-1}H_i})$, $j < i$

until we reach a point at which

$$p(\overrightarrow{H_{i-j}H_{i-j+1}\ldots H_{i-1}H_i}) = p(\overrightarrow{H_{i-j+1}H_{i-j+2}\ldots H_{i-1}H_i}) \quad (18.7)$$

When this occurs, the choice of H_i depends on the previously occurring harmonies counting back to H_{i-j+1}, but not on harmonies prior to that, i.e., H_{i-j}. The number, j, will not, of course, be the same for each specific H_i, but it is almost certainly true that such a point exists.

Second, we test to see whether the same is true of durations. If L_i is defined to be the duration of H_i, then we calculate by analogous means:

1. $p(L_i)$

2. $p(\overrightarrow{L_{i-1}L_i})$

   . . .

n. $p(\overrightarrow{L_{i-k}L_{i-k+1}\ldots L_{i-1}L_i})$

If the results of these computations demonstrate that L_i is dependent on previous durations back to, and including, L_{i-k}, and that H_i is dependent on previous harmonies back to, and including, H_{i-j}, it will then be possible to calculate the conditional probabilities:

$$1.\ p(\overrightarrow{L_{i-k}L_{i-k+1}\ .\ .\ .\ L_{i-1}L_i}|H_i)$$

$$2.\ p(\overrightarrow{H_{i-j}H_{i-j+1}\ .\ .\ .\ H_{i-1}H_i}|L_i)$$

and if

$$p(\overrightarrow{L_{i-k}L_{i-k+1}\ .\ .\ .\ L_{i-1}L_i}|H_i) = p(\overrightarrow{L_{i-k}L_{i-k+1}\ .\ .\ .\ L_{i-1}L_i}) \qquad (18.8)$$

then, L_i may be chosen without regard to the values assumed by H_i. Or, if

$$p(\overrightarrow{H_{i-j}H_{i-j+1}\ .\ .\ .\ H_{i-1}H_i}|L_i) = p(\overrightarrow{H_{i-j}H_{i-j+1}\ .\ .\ .\ H_{i-1}H_i}) \qquad (18.9)$$

then H_i may be chosen without regard to the values assumed by L_i.

Furthermore, one of the above can be true without the other being true. If we use the notation $y = f(x)$ to mean that x is the independent variable upon which y depends, then there are four possibilities:

a. The second is true but not the first: $L_i = f(H_i)$.

b. The first is true but not the second: $H_i = f(L_i)$.

c. Both are true: H_i and L_i may be chosen independently.

d. Neither is true: the intersection, H_iL_i, must be treated as a single variable dependent on others.

The writers believe, because of compositional experience, that b. will prove to be true for certain L_i, and c. true otherwise.

Third, it is also necessary to account for the position within the measure at which the progression takes place. If P_i denotes the eighth-note position at which H_i (and L_i) commence ($1 \leqslant P_i \leqslant 8$), then P_i is certainly a function of the preceding durations, i.e., assuming common time,

$$P_i = 1 + (L_1 + L_2 + \ldots + L_{i-1}, \text{ modulo } 8) \qquad (18.10)$$

Since L_i is also a function of the preceding durations, there is a relationship between L_i and P_i. Clearly the choice of P_i precedes the choice of L_i, since P_i is uniquely determined by $L_1L_2L_3 \ldots L_{i-1}$ and not by L_i.

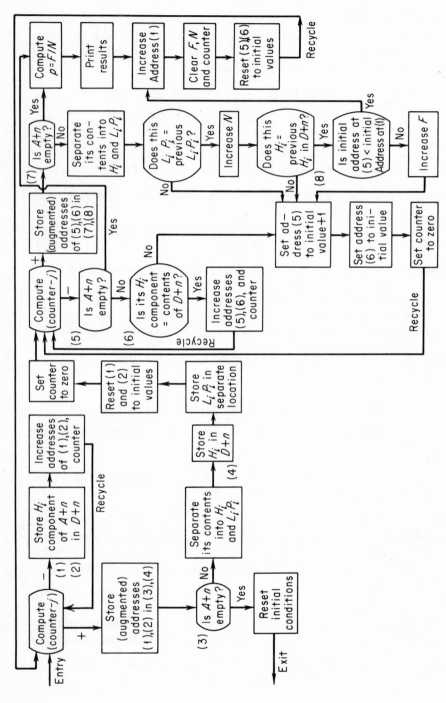

FIGURE 18.5 Flow diagram of program for determining the dependence of a structural element.

Since the sequence $L_{i-k}L_{i-k+1} \ldots L_{i-1}$ could have begun at any position within the measure, we shall also have to calculate

1. $p(\overrightarrow{L_{i-k}L_{i-k+1} \ldots L_{i-1}L_i}|P_i)$

2. $p(\overrightarrow{H_{i-j}H_{i-j+1} \ldots H_{i-1}H_i}|P_i)$

to determine whether the probabilities of L_i and H_i are affected by P_i. Details of the programing of these computations are provided by the block diagram shown in Figure 18.5. The method above should either confirm or refute the hypothesis that the variable with the fewest possible outcomes may be considered the independent variable. Generally speaking, there are far fewer possible durations than harmonies. When considering harmonic rhythm, we generally do not consider durations below the eighth-note level at a moderate tempo. A harmony rarely lasts much beyond the length of a whole note. Consequently, L_i is usually confined to the range $1 \leqslant L_i \leqslant 8$ eighth notes. Our hypothesis, then, is that

$$L_i = f(P_i), \qquad H_i = f(L_i, P_i) \qquad (18.11)$$

In other words, the composer normally chooses first duration, then harmony, thereby insuring a maximum amount of freedom in choosing the final variable.

Why might a composer wish to insure for himself this freedom? Because he thereby reduces his chances of having to reconsider his earlier decisions. If we imagine a composer faced with a choice of duration and harmony at some point in the music, we might further imagine him following both possible sequences: If he chooses first the harmony and then duration, and if some harmonies are mutually exclusive with certain durations, the choices for duration will become few and might interfere with a good harmonic rhythm. He might then have to reconsider his choice of harmony. On the other hand, if he chooses first the duration, even though this rules out certain harmonies, enough other possibilities remain to assure a smooth harmonic progression, so that his chances of having to reconsider the original decision are smaller.

18.5.2 Larger Harmonic Structures. Once having described "style" in terms of probabilities, we shall want to investigate harmonic structures that exist between non-adjacent harmonies. Commonly in music, certain harmonic progressions involving a set of four or five chords are used as larger structures, other chords or chord progressions being inserted between the individual members of the main progression. For example, the common progression, I, V, VI, II, V, might be expanded by the insertion of secondary dominants between each of the chords as illustrated by the example in Figure 18.6. Such insertions need not be confined to secondary dominants, of course. If we denote by X_i a chord or a set of chords form-

FIGURE 18.6 Larger harmonic structures.

ing a progression between the members of the larger progression H_i' and $H_{i'+1}$, we may describe such a structure as

$$(X_{i-1})H_i'X_iH_{i'+1}X_{i+1}H_{i'+2}X_{i+2} \ldots X_{i+j-1}H_{i'+j}(X_{i+j})$$

with the parentheses indicating that the element enclosed may or may not be present. Several questions should be raised here:

a. How are the probabilities of H_i' affected by these insertions?

b. Which simple progressions are suitable for expansion into a larger structure? Are any new?

c. Is X_i dependent on H_i' or on $H_{i'+1}$ or on both?

d. Is there a larger rhythmic structure governing the larger harmonic structure?

e. How is the larger structure made perceptually apparent?

Without going into the details of this analysis, it is apparent that many of the previous methods for analyzing style can be again used here to analyze larger harmonic structures. Thus, if a certain structure, S, is found to have frequency f and the total number of structures found in the sample is n, then

$$p(S) = \frac{f}{n} \tag{18.12}$$

Question b. then can be answered by a comparison of this with the progressions found to be frequently occurring in the previous section. (We consider "suitable" to mean "having the highest frequency of occurrence.") The writers predict that many of the larger structures will prove to be identical with the smaller; however, there may well be new progressions found also.

Concerning Question c., we shall have to define some chord, H_m, between H_i' and $H_i'_{+1}$, such that $H_m = f(H_i'_{+1})$ and $H_{m-1} = f(H_i')$. If H_m is also $f(H_i')$, we may call this the "pivot chord" analogous to the "pivot chord" of a modulation. All modulations do not contain pivot chords, but there is always a point between the two keys, K_i' and $K_i'_{+1}$, at which the harmonies cease to be a function of the preceding key and become a function of the following key. The same may be said of larger harmonic structures not involving a modulation. Accordingly, we shall have to compute some further probabilities, i.e., the probability of H_m preceding H_{m+1}, and so on. It should be noted that the probability of A following B is *not* the same as the probability of B preceding A.

18.5.3 *Tonal Structure.* Our hypothesis is that harmonic progressions form larger harmonic structures which, in turn, may form still larger harmonic structures. These larger harmonic structures eventually become a series of modulations from key to key, forming the key structure, and certain of the keys form the structure of the composition in the largest sense, the tonal structure. If such is true, tonal structure would in the largest sense be an ever-broadening form of the simplest harmonic progressions. All levels of structures must be investigated in order to determine not only the probabilities of the various elements, but also to determine whether the "procedural" logic of one level is also valid for higher or lower structural levels. We believe such will be the case, although the probabilities of specific elements may change somewhat from level to level. If the hypothesis is correct, the sequence of choices to be made for a structure, such as shown in Figure 18.7, subject to prior choices of position and length in each case, would be indicated by the arrows. In such a procedure, the structural levels might be indicated as shown. It is toward this type of scheme that our programing of the "dummy model composer" is directed.

18.6 PROGRAMING FOR MUSIC SYNTHESIS

The present programs for music synthesis by the ILLIAC already provide certain basic procedures later to be incorporated into the "dummy model" structure. These programs generate tones, harmonies, rhythms, and so on, but without the incorporation of style data. Therefore, the output so

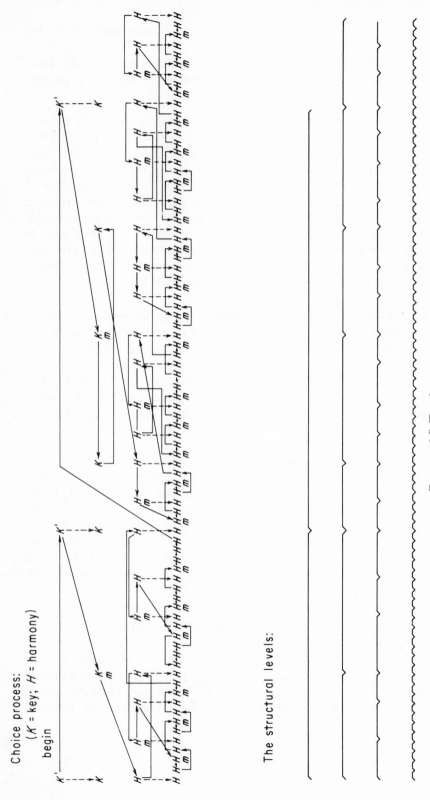

Choice process:
(K = key; H = harmony)

The structural levels:

FIGURE 18.7 Tonal structures.

far produced is highly random in structure; more so, in fact, than any of the samples of random music included in the *Illiac Suite,* because this time we have permitted a much wider range of choice of tones and rhythms.

First, we wrote a program to generate random numbers within certain specified limits. This program was tested for randomness and the maximum difference in the probabilities of any two outcomes was found to be less than 0.001. Either equal probabilities (to yield random music) or unequal probabilities (to yield non-random music) may be subsequently imposed by dividing 1000 into equal or unequal blocks dependent on the set of probabilities desired. For instance, for the situation of choosing among 88 *equally* probable tones, 1000 is divided by 88 ($\cong$ 11). A number is then generated randomly between 1 and 1000, and whichever block of 11 it falls into is the outcome. (In this particular instance, the left-over 32 integers are discarded.) If, however, we desire unequal probabilities of, say, 0.25 for one of the outcomes and the rest equal, then a block of 250 is provided for the element having a probability equal to 0.25 and a block of 750 $\div$ 87 ($\cong$ 9) for each of the others. The numbers are associated in every instance with specific choices of elements being composed.

Second, a "dummy" program has been written that generates melodic tones and rhythms for two voices for n bars. A flow chart for this program is shown in Figure 18.8. Since

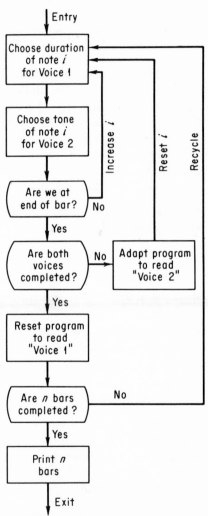

FIGURE 18.8 Flow diagram of program to generate melodic tones and rhythms for two voices.

no interrelation between the two voices is intended at this time, the sequence of choosing events is quite simply Voice I, then Voice II, for one bar, then recycling until n bars are completed. This sequence of procedural logic will be altered, once tests for correlation of voices with one another are added. In other words, it is not reasonable to expect that one voice may be completed for a space of one bar before the next voice is written, unless we use a *cantus firmus* type of procedural logic. For testing the rhythm and note generation routines, however, this is a simple yet acceptable method of progressing.

Concerning the choice of rhythms available, we have thus far confined ourselves to the most usual subdivisions of the whole note and programed only for common time, i.e., $\frac{4}{4}$ meter. The subdivisions employed include all duple subdivisions down to, and including, the thirty-second note ($\frac{1}{32}$ of a measure) and all triple subdivisions down to, and including, the sixteenth note triplet or "twenty-fourth note" ($\frac{1}{24}$ of a measure). This provides eleven possible values, all of which can be combined in any way through the use of ties to provide additive durations.

In all, then, we have the possibility of forming all possible durations which can be expressed in the form:

$$\frac{1}{32} \leqslant \frac{i}{32} + \frac{j}{24} \leqslant 1 \qquad (18.13)$$

where $i = 1, 2, 3, \ldots, 32$ and $j = 1, 2, 3, \ldots, 24$ for one measure. Furthermore, these values can be tied over the bar line, which is primarily an indexing device rather than an indication of metrical stress. This provides, theoretically at least, a virtually unlimited number of combinations of duple and triple rhythms.

The generation of tones thus far is considerably less elaborate and amounts merely to random generation of integers between 0 and 87, corresponding to the 88 tempered tones of the ordinary chromatic scale. A sample of ILLIAC output combining these two schemes of rhythm and tone generation is shown in Figure 18.9. This highly random material serves as "raw material" from which we expect to fashion more meaningful musical structures.

Third, some studies have been completed on routines to generate harmonic rhythm and root tones. In a random situation, the generation of the harmonic root is simply a choice of an integer between 0 and 11, corresponding to the 12 tones of the tempered scale, and presents no more difficulties than the generation of melodic tones. The means of gene-

FIGURE 18.9 A sample of ILLIAC output.

rating the harmonic rhythm is somewhat more difficult, however, in that we have classified harmonic rhythms into types and variations of these types. The types correspond to the number of roots present in a bar. The variations correspond to the placement within the bar of these roots and are classified into zero, first, second, or third order, depending on the correspondence or noncorrespondence of the positions of roots with the *a priori* positions of "strong" beats within a common time measure. The rhythm exhibiting the most syncopation is classified as third order; that exhibiting the least syncopation as zero order. Moreover, a third order structure is considered a variant of a zero order structure. For our present purposes, an exact description of these classifications is unnecessary, but to show that it provides useful results, we reproduce in Figure 18.10 a sample of the rhythms and roots so generated.

FIGURE 18.10 Sample of generated harmonic rhythm and root tones.

All types and orders are considered equally probable in this example, so it is, consequently, once again quite random in nature. For harmonic rhythm we consider subdivisions down to the eighth note only, and do not include triple subdivisions. All durations here may be expressed as $i/8$, where $i = 1, 2, \ldots, 8$, for one measure. Ties across the bar line can occur only if the root generated for the beginning of one measure is the same as the last root generated in the preceding bar. The flow chart for this program is shown in Figure 18.11.

To be sure, then, these programs represent some of the actual means of achieving a choice of the various elements required. What remains to be done at the time of writing is to combine these various routines into a

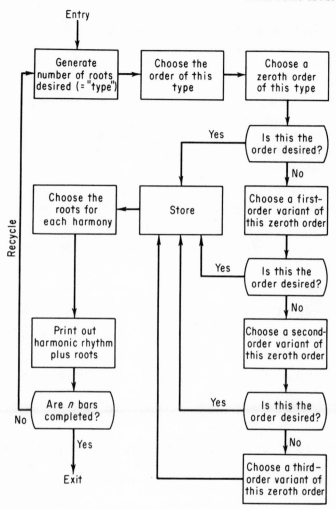

FIGURE 18.11 Flow diagram of program to generate harmonic rhythm and root tones.

sequence of events wherein each is entered at the most opportune time to produce the most accurately stylistic music. Both the determination of this compositional sequence and the reduction of randomness of choice by the introduction of appropriate subroutines await analytical results. We contemplate three types of tests of the validity of the synthesis:

a. Subjective tests asking qualified musicians to discuss the synthesized music in terms of stylistic integrity, structural cohesiveness, and general musical interest.

b. Analytical tests by the computer itself, having the computer regard its own music as the sample and compute the probablities involved. These probabilities would then be compared to the probabilities computed for the original sample.

c. Specific choice tests. A section of a piece of music would be inserted into the computer and analyzed. The computer would be instructed to choose a succeeding element based on the probabilities found from the original sample. This choice would be compared with the actual choice made by the composer.

Dependent on the success of the noted investigation, future experiments are envisioned. One logical sequence of investigations is the following:

a. An investigation of harmonic elements (including inversions of triads). This is the present study and includes the melodic aspect of the bass line.

b. A study of melodic elements (monophonic music).

c. A study of the combinations of a. and b. above (homophonic music).

d. A study of melodic and harmonic combinations of four or more voices (polyphonic music).

The completion of these studies will enable us to program large-scale musical structures in any "style" reasonably compatible with the "dummy model" structure. Provisionally, we think that the fugue and variations forms might well provide good tests of this kind of synthesis.

An inspection of the resultant musical structures should permit at least some inferences concerning the validity of the flow charts thus far set up as representations of the logical processes required by creative musical thought.

REFERENCES

1 Bean, C., Jr., Information Theory Applied to Analysis of a Particular Formal Process in Tonal Music. (Unpublished thesis.) Univ. of Ill., 1961.

2 Hiller, L. A., Jr., Computer Music, *Scientific American, 201* (No. 6), December 1956, 109.

3 ———, Electronics and Music, *I.R.E. Student Quarterly,* 1960.

4 ———, and Isaacson, L. M., *Experimental Music.* New York: McGraw-Hill, 1959, 134–35. It should also be noted that a review of Schenker's ideas has recently appeared. For a description of his analytical method, see Forte, A., Schenker's Conception of Musical Structure, *Jour. Music Theory, 3* (No. 1), 1959.

5 ———, and ———, *Experimental Music.* New York: McGraw-Hill, 1959.

6 ———, and Isaacson, L. M., *Illiac Suite for String Quartet,* New York: New Music Edition, 1957; now available through Theodore Presser Company, Bryn Mawr, Penn.

7 Moles, A., La Musique Algorithmique, Premiere Musique Calculée, *Revue du Son, 93* (No. 1), 1961, 28.

8 Zavipev, R. Kh., An Algorithmic Description of the Music Composing Process, *Doklady ANSSB, 132,* 1960, 1283.

W. Ross Ashby

19/SIMULATION OF A BRAIN

*Professor W. Ross Ashby was
born in London, in 1903. Educated at
Cambridge, he qualified in medicine, specialized
in psychiatry, and since 1928, has given
most of his attention to the problem:
How can the brain be at once mechanistic and adaptive?
He obtained the solution in 1941,
but it was not until 1948 that the Homeostat
was built to embody the special process, which
was described in 1952 in* Design for a Brain. *Since
then he has worked to make the theory of
brainlike mechanisms clearer.* An Introduction
to Cybernetics *(1956) gives his later
work. It has been translated and published
in the U.S.S.R. and has also been
translated into French, Spanish, Polish, Czech,
and Hungarian. He is now at the University
of Illinois, where he is teaching cybernetics
and continuing his research.*

19.1 WHAT IS "BRAINLIKE" BEHAVIOR?

No better introduction to the topic has been given than that offered by Turing, one of the founders of modern computing. "The brain," he said, "has the consistency of cold porridge; therefore a bowl of cold porridge is a model of the brain, so far as it goes." Such a statement leads to the realization that to create a model which is to be more than a mere collection of gadgets, one must build from the foundations.

The subject of "models of the brain" has been totally changed in the last twenty years. In the 1930's, *any* machine that copied *any* function of the brain was of interest; since on the basis of the "null" hypothesis no function could be copied, every exception was significant. Then came the general purpose computer and a realization that mechanisms existed that could carry out *any* defined piece of behavior. With the advent of the computer, the model was required to do more than merely demonstrate that it *could* perform some function, however high in behavioral level—the interest, if any, now lay elsewhere.

It does not seem to be widely appreciated that a somewhat similar change

453

occurred when Pitts and McCulloch [7] showed that a net with the simple properties that are found in all nerve nets could produce all behaviors. Today, however, demonstrating that a particular net can produce a particular behavior seems less significant; interest has centered elsewhere. (But see Chapter 20.)

For these reasons, "simulating the brain" requires new justifications. What these are will be outlined below.

19.2   THE TWO MEANINGS OF "BRAINLIKE"

The state of science has changed grossly in the last twenty years. Before World War II, our attitude toward the brain was partly superstitious; we considered the brain to be essentially miraculous in certain aspects, and we could put no bounds on the extent of its powers. We believed that "genius" could do everything, just as the elderly gentleman who saw sparks when Sam Weller's fist hit his nose felt that "electricity" could do everything. Today we know better. The logic of mechanism has forced us to conclude that the brain is remarkable in just two respects, and no more.

The two respects are clearly distinguished by whether the brain's activity is or is not being considered in relation to a defined, and previously given, goal; more precisely, in relation to the "focal condition" defined by Sommerhoff.[9] Note, for instance, the sentence from a newspaper: Despite these difficulties, the pilot landed the plane safely. (In this example, whether the pilot was human or automatic is irrelevant.) The criterion of the pilot's cleverness is the word *safely*. In the landing of aircraft, there is a well-understood goal or "focal condition" that is *given*. The pilot lands and shows his cleverness by whether he does (or does not) keep several essential variables within assigned limits:

   a. The shock to the landing gear not to exceed so much force
   b. The touchdown to occur within a certain area
   c. The aircraft not to turn over, etc.

19.2.1 *A Highly Selective System.*   A vast amount of brainlike activity can be summed up as showing high selectivity for the focal condition. This is the activity of the automatic pilot, of the control mechanisms in the petroleum refinery, of the navigator who makes an exact landfall. By what route the focal condition is reached is often irrelevant; in fact, use of an unusual route is often regarded as emphasizing the braininess,

as when a chess master in a tournament achieves his mate by a route that no bystander had thought of. Be that as it may, a system's behavior is brainlike (in the first way) when it shows any remarkable power of achieving the focal condition in circumstances that make the achievement evidence of intense *selection*.

19.2.2 *A Sensitive-complex-active System.* The other type of behavior that can be called brainlike occurs when the brain demonstrates that it is almost unique on this earth as a system that is

  a. extremely sensitive,
  b. extremely complex and richly connected internally, and
  c. extremely active.

Today, of course, we know that electronic and other networks can readily provide these properties. From the days of the Greeks until World War II the brain was the sole possessor of these properties; hence all properties belonging to the sensitive-complex-active system were regarded as brainlike. They are, however, sharply distinguishable from the first type because they are neither good nor bad in themselves; they are like oxidation —neither good nor bad in itself, just a natural or inevitable process under certain conditions, and capable of being used, *or suppressed,* according to the demands of any given focal condition.

19.2.3 *Some Comments Concerning Brainlike Activity.* At the moment, little is known of these processes, though a start has been made. The Monte Carlo methods in the computer provide examples of various sensitive-complex-active processes, and much of statistical mechanics in the past has been of this type. The theory of epidemics provides another example; and the mechanism given by the author [4] to show why habituation is so common is of the same type.

Since all brainlike activity can be examined within these two types, there is no room today for a merely superstitious attitude that accepts the brain (whether of a "genius" or not) as capable of anything. On the contrary, today the brain's capacity is recognized to be *strictly limited*. It is obviously limited in the second type of process, for as a material system, it is going along its physically and chemically determined trajectory, no more able to produce the magical in its impulse transmissions than it can produce the magical in its oxidations. The properties that it shows are those of any system that is increasing in entropy, and those of any Markoff process as it tends to equilibrium.

But the other type of activity, the goal-seeking, is equally bounded, though this is *par excellence* the behavior that in moderate degrees is called "intelligent" and in extreme degrees "the work of genius." Yet the work of genius is ultimately one of selection, and for selection there is the axiom [2] true for computer and brain alike: Any system that achieves appropriate selection (to a degree better than chance) does so as a consequence of information received.

Thus the living brain is as bounded as is the computer. The superstitious idea that a "genius" can do anything is in headlong collision with the *quantitative* limit expressed in the law of requisite variety and in Shannon's Tenth Theorem. [8] If the brain, especially the human brain, seems sometimes to transcend this limit, it is because *we* fail to appreciate that what the species has learned in 2 billion years of experiencing terrestrial problems, and what the individual has learned in the years of childhood, are together providing information relevant to the problem in hand. Human beings, for instance, are peculiarly gifted when dealing with problems in three-dimensional geometry (in which they and their ancestors have lived for aeons), but when they come to topologies that are very different—that of five-dimensional geometry, for example, or that of the partly ordered set—they show much less flair. Thus, brainlike activity is to be conceived in one of these two exact senses: either it refers to a process by which information received is transformed into an appropriate selection, or it refers to any process, subject to exact laws, that is unusually complex and active and also happens to be used by the living brain.

19.3   THE DISCIPLINE OF SIMULATION

A feature of attempting to simulate brainlike activity, commented on by all who have undertaken to do so, is the rigorous, but most salutary, discipline that it imposes on the thinking of the would-be designer. First, he must define his aims precisely. Does he wish to demonstrate "coordination between muscles"? Then he must define these concepts in terms of actual behavior. It is of little practical use today to explain "coordination" in terms of "integration," the latter in terms of a "higher level," and "higher level" in terms of "consciousness," etc. It is necessary to keep to one *region of discourse,* and the substitution of one word for another offers no solution. Even if an attempt at simulation achieves nothing in hardware, it is usually a most instructive activity, leaving the worker with a far deeper insight into the nature of the proposed phenomenon than he previously had.

19.3.1 *Logical Deduction.* Simulation has so displayed the essential features of logical deduction that today any complicated logical problem (e.g., that set up by an insurance policy with many highly conditional and interrelated clauses) can be solved directly by some mechanical process that carries out the necessary operations. Again, the problem of mechanical translation has resolved itself simply into a study of the mechanics of translation—of finding in what way the given language does actually possess structure and conditionalities internally. It is this information that must be given to a translator, whether to a machine being programed or to a child learning the language. The older idea that there was a *mystique* of translation must now be dismissed as a superstition based on ignorance.

19.3.2 *Problem Solving.* The same problem confronts the would-be programer of a machine to play chess, or to write music like Bach's. The real problem is not to assemble the hardware, but to find the constraints, the laws, short-term and long-term, that impose on the output something of the essential structure of chess playing or Bach writing. "What do I mean by music like Bach's?" is the essential problem to be solved. This is difficult; once the answer is known, making a machine to do it is today a mere matter of routine. (See Chapter 18.)

19.3.3 *Simulation Models.* This type of analysis *forced* a recognition that to model an organism that would adapt to an environment implied that one must also *model an environment*—the situation is meaningless, otherwise. Here the modelmaker must seriously consider what sort of an environment he is thinking of, whether it is properly representative of some biological environment, and if not, of exactly which set of environments it *is* representative. Hence, it is true to say that today we not only understand better what is meant by "brainlike," but we can also see more clearly the peculiar and pervading features of the world we live in—the world that has imposed so many special characteristics on the creatures that have evolved in it.

The same analysis forces an early recognition of the *essential* relation between the phenomenon of "memory" and the fact of non-observability of some of a system's parts. If not all of a system is observable, so that its behavior is not wholly predictable (for lack of information about the states of the unobservable parts), then predictability may be restored if the observer takes into account what the observable parts have done earlier. Explaining what happens in the present by reference to what happened in the past is the core of the phenomenon of the objective (behavioristic) aspect of memory. The attempt to simulate "memory" brings these facts very quickly to the fore.

19.4   THE NEW DYNAMICS

The "logic of mechanism," [1, 3] or of mathematics, which has been developed, does not attempt to dogmatize about what the real world may or may not be; its aim is to provide an absolutely unambiguous and rigorous framework of concepts and theorems in which ideas about the real world may find their exact expression. A similar and well-known example is given by the calculus, which enables the trained student to discuss velocities, rates of change of velocities, rates of change of rates of change of velocities, etc., without the least confusion. With this conceptual machinery, the student can tackle problems in the real world (that involve, say, fluctuating acceleration) with a security that is quite inaccessible to the untrained. The aim of the new logic of mechanism is to give security in discussion, not merely when the discussion is between two workers, but also when the worker discusses matters with himself, i.e., in his own thinking processes about the matter.

We will now examine some of the elementary concepts relating thinking processes to the operation of a general purpose computer. Any particular machine is defined by a set M of states. A watch may have its mainspring in many degrees of being wound up and its balance and other wheels in various positions; all these states form the set M. On the other hand, the state in which the mainspring is in three pieces, lying between the wheels, is not (usually) included in M. So to define M means simply to define and put bounds on what we are going to talk about.

Under the drives of nature—gravitational, electrical, chemical, etc.—things change; i.e., go from state to state. Of outstanding importance are those systems with the characteristic that their next state is uniquely determined by their immediately preceding state. This postulate is true of the great majority of systems that are treated in physics, and it is slowly being made true for the systems studied in physiology and psychology. When it is true, a *machine* can then be defined as a system whose behavior corresponds to a mapping of M into M. This definition has this advantage: it directly relates the essentially behavioristic concept of "machinelike behavior" to one of the fundamental concepts of mathematics. Once joined in this way, the concept can be related, as Bourbaki [5] has shown, to the whole rigorous world of mathematics.

If the machine has an input, then the mapping will have the form, essentially, of a table of double entry (though it may *look* very different if written in some other form). Thus if the machine M has states m_1, m_2, . . . and its input has values i_1, i_2, . . . , the canonical representation will be of the form shown:

		M			
		m_1	m_2	m_3	. . .
I	i_1	m_j	m_k	. . . .
	i_2	m_h	. . . .
	. . .	. . . .

If the machine is at state m_1, and the input is at state i_1, then the machine will move to m_j (where m_j is some state in M), and so on.

Such a form can obviously be represented in a computer, and the computer can readily be programed so that if the store I contains value (number) i_1, and the number in store M is m_1, then the number in M shall be changed to m_j, which it will find in the block of stores that are carrying the canonical representation.

In general, in the fully arbitrary machine, the mapping must be carried simply as a table which is to be read. Often, however, the mapping has internal relations, so that the computer can find the next value of M by some process. Such would happen if the new value were always $i_j + m_k$. When the computer copies some machines in this way, it is usually said to be "solving a difference equation."

There is no room here to develop the logic of mechanism fully. *Eléments de Mathématiques* [5] gives the principles; the mathematical details can be found in *Théorie des Ensembles*, especially in *Fascicule de Résultats*.[6]

19.5   WHAT IS A MODEL?

The new logic of mechanism has made possible an unequivocal answer to this question. The concept of "similarity" is well understood and exactly defined in the mathematical world of mappings, for these problems have been studied long before they were thought to have applications to brain physiology and psychology. In general, *simplifying* means "applying an equivalence relation," so that the set M is reduced, by grouping of its states, to a smaller set (called the "quotient" set). But if the simplifying is not to lead to mere nonsense, the simplified form must still be a machine, i.e., a mapping. So follows the consequence that a "model" must be *the quotient set of an equivalence relation that is compatible with the original mapping,* where *compatible* means "not losing the original property of being a machine."

This definition may seem somewhat distant from everyday practice, but it has the great value that it puts an absolute stop to vague disputes about whether something is a "proper" model of something else. It makes clear that all machines that resemble another machine in some well-defined way stand in the same fundamental "model" relationship to it. It also makes clear that all models (of a given system, such as a brain) can be related (by partial ordering) in their degree of closeness to the given system.

For example, a physicist may make a model, of jelly, shaped exactly like a brain, in order to study how concussion waves travel through it. In contrast, an electrician may use, as his model of the brain, a network of wires and hardware, to study how electrical impulses travel through it. Each model might be valid and yet the two might have no point at which they could be made comparable.

Not only has the new logic completely clarified the logical basis of what is meant by a "model"—it has also shown that there is no natural reason for restricting the concept to forms made in hardware. The quotient set may be in *any* form, perhaps in states of hardware or other physical forms, and also in mathematical or other symbolic forms, extending eventually even to the purely verbal form (i.e., to plain English) *provided the latter behaves with the strictest rigor and discipline.* Thus, in answering the question, "Of what use is a model?" one must bear in mind that the world of models includes the mathematical and even the precisely defined conceptual.

Since every machine corresponds to a mapping, which can always be represented by a process in a computer, and since every model of the machine is another mapping, it follows that the general purpose computer can, in principle, behave as any model of the original machine. Thus today, not only can the computer "model" the behavior of an airplane wing in flutter, it can also "model" the computational procedures of another computer. (This use of simulation proves to be a valuable aid in checking a computer's reliability, when a second computer of proven reliability is available.) Computer II is performing, step by step, the processes that computer I will execute if it follows its program correctly. The word "model" today means far more than it did twenty years ago!

With such facilities available, the research worker is challenged to use his imagination and then to use the facilities. Some of the ways in which models, in the general sense, can be of use in psychology, neurophysiology, and the social sciences will now be discussed.

19.6 VALUES OF SIMULATION MODELS

19.6.1 *Simulation for Vividness*. Simulation may be employed to emphasize and clarify some concept. Statements about machines in the abstract tend to be thin, unconvincing, and not provocative of further thinking. A model that shows a point vividly not only carries conviction, but stimulates the watcher into seeing all sorts of further consequences and developments. No worker in these subjects should deprive himself of the very strong stimulus of seeing a good model carry out some of these activities "before his very eyes."

A good teaching course today (to show the relations between mechanism and brainlike behavior) should contain the following demonstrations, which I believe to be minimal.

As an introduction, the Tortoise of W. Grey Walter [11] is ideal. Its principles are simple (if the engineering details are ignored), and it vividly demonstrates that a few primary rules, operating in a suitable environment, can lead to a remarkable complexity of goal-seeking behavior. At one stroke, the Tortoise disposes of a vast number of pseudo-philosophical questions, leaving the observer well prepared to proceed further in the theory of the subject.

After the Tortoise has given its display of rich protozoon-like behavior, a return to more disciplined thinking is desirable. The next step is to display what can be done by a formal "machine," as a mapping. It is easily made, using discreet states and steps in time, by a set of relays whose state (at time t) changes to a state (at time $t + 1$) that is a determinate function of what was the state at time t, and also what was the state of a set of "input" relays. The determinate function can be set up on a plugboard. The author built such a machine a few years ago, and it has proved invaluable for showing how various elementary types of behavior can be analyzed into an exactly defined mapping, and how this mapping will lead to behavior (on a row of lamps) that is obviously of the required type. This machine makes vivid the logic of mechanism, turning it into actual behavior while relinquishing nothing of the basic rigor. (See also Chapter 20.)

The student is now far removed from the vague and windy world of philosophy in which most beginners live when approaching the subject of mechanism and behavior. The next step for him is to advance to more complex behavior while still retaining a completely rigorous grasp of what is happening. One possible machine suitable for this step is the author's Homeostat,[3] which shows how a second-order degree of complexity in goal-seeking is logically implicit in certain general functional relationships. Other models are certainly possible here and should be made; but at the time of writing, the author knows no other.

When the student is sufficiently familiar with these machines to be able to dismiss them and their lessons as obvious, he will be ready to proceed on his own. But he himself, when he develops new processes and tries to explain them to others, will almost certainly find himself impelled to "dress up" the presentation, till it appears as a little stagelike show. For often, only when the onlooker sees the process in that form can he suddenly say, "I see what you mean." Thus, "simulation for vividness" can be regarded as a proper and important method by which science can advance.

19.6.2 *Simulation as Archive*. A second use of the model is one that has not so far developed appreciably; yet it is bound to become important in time. I refer to the use of a constructed model as an archive and repository for collected knowledge. A good example is given by our knowledge of the mechanisms at the base of the brain. Year by year, the physiologists and psychologists are adding fragments to the accumulated knowledge, and it is becoming only too evident that the parts are interrelated in a fearfully complex way. The neuronic centers responsible for reflexes and instincts act on the centers for the vegetative nervous system and on the endocrines; these act on each other, on the cerebral cortex, and on the muscles; these interact and have effects on the emotional centers, and so on, through a number of parts whose list is being added to almost daily. To describe all these parts piecemeal in a textbook of physiology and to expect the student to work out the interactions in his head is to give him a quite impossible task. It seems likely that a model must be built, either as an analog or as a program that can be added to, so that the student and advanced worker (and perhaps the diagnostician) will have available something that can answer the various questions that can arise. The model would then itself be both archive and computer.

Something of this type has happened in economics. Tustin [10] shows how models can be used to represent economic theories and to answer questions about their consequences. (See also Chapter 24 on simulation of international relations.)

19.6.3 *Simulation for Deduction and Exploration.*

Perhaps the most compelling reason for making models, whether in hardware or by computation, is that in this way the actual performance of a proposed mechanism can be established beyond dispute. In the past (as exemplified in Newton's *Principia*), questions about the behavior of a proposed mechanism were either solved by mathematics or they were merely talked about. In practice, for two thousand years, *mathematics* has meant "such processes as can be carried out with simple writing materials on not more than a few square feet of material." So mathematics tended to confine itself to the linear cases, in which solutions are often readily obtainable. This restriction was not serious in the physical sciences, in which the linear is common, but it was almost fatal in the biological, in which the nonlinear is ubiquitous and important. As a result, many biological theories and models remained untested, and doubtless many bad ones survived longer than they should have. Note, for instance, the idea that the molar functioning of the nervous system might be explained if every passage of a nervous impulse across a synapse left it increasingly ready to transmit a subsequent impulse. Such a property at the synapse must impose many striking properties on the organism's behavior as a whole, yet for fifty years no opinion could be given on its validity, for no one could deduce how such a system would behave if the process went on for a long time; the terminal behavior of such a system could only be guessed.

Today, such a process can readily be programed into a general purpose computer, and the ensuing behavior actually displayed. We may fully expect in the next decade or two to witness first a thorough re-examination of the well-known hypotheses that have come to us from the past, then the rejection of some as being quite foolish, and finally the emergence of modified forms that are ready for further testing.

Another of the questions that requires thorough testing is just what would happen if an organism lived *strictly* according to the rules of the conditioned reflex. Would it not tend to sink into an invariable routine of self-reinforcing reflexes, leading to its ultimate destruction by inflexibility? Again, what are the dynamics of a system of conductors that affect each other through a "threshold"? Such a system is very like a forest dry enough to be on the verge of spreading a fire: if the threshold (of inflammability) is just below the critical value, any fire tends to peter out; if it is just over the value, any fire tends to increase without limit, till the whole forest is burned out. This behavior does not sound very brainlike, but the matter cannot be discussed rigorously, for the dynamics are grossly non-linear and the mathematics too difficult for practical use. On a computer, however, such a process can be set in motion, and one can observe what actually happens.

Closely similar to this application of models is their use for exploration. There must be many new properties to be found in a system as unusual as a nerve network—and even more in a generalized dynamics—which is subject to enough constraint to give it structure (in the algebraic sense), yet free, as the brain is, from the constraint of energy conservation. In such systems, the trend toward equilibrium implies that the dynamic laws are acting selectively to the development of states that are *peculiarly self-preserving in relation to those laws*. These and a host of other interesting possibilities still await investigation.

Among the possibilities is one that deserves special mention. Equilibria are fundamentally important in biological systems. Homeostasis is simply another name for it, as are survival and adaptation.[3] But the ordinary system considered in physics is usually very poor in equilibria, either having only a few, or one, or (if it is ergodic) none at all—only a perpetual wandering. Very little attention has been given to, and very little is known about, *systems with many states of equilibrium*. Yet such systems must be important in biological theory. To have much "memory" is to be able to keep traces of physical events *unchanging in time;* and this invariance is an essential component of the concept of equilibrium. At the present time, the only non-living systems we know of with this property are such trivialities as a dish of sand, whose grains can rest in any one of a great number of configurations. However, this system is too little dynamic to show much of interest. The computer is clearly the device of choice with which to explore this interesting topic.

19.7   DIGITAL OR ANALOG?

It must be admitted at once that today's digital computers are not well suited to carrying out a process that represents the behavior of large numbers of parts, such as those in a nerve net, that in reality act simultaneously. The reason is that today's computers mostly act by finding what part 1 would do, then part 2, and so on. Only when *all* the parts' next values have been computed can the machine compute the next value of the whole. As a result, if the net is, say, 1000 by 1000 in parts (i.e., a million in all) and if the computation for one part takes a millisecond, the whole will take over a quarter of an hour to advance by one step in time. If the system were made of relays, able to act simultaneously, the steps could be achieved at about 10 per second, i.e., about ten thousands times as fast. True, some computers are now being designed so that several computations can go on simultaneously, but those who wish to explore processes of this type would do well to consider whether some analog of parts that can all act simultaneously would not be preferable.

Today's so-called general purpose computer is really very specialized: it can carry out an *arbitrary* process only after the programer has exercised some ingenuity. Thus, although it can carry out an operation, such as "multiply two numbers," readily, the programer must impose on to it a very artificial and selected sequence if it is to carry out so simple an operation (on two strings of digits) as "in between the digits of the one insert the digits of the other," though this operation, on the digits, is much simpler than the multiplication.

The truly general computer, as the logic of mechanism shows, would be a machine on which could be represented any mapping of a product set into one of its components, of $I \times M$ into M, for instance. Changes on M here represent the process, and changes on I represent arbitrary changes, imposed by the operator, on the input. So far as I know, only one machine of this type has been made (and that almost a toy). The possibility that further developments in this direction might be of use in the behavioral sciences may be worth consideration.

19.8   SUMMARY

"Simulation of the brain" can be carried out in a variety of forms, and some deep thinking on matters of principle is called for, if the result is not to be an example of advanced technique being used to achieve a result that conceptually is merely medieval.

Worthwhile reasons for simulation include:

a. The presentation of a relation between structure and function in some way that, by its vividness, enables the onlooker to grasp the significance of the relation much more fully than when it is stated in colder and more abstract form.

b. The building of a complex system to be an accurate analog of some other system that is too complex to be treated either in words, or in mathematical form, or in thought. A model of a river estuary, to show silting and its changes, would be of this type. So would be a model to bring together all the facts known about the instinctive, reflex, endocrine, and related systems lying at the base of the brain.

c. Building an analog of a theory, so that the analog could show, relatively quickly and easily, what are the consequences, especially the ultimate consequences, of the given theory.

REFERENCES

1 Ashby, W. R., *An Introduction to Cybernetics*. London: Chapman & Hall, 1956.

2 ———, Computers and Decision-making, *New Scientist, 7*, Mar. 24, 1960, 746.

3 ———, *Design for a Brain*. 2d ed. London: Chapman & Hall, 1960.

4 ———, The Mechanism of Habituation, *Symposium Mech. Thought Proc.* London: Her Majesty's Stationery Office, 1958.

5 Bourbaki, N., *Eléments de Mathématiques*. Paris: Hermann et Cie., 1939–. (First of several volumes.)

6 ———, Théorie des Ensembles; Fascicule de Résultats, *A.S.E.I.* (No. 1141), 1959. Paris: Hermann et Cie.

7 Pitts, W., and McCulloch, W. S., A Logical Calculus of the Ideas Immanent in Nervous Activity, *Bull. Math. Biophys., 5* (No. 4), December 1943, 115–33.

8 Shannon, C. E., and Weaver, W., *The Mathematical Theory of Communication*. Urbana, Ill.: Univ. Illinois Press, 1949.

9 Sommerhoff, G., *Analytical Biology*. Oxford: Clarendon Press, 1950.

10 Tustin, A., *The Mechanism of Economic Systems*. London: Heinemann, 1953.

11 Walter, W. Grey, An Imitation of Life, *Scientific American, 182*, May 1950, 42–45.

James T. Culbertson
20/NERVE NET THEORY

*James T. Culbertson, Yale '34,
majored in zoology while an undergraduate,
then studied philosophy and taught logic
and ethics at the University of Pennsylvania
until 1937 when he returned to Yale.
Since graduating from college, his main interest
has always been the mind-brain problem,
as evidenced by his doctor's thesis in the
philosophy of science, The Place of the Sense World
in Physical Theory, Yale University,
1940. He taught mathematics and physics
in a Navy program and then philosophy at Michigan
State. He worked with nerve nets on the
Committee on Mathematical Biology at Chicago,
1947–49, and taught philosophy at
the University of Southern California until 1951.
He was then on the "robots team" at The
RAND Corporation as research associate for
two years before coming to California State Polytechnic College
where he now teaches philosophy and mathematics.*

20.1 INTRODUCTION

The psychologist wishes to understand organic behavior—the stimulus-response or input-output properties of animals and human beings. Until recently there had been no psychologically interesting artificial behavior. But now we have computers and automata. The behavior of these man-made objects shows some interesting parallels to the behavior of natural organisms, and the study of these stimulus-response machines has suggested many possible brain mechanisms to the psychologist.

But a much more basic behavioral study investigates the general principles of behavior regardless of how they may happen to be exhibited in this organism or that machine. This general theory of automata, or nerve net theory, uses the neuron as a universal element.

Neurons, as herein defined, are called "universal elements" because any given behavior (set of stimulus-response properties) can be mediated by some assemblage of them. For any specified behavior, we can design some nerve net to exhibit that behavior. Thus human behavior, whatever may be its mechanisms, has some place within this general theory,

and the further the psychologist extends nerve net theory the more behavioral possibilities it will reveal.

There is a great variety of hardware in electronic computers and other
digital "robots." But whatever their components, the logical structure of
any such devices can be represented by "neurons," very simple conducting
elements, all essentially similar. The theory of automata, which includes
the study of computers as a special case, analyzes robots into these logically
primitive components.[7]

Neurons can form nerve nets in an infinite number of ways. The receptor
neurons receive stimuli so as to start impulses into the net, which may have
any number of central neurons, while impulses from the net can leave
through the effector neurons to cause responses.

FIGURE 20.1 Receptor
neuron with one end-
bulb.

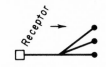

FIGURE 20.2 Receptor
neuron with three
endbulbs.

Each neuron under consideration here has one entrance and
one or more exits. In the illustrations, the left end of any
neuron is its entrance and the
right ends are exits. Thus the
neuron in Figure 20.1 has one
exit. The neuron in Figure
20.2 has three exits, etc. Like-
wise in the nerve nets (Figures 20.6–20.13), the exits of each neuron are
easily seen. In Figures 20.6 and 20.7, each neuron has one exit. In Figure
20.8, three of the neurons have one exit, and the other two each have
two exits, etc.

An impulse starting from a neuron's entrance travels to each of its exits.
If there is more than one exit as, for example, in Figures 20.2 and 20.4,
it reaches all of them simultaneously. The time it takes for an impulse to
pass all the way through a neuron and then start an impulse in another
neuron (or start a response if it is an effector neuron) is the same via all
exits and is called the "action time" of the neuron. Customarily, this action time—specified as the same for all neurons—is taken as the unit for
measuring time. For convenience, let the action time be 1 millisecond.[7]
If an impulse starts in the receptor neuron in Figure 20.6, then an impulse
starts in the next neuron 1 ms later; in the next, 2 ms later; and in the
effector neuron, 3 ms later; then, this impulse starts a response 4 ms later.

In the nerve nets below, all impulse paths through a net traverse the same
number of neurons, and there are no cyclic paths. Hence the time it takes

for an impulse to go all the way through any given net is the same regardless of the path it takes. This is called the "reaction time" of the net. In Figure 20.7, the reaction time is 2 ms. In Figures 20.8 and 20.9, the reaction time is 3 ms. In Figure 20.10, it is 6 ms.

20.2   THE THREE KINDS OF NEURONS

The entrance to a *receptor neuron* is a receptor ($\square$) and each exit is an endbulb ($\bullet$ or $\circ$), as shown in Figures 20.1 and 20.2. Endbulbs are either excitatory ($\bullet$) or inhibitory ($\circ$), both kinds being shown, for example, in Figure 20.8. Each excitatory bulb, when active, tends to start an impulse from the synapse it contacts, as will be explained later; each inhibitory bulb tends to prevent such an impulse from starting.

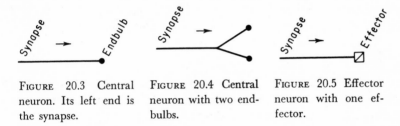

FIGURE   20.3   Central neuron. Its left end is the synapse.

FIGURE   20.4   Central neuron with two endbulbs.

FIGURE   20.5   Effector neuron with one effector.

The entrance to a *central neuron* is a synapse and each exit is an endbulb, as shown in Figures 20.3 and 20.4.

The entrance to an *effector neuron* is a synapse and each exit is an effector, as shown, for example, in Figure 20.5.

Using these three kinds of neurons, we form nerve nets by bringing endbulbs and synapses into contact. Thus the endbulb of each neuron in Figure 20.6 "contacts" the synapse of the neuron at its right, and each receptor neuron in Figure 20.7 has an endbulb on the effector neuron, whereas in Figure 20.8, the synapse of the central neuron is contacted by five endbulbs. The two rules of nerve net construction are *(1) each endbulb must contact exactly one synapse; (2) each synapse must be contacted by at least one endbulb.*[2]

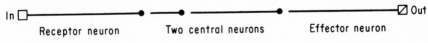

In $\square$ ——————————•   •———————•   ————————$\square$ Out

Receptor neuron   Two central neurons   Effector neuron

FIGURE   20.6 Stimulus fires receptor. Neurons conduct the impulse to effector. Effector activates some output devices. Each neuron fires one ms after the one before. Reaction time is 4 ms.

20.3   NEURON ACTIVITY. THRESHOLDS. PULSE REGULATION

If an impulse starts from the entrance of a neuron, then that neuron is said to "fire." Also we may say that its entrance (receptor or synapse) fires, which is taken to mean the same thing. Receptors fire because of stimuli from the environment, whereas the firing of synapses is controlled by the endbulbs contacting them. When a neuron fires, the impulse proceeds to all its endbulbs (or effectors), making them active, and then the endbulbs (or effectors) cease their activity and "die." This is merely a convenient term for whatever it is that happens in each endbulb. So, in regard to terms, receptors and synapses *fire,* and endbulbs and effectors *die.* In this analysis, the actual physical nature of the endbulb activity is as logically irrelevant as the nature of the impulse that leads to it. The logically important statement is merely: *If a neuron fires at any time* t *then all its endbulbs (or effectors) die at* t + 1. The time $t + 1$ is, of course, 1 ms after t since time is measured in milliseconds.

Whether a synapse fires is determined, in part, by its *threshold.* The threshold of any synapse is designated by θ and equals some integer. Roughly speaking, the higher its threshold the harder it is to make it fire. Thus $\theta = 2$ on the synapse in Figure 20.7 and $\theta = 2$ on the central neuron in Figure 20.8, etc. If the value of θ is not indicated on a synapse, it is understood that $\theta = 1$. In Figure 20.6, for example, $\theta = 1$ at each synapse.

Synapse-firing rule: *A synapse fires at any time if and only if* $E - I \geqq \theta$ *where* E *is the number of excitatory bulbs contacting it which die at that time and* I *is the number of inhibitory bulbs contacting it which die at that time.*

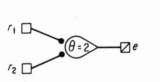

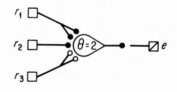

FIGURE 20.7 The synapse is enlarged for convenience.

FIGURE 20.8 The third receptor neuron has two inhibitory bulbs.

If just r_1 in Figure 20.7 fires at any particular time t, then only one of the excitatory endbulbs contacting the synapse dies at $t + 1$. So $E = 1$

at $t + 1$ and $I = 0$, since no inhibitory bulbs contact the synapse. Since $E - I$ is less than θ, the synapse does not fire at $t + 1$. The same is true, of course, if just r_2 fires. On the other hand, if both receptors fire at t, then $E - I = 2$ at $t + 1$, so the synapse fires at $t + 1$.

In Figure 20.8, note the influence of inhibitory bulbs on the synapse of the central neuron. For example, suppose all three receptors fire at t. Then at $t + 1$ we have $E = 3$ and $I = 2$. So this synapse does not fire at $t + 1$, since $E - I$ is less than θ. On the other hand, if just r_1 and r_2 fire at t, then $E - I \geqq \theta$ at $t + 1$, so it fires at $t + 1$.

It is assumed that the receptors in a net are *pulse regulated* in the sense that they can fire only at integer values of t. Thus the receptors can fire only when $t = 1$, or 2, or 3, or some other integer, time being measured in milliseconds from some time origin. They cannot fire when $t = 2\frac{1}{2}$ or $3\frac{1}{4}$ or any other non-integer. Obviously, with the receptors pulse regulated, the entire net becomes pulse regulated, because the action time of each neuron is 1 ms.[2]

20.4 INPUT-OUTPUT PROPERTIES

In a nerve net, the receptors that fire cause impulses to start into the net, and which receptors fire determines which effectors the impulses ultimately reach. These stimulus-response properties of the net can be conveniently expressed by listing for each input the resulting output. Let the receptors be labeled r_1, r_2, r_3, . . . , r_k, . . . , r_n.

The set of receptors firing at any time is the *input* at that time. The input is represented by a binary number. The rightmost digit of this number is a 1 if r_1 fires and a 0 if r_1 does not fire. The second digit (from the right) is a 1 if r_2 fires and a 0 if r_2 does not fire. The third digit (from the right) is a 1 if r_3 fires and a 0 if r_3 does not fire, etc.

In general, the input is indicated by the binary number whose kth digit (from the right) is 1 if r_k fires, and 0 if r_k does not fire. Thus, in Figure 20.7, 01 represents the input where r_1 fires and r_2 does not fire. The case where neither receptor fires is called the "null" input, 00. The net in Figure 20.7 has four possible inputs: 00, 01, 10, and 11. The input-output properties of this net are therefore completely expressed by the table

in	00	01	10	11
out	0	0	0	1

In the output row we have a 0 or a 1, according as the effector is or is not activated. So the last column, for example, shows that when both receptors fire the effector is activated. (If we altered the net so as to make $\theta = 1$ on the synapse, then the output row would read 0, 1, 1, and 1.)

Look now at Figure 20.8, which is an arbitrarily chosen illustration. There are three receptors, so there are the inputs shown in the following table where we see that only two inputs, 001 and 011, lead to a response.

in	000	001	010	011	100	101	110	111
out	0	1	0	1	0	0	0	0

Raising the threshold decreases the number of inputs that cause a response: e.g., if we let $\theta = 3$ on the central neuron, we would get the output row 0, 0, 0, 1, 0, 0, 0, 0. On the other hand, lowering the threshold gives more 1's in the output row. Thus if we let $\theta = 1$ we would have 0, 1, 1, 1, 0, 0, 0, 1. And if we let $\theta = 0$ we would have 1, 1, 1, 1, 0, 1, 0, 1. (Note that if $\theta \lesssim 0$, a synapse fires spontaneously every millisecond, except insofar as it may be prevented by inhibitory bulbs.) Suppose the threshold was still lower. If we let $\theta = -1$ the output row would be 1, 1, 1, 1, 0, 1, 1, 1; and finally for $\theta = -2$, e would respond for any input.

20.5   A COUNTING NET

We shall consider now a case involving several effectors. The counting net in Figure 20.9 is so constructed that its response indicates the number of receptors that fire. We may think of effector e_1 as causing a "1" to appear, e.g., lighting a light bulb with a "1" on it. Similarly a "2" appears if e_2 is activated and a "3" if e_3. Thus the number of receptors firing at t is indicated by the response at $t + 3$; e.g., if any two receptors fire, then only e_2 is activated, as shown by the fourth, sixth, and seventh columns of the in-out table.

in	000	001	010	011	100	101	110	111
out	000	001	001	010	001	010	010	100

The reader should examine the net to see that it has the counting properties specified above. For instance, note that if r_2 and r_3 fire, then the first two central cells fire, and then just e_2 responds, as specified in the next to the last column.

20.6   LARGER COUNTING NETS

Using four receptor, four central, and four effector neurons we can construct a net for counting up to 4. Each receptor neuron will have an excitatory bulb on each central neuron, and the fourth central synapse will have $\theta = 4$. Using this method, nets can count any number of simultaneous receptor firings.

Note that the in-out table doubles for each receptor added to the net. For three receptors there are eight possible inputs, and hence eight columns as shown in the above table; for four receptors there are 16 possible inputs:

$$0000, \ 0001, \ 0010, \ 0011, \ 0100, \ 0101, \ 0110, \ 0111,$$
$$1000, \ 1001, \ 1010, \ 1011, \ 1100, \ 1101, \ 1110, \ 1111$$

namely, the first 16 binary numbers starting from 0000. For five receptors there are 32 possible inputs—the first 32 binary numbers starting with 00000.* In general, the number of possible inputs equals 2^n, where n is the number of receptors. Hence as n increases, the table soon becomes unhandy. But the in-out properties of these counting nets are completely specified just by n and the statement of function in Figure 20.9, so no long in-out tables are necessary. Likewise, in any net to satisfy some sufficiently simple functional relation between input and output, the statement of the function would soon become handier than the in-out table as n increases.

20.7   USING THE SIMPLEST COMPONENTS

In any counting net built as in Figure 20.9, each receptor neuron has n endbulbs, and n endbulbs contact each central synapse. We shall assume, however, some maximum number of endbulbs that a neuron can have and also a maximum number of bulbs that can contact one synapse. If the number of receptors exceeds these maxima, some question might arise as to whether the counting net could be constructed. But there is no difficulty: *For any net (counting net or any other net) there is a net satisfying the same in-out table and containing no neuron with more than two endbulbs and no synapse contacted by more than two endbulbs.* In other words, we never need neurons with more than two bulbs and we

---

* Of course the number of possible inputs, and hence the number of columns in the in-out table, depends only on the number of receptors, not on the type of net nor on the number of effectors.

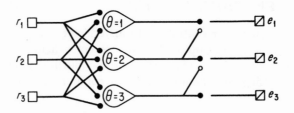

FIGURE 20.9 A counting net. If k receptors fire at t then just e_k responds at $t + 3$.

never need more than two bulbs at any synapse, provided, of course, that we may increase the reaction time and also the number of central neurons.

To prove that any neuron with more than two bulbs can be replaced by a plurality of neurons each with only one or two bulbs, let a two-bulb neuron, x, contact two different two-bulb neurons. Let these two neurons each contact two different two-bulb neurons, and then let these four neurons each contact two different two-bulb neurons, etc. We see that if x fires at t then 2^k bulbs die at $t + k$. Also, substituting one-bulb neurons for two-bulb neurons anywhere desired, it is obvious that if x fires at t then 2^k bulbs *or fewer* can be made to fire at $t + k$. Hence, for any net there is some net satisfying the same in-out table and using only one-bulb and two-bulb neurons. (It is understood that time delays are introduced wherever needed by inserting neurons so that the reaction time of the net is the same for all inputs.)

To prove that any neuron contacted by more than two bulbs can be replaced by a plurality of neurons each contacted by one or two bulbs involves a proof more lengthy than the above, but perfectly straightforward, and we leave it as an exercise for the reader.

How can one design a counting net in such a way that the complexity of the components does not increase with the number of receptors? To illustrate, let us use the simplest components possible: Each neuron has only one or two bulbs and only one or two bulbs contact any synapse. Figure 20.10 shows a method whereby we can count any number of receptor firings using only these simplest components. If $n = 6$, how many central neurons would be required using this method? Note that, in general, the simpler the components, the more central cells must be used and the longer the reaction time.

These simplest components can always suffice, but to illustrate the general principles of nerve net construction, we shall hereafter use neurons with as many branches as we wish and synapses as large as we wish.

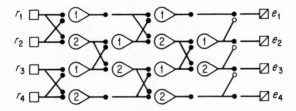

FIGURE 20.10 A counting net.

20.8 SOME OTHER NERVE NETS

There are many kinds of counting nets. Instead of a different effector responding for each different number of receptor firings, the net may count directly in the binary system. In this case, the "readout" can appear in a register in which e_1 controls the first digit window (the rightmost) and e_2 controls the second digit window, etc. The first (rightmost) digit is a 1 if e_1 responds and a 0 if e_1 does not respond. The second digit is a 1 if e_2 responds and a 0 if e_2 does not. Similarly for e_3, etc. Thus, if any one receptor fires, then the register shows the number . . .0001. If two fire, it shows . . .0010, etc. If, for example, eleven receptors fire, the number . . .001011 appears in the register. The number of 0's at the left is determined, of course, by the size of the register. Let the number of receptors be three, i.e., $n = 3$. Then there are just two effectors e_1 and e_2. We can use a two-place register and the output row of the in-out table (see table in Section 20.5 above) would read 00, 01, 01, 10, 01, 10, 10, 11.

The student should see how to construct this nerve net using three receptor neurons, three central neurons, and two effector neurons. The net is exactly like Figure 20.9 until we come to the connections from the third central neuron to the effector neurons. This neuron has an excitatory bulb on each of the two effector neurons (remove the third effector neuron). Thus, if h receptors fire, then the number h (expressed in the binary system) occurs in the register. The reader should now diagram a binary counting net for $n = 4$, by putting in another receptor cell, another central cell, and another effector cell. Thus he will become more skilled in this game of small nerve nets, where general principles of in-out digital devices can be illustrated in miniature.

The effectors of the counting net could operate a register in which the readout was in the decimal system. This would obviously require more central neurons.

Counting nets can be used to discriminate lengths, areas, and intensities, or any other properties of the stimulus configuration that can be measured by a number. Also they can form parts of numerical nets for adding, subtracting, multiplying, and dividing.[1] To illustrate, the student might design a subtracting net, say with two receptors labeled p_1 and p_2 and two receptors labeled q_1 and q_2. We want the response to indicate the number, m, of active p-receptors minus the number, s, of active q-receptors. The effectors can be labeled e_{-2}, e_{-1}, e_0, e_1, e_2, the subscripts being the five possible values of $m - s$. He should construct the net so that if m p-receptors fire and s q-receptors fire then just e_{m-s} responds Δ ms later, where Δ is the reaction time. For instance, if two of the p-receptors and one of the q-receptors fire at t, then just e_1 responds at $t + \Delta$. Should he find this miniature subtracting net interesting, he might design a multiplying nerve net: The response is to indicate the number of active p-receptors times the number of active q-receptors.

We have examined counting nets for counting simultaneous events but there are also nets for counting successive events and nets for any other numerical or logical operations.[2] We have stressed the counting net only because it is an easily understood example for illustrating certain properties true of any net.

20.9   FORM PERCEPTION

Let us see how a net can perceive shape or form. In the nets below, the form is not abstracted from its position, size, and rotation. This is a very serious restriction, because the shape the net is constructed to recognize can elicit the response only if it has some fixed position, size, and angular rotation. There are nets, larger than we can examine here, that can perceive the specified shape or shapes abstracted from the Gestalt transformations of position, size, and rotation. Thus a net can be designed to recognize, for instance, an **F** wherever it may fall on the retina (array of receptors over a surface) or whatever size it may be (within obvious limits) and however it may be tilted.[1, 4, 5, 6]

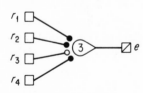

FIGURE 20.11 Effector.

In Figure 20.11, effector e responds at $t + 2$ if, and only if, r_1, r_2, and r_4 fire at t and r_3 does not fire at t. This is a response to an extremely simple image, 1011. The method illustrated is completely general, however complex the image. It is required that effector neuron g fire only for some given subset S of the net's receptors. On g, let each receptor neuron have either an excitatory or an inhibitory bulb, according as either it is or is not a member of S, and let $\theta = m$ where m is the number of members of S. Then g fires only for S.

The student should design the following nerve net using the method described and illustrated above: Given seven receptor neurons and an effector neuron g, design a net such that g fires just for the image 1101101. Remember the right-to-left convention, whereby the state of r_1 is indicated by the rightmost digit.

Clearly we may have any number of effectors, each recognizing a different image: Given six receptor neurons and two effector neurons, g_1 and g_2, design a net such that g_1 fires just for the form 101110 and g_2 just for the form 110101. Here each receptor neuron will have two branches, one going to g_1 and the other going to g_2.

20.10 NETS TO SEE IMAGES RESEMBLING A GIVEN IMAGE

Certain images resemble each other more closely than do others. Thus 1001 resembles 1011 more closely than 0100 resembles 1011. The net in Figure 20.11 responds just to 1011 as shown in the in-out table below. Now we wish to alter the net so that it responds not only to this "just right" image, but to the four other forms that most closely resemble this just right image, namely, 0011, 1001, 1010, and 1111. (Each of these differs from 1011 in only *one* digit.) What change must we make in the net? Obviously, all we need to do is lower the threshold from 3 to 2. The resulting output is shown in the third row of the table. Furthermore, suppose we wish the net to respond not only to 1011 and to the four images that differ from 1011 in just one digit but also to the eleven that differ from 1011 in *two* digits. For this, we lower the threshold to 1, as shown in the fourth row.

in	0000	0001	0010	0011	0100	0101	0110	0111	1000	1001	1010	1011	1100	1101	1110	1111
$(\theta = 3)$ out	0	0	0	0	0	0	0	0	0	0	0	1	0	0	0	0
$(\theta = 2)$ out	0	0	0	1	0	0	0	0	0	1	1	1	0	0	0	1
$(\theta = 1)$ out	0	1	1	1	0	0	0	1	1	1	1	1	0	1	1	1
$(\theta = 0)$ out	1	1	1	1	0	1	1	1	1	1	1	1	1	1	1	1

In general, consider any net constructed so as to respond to one just right image where the net has n receptors and m of them are in S. Then, on g, $\theta = m$ as indicated in Figure 20.11. Now lower the threshold so $\theta = m - k$. Then the net will respond to exactly N images each differing from the just right form in k digits or less, where

$$N = \sum_{i=0}^{k} {}_{n}C_{i}$$

Here ${}_{n}C_{i}$ means the number of combinations of n things taken i at a time.

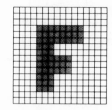

FIGURE 20.12 Receptors in a retina.

In Figure 20.12, the little squares are receptors in a retina. Suppose the blacked squares indicate the particular image that the net (not shown) is to recognize. Following the method outlined in Section 20.9, we let each blacked receptor neuron have an excitatory bulb on the effector neuron g and each unblacked neuron have an inhibitory bulb on g. (See also Section 20.7.) And we let $\theta = m$ where m is the number of blacked receptors. Then g will fire if, and only if, the **F** image falls on the retina precisely as shown in the figure. This is a very strict requirement. There is a response if, and only if, every blacked receptor fires and no other receptor fires. Only the specific image is adequate. Suppose we constructed this nerve net with all the accessories and environment of a bibliophile, lenses for focusing images, nerve nets for turning pages, etc. Still the probability of the just right **F** image hitting the retina might be very small.

Making $\theta = m - 1$ would be slightly more practical, since not only the just right image but any one of n other nearly right images could fire g; that is, any image resembling the just right image except that either one unblacked (background) receptor fires or else one blacked (figure) receptor fails to fire.

Making $\theta = m - 2$ would allow $_nC_2$ additional inputs to fire g, these resembling the just right image a little less closely. Making $\theta = m - 3$ would allow $_nC_3$ more inputs to fire g, etc. As we lower the threshold, considerable image tolerance develops. The image can be wobbled around a little or be slightly deformed, small lacunae can occur within the figure and small islands outside it in the ground. There would be some optimum value of θ, depending in part on the size of the retina and on how much we would allow an image to differ from the standard **F** image and still be able to elicit a response.

This net recognizes a form in a particular position and size with as much tolerance as we want, as mentioned above. But it does not recognize the abstract form. That is, we cannot move the **F** sidewise or vertically, or change its size, or rotate it except within the limits of tolerance. There are, however, as we have already said, some very nice form abstractors, such that g would fire even though the **F** image was moved about on the retina, or changed in size, or rotated, or replaced by its mirror image. These nets have many central cells and would require a longer discussion than we can give here. But the above net is a very important accessory whereby we could get very good results with a very "cheap model" form abstractor. Of course, many different images can be run through the same form abstractor and then diverted to their different appropriate effectors.

20.11 NETS SATISFYING IN-OUT TABLES AND OTHER CONSTRAINTS

Given a net, it is easy, though perhaps tedious, to determine its in-out properties by examining thresholds and endbulbs at synapses. We can express these properties by an in-out table so that for any input we can read, from the table, the resulting output.

It is, however, the more interesting reverse problem that we wish to examine here. Given the in-out table, how can we construct a net that will satisfy that table? In addition to the in-out table there may be some other constraints, such as limiting the number of central neurons allowed or the reaction time.

We shall continue to use our miniature nerve nets as illustrations. A typical problem would be—using only two central neurons, design a net satisfying the in-out table:

in	000	001	010	011	100	101	110	111
out	1000	1011	1000	1011	1000	0110	0110	0110

In working out this problem, we note first of all that there are three receptors, since each input is a three-place number, and there are four effectors. Draw in the receptor neurons r_1, r_2 and r_3 and the effector neurons with effectors e_1, e_2, e_3, and e_4, leaving enough room for the central neurons. Then figure out how to connect the receptor neurons to the two central neurons and then the central neurons to the effector neurons and the thresholds so that the above in-out table is satisfied.

The beginner may encounter difficulty in solving certain problems in this game of miniature nerve nets. (If the reader finds difficulty with the foregoing problem, he might try the simpler nets in the next paragraph first.) For any problem to be meaningful, it must, of course, present a bona fide in-out table; e.g., the outputs must all have the same number of digits and the number of columns must be 2^n where n is the number of digits in each input. For a solution to be possible, the constraints must be such that a net satisfying them can actually be designed. For each in-out table, some minimum number of central neurons is required. We can use more than this minimum number of neurons in designing the net, but of course we cannot use fewer.

Consider, for example, the problem: Without using any central neurons, design a net satisfying the in-out table whose output row is 0, 0, 0, 1. The solution is shown in Figure 20.7. Also consider the same problem except that the output row is to read 1, 1, 0, 1. Again the solution is very simple. But now consider the problem: Without using any central neurons, design a net satisfying the in-out table whose output row is 1, 0, 0, 1. This problem has no solution since two central neurons are needed for these in-out specifications. The student should draw this net using two central neurons. Also he should do the same given the output row 0, 1, 1, 0.

Without using any central neurons, design a net satisfying the in-out table whose output row is 001, 000, 011, 010, 101, 100, 111, 100. Using no neurons with more than two endbulbs and no synapses contacted by more than two endbulbs, design a nerve net satisfying the in-out table whose output row is 000, 011, 000, 011, 000, 110, 110, 110.

In Section 20.13 we shall see that for any given in-out table it is theoretically possible to design a net that satisfies that table. By *theoretically possible* we mean that there is no uncertainty as to procedure. Of course, for a large net it might not be feasible to design the net, just as it would not be feasible to write down the first 10^{100} integers using paper and pencil, although this is theoretically possible; i.e., there is no uncertainty about the procedure.

20.12   THE NUMBER OF BEHAVIORALLY DIFFERENT NETS

To speak of the behavior of a nerve net we shall suppose it is to be inserted in, and part of, a robot. The receptors are at fixed places on, or in, the robot, and the effectors contact output power devices of some kind (muscles, motors, etc.). The receptors differ in position and they may also be of different kinds (photoceptors, chemoceptors, tactile receptors, etc.), so the firing of one set of receptors is always a different input from the firing of any other set of receptors. Similarly, the effectors differ in position and perhaps also in kind, so the activity of one set of effectors is a different output from the activity of any other set of effectors.[3]

Now let us consider a robot with n receptors and μ effectors and see how many behaviorally different ways the n receptors and μ effectors could be interconnected by a nerve net. We may think of the n receptors and μ

effectors as already fixed in the robot, and now we wish to investigate the number of behaviorally different ways a net could interconnect them.

The input row in the table of any net is determined merely by how many receptors it has, and then the output row is filled in according to the in-out properties of the net. It is interesting to see how many different in-out tables there are for n receptors and μ effectors. It is interesting because the number of such in-out tables (for a fixed value of n and a fixed value of μ) is so much larger than one might at first suppose.

Consider, for example, nets with three receptors ($n = 3$) and three effectors ($\mu = 3$). How many behaviorally different nets are there? Two nets differ behaviorally if, and only if, their in-out tables differ. Here a little arithmetic shows us that there are 16,777,216 behaviorally different nets with three receptors and three effectors. Each of these is indicated by a different way of filling in the output row below.

in	000	001	010	011	100	101	110	111
out								

There are eight ways to insert the output for the input 000 and eight ways to insert the output for the input 001, etc. Hence there are 8^8 behaviorally different nets having three receptors and three effectors. Each would give us a behaviorally different robot.

Of course, one robot is completely paralyzed (all 0's in the output row), and 195,840 of them are partially paralyzed (one or two effectors never respond), but the vast majority of them make use of all their effectors.

A small percentage of the robots are partly or completely paralyzed as just mentioned, and also the same small percentage have one or more continously active effectors, and likewise a few have only two or three responses. There are, however, $8! = 40,320$ of them that give a different response to each input, while only eight give the same response to all inputs.

It might be interesting to classify the behaviorally different cases, but that is not our purpose here. In this section, we merely wished to point out that if a nerve net has n receptors and μ effectors, then there are $2^{\mu 2^n}$ behaviorally different ways it could be constructed.

20.13   NETS SATISFYING ANY GIVEN IN-OUT TABLE

In Section 20.11, we were given in-out tables and then found nerve nets to satisfy them. In each case, we designed a net with behavioral properties satisfying the table. One might ask whether there is any in-out table for which no net can be designed. The answer is "no." Given any in-out table there is some net satisfying it. Moreover there is a general method for constructing the net. We wish to explain this general procedure here. By this means, we can design a net having any in-out properties we want.

All reaction times will be 3 ms, using this method, and the essential feature of the method is that there is a different central neuron for each input—each input causes its specific central neuron to fire. Only one central neuron can fire at a time, the one specific to the input that has occurred 1 ms before.

Perhaps the easiest way to explain will be to take a simple example first and then give the completely general directions later. Let us construct the net satisfying the in-out table

in	00	01	10	11
out	011	010	100	110

The table shows two receptors (and hence $2^2 = 4$ inputs) and three effectors. We proceed as follows:

1. Draw in the two receptors r_1, r_2, the three effectors e_1, e_2, e_3, and four central neurons.
2. Label the central neurons with the input numbers.*
3. On each central neuron let θ equal the number of 1's in its label.
4. On each effector neuron let $\theta = 1$.
5. Let r_k have one bulb on each central neuron. This bulb is excitatory or inhibitory, according as the kth digit in the neuron's label is a 1 or a 0.

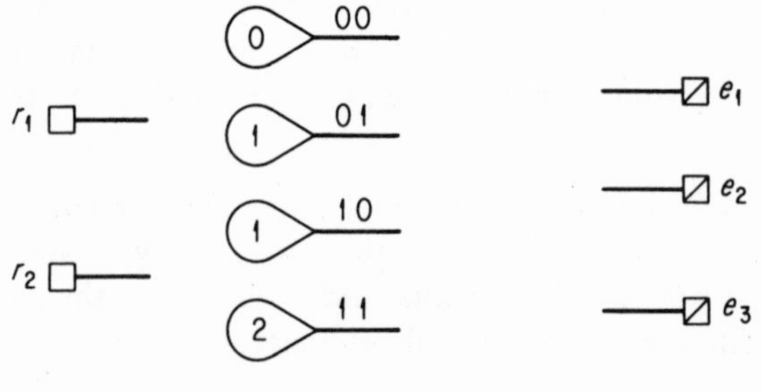

FIGURE 20.13 The general method.

6. Let each central neuron, c, have an excitatory bulb on e_j if, and only if, the jth digit in the output for the label of c is a 1.

* The first four steps are shown in Figure 20.13, the remaining steps in Figure 20.14.

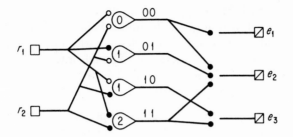

FIGURE 20.14 The completed general method.

Regarding step 5, note that r_1 has an inhibitory bulb on the first central cell because the first (rightmost) digit in the cell's label is a 0, and r_1 has an excitatory bulb on the second central cell because the first digit in that cell's label is a 1, etc. Similarly r_2 has an inhibitory bulb on the first central cell because the second digit in the cell's label is a 0, and r_2 has an inhibitory bulb on the second central cell because the second digit in its label is a 0, etc.

Regarding step 6, note that the first central cell contacts e_1 and e_2. This follows from the fact that input 00 is to have the output 011 according to the in-out table. Similarly step 6 indicates the other throughput to output contacts.

The student should check the net carefully to see that its behavior is that specified by the in-out table. Also he should try one or two other examples to develop confidence that he can design a nerve net with any given in-out properties. The procedure is made general by substituting the following for step 1: Draw in the n receptors $r_1, r_2, \ldots, r_k, \ldots, r_n$, the μ effectors $e_1, e_2, \ldots, e_j, \ldots, e_\mu$, and 2^n central neurons.

Use the general method to design a net satisfying the in-out table whose output row is 01, 01, 01, 00, 10, 11, 00, 10. Fill in the output row of an eight-column table in any way and then design the net having the indicated behavioral properties.

The general method always uses more central neurons than needed; i.e., no in-out table requires 2^n central neurons; however, it is a completely systematic method.

In this general method, each receptor neuron has n endbulbs, and n endbulbs contact each central neuron. But the general method can easily be modified so that no neuron has more than two endbulbs and no more than two endbulbs contact any synapse.[3]

The general method can be applied to inputs over time so that the output at $t + 3$ can be a function of *all* the inputs before t. This gives a "complete" robot, able to respond in any desired way to any given circumstances and past history of experience. Though interesting in principle, the general method could not be applied in any actual case unless the number of receptors was quite small.

By means of nerve nets, we can design any prescribed artificial behavior, including, for example, the simulation of human behavior. Note, however, that nerve net theory, as part of the general theory of automata, is quite independent of animal and human neurophysiology. Nerve net theory merely says that if neurons (as herein defined) are put together in such and such ways, then certain behavioral properties will result, and if they are put together in such and such other ways, then other behavioral properties will result. Nerve net theory implies nothing at all about animal or human nervous systems. It is not an empirical investigation.

20.14 ARTIFICIAL SUBJECTIVE PHENOMENA

In the nerve net analysis of artificial behavior, we saw how the state of the nerve net at any time was determined by the preceding state, and we traced these states through the nerve net from the receptors to the effectors. In the analysis of artificial behavior, we were interested in showing how the structure of the net gave it certain in-out properties.

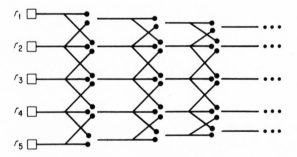

FIGURE 20.15 A nerve net.

If, on the other hand, we examine the structure of the *impulses* passing through the net, we have a possible analysis of the mental events or subjective phenomena that accompany the net's activity. The impulses passing through the net join together at synapses and separate where neurons branch. Thus the impulses passing through a nerve net form a network of impulses in space-time. Consider, for example, the nerve net in Figure

20.15. The space-time network of impulses passing through this net is determined by the input and by the properties of the net. Suppose, for example, that r_1, r_2, and r_5 fire at some time t. The resulting network of impulses is shown in Figure 20.16. In this space-time graph of neuron impulses, the point ρ_1 for instance, is the firing of r_1 at time t.

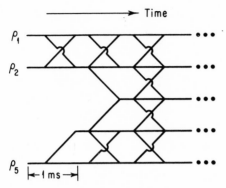

FIGURE 20.16 Impulse network for input 10011.

The network of impulses in Figure 20.16 is a subspace of space-time in which it is embedded. Let us define this particular network (Figure 20.16), or subspace, as the "psychological space" of the net (Figure 20.15) for the input 10011. When distances are measured in this psychological space, they must be measured *along the impulse network*. For example, what is the psychological distance (as opposed to physical distance) between the firing of r_1 and the firing of r_2? Measuring along the network, we find that it is 2 ms. (We take 1 ms as the unit of *distance* in the psychological space.) On the other hand, the distance between the firing of r_2 and the firing of r_5 is 4 ms.

Proceeding in this way, considering the network of impulses (a subspace of space-time) as a "psychological space," we can work out the rules of measurement in this space. This gives us, we believe, an analysis of artificial sense data.[3]

20.15 CONCLUSION

Nerve net theory, in describing the relationships of the logically simplest element, which is called the neuron, provides a basis for effectively designing input-output devices. Neurons are universal elements, in the sense that any artificial behavior can be described in terms of their behavior. Methods of mathematical logic can be used in the analysis of nerve nets, though we have not discussed this matter, and many researchers are now active in this field.

Since any behavior can, in principle, at least, be simulated by nerve nets, they provide a powerful method for investigating biological behavior. Also, as briefly claimed above, they enable one to construct artificial states of consciousness.

REFERENCES

1 Culbertson, James T., *Consciousness and Behavior*. Dubuque, Iowa: Wm. C. Brown, 1950, 32–48.

2 ———, *Mathematics and Logic for Digital Devices*. Princeton, N.J.: Van Nostrand, 1958.

3 ———, *The Minds of Robots*. Urbana, Ill.: Univ. Illinois Press, 1962, chaps. 3, 4 (in press).

4 Pitts, W., and McCulloch, W. S., How We Know Universals, the Perception of Auditory and Visual Forms, *Bull. Math. Biophysics, 9* (No. 3), September 1947, 127–47.

5 Rashevsky, N., *Mathematical Biophysics*. Revised ed.; Chicago: Univ. Chicago Press, 1948.

6 Rosenblatt, F., The Perceptron: A Theory of Statistical Separability in Cognitive Systems, *Report VG-1196-G-1*. Buffalo, N.Y.: Cornell Aeronautical Laboratory, Jan. 1958. The Perceptron not only recognizes preassigned shapes but can learn to recognize new shapes.

7 Shannon, C., and J. McCarthy, eds., *Automata Studies*. Princeton, N.J.: Princeton Univ. Press, 1956. Contains articles on nerve nets and also some references to other works on nerve net theory.

Robert S. Ledley
21/ADVANCES IN BIOMEDICAL SCIENCE AND DIAGNOSIS

*Robert S. Ledley is primarily
interested in digital computer engineering
and the application of computers to
biology and medicine. He was born June 28, 1926,
received an M.A. (mathematical physics)
from Columbia University, 1949; D.D.S., New York University,
1948. He is now President, National Biomedical
Research Foundation, 1960–. His past positions include:
Consultant Mathematician, National
Bureau of Standards, Data Processing Systems Division,
1958–61; Staff, National Academy of Sciences–
National Research Council/Medical Sciences Division, 1957–61;
Associate Professor of Electrical Engineering (final rank),
The George Washington University, 1957–60;
operations research analyst, Johns
Hopkins University, 1954–57; physicist, Electronic
Computer Laboratory, National Bureau of Standards
1951–54; Captain, United States Army, 1951–52.
He is a Fellow, American Association for the Advancement
of Science, and a member, American Physical
Society, American Mathematical Society, Operations
Research Society of America, Institute of Radio
Engineers. He is the author of* Digital Computer
and Control Engineering *(New York: McGraw-Hill, 1960).*
Programming and Utilizing Digital Electronic
Computers *(New York: McGraw-Hill, 1962).*

21.1 INTRODUCTION

21.1.1 *The Need.* Already there has been extensive use of computers in technology, business, and the physical sciences. But in the biomedical sciences their use has barely begun. In the future, however, perhaps the greatest utilization of computers will actually be in the biomedical sciences.* The problems that arise here characteristically involve large masses of data and many complicated interrelating factors, and it is just these types of problems for which computers are primarily suited. Also of great significance are the recent dynamic changes taking place in the biomedical fields themselves. For example, biological processes are now being examined in terms of atomic structures, energy levels, binding forces, molecular configurations, and the kinetic and thermodynamic details of biochemical reactions. Increasing quantization, with concurrent emphasis on the biophysical and physiochemical bases of biological systems, is rapidly bringing a large portion of biomedical science to a point where complicated mathematical manipulations and mass data reduction and analysis are absolute prerequisites to further progress.

At the present time, however, only about 5 per cent of digital computer time in university laboratories is devoted to biomedical research. For example, the Cooperating Colleges of New England, comprising some thirty universities and colleges which utilize the computer laboratory at

---

* See R. S. Ledley, *Use of Computers in Biology and Medicine.* New York: McGraw-Hill (in press); also R. S. Ledley, Digital Electronic Computers in Biomedical Science, *Science, 130* (No. 3384), Nov. 6, 1959.

the Massachusetts Institute of Technology, report * that only 6.8 per cent of the computer time is spent in the biological sciences, and of this 1.7 per cent is used in crystallography, 0.8 per cent in agriculture, and 3.9 per cent in psychology, leaving only 0.4 per cent of the computer time for use in what might be called "pure" biomedical research. Hence the need arises for biomedical research workers to have a greater understanding of the capabilities and advantages of electronic computers and for a greater stimulation of the use of computers in biomedical research.

21.1.2 Main Advantage. Of course, currently many hundreds of applications of computers are being studied throughout the country in the biomedical sciences. Most of these are being made by relatively isolated research workers who, with only few exceptions, have extensive cross-disciplinary backgrounds. They include professors of anatomy who are also X-ray spectroscopists, physicians who were once electrical engineers, biophysicists and physiologists who were originally physicists, psychologists with extensive mathematical background, and others. As in any new field, the research workers involved are only recently becoming aware of each other's work.

Many of these applications utilize the computer as a rapid calculator that can perform complex mathematical and logical operations more conveniently and often more economically than could be done by manual means. However useful computers may be for such jobs, their greatest advantage does not derive merely from ability to calculate rapidly. Rather, electronic computers are significant because they *can make feasible the solutions to problems that could not otherwise be approached.* Thus computers can enable theories to be explored, experiments to be performed, and data to be collected which would otherwise be impracticable; thus, computers greatly extend the biomedical research worker's range of capabilities.

21.1.3 Point of View. It is, of course, impracticable to review here those hundreds of applications already in progress, or the many more that are being proposed. Hence, we shall mention only sufficient applications to indicate the immense potential of this powerful new tool. It is most convenient to consider the applications in four basic (but inevitably overlapping) categories:

    a. Numerical solution to equations of biological importance
    b. Simulation of biological systems
    c. Biomedical data processing
    d. Computer aids to medical diagnosis

* Semi-annual *Report,* July 1960, No. 7. Massachusetts Institute of Technology, Cooperating Colleges of New England Computational Center.

After a general discussion of these categories, specific illustrations will be cited in order to give the reader a concrete idea of the role of the computer in advances in biomedical science and diagnosis.

21.2 NUMERICAL SOLUTION TO EQUATIONS OF BIOLOGICAL IMPORTANCE

21.2.1 *Biological Equations.* One method for studying a biological phenomenon is to make some hypothesis concerning its mechanism, write the corresponding (in general, differential) equations, and compare the solutions of the equations with experimental data. If the solutions do not agree with the data, the hypotheses are altered, and the process is repeated. This method has been used for centuries in the physical sciences. In many instances, it is not too difficult to write mathematical equations to describe a complex phenomenon reasonably; more often than not, however, such equations cannot be solved by conventional analytic methods. Yet with the utilization of electronic computers, they may frequently be solved numerically. Indeed, the numerical solution is often the most desirable, since it can be compared directly with the experimental data.

To illustrate the role of the computer in generating numerical solutions to biological equations, we shall briefly consider three examples: (1) analysis of the pupil servomechanism; (2) theory of neuron signal conduction; and (3) calculation of compartmental rate exchange parameters. The first of these examples describes the work of L. Stark in quantitatively investigating a problem in biocontrol engineering (or analysis of reflex actions). The application of servo-control engineering to the analysis of reflexes by means of computers opens a new approach to a quantitative and unified understanding of reflex controls and interrelationships of the human nervous system. The second example is concerned with the now famous Hodgkin-Huxley equations, whose work was actually carried out by hand computation. The third example describes a development made important by the extensively used radioactive tracer techniques which are applied to diagnosis and clinical research.

21.2.2 *Pupil Servomechanism.* The reflex under study [19] was the change of size of the pupil with light intensity entering the eye. The changing size of the pupil was measured for various light intensities by means of a pupillometer (see Figure 21.1). Critical experiments were performed by having the incident light intensity under the control of the pupil size by means of an external feedback loop, as shown in Figure 21.1. The reflex control loop under study is diagramed in Figure 21.2, where the goal was to find the precise mathematical expression for the "transfer function" $G(s)$ which describes in quantitative terms the relation between

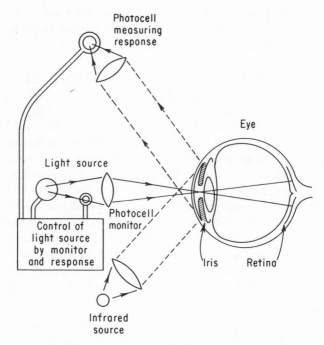

FIGURE 21.1 Diagram of pupillometer. Illustration shows setup with infrared response-measuring instrumentation and light source disturbance. The experimental apparatus contains a feed-back loop of its own to control the light source by monitoring the pupil response.

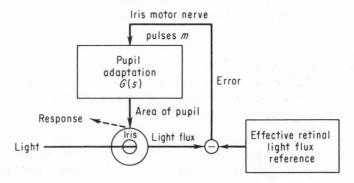

FIGURE 21.2 Diagram of a simplified closed-looped pupil-control system. The difference between the incident light and the amount of light the retina "can safely receive" is called the "error." This error is the input into the control mechanism that determines the pupil adaptation response given by the transfer function $G(s)$.

the incident light and the pupil adaptation as controlled by the brain's reflex mechanism. Of course, the method is to guess at certain forms for the function $G(s)$, and then check the computed result with the experiment. However, other experiments (see Figure 21.3) can assist in determining $G(s)$. For instance, by utilizing a small beam, the changing size of the pupil will not affect incident light intensity—this is called "opening the loop." By putting the beam of light on the edge of the pupil, a small change in pupil size will have a larger effect than normal—this is called instituting "high gain." The pupil response to such artificial stimuli was

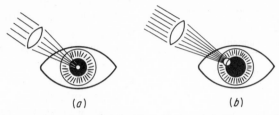

(a)   (b)

FIGURE 21.3 Placement of incident light: (a) For open-loop response; (b) For high-gain effect.

used to aid in studying the function $G(s)$. In this way, Stark has shown that a reflex can be analyzed in a manner similar to that for an electronic feedback control or servomechanism, and in fact, the same mathematical methods employed by the servo-engineer and developed for feedback control analysis can be used for the biocontrol systems as well.

21.2.3 Neuron Signal Conduction. A major advance in neurophysiology has been made by A. L. Hodgkin and A. F. Huxley by their mathematical formulation of equations for nerve membrane currents,[6, 7, 16] which also may apply to muscle membrane. These equations have been extremely effective in predicting many phenomena of classical axon physiology, including thresholds, action potentials, and excitation changes (such as prolongation of action potentials) due to variation in temperature and drug effects. The equations themselves are based on a model, but the form of the functions, as well as constants that enter into the model, are essentially empirical and based on experimental curve fitting. In this sense, many questions are left unanswered concerning origins of the mechanisms described by the equations. On the other hand, the accuracy and range of predictions that can be produced by computations using these equations are great. Thus the results of various numerical computations based on the equations can be an effective aid to the precise formulation of further investigations and analysis of future experimental results. The equations are sufficiently complicated to require the use of a computer for predictive or other numerical investigations.

Figure 21.4 illustrates the propagation of the action potential and Figure 21.5 the electrical circuit equivalent of an axon. To describe the mechanism of nerve conduction briefly, we can consider the nerve fiber as a long cylindrical tube with a surface membrane separating two aqueous solutions. In the outside medium, more than 90 per cent of the osmotic balance across the membrane is made up of sodium (Na) and chloride (Cl) ions; while inside most of the osmotic balance is made up of potassium (K) and various organic anions, less than 10 per cent being accounted for by the Na and Cl ions. By using very fine micropipettes, it is possible to penetrate the membrane without serious

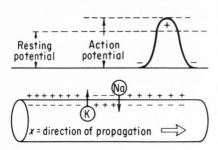

FIGURE 21.4 Propagation of the neural action potential. As the action potential is propagated, Na ions enter the fiber and charge the interior positively; then K ions leave the fiber and restore the initial membrane potential.

mixing of the inside and outside aqueous fluids and to measure the potential difference between inside and outside. This difference is about 80 millivolts (mv) across the membrane, and there are no detectable

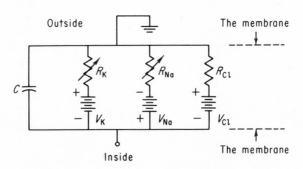

FIGURE 21.5 Electrical equivalent of an excitable membrane.

potential differences within the interior. If the voltage is applied to the inside of the membrane by a microelectrode, the membrane potential inside is raised, and then dies out, unless the inside potential is raised above the threshold, in which case the complete action potential develops. After the action potential decays, the nerve fiber in that area becomes temporarily inexcitable. The explanation of these phenomena—i.e., the model upon which the Hodgkin-Huxley equations are based—is roughly as follows: The Na permeability of the membrane is raised by the stimulating depolarization of the axon. If the threshold level is reached, the Na conductance of the membrane increases rapidly, and the interior of the fiber becomes positive. The Na permeability is then switched off, the membrane becomes permeable to K, and a large K conductance is developed, lowering once more the inside potential to its resting state. Note that the electrical return of the system is not brought about by a reversal of ionic movement, but rather by successive permeability changes, at first to Na and then K. The rate constants of these changes and their time course of decline have been determined experimentally by A. L. Hodgkin and A. F. Huxley. Although for one stimulation the total ion transfer is very small, it is clear that there must be a way to pump the Na out of the inside of the membrane and to replenish the K. These are evidently long-term phenomena that can be ignored during an action potential description.

In Figure 21.5 we have included a membrane capacity C and a leakage aspect, as well as the K and Na conductances, which are $1/R_K$ and $1/R_{Na}$ respectively. Thus, if V is the inside potential difference from its resting value, a is the radius of the axon, R is the inside resistance per unit length, x is the distance along the axon, and t is time, then

$$\frac{a}{2R}\frac{\partial^2 V}{\partial x^2} = C\frac{\partial V}{\partial t} + \frac{1}{R_K}(V - V_K) + \frac{1}{R_{Na}}(V - V_{Na}) + \frac{1}{R_{Cl}}(V - V_{Cl})$$

is a partial differential equation describing the function $V(x, t)$. Actually the situation is more complicated than this, since $1/R_K$, $1/R_{Na}$, and $1/R_{Cl}$ are themselves each determined by differential equations, because they are time dependent.

21.2.4 *Compartmental Rate Exchange.*

Radioactive tracer measurements require extensive computer-aided reduction if they are to be used quantitatively and accurately for diagnostic purposes. For example, a certain amount of radioactive iodine may be injected into the patient for an investigation of hyperthyroidism. Then the amount of radioactive substance is measured as a function of time in such "compartments" as the blood iodide, thyroid gland, protein-bound iodine, feces, and the excreted urine—see Figure 21.6(a). Then, if $q_i(t)$ represents the amount of radioactive material in compartment i at time t, the rates of change of radioactive material can be expressed by

$$\frac{dq_i}{dt} = \sum_{\substack{i \\ j \neq i}} (\lambda_{ij}q_j - \lambda_{ji}q_i)$$

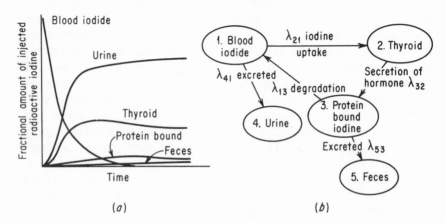

(a)   (b)

FIGURE 21.6 Radioactive tracer functions. Computer-aided data analysis could facilitate the work in projects such as this.

where the constant λ_{ij} is the fractional turnover rate of radioactive material from compartment j to compartment i. These are called "rate exchange equations." For the simple model of Figure 21.6(b), we have five compartments (where we have taken $\lambda_{12} = \lambda_{23} = \lambda_{31} = \lambda_{14} = \lambda_{35} = 0$). The computer problem is to fit the data measured from the patient to the solution of a set of such equations in order to determine the λ_{ij} for the patient. Then, for example, $\lambda_{21}/\lambda_{41}$ or λ_{32} may be indexes of disease, i.e., symptoms. Many problems associated with such a technique—such as uniqueness of the computed results, consistency of redundant information, statistical variations, etc.—are still being worked out.[2] The method is not unique to thyroid dysfunction. Radioactive chromium and cobalt are traced in connection with the leukemias and anemias; radioactive iodine and copper are traced for kidney and liver dysfunction tests, pancreatic insufficiency, gall bladder disease, circulatory diseases; radioactive-carbon-tagged chemicals can be used for pinpointing specific metabolic pathway dysfunctions.[17] Computer-aided quantitative tracer analysis opens up entire new fields of specific diagnostic analysis.

21.3   SIMULATION OF BIOMEDICAL SYSTEMS

21.3.1 Biomedical Systems. Complicated and highly involved phenomena, such as entire biological systems, can be analyzed by means of computer simulations. Usually a great deal is known about the local-component aspects of such a system, but a study of how these many complicated parts combine to make the whole has not heretofore been generally feasible because of the immense amount of calculation required.

These calculations can frequently be accomplished, however, if the functional equations of the component parts and their interaction rules are assembled on a digital computer. A computer simulation can advance (1) the study of a complicated system as an integrated result of many individual, interacting component parts, (2) the evaluation of the relative influence of each small component in relation to the whole system, (3) the testing of hypotheses about a part of a system for consistency with known data about the whole system, and (4) the designing and planning of future, more critical experiments concerning still unknown components of the system. Unfortunately, although many large-scale system simulations have been carried out on digital computers in the military and business fields, few if any have been accomplished in the biomedical field.

We now present three examples of the simulation of biomedical systems. (Brain and neuron net simulations are discussed elsewhere in this book; hence we shall not consider these important simulations here.) The first simulation to be briefly described is that of the circulatory system; the second, that of "teaching" a rat; the third concerns word-frequency distributions. In order to present the concepts involved, we have chosen to present stylized and grossly simplified versions of such research, containing the essence of the simulational technique and concepts utilized.

21.3.2 *Simulation of the Circulatory System.* H. Warner investigated a simulation of the heart and circulatory systems by means of an analog computer.[20] The simulation itself consists of a hypothesis about the interrelationships between the heart and the rest of the circulatory system, in the form of simultaneous differential equations. Figure 21.7 shows the division used of the heart and circulatory system into six compartments for the purposes of the simulation. These compartments are (1) right ventricle, (2) pulmonary arteries, (3) pulmonary veins and left atrium, (4) left ventricle, (5) aorta and arterial bed, and (6) body system veins and right atrium. The order in which these compartments are named is also the order in which the blood passes through them. Of prime interest in the simulation are the relationships between the blood pressure, P_i, and volume, V_i, within each compartment, and the flow, F_i, of blood from one compartment to the next (see Figure 21.8).

The different roles played by the ventricles during systole and diastole (i.e., contraction and subsequent expansion of the heart, pumping blood out and being refilled, respectively) should be observed. During the systole, the blood flow between the right atrium and the right ventricle, F_1, and the flow between the left atrium and the left ventricle, F_4, both become zero; the ventricles are pumping blood into the pulmonary and sys-

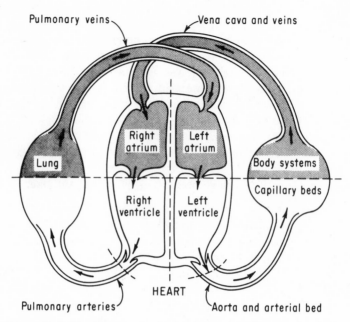

FIGURE 21.7 The heart and circulatory system. Diagramatic illustration of the six compartments of the heart and circulatory system
used for the purposes of this simulation. Dashed lines show separation of compartments, arrows show direction of blood flow.

tem arteries. Analogously, during diastole, F_2 and F_5 both become zero;
the ventricles are being refilled from the atria. This is illustrated in Figure
21.8 where the ventricles have been repeated, once for systole and once
for diastole, since different sets of equations govern them at those times.
The initial conditions at P_1 and V_1 for systole are the final values of P_1
and V_1 resulting from diastole; conversely, the initial conditions at P_1 and
V_1 for diastole are the final values of P_1 and V_1, resulting from systole.
Similar remarks apply to P_4 and V_4. These observations are indicated by
the dashed lines in the figure.

A more complicated simulation might also include the effects of the temperature, heart rate, blood chemistry, etc. Were its parts proved reasonably
accurate, such a simulation could be applied directly for clinical use. For
example, suppose the state of a patient's circulatory system, as measured
by clinical and laboratory tests, was entered into a computer coded to
simulate the circulatory system. The computer could then determine the
future course of the patient's circulatory system. Were this course predicted to be unsatisfactory, various therapeutic measures could be evalu-

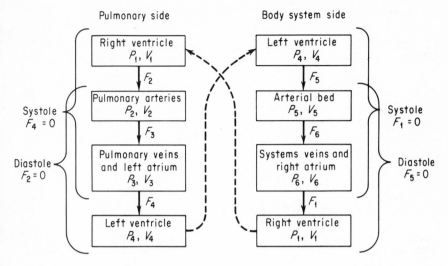

FIGURE 21.8 Relationships between blood pressure and volume. Summary of conditions during systole and diastole indicating that $F_1 = F_4 = 0$ during systole, and $F_5 = F_2 = 0$ during diastole.

ated *by means of the simulation* until some maximum effective measures were determined.

21.3.3 *Teaching a Rat.* This study is concerned with the simulation of animal learning; it presents an excellent example of the Monte Carlo technique.[5] The computed simulation-model results can be compared with data obtained from laboratory animals. By adjusting the ingredients of the model until it compares favorably with experiment, the learning process may be studied; when an "accurate" model has been obtained, the effect of varying parameter values may be investigated on the computer; based on this information, new and more critical experiments may be designed, and so forth.

The particular model to be described assumes that a rat is presented with a decision-making problem in order to obtain his food. The animal is repeatedly confronted with the same set of n alternatives, say n doors in different shapes. The rat is rewarded for a "correct" choice by food; it is punished for "incorrect" choices by a shock. To be specific, let us say there are four possible mutually exclusive and exhaustive choices (i.e., the rat chooses one and only one of the four doors), and let p_0, p_1, p_2, p_3 represent, respectively, the probabilities of the four outcomes of the "choosing event." These probabilities represent the random factors of the animal's *actions* in the choice. Associated with each choice, for example, the ith choice, is another event, the "learning event" which, say, has three possible mutually exclusive and exhaustive outcomes, with probabilities respectively $(\pi_{i0}, \pi_{i1}, \pi_{i2})$; these probabilities reflect the random factors associated with the learning effect of the "reward" or "punishment" following the ith choice. The outcome of the "learning event" in turn influences the "choice" probabilities. This is taken into account by associating with each learning outcome, say the ikth outcome, a set of "reinforcement" values $(\beta_{ik}^{(0)}, \beta_{ik}^{(1)}, \beta_{ik}^{(2)}, \beta_{ik}^{(3)})$, which are then used to modify the choice probabilities (p_0, p_1, p_2, p_3) as follows:

$$p_j' = \frac{\beta_{ik}^{(j)} p_j}{\sum\limits_{\mu=0}^{3} \beta_{ik}^{(\mu)} p_\mu} \qquad (j = 0, 1, 2, 3)$$

where p_0', p_1', p_2', p_3' are the new or reinforced-choice probabilities for the next round. In this way the choice probabilities become changed as the animal "learns"; in fact, the successive values of the probabilities on successive rounds of the teaching process represent the process of learning by the rat.

Summarizing, then, the procedure is as follows: A random number is chosen, and one of the choice-event outcomes is thereby determined according to the probabilities (p_0, p_1, p_2, p_3). Associated with each choice is another set of outcomes to the learning event, to which are also associated a set of probabilities, i.e.,

Choice outcomes	Probabilities	Learning outcomes 0	1	2
0	p_0	π_{00}	π_{01}	π_{02}
1	p_1	π_{10}	π_{11}	π_{12}
2	p_2	π_{20}	π_{21}	π_{22}
3	p_3	π_{30}	π_{31}	π_{32}
		Probabilities		

where for each of the $4 \times 3 = 12$ choice-learning-outcome combinations there is a set of reinforcement values $(\beta_{ik}^{(0)}, \beta_{ik}^{(1)}, \beta_{ik}^{(2)}, \beta_{ik}^{(3)})$. Thus, a second random number is chosen, and one of the learning events is thereby determined from the appropriate set of probabilities $(\pi_{i0}, \pi_{i1}, \pi_{i2})$. Having determined, therefore, a particular ikth choice-learning outcome for the rat's behavior, the reinforcement values are utilized to determine the new set of choice probabilities for the next round.

Will such a process "settle down"; i.e., will the choice probabilities (p_0, p_1, p_2, p_3) approach limiting values, or will they tend to oscillate? What is the effect of the constant parameters π_{ik} and $\beta_{ik}^{(j)}$ on the behavior of the choice probabilities? Can variation of the parameters π_{ik} and $\beta_{ik}^{(j)}$ be produced experimentally by varying the value of the reward and punishment to the rat? What is the effect of increasing the number of choices? What is the minimum number of learning outcomes that must be obtained for the model to compare favorably with experiment? What is the effect on the model itself of varying the number of learning outcomes considered? These and many more interesting questions can be approached, but the project becomes feasible only because of the availability of the high-speed digital computer.

21.3.4 *Word-frequency Distributions Simulations.* Perhaps the most remarkable feature of the human brain is its ability to direct the process of speech. Each word must be precisely chosen and integrated into a flow of word sequences, with the purpose of expressing a thought. It is reasonable therefore to study the words uttered by an individual as perhaps providing a key to the mechanisms of the brain or to pathological disturbances. Let us suppose, for example, that we recorded 100,000 words spoken by an individual and counted the number of times each word was repeated, i.e., determined the *frequency, f,* with which each word was used. Next, let us *order* the words according to their frequency of use, and let the position of each word in this order be called its rank, r. If we now make a graph of f versus r, we shall obtain a graph similar to that of Figure 21.9. For example, r_i words were used more than f_i times, as shown in the figure. Zipf's law states that the f versus r curve is given by

$$f = \frac{c}{r}$$

where c is a constant. Another form of Zipf's law can be obtained if we let n be the number of words at a given frequency; then,

$$n = \frac{c}{f^2}$$

which means, for example, that four times as many words occur approximately 100 times as occur approximately 200 times. To see this, we note that the difference in rank between two words, Δr, is approximately equal to the number of words that have frequencies lying

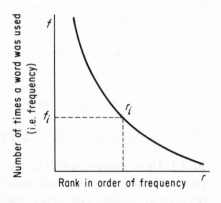

FIGURE 21.9 Word frequency as a function of rank. Typical distribution frequency f versus rank r.

---

* This section is based on private communication with N. Geschwind, Boston Veterans Administration Hospital.

between f and $f + \Delta f$; that is, $\Delta r = n[(f + \Delta f) - f] = n \Delta f$ or, on taking limits, $n = dr/df = d(c/f)/df = c/f^2$ as desired.

The distribution described by Zipf is the simplest first approximation to the word-frequency distribution law. It has been shown by many workers, however, that in the simple form given above, it does not fully explain all the details of the distributions. Significant further contributions have come from the work of Mandelrot, Howes, and others; however, consideration of these is beyond the scope of the present treatment.

Various theories can be proposed that might describe this phenomenon, but many of these theories must be tested by Monte Carlo simulations with a computer. For example, consider the theory that the probability of a word's being used is proportional to the frequency with which it has been used. To simulate this hypothesis on the computer, we might program the computer to select words from a given list of k words, according to certain probabilities as follows: Initially, let the probability of any word being selected by the computer be $1/k$. When, say, the ith word is chosen, then the probability p_i of selecting that word in the future is increased by the computer by some amount Δq. Of course, all the probabilities will then have to be renormalized so that

$$\sum_{i=1}^{k} p_i = 1$$

This process is continued until a stationary distribution is obtained for frequency versus rank. This procedure has a great many variations: the initial distribution need not be uniform; the increment Δq might depend on various factors, such as the frequency itself; and so forth. Clearly, a computer is required for such experiments. Further experiments may study how the final distribution changes with a change in the parameters (that is, Δq, or the total number of words, k) under consideration; or it may be possible to simulate the frequency distribution obtained experimentally from aphasics or from persons with other mental disorders.

21.4   BIOMEDICAL DATA PROCESSING

21.4.1 *Data Processing.* There are a great many applications of computers in the straightforward statistical analysis of medical records, experimental results, and other data. Notable is the large variety and amount of psychological research being accomplished: the psychologists always seem to be among the first to take advantage of the computer in a newly established computing center. Computers are aiding the statistical evaluation of new drugs, correlation of disease with various possible etiologies, studies of the effectiveness of new cures and preventives, etc.

Many special purpose clinical data processing computers have been introduced in the biomedical sciences. One of the most notable, described below, is the general anesthetic administrator machine that utilizes the patient's electroencephalograph to monitor the anesthetic administration. A different kind of data reduction problem is involved in connection with various continuous recordings—such as electrocardiograms, electroencephalograms, gastroenterograms, and electromyograms—obtained from living animals. Much work has been accomplished in applying the computer to the problems of electroencephalograms, and some of these studies will be briefly described below.

21.4.2 General Anesthetic Machine. Agents for general anesthesia can be gases, such as ether, nitrous oxide, etc., which are inhaled by the patient, or liquids, such as sodium pentothal, which are injected into the patient's blood stream. Sometimes combinations of agents are used. The drug is picked up by the circulation and transmitted to the brain. As the concentration in the brain increases, the patient goes through four successive stages of reaction: the induction or first stage, the excitement or second stage, the surgical or third stage, and the danger or fourth stage. Conventional methods for distinguishing these phases are by observation of certain physiologic indices, the four most important being (1) diameter of the eye pupil and reaction to light, (2) character and depth of respiration, (3) rate and character of pulse, and (4) blood pressure. These and other indices are continually observed by the anesthetist during the induction of anesthesia and performance of the surgical operation. Figure 21.10 roughly indicates the relationship of the four main indices with respect to the four stages of anesthesia. During the first stage, the patient

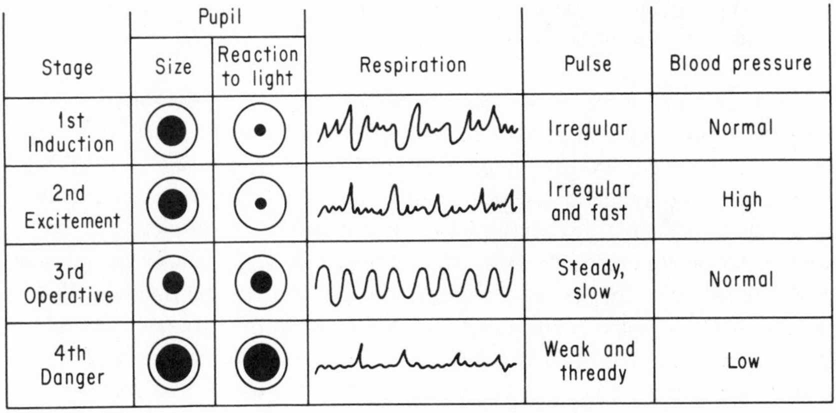

Stage	Pupil		Respiration	Pulse	Blood pressure
	Size	Reaction to light			
1st Induction	◉	⊙	∿∿∿∿∿	Irregular	Normal
2nd Excitement	◉	⊙	∿∿∿∿∿	Irregular and fast	High
3rd Operative	◉	◉	∿∿∿∿∿	Steady, slow	Normal
4th Danger	⬤	⬤	∿∿∿∿∿	Weak and thready	Low

FIGURE 21.10 Four principal indices with respect to the four stages of general anesthesia.

loses consciousness; during the second, the patient has a tendency to be restless or even unruly; during the third, surgical procedures can be performed; the fourth stage is that of cardiac and respiratory paralysis and death.

Clearly, due to human error and individual variability of the patient, the successful administration of a general anesthetic is a difficult procedure. But the electrical activity of the brain as recorded by the electroencephalograph varies with the different stages of anesthesia, as shown in Figure 21.11.

Relation of brain activity to depth of anesthesia

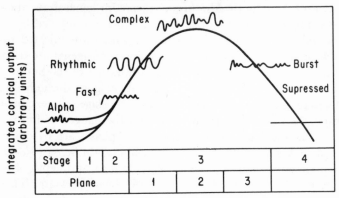

FIGURE 21.11 Illustration of electroencephalogram patterns and their relationship to the progressive stages of general anesthesia. The third, or operative stage, is usually divided into three planes characteristic of light, medium, and deep anesthesia. Various operations require different planes. The characteristic electroencephalogram patterns are also shown for these planes.

By appropriately integrating the output of the electroencephalograph, properly filtered, etc., it is possible to determine automatically the stage and plane of the patient during anesthesia.[3] The output of the integrator is translated into an electrical pulse, the time density of which is controlled by the brain activity. For example, during stage 2, a high electrical pulse density will be generated to bring the patient into stage 3. As the patient goes progressively deeper into stage 3, the density of the pulses will decrease due to decreased activity of the brain. Administration of the anesthetic agent can be directly controlled by the pulse density, the higher the density, the more being administered. Again, a control can be used to calibrate manually the depth of anesthesia desired. This process is diagrammatically illustrated in Figure 21.12. This procedure has been successfully utilized in the operating room for human anesthesia.

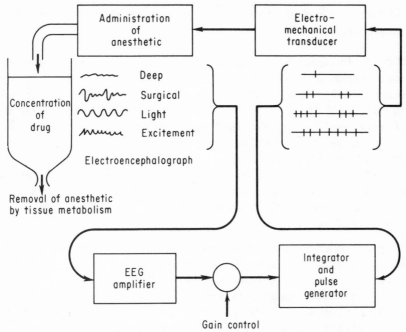

FIGURE 21.12 Diagramatic representation of servoloop in anesthetic regulation.

The technique has the advantage of minimizing the chance of human error and enabling the anesthetist to concentrate more fully on the individual-patient variability factor and on emergencies that may arise. Of greatest importance is the computer's smaller delay time in feedback control, as compared with that of the human anesthetist; this results in greater uniformity in the control of the depth of the anesthesia.

Another advantage is concerned with surgical techniques in situations such as heart surgery, where curarization of the patient has been increasingly employed. One result is that the anesthetist can have *no* information of the conventional kind even to estimate whether the patient is conscious or not. In fact, instances have been reported in the literature in which a curarized patient has undergone an operation and been conscious throughout. In such cases, the electroencephalographic control of anesthesia may be the only available method for monitoring curarized patients.

21.4.3 Neuroelectric Data Processing. As illustrations of the use of computers in analyzing neuroelectric data * we consider two approaches:

* See Siebert [18] for a fine review of the work accomplished at the Massachusetts Institute of Technology by one of many outstanding groups working in this area.

(1) averaging evoked responses; and (2) studying patterns in the electro-encephalogram.

21.4.3.1 *Averaging Evoked Responses.* An *evoked response* is the reaction to a controlled stimulus; this stimulus may be, for example, a clicking sound, a flash of light, or the turning on or off of a sound or light, etc. All these kinds of stimuli have one characteristic in common; there is a reference point in time that characterizes each repetition of the stimulus, e.g., when the click or the flash occurs, when the sound or light is turned on or off, etc. If we observe the neuroelectric potential waveforms from the time-reference point of the stimulus, the result is apparently random in nature; i.e., the evoked response, if it exists, is buried in the noise of the virtually random fluctuations from other sources. The problem is thus reduced to isolating the evoked response.[1]

Let us consider a repetition of one such stimulus: a sound click. We shall assume that the neuroelectric response evoked by each click is in-variant, i.e., remains approximately the same for each click, and that all other neuroelectric fluctuations are random in nature and therefore, of course, nonrepetitive. Then, if we measure the total response composed both of evoked response and random components and if we average the duration of many of these, using each stimulus as a reference point in time, the random component should average out, leaving only the desired estimate for the isolated, evoked response.

To be more specific, let us consider a neuroelectric pattern $v(t)$ associated with a sequence of clicks, as illustrated in Figure 21.13(a). Suppose

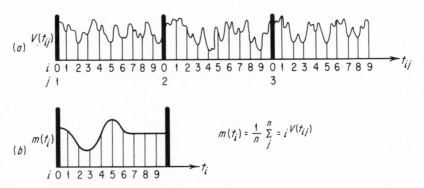

FIGURE 21.13 A neuroelectric pattern associated with a sequence of clicks. (a) The vertical bars represent the times of the clicks; (b) The average of over 100 of such pattern segments, clearly indicating the evoked response.

we divide the time scale into segments starting from each click, indexed by i, where the click itself is indexed by j. Then a point on the time scale can be denoted by t_{ij}, that is, the ith point after the jth click. Now suppose we average $v(t_{ij})$ for the times $v(t_{0j})$ and call the result $m(t_0)$, and do the same for $v(t_{1j})$, calling the result $m(t_1)$; for $v(t_{2j})$, the result $m(t_2)$, etc. For example,

$$m(t_3) = \frac{1}{n} \left[v(t_{31}) + v(t_{32}) + v(t_{33}) + \cdots + v(t_{3n}) \right],$$

where n is the number of clicks considered. In this way the points of the function $m(t_i)$ are formed, as illustrated in Figure 21.13. The function $m(t_i)$ is an estimate of the evoked response, the random components having been averaged out.

This method of isolating estimates of evoked responses can be applied to an awake human or animal subject with electrodes on the scalp. In this way, psychophysical and physiological responses can be studied. For example, for the clicking evoked response, $m(t_i)$ was obtained for clicks of differing intensity, and the subjects' threshold for response observed and compared with the subjective findings. A computer is required to obtain these averages, because from 100 to 3,000 or more stimuli are required for the average to "converge," i.e., to remain relatively stable. It is clear that the electroencephalograph includes some composite function of all the specific responses of the brain to external stimuli; this function may be, but is not necessarily, basically additive. In this view, the total electroencephalogram is then composed of these composite responses, together with a similar function of all other, or internally stimulated, responses. Can the contributions of these stimuli be analyzed in such a way that they can then be resynthesized to predict an electroencephalographic record? The method of averaging evoked responses, together with the capabilities of a digital computer, makes an approach to such problems feasible.

21.4.3.2 *Study of Patterns in the Electroencephalogram.* This study represents an effort to have a digital computer carry out an analysis that is analogous to that of an electroencephalographer who visually examines an EEG (electroencephalogram) for various characteristic patterns as an aid to making a diagnosis. The approach is empirical, based on a trial-and-error procedure. The technique differs from that described in the last paragraph in that attention is focused on particular patterns in a waveform, without involving averaging or other mass processing of the EEG response. Such pattern-recognition research, however, must initially be made on a digital computer which can be logically programed in a flexible manner to use various criteria with respect to selected segments of the EEG.

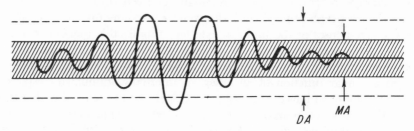

FIGURE 21.14 Illustrations of so-called "α-bursts" in an EEG.

A study based on recognizing the "α-bursts" of an EEG has been made.[4] These α-bursts are one of the most striking properties of an EEG (see Figure 21.14). It is frequently important to know the "alpha index," defined as the percentage of the record that contains alpha rhythm. In order to have the digital computer calculate this index, three criteria for recognizing an α-burst were set up. First, a section of the record must have at least a certain minimum peak-to-peak amplitude in order to be considered at all. For a particular EEG being analyzed, this peak-to-peak amplitude factor, called the *amplitude parameter* or *AP*, is defined as the ratio of the *minimum amplitude*, or *MA*, and the *median amplitude*, or *DA*. Thus $(MA) = (AP)(DA)$. The greater the *AP*, the smaller will be the part of the EEG considered; the smaller the *AP*, the greater the part of the EEG considered (see Figure 21.15). If a section of the EEG meets the first criterion, then the second criterion is considered; namely, that the interval between two successive zero crossings, or the *IZ* of the curve,

FIGURE 21.15 Illustration of the first criterion, where we have drawn $MA = \frac{1}{2} DA$, or $AP = \frac{1}{2}$.

be less than some given length. This factor was given by the median zero crossing interval, or *MI*, for the whole EEG record, plus or minus a certain fraction of the median length, this fraction being called the interval parameter, or *IP*. Thus $(IZ) = (MI) \pm (IP)(MI)$, as illustrated in Figure 21.16. The third criterion requires that at least five consecutive zero-crossing waves meet both the first, or amplitude, criterion and the second, or interval, criterion. Those segments of the EEG record satisfying all three criteria are defined as segments of *rhythmic burst activity*.

Investigation techniques of this type open a whole new area in the quantitative evaluation of electroencephalograms and their relation to diagnosis.

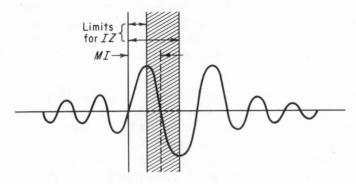

FIGURE 21.16 Illustration of the second criterion where we have drawn

$$IZ = MI \pm \tfrac{1}{2}MI, \quad \text{or} \quad IP = \tfrac{1}{2}.$$

21.5 LOGICAL REASONING IN MEDICAL DIAGNOSIS *

21.5.1 *Symptom-disease Complex and Medical Knowledge.* Mathematical logic (the propositional calculus) is employed in order to make a computer list diagnostic possibilities for the symptoms presented by a patient. The use of logic for this purpose is closely related to the concept of symptom-disease complexes (sdc's). A symptom complex is a list of the symptoms that a patient does and does *not* have; a disease complex is a similar list of diseases. A *symptom-disease complex* is a list of both symptoms *and* diseases that a patient does and does *not* have. For example, consider Figure 21.17 where, for simplicity, our attention is limited to two symptoms, $S(1)$ and $S(2)$, and two diseases, $D(1)$ and $D(2)$.

Each column represents a symptom-disease complex, where a unit in the row signifies that the patient has the corresponding symptom or disease, and a zero signifies that the patient does not have the symptom or disease. Thus the column in the rectangle of Figure 21.17 represents the symptom-disease complex of the patient having symptom $S(1)$, not having $S(2)$, having

$S(1)$ 1 1 1 1 |1|1 1 1 0 0 0 0 0 0 0 0

$S(2)$ 1 1 1 1 |0|0 0 0 1 1 1 1 0 0 0 0

$D(1)$ 1 1 0 0 |1|1 0 0 1 1 0 0 1 1 0 0

$D(2)$ 1 0 1 0 |1|0 1 0 1 0 1 0 1 0 1 0

FIGURE 21.17 Logical basis for two symptoms, $S(1)$ and $S(2)$, and two diseases, $D(1)$ and $D(2)$.

* This and the next section are excerpted from R. S. Ledley and L. B. Lusted, The Use of Electronic Computers in Medical Data Processing, *I.R.E. Trans. Med. Elec.*, January 1960, *ME-7*, 31–47. See also references 8, 11, 12, and 15.

$D(1)$, and having $D(2)$. The columns of Figure 21.17 represent all conceivable sdc's that can be formed from two symptoms and two diseases. If p symptoms and q diseases are under consideration, then clearly there are 2^{p+q} conceivable sdc's. For our example, $p = 2$, $q = 2$, whence there are $2^{2+2} = 16$ columns.

We use the phrase "all *conceivable* sdc's," but not all of these are *possible* or actually occur. It is *medical knowledge* that informs us which sdc's do or do not occur. For example, suppose that for the particular symptoms and diseases under consideration, medical knowledge informs us that if a patient does not have $D(1)$ and does not have $D(2)$, then he cannot have $S(1)$ and he cannot have $S(2)$, and conversely. Such a statement can be symbolized in terms of mathematical logic as

$$\overline{D(1)} \cdot \overline{D(2)} = \overline{S(1)} \cdot \overline{S(2)}$$

where the bar "—" represents NOT and the dot "·" represents AND. The effect of such a statement of medical knowledge is to eliminate from consideration some of the conceivable sdc's which are not possible. For example, the following columns

$S(1)$	110	000
$S(2)$	101	000
$D(1)$	000	110
$D(2)$	000	101

represent the sdc's that cannot happen according to our rule of medical knowledge; the left-most three columns represent sdc's where the patient has no diseases but does have the symptoms, and the right-most three columns represent sdc's where the patient has no symptoms but does have the diseases. In Figure 21.18 these columns have been crossed off.

Suppose, for example, another assertion of medical knowledge is that if the patient has disease $D(2)$, then he must have symptom $S(1)$, which can be symbolized as

$$D(2) \longrightarrow S(1)$$

This means, in addition, that the sdc's represented by the following columns cannot occur

$S(1)$	0	0
$S(2)$	1	1
$D(1)$	1	0
$D(2)$	1	1

for they are contrary to the assertion of medical knowledge. These columns have also been crossed off in Figure 21.18.

The logical effect of medical knowledge is to reduce the totality of all conceivable sdc's to those which are possible or compatible with the assertions embodied in medical knowledge.

Figure 21.19 represents all possible sdc's for our illustrative situation. In general, medical knowledge is stated in the form of our second assertion: If the patient has a certain disease complex, then he can have the following symptom complexes. This is why most medical textbooks are organized by diseases and discuss symptoms associated with each disease.

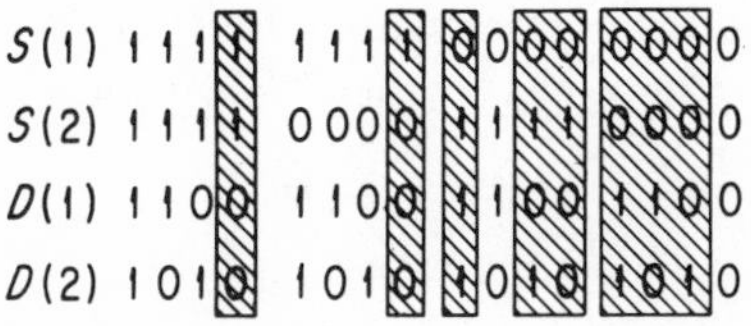

$S(1)$ 1 1 1   1 1 1   0 0 0   0 0 0 0

$S(2)$ 1 1 1   0 0 0   1 1 1   0 0 0 0

$D(1)$ 1 1 0   1 1 0   1 1 0   1 1 0 0

$D(2)$ 1 0 1   1 0 1   1 0 1   1 0 1 0

FIGURE 21.18 Reduced logical basis resulting from the application of medical knowledge.

$S(1)$ 1 1 1   1 1 1   0   0

$S(2)$ 1 1 1   0 0 0   1   0

$D(1)$ 1 1 0   1 1 0   1   0

$D(2)$ 1 0 1   1 0 1   0   0

FIGURE 21.19 Reduced logical basis; rectangle indicates case of patient having symptom $S(2)$ but not $S(1)$.

21.5.2 Listing Diagnostic Possibilities. Suppose a particular patient presents a symptom complex as follows: The patient does not have symptom $S(1)$ but does have symptom $S(2)$. Written symbolically, this is $\overline{S(1)} \cdot S(2)$. To make the diagnosis, we look at Figure 21.19, which contains all possible sdc's, for those columns which contain the symptom complex $\overline{S(1)} \cdot S(2)$. There is only one such column, namely

$$S(1) \quad 0$$

$$S(2) \quad 1$$

$$D(1) \quad 1$$

$$D(2) \quad 0$$

Thus, the logical analysis informs us that the patient with symptom complex $\overline{S(1)} \cdot S(2)$ has disease complex $D(1) \cdot \overline{D(2)}$, i.e., the diagnosis is that the patient has disease $D(1)$ but not disease $D(2)$. Suppose another patient presents $S(1) \cdot \overline{S(2)}$. The columns of Figure 21.19 containing this symptom complex are

$$S(1) \qquad 111$$
$$S(2) \qquad 000$$

$$D(1) \qquad 110$$
$$D(2) \qquad 101$$

Thus, the patient may have both $D(1)$ and $D(2)$, or else $D(1)$ and not $D(2)$, or else $D(2)$ but not $D(1)$. This means that the symptoms considered are insufficient in this case to distinguish between $D(1)$, $D(2)$, or both $D(1)$ and $D(2)$. Therefore, the logical analysis can result in a list of possible diagnoses consistent with the symptoms presented by the patient.

A more formal statement of our logical analysis is as follows: Let $D(1)$, $D(2)$, . . . , $D(n)$ be the diseases under consideration, and let $S(1)$, $S(2)$, . . . , $S(m)$ be the symptoms under consideration. Then medical knowledge appears as a Boolean function

$$E = E[D(1), \ldots, D(n), S(1), \ldots, S(m)]$$

The symptom complex of the patient is the Boolean function

$$P = P[S(1), \ldots, S(m)],$$

and the logical aspect of the medical diagnostic problem is to determine a function

$$f = f[D(1), \ldots, D(n)]$$

of the list of diagnostic possibilities such that the following Boolean equation is satisfied:

$$E \longrightarrow (P \longrightarrow f)$$

21.5.3 Determining Further Tests. The ease with which medical symptoms or test results can be obtained varies greatly with the complexity of the examination, cost, inconvenience to the patient, etc. Thus, in any particular medical specialty, the examinations could be classified using difficulty of execution as the criterion. For example, it is often a straightforward matter to obtain some aspects of the patient's medical history; some parts of a physical examination are more convenient to do than others; some blood tests and X-ray examinations are more costly than others; certain tests, such as biopsies or exploratory operations, are used when no other techniques provide needed information. It becomes clear that it is not feasible first to make all possible tests on a patient and then to determine the diagnosis. The more realistic method uses iterated stages:

making tests; determining how precise a diagnosis can be made from the results so far obtained; determining what further tests should be made; making these tests; determining how precise a diagnosis can be made from the additional results obtained; determining what further tests should be made; making these tests; and so forth, until a satisfactory diagnosis has been accomplished.

This problem can be formulated in terms of our logical considerations of the previous section. The formulation will be described by means of an illustration. Figure 21.20 shows a set of sdc's associated with 14 symptoms and 8 diseases. For this illustration, the symptoms have been classified into history, physical examination, laboratory blood tests, and bone marrow tests, arranged in order of increasing difficulty of performance. Notice that $S(1)$ actually contributes nothing to the diagnosis because, having a unit in every column, it does not distinguish between any columns. Suppose, for illustration, that the patient has both $S(2)$ and $S(3)$. Then the diagnosis so far is that the patient has a disease complex associated with one of the left most eleven columns. Thus, because of the patient's symptoms, we eliminate from consideration the rest of the columns, as shown in Figure 21.20. Of the physical ex-

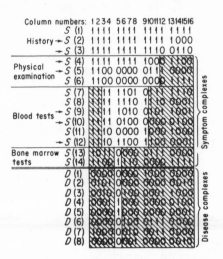

FIGURE 21.20 Logical basis for symptom-disease complex associated with fourteen symptoms and eight diseases.

amination symptoms $S(4)$, $S(5)$, and $S(6)$, only two are necessary, for all three cannot differentiate between the remaining columns better than can any two. Suppose $S(4)$ and $S(5)$ are taken, and the patient has $S(4)$ and *not* $S(5)$; then only seven columns remain as possible diagnoses, namely columns, 3, 4, 5, 6, 7, 8, and 9. The choice among the blood tests $S(7)$, $S(8)$, $S(9)$, $S(10)$, $S(11)$, and $S(12)$ is not as easy to make. It can be shown that only three of these six tests need be made, namely, $S(9)$, $S(10)$, and $S(12)$. Suppose the patient presents positive results for tests $S(9)$ and $S(12)$, and a negative result for test $S(10)$. Then only a single column remains, namely column 5. Thus the bone marrow tests need not be made, and the patient has a combination of both diseases $D(4)$ and $D(5)$ but none of the other diseases. Suppose, on the other hand, that at the physical examination the patient had both $S(4)$ and $S(5)$. Then only columns 1 and 2 would remain; the blood tests will not distinguish between them, and bone marrow test $S(13)$ would have to be made.

21.6 CALCULATING THE ALTERNATIVE DIAGNOSTIC PROBABILITIES

21.6.1 *Probability in Medical Diagnosis.* Frequently it is not feasible, nor desirable, to make further tests to distinguish between alternative possible diagnoses. The problem then resolves itself into answering the question: In the light of the patient's present symptom complex, what is the probability that he has a particular disease complex? We are asking for a conditional probability: Given the patient's *symptom complex, s_j*, what is the probability of his having a *disease complex, d_i*? This is frequently denoted by $p(d_i|s_j)$, where the symbol to the right of the slash is the condition, and the symbol to the left of the slash is the occurrence whose conditional probability is desired.

The well-known Bayes' formula offers important information concerning the composition of $p(d_i|s_j)$.

$$p(d_i|s_j) = \frac{p(d_i)p(s_j|d_i)}{\sum\limits_{\text{all } k} p(d_k)p(s_j|d_k)}$$

where $\sum\limits_{\text{all } k}$ indicates a summation over *all possible disease complexes d_k* under consideration. Let us focus our attention on the two terms in the numerator, namely,

$$p(d_i)p(s_j|d_i)$$

since the denominator merely acts as a normalization factor. The term $p(s_j|d_i)$ is the probability of having the symptom complex s_j when it is known that the patient has the particular disease complex d_i. This is precisely what is described in medical textbooks when a particular disease is under consideration. Of course, textbooks do not at the present time assign numerical values to $p(s_j|d_i)$, but they do state that associated with a certain disease particular symptoms are common, frequent, rare, etc. The reason for discussing $p(s_j|d_i)$ rather than $p(d_i|s_j)$ is that the etiology of the symptoms is related to, or stems from, the disease. *Thus $p(s_j|d_i)$,* i.e., the symptoms resulting from a disease, *is a constant for the particular disease complex under consideration, being relatively independent of other circumstantial factors.*

On the other hand, consider the term $p(d_i)$. This is the probability that, of the particular population of patients involved, any particular patient has this disease complex d_i. By "particular population of patients," we mean that population from which the patients can be considered as chosen *at random* in the technical sense. For example, the population may be that of the entire United States, or that of a particular clinic in a particular hospital, etc.; in each case, $p(d_i)$ will, in general, be different. *This term relates the influence of geographical, seasonal, epidemiological, social, and other such factors to the diagnosis.* Thus, in the tropics one is more apt to find tropical disease; during an Asian flu epidemic, the symptoms of a cold are more likely to be relegated to Asian flu; some diseases, like poliomyelitis, have a seasonal variation, etc. A little reflection indicates clearly that both these factors—the circumstantial or local, and the constant relating to the disease-symptom syndrome—influence the diagnosis.

21.6.2 *Problems in Computing Statistics.* As we have noted above, the statistics in which we are interested, i.e., $p(d_i|s_j)$, reflect local changes in place and time, and therefore must be collected locally. In order to be valid, however, "sufficiently large" data must be used, which may not be available locally. Bayes' formula comes to our aid under such circumstances, for it is clearly not necessary to have as large a sample to determine $p(d_i)$ as to determine $p(d_i|s_j)$. Thus, since $p(s_j|d_i)$ is a constant, not dependent on local conditions and independent of time, nationwide statistics collected over a long period of time can be used for this purpose. Then, locally, only $p(d_i)$ need be derived from collected data, and Bayes' formula used as illustrated above to determine $p(d_i|s_j)$. Notice also that the local collection of statistics to calculate simply $p(d_i)$, where no symptoms enter, is a much simpler process than that which we have just described. Thus, the use of Bayes' formula presents important practical advantages.

Another important problem arises in connection with *rare diseases*. If we had a clinic for rare diseases, then for the population of this clinic, the diseases would not be rare and the problem would be solved. Patients having rare diseases must be referred to this clinic, however; hence, the rare diseases must be diagnosed even under conditions of "rarity." The columns or sdc's corresponding to rare-disease complexes *cannot* be allowed to have a zero tally, for then they would be missed. Thus, a minimum but *greater than zero* tally must be kept for these rare sdc's at all times. This minimum tally will give wrong probabilistic results, i.e., in general, too large results; but the minimum non-zero tally should be warning enough. Actually, when comparing non-rare diseases, the probabilities will not be misleading, but when comparing rare with non-rare diseases, the probabilities will have no meaning.

Finally, consider the problem of the delay with which our "current" statistics reflect time-dependent changes. Obviously, even though we are dropping old statistics at the same rate as receiving new statistics, the initiation of an epidemic, for example, will be observed with a finite delay, as will the end of an epidemic. This is a practical problem that exists no matter how the statistics are taken, and it applies to all public health and other such fields, as well as to medical diagnosis. It simply reflects the delay in current information gathering and processing. It might be observed that an "uncertainty principle" applies here, analogous to the well-known uncertainty principle that appears in quantum mechanics, namely,

$$(\Delta L)(\Delta t) > \epsilon$$

For, if we wish to make our statistics more sensitive to time changes (i.e., decrease the delay time Δt), then we must accept more statistics per unit time (i.e., collect statistics from a larger area) thereby increasing ΔL, the geographical locality factor. On the other hand, if we limit the area in which we collect statistics (i.e., decrease ΔL) we shall have to compensate for the smaller rate of incoming statistics by waiting a longer time (i.e., increase Δt). The situation is far from hopeless, however, for there are many techniques for handling such situations. For example, physicians are alerted at the time of the seasonal occurrence, say, of poliomyelitis. Similarly, the statistics can be tampered with by artificially raising certain tallies from previous epidemiological experience. In this way, the lead in incidence over statistical reflection can be reduced. After the initial priming, the usual tallies can then take over.

21.7   DISCUSSION OF COMPUTER AIDS TO MEDICAL DIAGNOSIS

It must be remembered that one cannot get out of a computer more than one puts into it; i.e., a computer can do no more than it is *programed* to do. If a certain disease-symptom relationship is not recorded in the computer memory, the relationship cannot enter into any computations. Incorrect data entered into the computer's memory can generate incorrect results. Incomplete history taking, incorrectly executed laboratory tests, incorrect interpretation of results of diagnostic procedures, etc., will all contribute to incorrect computer outputs. These remarks, of course, apply to any method of making the diagnosis and formulating the treatment plan; the computer has no magical properties from this point of view.

Although it is important to understand the limitation of the computer, it is also unwise to underestimate its capabilities. For example, a computer can be made to (1) "check" the input information for logical inconsistencies, (2) "learn" from the statistical experience of current data that may be continually fed into its memory, (3) "organize" current information for coordinate retrieval, (4) "read" an article and extract pertinent diagnostic information, (5) carry out complicated "reasoning" processes, (6) "evaluate" an optimum or near-optimum course of action for given circumstances, and so forth.[9, 10, 13, 14] Nevertheless, it is the scientific ingenuity of the human mind that "tells" the computer how to perform these remarkable feats.

There are other problems associated with the use of computers besides those of input data accuracy and data omission. First, standardization of nomenclature is a practical necessity. The computer can be made to recognize different words as denoting the same idea, but it obviously cannot distinguish between different ideas denoted by the same word. Second, standardization of the coding procedures is needed so that, for example, medical records from different hospitals will have directly compatible codes. Third, standardization of test interpretations is an ever-present problem. For example, at what point does the blood sugar level test indicate diabetes? No matter where the line is drawn, the test results will be positive for some patients who do not have diabetes and negative for some who do. The test results must be interpreted to minimize the errors, keeping in mind that such errors cannot be totally eliminated. Observe that these problems arise simply because the use of a computer requires logical self-consistency, together with the preliminary analysis of all possible relevant outcomes.

Although computers can serve the physician in many ways, we do not mean to imply that computers will make the physician's job easier. On the contrary, to utilize computers the physician must learn how to communicate with them and how to evaluate correctly the information obtained from them. But we believe that ability to make a more precise diagnosis and a more exact determination of the best possible treatment plan will more than offset these difficulties.

ACKNOWLEDGEMENT. This chapter is based on work performed under National Institutes of Health research grants RG-5626 to the National Academy of Sciences, RG-6346 to The George Washington University, and RG-7844 to the National Biomedical Research Foundation.

REFERENCES

1 Barlow, J. S., An Electronic Method for Detecting Evoked Responses of the Brain and for Reproducing Their Average Waveforms, *Electroencephalog. and Clin. Neurophysiol., 9*, 1957.

2 Berman, M., and Schoenfeld, R. L., Information Content of Tracer Data with Respect to Steady-State Systems, *Symposium on Information Theory in Biology.* New York: Pergamon Press, 1958.

3 Bickford, R., Electronic Control of Anesthesia, *Electronics, 23*, September 1950.

4 Farley, B. G., *et al.*, Computer Techniques for the Study of Patterns in the Electroencephalograph, *Tech. Rept. 337*, Research Lab. of Electronics, MIT, 1957.

5 *First Annual Report*, Philadelphia: University of Pennsylvania Computer Center, 1959, 34–36.

6 Freygang, W. H., Some Functions of Nerve Cells in Terms of an Equivalent Network, *Proc. I.R.E., 47* (No. 11), November 1959.

7 Hodgkin, A. L., and Huxley, A. F., A Quantitative Description of Membrane Current and Its Application to Conduction and Excitation in Nerves, *Jour. Physiology, 117* (No. 4), 1952.

8 Ledley, R. S., and Lusted, L. B., Computers in Medical Data Processing, *Operations Research, 8* (No. 3), May–June 1960.

9 ———, *Digital Computer and Control Engineering*, New York: McGraw-Hill, 1960.

10 ———, Mathematical Foundations and Computational Methods for a Digital Logic Machine, *Operations Research, 2*, August 1954.

11 ———, and Lusted, L. B., Reasoning Foundations of Medical Diagnosis, *Science*, July 3, 1959, *130* (No. 3366).

12 ———, and Lusted, L. B., The Use of Computers to Aid in Medical Diagnosis, *Proc. I.R.E., 47*, November 1959.

13 ———, Tabledex: A New Coordinate Indexing Method for Bound Book Form Bibliographies, *Proc. Intl. Conf. on Scientific Information, 1958.* Washington, D.C.: Natl. Acad. of Sciences–Natl. Research Counc., 1959, Area V.

14 Luhn, H. P., The Automatic Creation of Literature Abstracts, *IBM Jour. Research and Development, 2*, April 1958.

15 Lusted, L. B., and Ledley, R. S., Mathematical Models in Medical Diagnosis, *Jour. Med. Educ., 35* (No. 3), March 1960.

16 Moore, J. W., Electronic Control of Some Active Bioelectric Membranes, *Proc. I.R.E., 47* (No. 11), November 1959.

17 Okita, G. T., Leroy, G. V., Tocus, E. C., and Rodin, B., Argonne Cancer Research Hospital, Univ. Chicago. (Private communication.)

18 Siebert, W. M., ed., Committee on Biophysics Group of Research Laboratory of Electronics, Processing Neuroelectric Data, *Tech. Rept. 351,* M.I.T., July 7, 1959.

19 Stark, L., Stability, Oscillations, and Noise in the Human Pupil Servomechanism, *Proc. I.R.E., 47* (No. 11), November 1959.

20 Warner, H., The Use of an Analog Computer for Analysis of Control Mechanisms in the Circulation, *Proc. I.R.E., 47* (No. 11), November 1959.

ADDITIONAL REFERENCES. Selected to be representative (but in no way complete) of the use of computers in biology and medicine.

Clynes, M. E., Respiratory Control of Heart Rate: Laws Derived from Analog Computer Simulation, *I.R.E. Natl. Conv. Rec.,* Pt. 9, 1959.

Cole, K. S., *et al.,* Automatic Computation of Nerve Excitation, *Jour. Soc. Ind. Appl. Math., 3* (No. 3), 1955; Corrections, *Ibid.* 6 (No. 2), 1958.

Farrar, J. T., Digital Computer Diagnosis of Gastrointestinal Disorders from Complex Intraluminal Pressure Record, *Proc. Conf. Diagn. Data Proc.,* Jan. 14, 1959; in *I.R.E. Trans. Med. Electr., ME-7* (No. 4), October 1960.

Hoffman, J. G., *et al.,* Digital Computer Studies of Cell Multiplication by Monte Carlo Methods, *Jour. Natl. Cancer Institute, 17,* 1956.

Krant, J., The Shape of the Chymotrypsinogen Molecule from X-ray Diffraction, *Biochem. Biophysics Acta, 30,* 1958.

Ledley, R. S., The Relation of Occlusal Surfaces to the Stability of Artificial Dentures, *Jour. Amer. Dental Assoc., 48,* 1954.

Lipkin, M., and Hardy, J. D., Mechanical Correlation of Data in Differential Diagnosis of Hematological Diseases, *Jour. Amer. Med. Assoc., 166,* Jan. 11, 1958.

Nash, F. A., Differential Diagnosis: an Apparatus to Assist the Logical Faculties, *Lancet, 1,* April 24, 1954.

Taback, L., *et al.,* Digital Recording of Electrocardiographic Data for Analysis by a Digital Computer, *I.R.E., Trans. Med. Electr., ME-6* (No. 3), 1959.

Talbot, S., Computers Applied to Ballistocardiography, *Ibid.*

Sydney C. Rome & Beatrice K. Rome

22/COMPUTER SIMULATION TOWARD A THEORY OF LARGE ORGANIZATIONS

Sydney C. Rome graduated from Harvard in mathematics and physics, but turned to logic, foundations of science, and epistemology for his doctoral work at Harvard, where he served as Special Research Associate in the Psycho-Acoustic Laboratory. Later, he headed the Project Information Section of the Polaroid Corporation's laboratories. As assistant to the president of the Sonotone Corporation, he was responsible for corporate organization and the administrative coordination of the research laboratories. He served as lecturer on the Graduate Faculty of the New School for Social Research and as Professor of Philosophy at William and Mary. With The RAND Corporation, he headed the data analysis and data control activities of the System Training Program, and now with System Development Corporation, he is the principal investigator of the Leviathan project.

Beatrice K. Rome was awarded her degrees at Radcliffe and Harvard, receiving her doctorate while Professor of Philosophy at William and Mary. Until she joined RAND, her principal interests were the philosophy of organism, cosmology, and seventeenth-century thought, particularly Malebranche and Descartes. At RAND and SDC she has written extensively in three fields: (1) the principles of designing problem situations for training large air defense complexes as total systems, (2) the codification of the human technology that supports SDC's computer simulation of air defense situations, and (3) the objectives of defense, including studies of NATO, Soviet strategy, the computerization of military intelligence, and the theory of command and control. She has made contributions to the Leviathan project on the levels both of basic theory formation and methodology and of developing the exploitation of logical or nonquantitative computer simulation for scientific investigations.

22.1 STRUCTURE AND DYNAMIC CHANGE IN LARGE SOCIAL GROUPS

22.1.1 *The Present-day Transformation of the Social Fabric.* The twentieth century is witnessing the effects of a threefold technological revolution, in production, transportation, and communication. These changes are perceptibly modifying the dynamics and structure of large social organizations. The quantity of productive or destructive output per executive, the wide, often global distribution of a single organization's personnel, investments, and resources, and the far-flung network of rapid transportation and communication—these have intensified and accelerated the executive decision-making process. This acceleration is producing what seems to be a radical, qualitative transformation in the entire fabric of our social existence, not solely in the military sphere but also in industry and government.

To understand these social phenomena, we are developing a conceptual framework to which we give the name "Leviathan." [1] In this chapter, we shall describe one aspect of our approach, namely, the use of a large digital computer to cause artificial social structures and social processes to develop according to sets of rules that we can experimentally prescribe and control. An IBM 7090 is employed for a purely automatic mode of operating our simulation, and a Philco 2000 machine is used when we wish to experiment with a limited number of live subjects.

22.1.2 *Large Social Groups.* In turning to computer simulation for scientific knowledge, we abstract general features of social process, features that remain invariant as our attention passes from one real organization to another of the same kind, and from kind to kind of social organization. We confine our attention to large social groups, including military organizations, that produce artifacts or services. In such large productive groups, much of the productive (or destructive) work is carried forward by means of one-way communications. Often these communications are secondhand, i.e., via intermediaries. When more than

523

perhaps a hundred or two hundred people are banded together in some common enterprise, it becomes physically impossible for every pair of members to meet and converse with each other face-to-face over any span of time.

In direct consequence, considerable numbers of members of a large organization are essentially faceless. Who files a letter or moves an article to its proper shelf in a warehouse is usually not significant, provided that the work gets done. Further, when face-to-face relationships are thus transcended, large groups generally exhibit more complex social structure than do small groups. Although large groups include face-to-face constellations, these subordinate units are, to some degree, organized as if they themselves were individuals. Thus, a squad can be ordered to perform a given mission, and with respect to the order, it may be meaningless to ask for the contribution of each specific member.

A purely formal, structural property of large groups thus becomes apparent: large groups have system levels. Whereas on one level a group behaves as if plural, consisting of individual persons or of subordinate groups, for a higher level, the plural group can act socially as if it were a collective individual. In large social groups there can be "individuals" composed of individual groups.

22.1.3 *The Technological System and the Governing System.* Once we look within a large productive system like an industry or governmental bureau or a military command, we can distinguish two basic subsystems: the technological system and the governing system. We define the *technological system* to consist of all those machines, messages, and applications of human energy that apply directly in the creation of the product or service of the entire social system. In the technological system is included everything that gets the product manufactured or the service delivered. The *governing system* includes the messages, machines, and social energy of a second order, which are about the technological work or service. Thus, any message or data concerning how many men, months, and work are required during a given period of time in order to produce a product would be a message that belongs in the governing system. Equally, a command to reallocate manpower or to change production schedules would probably belong in that system (see Figure 22.1).

Time flows in different ways through the two systems. In the technological system, the flow of time is linear. Raw materials enter at a given date

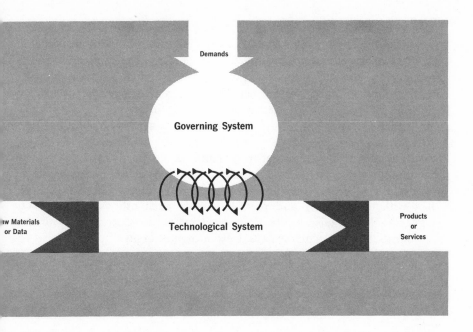

FIGURE 22.1 Technological system and governing system.

and leave at a later date. We may think of the flow of time in the technological system as analogous to the advance of a wavefront. In the governing system, on the other hand, time tends to have a cyclical character. Suppose some event occurs in the technological system, requiring the intervention of the governing system. Perhaps a machine breaks down and production (or destruction) stops, or perhaps the quality of the product being produced shows signs of falling below an acceptable level. This event occasions an intervention. The executives in the governing system seek to diagnose the problem and to cope with it. Finally, a decision is made, and a change is effected in the production process. While this entire chain of events takes place, it is quite possible that the product that occasioned the chain has reached completion and has been delivered to the customer. Then the intervention, which actually changes the production system, is effected on a new generation of products. It takes effect at a much later time than the date of the event which occasioned the intervention. A cycle has been completed; if further intervention is required to produce further improvement in the process, the activity goes again around a similar cycle.

22.1.4 *Structure and Change*. It would be oversimple to suppose that governing and technological processes are just two self-contained systems. A productive system can, of course, for some purposes, be viewed as a simple combination of subsystems, while the aggregate of subsystems comprises a simple net like a nerve net. Then we generate a larger system by flowing the output of one subsystem into the input of another. But a governing system, in contrast, rarely exhibits such aggregational simplicity. Myriad activities temporally proceed in parallel at diverse levels of organization. Novel syntheses of intelligence, of strategies, of norms, of responsibilities, and of spans of authority emerge and hold sway over and over again at successively higher levels of integration. Often they conflict with one another and partially nullify each other's effects. Each higher-level synthesis absorbs lower-level integrations, in analogy to the organization of molecules in cells, cells in organs, organs in animals.

In point of fact, then, technological and governing systems are mutually adaptive to one another, and thus become fused in a single total system. As a result, an entire system can be viewed from the two points of view of change and of structure.

One can consider the system as a maze of channels through which flow progressively completed products and messages. Both work and communications move from station to station. Operations on the work transform the product or service that is being formed or performed. Interpretations and decisions alter the content of communications. The social system from this point of view is social process or functioning.

An equally true view of a social system focuses on its formal structure. A social system is at least that which is represented in an organization chart. It also, of course, includes as part of its formal structure what a behavioral scientist would denominate its informal organization. By *informal organization* is meant the patterns of interaction that depend more on friendship and interpersonal associations than on publicly acknowledged standard operating rules. Another element is the *formal coordinative,* or *lateral, structure.* By this is meant the publicly approved rules and channels of communication between independent subordinate trees in the formal organizational chart. Thus a coordinating committee, socially established by the governing system, is an example of formal lateral structure. Formal line structure and informal and formal lateral structure combine with the technological system of any large productive organization to guarantee that structure be as essential to operations as are dynamic interactions.

The fusion of structure and dynamic interaction raises problems for behavioral scientists, because complex structure complicates the interrelationships between micro-operations. Even if a given activity is repeated identically in ten different channels, it makes a difference to the operations of the system through which channel the activity flows. Aside from the relationship of suitability between message and channel, the same message through different channels can have different meanings for the total system. A statement that drill press no. 3 is down will obtain assistance from the maintenance department if it flows through one channel, and it might occasion reprimand from a first-level supervisor. From a higher-level executive, the statement might initiate an investigation into the performance of the maintenance department. Finally, such a statement might be declared unsuitable for admission into the office of the president without prior filtering at an intermediate level.

22.1.5 *Computer Simulation.* How should the complex interplay of structure and change in large social groups be studied? At the present stage of development of the social sciences, we lack scientific hypotheses sufficiently simple in consequences and sufficiently fecund in implications to reduce this complexity to propositions that would be encompassed by currently widespread analytic techniques. One innovation, the large digital computer, because of its high speed and large storage capacities, may possibly be the single instrument that will assist social scientists to achieve mastery over the complexity. The rest of this chapter discusses how to go about using a digital computer to achieve what can well be called analog simulation of social structure and process. We begin to construct our social group from the technological system and proceed upward. First, raw material is introduced; then the work of an organization gets done; then information is generated about the performance of the work; and finally the technological process is modulated and controlled.

22.2   THE COMPUTER PROGRAMS

22.2.1 *The Technological Task.* We begin our simulation by inventing a perfectly concrete, particular, and brute or surd task for Leviathan to perform. What shall this task be? If we were writing in the nineteenth century, we would probably seek to represent some activity that could be performed by a factory with the aid of natural power, for example, the production of flour from grain in a mill. Or we might want to represent effects of bombarding a fortress during a siege. In the twentieth century, it is more interesting to construct a productive process that involves communication of symbolic material. In our initial computer programs (which are reaching the operational stage as this is being written), we introduce encrypted messages coded by a special series of rules that we invent, and the task of the technological system is to restore these messages to their original clear form. The rules for decrypting, and the assembly lines that perform the decoding tasks, are held invariant through successive experimental investigations that employ Leviathan's programs. What do undergo fluid and adaptive change are executive interactions, organizational structure, and deployment of manpower.

22.2.2 *The Program System.* In Figure 22.2, are diagramed the computer programs for Leviathan. The constellation of programs can be envisaged as comprised of five groups.

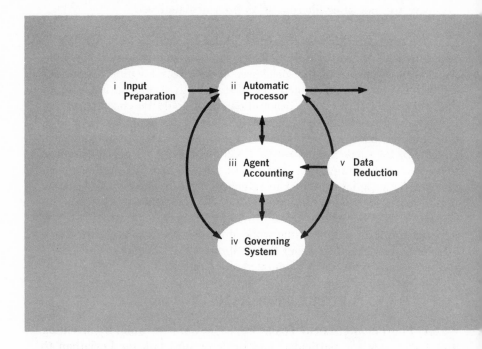

FIGURE 22.2 The five groups of computer programs.

The first programs (*input preparation*) receive messages that consist of words expressed in Latin letters. The letters of the words are converted to numerical values according to the Hollerith-like code:

$$A = 11, B = 12, \ldots, Z = 36$$

Three sets of clues (explained in Section 22.3.2) to the clear form of the original words are then generated; extra letters are supplied by a pseudo-random number generator until a total of eight letters occurs; and the resulting combinations of original letters and "random" letters in each word are scrambled by means of a second use of the "random" number generator. The resulting disguised words, each word accompanied by its proper three sets of clues, are read out on magnetic tapes. In turn, the tapes constitute a library of pre-prepared inputs (or "stimuli") for the second, third, and fourth groups of programs.

The second programs (the *automatic processor*) decrypt the disguised words with the aid of their accompanying clues. We say that these programs execute the technological tasks accomplished by the represented society. They simulate what is accomplished in a productive (or destructive) social group by the hands and machines that contribute directly to the services or products issuing from the group.

The third programs (*agent accounting*) attribute the simulated technological work of the represented social group to the directly productive energy in the technological system.

The automatic processor and the agent accounting programs together symbolize the technological system of any social organization simulated by the entire set of programs.

The fourth programs (*governing system*) represent the governing pyramid of control and command. Here are represented the flow of internal messages about the underlying technological work, the interpretation of these messages, the evolution of strategies for accomplishing the missions of the represented social group, command and control decisions, and the production of directives or orders. Demands of the environment will be represented in future programs.

Finally, the fifth programs (*data reduction*) perform data reduction on intermediate developments within the second, third, and fourth programs.

22.3   SIMULATION OF THE PRODUCTIVE PROCESS

22.3.1 *The Automatic Processor.*
The automatic processor can be viewed as a three-stage filter. In the first stage, parallel tests are made to determine whether each disguised word satisfies one of 25 possible versions of the first of the three clues that are provided for decrypting that word. In the second stage eight parallel tests seek to determine the form in which the second clue is satisfied. The third stage consists of eight similar

parallel tests. Viewed as a filter, the three stages of the processor successively eliminate equivocation and ambiguity.

At the entrance into the processor, there is a waiting line or storage queue. From this queue, each disguised word goes to all 25 first-stage subprocesses, each subprocess accepting a disguised word only when it is ready to work on it. After each subprocess has completed its work for a given disguised word, if the word does not meet the necessary conditions for the category under test by that subprocess, it is discarded from the subprocess. If it does meet the condition, however, it is passed along to the first intermediate storage queue.

There are 25 first intermediate queues, one associated with each subprocess (see Components III, Figure 22.3). The words which survive the

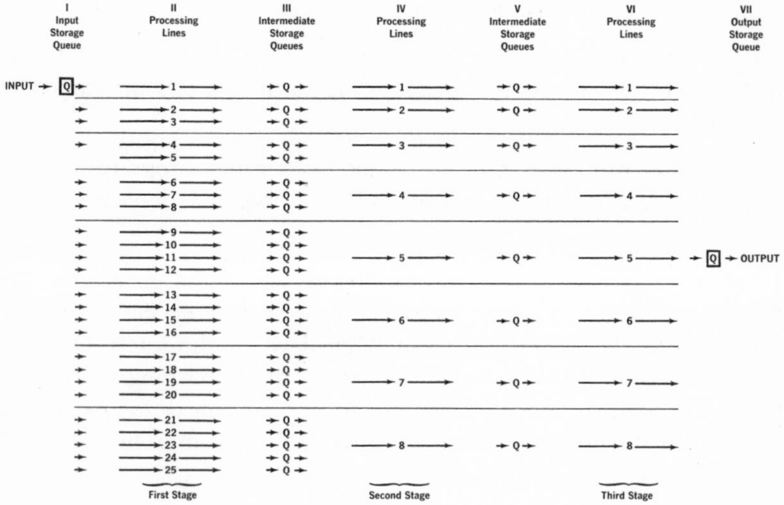

FIGURE 22.3 Processing lines and storage queues in the automatic processor programs.

first-stage subprocess and enter the first intermediate storage queues fall into two groups: (1) those which satisfy the first necessary condition, because in their original clear form they happen to belong to the category with which the storage queue and subprocess is associated; (2) those which accidentally satisfy the necessary condition, but really are spurious identifications.

The 25 intermediate storage queues (Components III) feed into eight second-stage subprocesses (Components IV), as shown in Figure 22.3. In the second-stage subprocesses (Components IV), tests are again applied, this time based on the second set of clues generated by the input preparation encrypting program. Words failing to meet the tests are discarded; partially identified words are delivered to the second intermediate storage queues, of which there are eight (Components V).

The eight second intermediate storage queues deliver their contents to the third and last subprocess (Component VI). These last-stage subprocesses correctly identify the original words.

22.3.2 *The Clues Prepared by the Input Preparation Programs.*
How does the elaborate network of processing lines and storage queues that constitute the automatic processor operate? To answer this question, it is first necessary to explicate in finer detail the encrypting discipline of the input preparation programs. These programs generate clues as follows:

a. *Gematric number.* The sums of the numerical values of the letters in the correct words are taken. We note that, in general, the least value that any such sum could possibly have in any word the Leviathan may receive is 11 (the value of the letter A) and the greatest value is 288 (8 times 36, or the sum of the letter values of ZZZZZZZZ). We engender equivocation by dividing the range of possible gematrics, namely, 11 through 288, into the six subregions: 11–60, 61–110, 11–160, 161–210, 211–260, 261–288. We subtract 50 repeatedly from the gematric of the correct word until the resultant value lies between 11 and 60. This value we give Leviathan with the understanding that the correct value is this least gematric mod 50.

Suppose that the correct word given to the input preparation programs is *SINGED*. The letter values of this word comprise the set [29, 19, 24, 17, 15, 14]. The sum of these letter values is 118. Subtracting 50 twice, we obtain the least gematric, $G_1 = 18$. Then $G_2 = 68$, $G_3 = 118$, $G_4 = 168$, $G_5 = 218$, $G_6 = 268$.

b. *Difference value.* The absolute value of the difference between the first and last letter of the correct word is also given to the simulated system. For the word SINGED, this is $|29 - 14| = 15$.

c. *Pair sums and differences*. As part of the encrypting discipline, the input preparation programs add randomly generated letters so that all words contain just eight letters. (Words longer than eight letters are converted by this procrustean process into two words, the first of which contains eight letters. The combination of the original word and the added random letters is called the "canonical" word. In the example of SINGED, let us suppose B and Z were added by the generator. Then the canonical word is SINGEDBZ.

We now form three subsets of clues in the following fashion. (1) Pairs of letters are taken together. The digits of their numerical equivalents in the tens position are stripped off and the sum of the remaining digits is taken. In SINGEDBZ, the first two letter values are 29 and 19 respectively. The 2 and 1 are stripped away from 29 and 19; and the remaining digits, 9 and 9, are added together to form 18. If the original pair of letters is in counter-alphabetical order, as they are in the SI of SINGEDBZ, 50 is added to this sum. (2) The sums of the first digits are taken. For the SI of SINGEDBZ, these are 2 and 1, and the first sum is 3. (3) The absolute values of the differences of the second digits are taken. For the SI of SINGEDBZ, we have $|9 - 9| = 0$.

Canonical word:	S	I	N	G	E	D	B	Z
Letter values:	29	19	24	17	15	14	12	36
Unit values:	9	9	4	7	5	4	2	6
Sums of pairs:	18		11		09		08	
P_1:	68		61		59		08	
Tens values:	2	1	2	1	1	1	1	3
P_2:	3		3		2		4	
P_3:	0		3		1		4	

FIGURE 22.4 Generation of clues.

The input preparation program now scrambles the order of the letters in the canonical word, using the random number generator to do this. Thus the automatic processor would receive from the input preparation programs an eight-letter word, say GDSBZEIN, or [17, 14, 29, 12, 36, 15, 19, 24], plus these clues: $G_1 = 18$, $D = 15$, $P_1 = [68, 61, 59, 08]$, $P_2 = [3, 3, 2, 4]$, $P_3 = [0, 3, 1, 4]$. Its task is to restore the given word to its original clear form.

22.3.3 *Operation of the Automatic Processor.* Records containing words encrypted in the foregoing fashion enter the processor and are stored in the input storage queue. Each of the first-stage subprocesses tests whether the words in this queue or waiting line can be made to satisfy the gematric clues.

In the case of GDSBZEIN, or [17, 14, 29, 12, 36, 15, 19, 24], the sums of the letters in the following combinations satisfy this gematric test: [15, 17, 36], [15, 24, 29], and [17, 12, 15, 24] equal 68 or G_2; [17, 29, 12, 36, 24], [14, 29, 36, 15, 24], [17, 14, 29, 15, 19, 24] and [17, 14, 12, 36, 15, 24] equal 118, or G_3. The survivors of the gematric test are stored in the first intermediate storage queues until the individual second processing stages are ready to operate on them.

In these second stages, tests are made for satisfaction of the differences condition. In our example, two combinations survive this test: In [14, 29, 36, 15, 24] and [17, 14, 29, 15, 19, 24] occur 14 and 29; and $|14 - 29| = 15$, the given value of the difference clue. D and S are identified as the terminal letters of the correct word. The survivors of this test are placed in the second intermediate storage queues.

The third processing stages test for satisfaction of the pair sums and differences condition. In our example, D or 14 cannot be the first letter of the correct word. This is because the first pair sum is 68, and $68 - 50 = 18$. Eighteen is the sum of the second digits of the first two letters of the correct word. The second digit of 14 is 4 but $18 - 4 = 14$; and no second digit can be 14.

Hence the first letter of the correct word is 29, or S. Its second digit is 9; $18 - 9 = 9$; the second letter must have a 9 for its second digit. This is the letter 19, or I. The last letter of the correct word must be D. Since I, or 19, does not occur in [14, 29, 36, 15, 24], the correct word must contain [17, 14, 29, 15, 19, 24].

We now know the letters that comprise the correct word and the first, second and last letters of this word. We have these letter values: [(29), (19), (15, 17, 24), (14)]. What can we learn from the fact that the value of the last letter of the correct word is 14? We know that this letter occurs in the third pair of letters of the correct word. The third pair sum is 59. Stripping off 50, 09 remains. Deducting the second digit of 14, namely 4, we find that the second digit of the fifth letter of the correct word is 5. Hence this letter must be 15, or E.

The remaining two letters in the correct word are 17, or G, and 24, or N. These must occur in counter-alphabetical order, because the second pair sum, namely 61, includes the increment 50. Also in the given word occur two letters added to the correct word to form the canonical word, namely, B and Z. These must occur in alphabetical order because the fourth pair sum, 08, does not include the increment 50.

The processor has now retrieved the canonical word and identified the original correct word: SINGED; BZ or [29, 19, 24, 17, 15, 14; 12, 36]. It confirms its identification by testing whether this word meets the second and third subsets of pair clues. If it does, the correct word in canonical form is placed in the output storage queue.

22.3.4 *Sequential Operations and the Clock.* The automatic processor consists of three stages of parallel operations. In the first stage are 25 subprocesses that operate in parallel, whereas in the second and third stages there are eight parallel processes. The computers we are employing are not parallel machines; their mode of operation is sequential. Hence the programs must scan out the various subprocesses in succession. Intuitively, we might think of a large productive organization stopped for an enduring instant in the flow of its activity. During this time, many pieces of many tasks are simultaneously executed. Perhaps a secretary says Hello, an executive dictates three words, and a drill press drills two holes in some work. For purposes of simulation, we say that one total scan through every action of the automatic processor represents all the work of an organization that takes place simultaneously during an extended moment. Now as the processor continues through scan after scan, the individual scans can be interpreted as successive moments of parallel operations. Sequential scans in the representing medium, the computer programs, are interpreted as successive simultaneous durations in the life of the simulated organization. Sequential scanning then defines a clock for the simulated organization. N scans comprise a period (we can think of an hour); M periods, an epoch (perhaps a day); and L epochs an era.

Notice that we do not first specify intervals of time and then measure the duration of our simulated social events as if they were contained in some absolute temporal box. On the contrary, we first create our social events and then measure time relatively, as one kind of relation among the absolutely existing events.

22.3.5 *Analog Simulation.* It is already possible to observe in what sense we assert that Leviathan's programs constitute analog simulation on a digital computer. The automatic processor actually performs the work that would be performed in any real productive system. The programs directly transform encrypted words into their original clear form; the programs literally retrieve the original forms latent in the disguised words and their associated clues. The subsequent programs—agent accounting and the governing system—also carry out this approach of directly performing operations in direct imitation of selected, important features of real social operations.

22.3.6 *Intermediate Behavioral Language.* The analog character of our simulation becomes even clearer if we consider a powerful technique that we employ in formulating it. The entire formulation is stated in an intermediate behavioral language. A typical operation in this language is "026. Test whether there is room in storage queue. If yes, X. If no, Y." Two other examples are "050. Add X to Y" and "040. Test: Does X = Y? If yes, V. If no, W." These operations in the intermediate language can support three interpretations: (1) The operations are directly translatable into the commands that cause the computer to operate. The computer operations really accomplish these activities, operating directly on the encrypted words that are being decoded. (2) The operations are such that they can be stated completely in the notations of mathematics or of set theory. (3) The operations can literally be accomplished by the overt behavior of live persons. Hence the operations are invariant across human behavior, mathematico-logical formulation, and computer operations.

For computer operations, this mode of formulation permits the designers of Leviathan to think in terms of human behavior, confident that the formulations can be performed by computing machinery. Any formulation that can be made to operate by live subjects following prescribed rules without further interpretation and that is coherent in the intermediate formulation, can be translated into machine operations. Hence formulation can proceed in a language "sealed off" from any particular machine, that is, invariant to reprograming from one machine to another.

For social investigations, the intermediate behavioral language guarantees strict, operational formulation. If every significant overt action in an experiment can be literally duplicated by computing machinery, then the experiment refers without remainder to overt, operational behavior.

Finally, because the intermediate language is exhaustively translatable into either mathematical or set-theoretic terms, we can be scientifically rigorous without being exclusively quantitative. We can express with precision many qualitative relationships essential to social structure and process. Also we guarantee an objective statement to any conclusions that we may derive from our formulations.

22.4   SIMULATION OF PRODUCTIVE AGENTS

22.4.1   *Productive Energy and Social Energy.* It is now time to introduce simulated agents. This we can do by extending our interpretation of the intermediate behavioral language. We designate the micro-operations in the language "atomic actions," and we arbitrarily assert that each micro-operation represents the expenditure of one unit of social energy. Ironically honoring the tradition that gave birth to therbligs, we call our units "taylors," after the industrial engineer, F. W. Taylor, who sought to rationalize human labor. Then each time an atomic action is executed in the automatic processor, one unit of human energy, 1 taylor, is said to have been expended. The atomic actions are thus shared between the productive and the social energy of the technological system.

Next we simply attribute the social energy to productive agents. At this point, a word of historical explanation is in order. In formulating the Leviathan technique for large-group analysis, we had two options. We could have either identified our agents with specific locations in the core storage of a computer or else built our agents around simple proper names. The first alternative seemed hardly suitable after Whitehead's strictures against misplaced concreteness and the fallacy of simple location. Any investigator possessing practical experience with organisms and adaptive systems is keenly aware that systems have a way of being neither simply where nor simply when. A system is excised from the total cosmological process by an act of abstraction. Autonomy is always relative. (Is the air we breathe, that is shared among people, part of the real internal constitution of a person?) Hence we follow the second alternative. We begin by naming our agents, starting with "0001." Once we give these proper names to our agents, the names serve as cores of identity about which we can accumulate, in lawful ways, events or properties that are brought into existence by the rules of our simulation. Provided an event or property is one that we would associate with an agent, it can be at-

001	STORE	Store X at Y
002	RECEIVE	Receive X from Y
004	PURGE	Remove X from Y
006	ARRIVED?	Test: Has X arrived at Y?
007	LEFT?	Test: Has X left Y?
010	SET	Set X to Y and discard X from Z
011	LOOK UP	Obtain definition of X from Y
015	EXTRACT	Extract X from Y, leaving Y vacant
016	INSPECT	Extract X from Y, leaving X in Y
026	ROOM?	Test: Room at X?
031	SEND	Send X to Y
033	ASSOCIATE	Associate X with Y
036	CONTROL	Request X to take control
040	EQUAL?	Test: $X = Y$?
041	PRODUCT?	Test: Do all X equal Y?
044	GREATER?	Test: X greater than Y?
050	ADD	Add X to Y at Z
051	SUMMATE	Take sum of items at X
054	SUBTRACT	$\lvert X - Y \rvert$

FIGURE 22.5 Definitions of atomic actions.

tributed to any one of our agents, regardless of its date or location. We shall explain later the degree to which we accumulate concreteness and specificity about our executive decision makers. As for the productive agents, on the other hand, submerged as they are in the technological system and representing hoi polloi—the workers in industry, the civil service clerks in government, and the enlisted men in military systems: for these, we provide only a very limited degree of specificity or individuality. To these directly productive agents, we attribute (1) skill profiles and (2) affiliation with particular squads or teams that report to first-level supervisors in the governing system.

22.4.2 Skill Profiles. In the intermediate behavioral language, 19 items comprise the total set of atomic actions that occur in the technological system (see Figure 22.5). These can be classified into six categories. Each category is said to be a class of skills (see Figure 22.6). This is the interpretation of *skill class:* Each productive agent has a variety of skills. Depending on how much of each skill he has, he can contribute so much of that kind of effort during an epoch toward accomplishing Leviathan's work. From this definition, it follows that atomic actions and skills are

I. Queue-processing	II. Data-coordinating	III. Message-clerking
001 Store 015 Extract 016 Inspect 026 Room?	006 Arrived? 007 Left?	002 Receive 004 Purge 031 Send

IV. Data-processing	V. Testing	VI. Computation
010 Set 011 Look Up 033 Associate 036 Control	040 Equal? 041 Product? 044 Greater?	050 Add 051 Summate 054 Subtract

FIGURE 22.6 Atomic actions assigned to skill classes.

closely associated. When an agent exercises a particular skill, he performs atomic actions associated with that skill. The table of skill classes defines for Leviathan what atomic actions can be performed, given any one of the six kinds of skills.

Once skill classes have been defined, we can introduce the notion of a "standard skill profile." Suppose that an organization wished to hire a message clerk. Given that there are the six categories of skills specified in Figure 22.6, little contribution would be expected from a message clerk in categories I (queue processing), II (data coordinating), IV (data processing), V (testing or quality control), or VI (computation), but the contribution from category III, which includes receiving messages, removing messages from files, copying or repeating and sending messages, would be maximal. A data clerk would have a different profile of skills (see Figure 22.7). Of course, it is not possible to tell a computer anything

	Amount of skill	
	Message-clerking	Data clerk
I. Queue-processing	Low	Low
II. Data-coordinating	Low	Higher
III. Message-clerking	High	Low
IV. Data-processing	Low	Higher
V. Testing	Low	Low
VI. Computation	Low	Higher

FIGURE 22.7 Requirements for typical standard skill profiles.

so general as that computational skills shall be "low" for one kind of newly hired person and "higher" for another. We need specificity. Fortunately, taylors give us what we need. For a given standard profile, we assign various amounts of taylors to each of the skill classes. It happens that up to 4096 taylors can be assigned to each skill class (2^{12}) or a maximum of $6 \times 4096 = 24{,}576$ taylors in all for any one productive agent. Thus standard skill profiles for typical message clerks and typical data clerks might resemble the values shown in Figure 22.8.

Skill class

	I. Queue-process-ing	II. Data-coordi-nating	III. Message-clerking	IV. Data-process-ing	V. Test-ing	VI. Compu-tation	Total
Message clerk	125	145	4000	550	150	75	5045
Data clerk	85	1550	1400	2525	150	850	6560

FIGURE 22.8 Examples of standard skill profiles.

From the standard skill profiles, we derive individual skill profiles. Although our enlisted personnel (or workers or government clerks) are essentially faceless, we do give them this much individuality—their skill profiles vary from one to another. The variation is specified in terms of increments and decrements over the values of taylors in the standard profiles.

The result of our formulations of skill classes, standard skill profiles, and individual variations are individual skill profiles. To each proper name of a productive agent, we attribute a unique individual skill profile. Later, we shall see that this skill profile is known to the experimenter who establishes the conditions (boundary parameters) for a given investigation employing Leviathan, but it is withheld from the executives who know the standard skill profiles but must infer inductively what are individual variations among productive agents.

Given individual skill profiles, it is possible to define "learning" for the productive agents, even though, besides individual skill profiles, little else is specified for each productive agent. Learning on the part of productive agents consists in attaining changes in individual skill profiles. Thus such learning is simple to define, has relevance to qualitative differences among agents (namely, differences in the respective skill classes, which are interpreted to be qualitatively distinct), and yet remains precise and measurable.

22.4.3 The Table of Atomic Actions and the Agent Accounting Table.

We have now explained the basic ingredients with which we simulate a technological system on a computer. What more is needed to set such a simulation into operation?

For an actual run, we should first have to specify four kinds of information that can vary from investigation to investigation, even though the programs remain the same:

a. *Number of agents.* How many productive agents should be included in a given investigation? This number need not remain the same throughout an experimental run on the computer, for it is possible with Leviathan to study expanding and contracting organizations, and the change in number of personnel can be controlled in three, non-exclusive, ways. A pattern of change in size and composition of the productive force can be prearranged to occur according to a desired time-scale, as certain events specified by the investigators occur, or at the command of the executives in the governing system.

b. *Standard skill profiles.* The next step would be determination of the standard skill profiles to be used during the progress of an investigation.

c. *Profiles assigned to agents.* These standard skill profiles would then be assigned to individual agents by the investigators.

d. *Individual variations in profiles.* From the standard skill profiles individual variations among the agents would be defined. The only limitations on individual variations are these: (1) that the result of combining standard skill profile and individual variations in every case result in positive values of taylors, and (2) that no skill class have a value exceeding 4095 taylors.

These four requirements are embodied in a table in the computer. The table consists of the proper name of each productive agent and his individual skill profile.

A fine adjustment can be added to the entries in the table. If an agent is absent, for example, on account of illness, operationally this means that during a particular period of simulated time the values of his individual skill profile are all zero; i.e., 'he can contribute no taylors to the productive or destructive work of the organization. Absenteeism can be individually controlled by a probabilistic formula specified by the investigators. The pseudo-random generator supplies "random" numbers, and, depending on the values of these numbers and the pattern contained in the formula, the individual agents are occasionally absent. Obviously, if this is important for some investigation, we can introduce contingent absenteeism, in which an agent has a pattern of probable absence that depends on kinds of events in the history of the simulated organization.

Now, once we have our table of individual productive agents and their skill profiles, we can interconnect the agent accounting programs with the automatic processor. This interconnection is the basic mechanism that permits us to simulate a technological system. How is the connection effected? By creating a second table in the following way:

a. *Name of atomic action.* At each point in the automatic processor where the computer program literally accomplishes the work specified by one of the atomic actions, we insert the name of the appropriate atomic action. Thus, if the atomic action happens to be "026" ("room?"), which tests whether a storage queue has room available to receive further work, "026" is inserted in the computer program immediately following the set of computer instructions in the automatic processor that do test for room in a given storage queue.

b. *Skill class of action.* For each atomic action listed in the automatic processor, the skill class to which the atomic action belongs is inserted in the computer code directly beside the respective atomic action.

c. *Name of agent.* If now we add the name of the agent assigned to perform the given atomic action, the computer can charge this agent with responsibility for performing his appropriate work in the technological system of the organization being simulated (but see Section 22.5.2 for more precise statement).

We are now ready to interassociate the items on two lists. One list contains the atomic actions in the order in which they occur, together with their respective skill classes and an indication of the agent who will be said to have performed the atomic action. We call this list the "table of atomic actions." Another list is the table of individual skill profiles associated with the respective productive agents. We call this list the "agent accounting table."

22.4.4 *The Operation of the Computer Programs that Simulate the Technological System.* The simulation of the technological system proceeds as follows: The automatic processor scans out the prescribed operations that constitute the technological work of the simulated organization. As each operation specified by an atomic action is completed by the automatic processor, the computer determines, from the table of atomic actions, which agent is responsible for performing the operation and what is the skill class of the operator. Control is passed in the computer to the agent accounting programs. These programs locate the proper individual productive agent in the agent accounting table, find the appropriate skill class for the atomic action being attributed to the agent, and subtract 1 taylor from the supply of taylors listed under the skill class. Then control is returned to the processor (see Figure 22.9). Like an inexorable loom, the computer executes an atomic action, charges the appropriate agent, executes the next action, charges the next agent, and continues to swing back and forth between the automatic processor, with its table of atomic actions, and the agent accounting table.

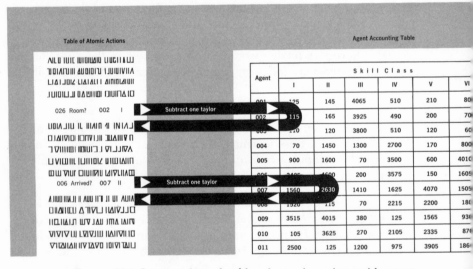

Figure 22.9 Interweaving of table of atomic actions with agent accounting table.

At the end of an epoch, the loom is halted, the taylors remaining in each individual skill profile are totaled, these totals are recorded, and in the agent accounting table, the individual skill profiles are reset to their original values. If learning is postulated, new values for the number of taylors in each skill category are set into the skill profiles that make up the accounting tables. The differences between the original and the subsequent values are measures of the amount of learning that may be said to occur.

As a result of the weaving action between the automatic processor and the agent accounting programs, the technological work of the simulated social organization is accomplished and the productive agents are charged with having made their proper contributions. The outcome of this activity is the simulation of a technological system.

22.5 THE GOVERNING SYSTEM

22.5.1 *The Hierarchy of Direct Command.* We begin our formulation of governing systems by building a skeleton. The skeleton represents the hierarchy of direct command or table of authority and responsibility, commonly shown as a tree on organization charts of productive social groups. We impose our skeleton on a governing system by incorporating it into the agent accounting table. This we do simply by grouping the agents represented in the table and interpreting each group of agents as a squad at the lowest level of command (see Figure 22.10). Next the squads are grouped together in ever larger aggregations (see Figure 22.11). Then, as the automatic processor grinds out the productive work of a simulated

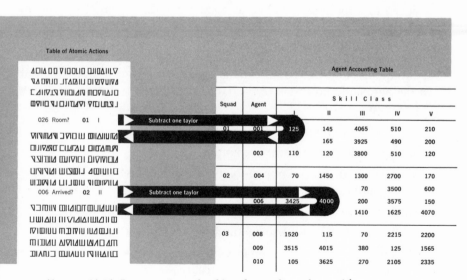

FIGURE 22.10 Interweaving of table of atomic actions with agent accounting table (agent accounting by squads).

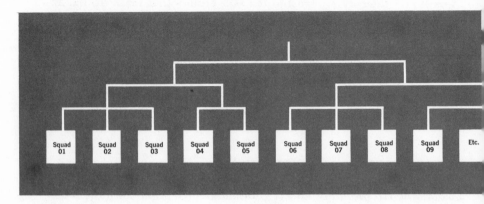

FIGURE 22.11 Squads aggregated into echelons of line command.

organization, each productive agent in each squad is charged with having performed a given atomic action. Because the squads are themselves grouped in ever more comprehensive groupings, each successively higher grouping of agents is *ipso facto* also charged with having performed that action.

22.5.2 *Organizational Responsibility for Performance of Technological Work.* Note that the responsibility for a given atomic action is not assigned to a specific individual as such, but rather to his organizational unit. In the table of atomic actions that we insert into the automatic processor, we specify (in addition to the skill class of each atomic action) the lowest-level organizational units to which the agents are assigned. Thus squads of agents, not individual agents, are assigned to specific tasks in the automatic processor. As a result, the programs operate as follows (see Figure 22.10):

a. Work is accomplished in the processor.

b. Control is passed to the accounting program.

c. The squad assigned responsibility for this work is located in the agent accounting table.

d. The skill class of the atomic action is located in the table.

e. The entire squad is scanned under this skill class.

f. The agent within the squad with the largest number of taylors remaining in this skill class is located.

g. This agent is charged with having performed the atomic action by the device of subtracting one taylor.

h. Control is returned to the automatic processor.

22.5.3 *Optional Varieties of Organization and Dynamic Reorganization.* The hierarchy of direct command is incorporated into our computer programs, as we have just seen, by imposing it as a skeletal structure on the table of productive agents. Now the list of atomic actions in the automatic processor specifies the flow of work in the technological system, whereas the agent accounting table specifies the formal structure of the organization. When the two tables are interconnected by the operation of the computer, the various organizational groups of executives in the hierarchical line organization are given responsibility for specific areas of productive work. How the line organization is associated with the production processes is completely at the control of the investigators.

Almost any form of formal organization that we can specify can be simulated by means of properly specifying the connections between the table of atomic actions and the social groups in the agent table. In particular, we can readily organize our simulated social groups:

a. By stage of completion of work, after analogy to an industrial combination with top-level divisions responsible respectively for obtaining raw materials, for example, from mines or oil wells, for intermediate processing into semifinished products, and for final processing for completed products.

b. By subprocesses, in a structure that might be exemplified by processing tax returns from the northeastern region, from the middle-eastern region, and so forth, until all regions are represented.

c. By predominant skill required to accomplish the technological work, for example, organization in terms of a division of engineers, of training specialists, of computer programers, etc., all combined to design a large, nationwide system of command and control over the flow of economic intelligence.

d. By allowing the pseudo-random number generator to provide a "random" organization for us.

In Figure 22.12 are suggested mixed forms of organization. The form of organization need not remain static during the operation of the programs, for the simulated executives can be made to restructure their own hierarchy of command dynamically as the simulation proceeds on the computer. This can be made to happen contingently on the occurrence of selected kinds of simulated events, for example, when consumer demand results in reducing the total kinds of products or services supplied by the total simulated system. The costs and consequences of different techniques for phasing over from one concrete form of organization to another

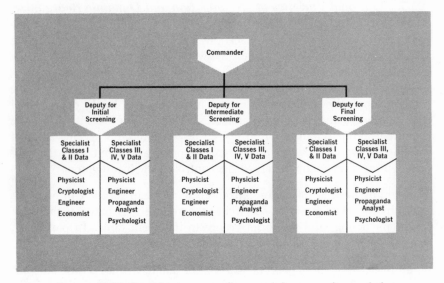

FIGURE 22.12 Organization according to (a) stage of completion of work, (b) subprocess, and (c) skill.

in large social groups provide a fertile field for the application of Leviathan.

22.5.4 *Information Generated in the Technological System.* Two basic kinds of information are generated by the technological system and are supplied to the executives in the governing system: information relating to production and information relating to manpower or social energy of the productive agents.

In the production area, the executives have access to information concerning the capacity of storage queues, the degree to which they are filled, the rate of entry of items into the subprocessing lines, and the quantity of items entering per epoch.

Information about manpower is generated in this way. At the end of an epoch, the taylors expended by each agent are extracted from the agent accounting table and recorded. Also, the taylors expended in each skill class are aggregated for each entire squad. If we think of the individual workers occupying rows in the accounting tables, the sum of taylors taken across each row at the end of an epoch is the total taylors expended per worker during that epoch. The totals of the columns represent the taylors expended per skill class by the entire squad. The original values set in the table at the start of each epoch represent, when aggregated by columns, the skill resources of the respective squads. Further aggregations of the squads furnish the skill resources and the expenditure of taylors by entire groupings on the first and higher supervisory levels in the pyramid of command.

Unless the investigators or the simulated executives specify otherwise, all information to the higher echelons of command during a simulation automatically follows the formal chart. This is true for information relating both to production and manpower. With time lags specified by the investigators, such information is sent in aggregate form to the executive offices in the command pyramid. Each office has access to information in the area of production and in the cadres of agents under its command. Each office receives this information in two forms: aggregated for the total area under its command and differentiated with respect to the organizational groups reporting to it.

In the information available at the higher echelons of command, the clumps of information may be too gross for many purposes of control and command. To obtain finer-grained information, specific messages requesting such data can be sent, interpreted, and answered. Of course, all such communication is subject to routine lags in times for delivery.

22.5.5 *Information Interpreted and Assessed according to Criteria.* Some information is tested by criteria and evaluated in the light of such criteria, and only the result of evaluation is passed forward to other executive offices. Suppose that in the agent accounting tables, taylors are insufficient to complete the work assigned to a given organizational group during an epoch. Criteria (simple numbers) are available to the executives to determine whether the insufficiency is so great that an agent should simply be transferred out of one group into the lacking group. Other criteria support decisions to interchange productive agents between pairs of groups for better fit of skills to skill requirements. The data relate to insufficiencies of specific amounts and skill categories. The assessment can be: we need an additional man. Many similar criteria are formed and assessments are made at various points in the command echelon.

22.6 DECISION MAKING

22.6.1 *Decision Making and the Development of Social Groups.* Decisions that significantly affect the operation of a social organization can conveniently be classified between two poles. One pole is that of control, tactics, administration, implementation; the other is that of command, strategy, and policy. Decisions of control are directed toward maintaining an organization within the direction of progress prescribed for it by decisions of command. For decisions of command, futurity is of the essence. These are choices that shape the future of an organization and open it to development, whereas decisions of control are far more closed in viewpoint, seeking to maintain an organization as prescribed by command. Because the interplay of structure and dynamics is of central concern for the Leviathan studies, the relationships between these two kinds of decisions become very important. Command prescribes new complexes of structure and function; control implements these prescriptions. But this is not all. Command transforms itself dynamically as an organization lives out its destiny. Very rarely can an executive or group of executives elect a future in a single act of choice and then realize that future with any precision. Like the headlamps of an automobile at night, command lights up the country that lies ahead, but does so for ever-varying distances; control remains closely bound to the present, even when it delivers what command exhorts, for where the roads lie and how they interconnect deeply affects the progress of the vehicle. Thus, decisions of command shape the future of an organization, and decisions of control implement these; but on a higher level of synthesis, viable command is constantly tested, monitored, and itself reshaped in a healthy organization.

According to this view, decision in the governing system is the essence of the executive process, because it is the key instrument by which the social organization constantly recreates and reestablishes itself. Thus, a just formulation of the executive decision-making processes becomes of crucial concern to Leviathan. For the formulation will dictate how the computer programs are written for Leviathan and how they enact or represent the command and control functions.

22.6.2 The Simulated Decision Makers. The governing system in any productive organization can be viewed as an elaborate set of transmission and decision nodes, connected by system links. In structuring such nets, we can attend to the links or to the nodes. What happens at the nodes?

In the computer programs, the decision makers are given bit relationships to represent individual traits. Values for these traits are parameters specified by the investigators as pure, logical variables, scaled from one to seven, with neutral point at four. If a tendency of an executive to make

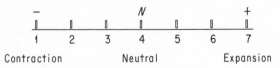

FIGURE 22.13 Scale of tendencies toward expansion.

decisions leading to expansion of his situation be scaled, *one* would represent strong tendencies to contraction; *two,* moderate tendencies; *three,* slight tendencies; *four,* neutral; *five,* slightly toward expansion; *six,* moderate; and *seven,* strong. In similar fashion, pure scale variables can be associated with speed of decision making, alacrity in execution, proclivity to delegate responsibility for decision making, tendencies to consult line, staff, associates, or supervisors for information or for direction in which to decide, tendency to centralize, quantity of parallel decision processes, prefiltering demands for decisions by importance, quantity of prefiltering, degree to which associates are informally consulted, tolerance of ambiguity, self-protectiveness, tendency to elaborate channels, and the like.

Once such sets of tendencies are chosen for individual executives situated at decision nodes in the formal organization, modifiers are introduced. The modifiers have the effect of altering the foregoing tendencies differentially, depending on the subject matter decided upon. Thus some executives will realize their extreme tendencies (for example, a tendency to caution) more fully with respect to human relations than with respect to problems of production. Or they may realize them more fully in economic matters than in setting priorities. Among the modifiers are those which take effect with respect to efficiency of manpower, effectiveness of manpower, production rates, products, capital, small issues in general, and large issues. In Figure 22.14 are expressed the cross effects of tendencies and their modifiers. Given a tendency, a row is selected in the matrix

		Tendency						
		−		N			+	
		1	2	3	4	5	6	7
−	1	1	1	2	2	3	3	4
	2	1	2	2	3	3	4	4
	3	2	2	3	3	4	4	5
Modifier N	4	2	3	3	4	4	5	5
	5	3	3	4	4	5	5	6
	6	3	4	4	5	5	6	6
+	7	4	4	5	5	6	6	7

FIGURE 22.14 Effect of modifiers on tendencies.

depending on the place an individual executive is made to occupy in the scale of seven. His modifiers are values represented in the rows. Once a column and a row are specified—a tendency and a modifier—then a cell in the matrix is determined, and the value in the cell is the resulting tendency employed in the simulation for that executive under those circumstances.

In addition to tendencies and modifiers, a further weighting factor is required before a given decision results. This is a relevance factor. The various tendencies are significant only to limited degrees, depending on the subject matter of the decision. In making decisions, men assess matters of semantic relevance. People fit their judgments to the objects concerning which judgments are made (while they always do this, they do not always do this well). Computers do not have this kind of semantic insight. Hence the investigators must build into the computer programs a comprehensive scheme of relevance factors.

22.6.3 *The Decision Sequence.* The remainder of the decision process is essentially a matter of behavioral mechanisms. This does not mean that the mechanisms will not result in very complicated sequences of interactions between executives. But complication can always be delegated to a computer, provided that the micro-operations are experimentally controlled. The investigator prescribes the stitches to be executed and the spools of variously dyed threads; the computer weaves out the social fabric. These are the stages in the individual decision processes as they will be incorporated in Leviathan's computer programs:

a. *Filtering.* When the time of decision making arrives for each simulated executive, many requests for decisions, originating both from other areas in the organization and from his inner driving interests, simultaneously press for satisfaction. Each executive initially filters these to select the objects about which his next decision will be concerned. Parameters that will be controllable include span of selection, rate of filtering, criteria for priority filtering.

b. *Elaboration.* Often the decision will be that more information is required. The decision process will temporarily be arrested as requests issue from him for further data. Or he searches his own store of impressions to collect the basis for making the decision. The result of elaboration is a perception of alternative choices open to him. Parameters include direction of consultation (up, down, staff, associates), rate, amount, relevance.

c. *Evaluation.* He next forms an estimate of the problem to be solved and the data available. Parameters include relevance, rate, and the disciplines for establishing criteria.

d. *Determining objectives.* Based on his perception of existing policy, he seeks to determine the answers to questions about the outcome of his process of deciding such as: To what end? What for? Parameters include relevance, rate, sources of objectives.

e. *Choice.* He chooses among the alternatives available, forming an estimate of the relevance of the various alternatives to the problem to be solved and the objectives currently acknowledged.

f. *Implementation.* He explores possibilities of implementation. Parameters are similar to those for elaboration.

g. *Command.* He issues an order to execute. Parameters include rate and organizational location of recipients.

h. *Follow-up.* He establishes within himself an intention to follow up to determine whether the command has been realized.

The outcome of the concerted activity of the executives will be the performance of the total organization. The executives, acting in concert, modulate the flow of work through the productive processes, the allocation of manpower, and the assignment of internal priorities. In short, they exercise control and command over the total system of which they comprise the governing complex.

22.7   CONCLUSION: THE LEVIATHAN COMPUTER PROGRAM AS A FACILITY

22.7.1 *Parameterized Programs.* Let us stand back and view the simulation that is accomplished by Leviathan's computer programs. Leviathan's programs provide it with a facility for many kinds of investigations. Parameters have been provided wherever specific quantitative values are needed. Time is parameterized, for a period is a number of scans through the automatic processor, an epoch is a number of periods, and an era a number of epochs, but each of these numbers is specifiable by the investigators. Organization is a pure variable, and the connection between organization and the production processes is subject to very fluid experimental control. The numbers and kinds of productive agents, the characteristics and organization of the executives, their specific modes of interaction: all these are parameterized; i.e., the investigators must state specific values for these before the computer can be made to operate.

22.7.2 *Data Reduction.* In the course of a run, in principle, every operation of the computer—literally every one—can be recorded. The total simulation is thus completely accessible to observation. The investigators can study precisely the instructions given to the computer and what happens when the computer obeys these instructions. Of course, no such torrent of data should or will be saved. For reference, magnetic tapes will be prepared containing in highly compressed form extensive selected records of what takes place. Then, in separate operations (the fifth group of programs, devoted to data reduction), the computer will again be used to search the tapes, reduce the data to forms which will constitute answers to questions explicitly framed by the investigators, and print out the results of the data reduction. Limited only by the ingenuity of the investigators in posing meaningful questions, the computer will be used to digest the results of investigations. The tapes themselves will be saved against the contingency that further questions will occur to the investigators as experiments proceed in orderly groups.

22.7.3 *Investigations at the Nodes.* The investigator can say what kind of executive shall occupy every node at which decisions are made in the governing system. The rate at which the executive makes his decisions, the ways he selects opportunities for deciding, his tendencies to delegate, to confer, to form coalitions, and many other characteristics can be specified and experimentally controlled. The computer converts all these modes of deciding at each node, plus all the data impinging on the node, into a synthesis at that node. Thus epoch after epoch in the life of the social organization, at node after node, the computer enacts the decision process of each individual.

These are the implications of this synthesizing activity for experimental design: We can conceive a governing system of a social organization as a collection of nodes or offices. At each node, we can specify, within rather wide limits, the traits of the decision makers. We can array the simulated decision makers in any way that may be conformable to the purposes of a particular investigation. We can, for example, arrange to have decision makers decide with a rapidity that is inverse to their status in the pyramid of command. Or we can make decisions tend to be increasingly trivial or fewer per epoch or warped from one area, such as production matters, to another, such as manpower allocation, as the decision makers occupy increasingly exalted status. In short, conceiving Leviathan's computer programs as a parallel array of nodal synthesizers, we can study the effects of individual modes of functioning on the operations of social organizations.

22.7.4 *Investigations of Total System.* The computer can also be conceived as synthesizing the total system. It welds the operations of the technological system with the governing processes of the command pyramid. Now with the computer, something impossible in real life can be done. In real life, neither real biological nor real social organisms can ever repeat their history in any literal sense. Organic life is inherently developmental. With the computer, we do simulate such development with considerable sophistication. But, further, any given operation of a computer can be repeated with perfect precision (assuming error-free operation of the computing machinery). Thus if the same initial value is set in a random number generator and Leviathan's programs are made to operate, they can exactly duplicate developmental processes that have previously been simulated. Change the initial value in the random number generator and everything about the simulation is subtly changed.

In consequence of these considerations, we can plan investigations with the computer programs in which every feature will remain the same in successive runs except one pervasive feature. The number, kinds, and characteristics of all productive and executive agents remain the same, as does the formal organization, the prescribed rules for organizational and local operating procedures, etc., but the informal organization is made to develop at a different pace and have a different degree of significance. Or formal lateral structure is allowed to develop to different degrees. Or certain kinds of communications are inhibited, for example, efforts at sharing views among executives below certain levels of command concerning the developing social norms of the organization. By this process, using the computer as a synthesizer of a total system, we can factor out the effects of a particular aspect of system operations in large social organizations.

22.7.5 *Computer Simulation.* Computer simulation is an important part of the Leviathan studies. If any structure or relation can be realized isomorphically in the computer, then the essence of that structure has been captured. The computer, furthermore, forces any structure to be realized in the form of operations, for the computer transforms. Hence it guarantees that where there is structure there is dynamic change. Therefore the important question of the relation of structure and dynamics is resolved in the machine by realizing a simulation. In addition, the computer does not tolerate ambiguity. Any realization is formal and precise— utter precision is guaranteed by computer realization. We conclude that if we can realize an abstract general analog of a social organization in a computer, then we realize more than the mere formal essence of any one social organization. For to the extent that our abstract analog structures are shared among many organizations in real life, we realize the common invariances that pervade productive social organizations.

Leviathan's programs, then, constitute a facility. Given these programs, a general purpose computer is converted into a laboratory instrument of great power for investigating many kinds of social relationships in large productive social groups. What results is an elaborate engine for determining the consequences of theories of an intermediate level between real life and the most general theory of social process.

REFERENCES

1 Rome, Beatrice K., and Rome, S. C., Leviathan, A Simulation of Behavioral Systems, to Operate Dynamically on a Digital Computer, and,
   Formal Representation of Intentionally Structured Systems, *Information
   Retrieval and Machine Translation*, Kent, A., ed. New York: Interscience, New York, 1960, chaps. 56 and 12. Also available from System Development Corporation as *SP-50* and *SP-82*.

2 Rome, S. C., and Rome, Beatrice K., The Leviathan Technique for Large-
   Group Analysis, *Behavioral Science, 6* (No. 2), April 1961, 148–52.

3 ———, Some Topological Measures for the Mark I Leviathan Programs,
   FN-4821, System Development Corporation, Dec. 17, 1960.

4 ———, Some Multivariate Informational Measures for Leviathan Mark
   I Programs, *FN-4827*, System Development Corporation, Dec. 8, 1960.

R. Clay Sprowls
23/BUSINESS SIMULATION

R. Clay Sprowls is
Associate Professor of Business Statistics
and Assistant Director
of the Western Data Processing
Center, the Graduate School of Business
Administration, the University of
California, Los Angeles.
He received his Ph.D. in business statistics
from the University of Chicago in 1951.
His present research interest is
in the use of electronic computers
to simulate business operations.
He is the author of a textbook,
Elementary Statistics, *and of papers*
on statistical methods.

23.1 DEFINITION AND EXAMPLES

"To simulate," according to Webster, is "to assume the appearance of, without the reality." This definition implies that simulation is concerned with the construction of models or prototypes of some part of reality. Models may be physical: for example, the model of an airplane which is flown in a wind tunnel to test the design and performance of the plane. They may be mathematical: for example, the set of equations describing the orbit of a satellite. They may be logical or input/output models: for example, the logistics of an air force described by a number of black boxes (including, perhaps, people) connected by rules of operations and decision making. Models need not be uniquely physical or mathematical or logical. They may involve elements of each of these classifications, especially the mathematical and logical.

Other examples of simulation are the study of maintenance operations, the design of a warehouse, and the scheduling of airplane traffic, job shop operations, and traffic patterns and flows in an urban area. Several chapters of this book are devoted to simulation: Chapter 19 to simulation of a brain, Chapter 22 to simulation of a behavioral system, and Chapter 24 to simulation of international relations and diplomacy.

The appearance of so much material in one book devoted to computer applications indicates that simulation is an important and interesting modern research tool of the behavioral sciences—as it has been in engineering and the physical sciences for a long, long time—and that a high-speed electronic computer is an integral part of many simulations.

23.2   SCOPE OF THIS CHAPTER

This chapter is concerned with one attempt to simulate the complete operations of a small business firm, named the Task Manufacturing Corporation, on a high-speed electronic digital computer.* One may immediately ask: Why such a simulation? Is such a simulation justifiable? Can one reasonably construct a model which gives the appearance but not the reality of the business firm?

As one moves further and further away from the individual worker in, say, the warehouse, and up into management levels, his conception of, and dealings with, the firm become more and more a study of information flows. The employee in the warehouse may be concerned primarily with moving boxes of finished product from a location in the warehouse into a box car; this is his daily job. The boxes must be moved as a part of the business operation, but involvement with the physical movement falls almost exclusively to this one man. Employees of other departments who are concerned with these shipments—for example, inventory control, sales analysis, or accounting—deal with recorded data about this movement. Higher levels of management know about the movement, make decisions based upon it, and change policies as a result of it, but only on the basis of information contained in a report. The facts of the physical environment may not be at all important to them because the business system appears as an information processing system consisting of transactions (of which the warehouse movement is one), information about these transactions, and decisions and policies relating to these transactions. Simulating the complete operations of a business firm is the task of modeling the information processing system.

* This simulation uses the electronic data processing equipment in the Western Data Processing Center, the University of California, Los Angeles. Professor Morris Asimow of the Department of Engineering has been a collaborator on the design of parts of the simulation. Financial support for the project has come from the Division of Research of the Graduate School of Business Administration and the Department of Engineering.

23.3   ASSUMPTIONS ABOUT THE TASK
MANUFACTURING CORPORATION

The appearance of reality can be given in many ways. For example, a time series of random drawings from a probability distribution may give a reasonable representation of the sales of a firm. As a model of the market, it is a simple and rather unsophisticated representation. A more elaborate statistical model is a multiple regression equation relating sales of the firm to several independent variables. This kind of model is used in many of the so-called management games.

The Task Manufacturing Corporation is based upon a different view of the nature of the models needed and is to be contrasted with management games in this as well as another way. The management game usually uses a simulated environment to study the behavior of individuals or teams of players or to instruct such individuals or teams. These games always involve the presence of players. Simulations may also involve players and be used for instruction, but primarily they are directed toward studying the behavior of the system either with the behavior of individuals given, or without them entirely. As a result, the type of model needed for simulation may be quite different from one that will suffice for a management game. The Task Manufacturing Corporation especially takes a different view of the type of model needed.

It starts with the premise that a business system is concerned with the origination of transactions (of many different kinds), with the recording of information in these transactions, and with the policies governing, and decisions based upon the processing of, the information in these transactions. The transactions in this simulation come from the subsystems of the firm.

The most important subsystems which give rise to these transactions are

    a. Employees, or workers in the production process,

    b. Machines, or productive units,

    c. Customers, or buyers of the product,

    d. Vendors, or suppliers of raw materials, and

    e. Financial institutions, or sources of financing.

Models of the subsystems describe *individual units* of each, for example, individual employees, machines, customers, vendors, and financial institutions, rather than an over-all work force, or production system, or market place with merely mathematical equations relating gross economic and engineering variables. A main task in the simulation is developing models of these individuals from mathematical and logical relationships which reflect some understanding of basic mechanisms underlying each of them and give rise to transactions which are the source of information for operating and controlling the business firm.

The simulation is not complete when models of these five subsystems are finished. Certain information processing and bookkeeping procedures must be established. These include accounting for accounts receivable and payable, general accounting, cost accounting, inventory control, and other routine record keeping.

More important, the models must be linked together with company policies and plans in order to have a total system. It is these linkages that are the interesting and important things to study. There is no intent to make, for example, a model of a customer that can be used to predict what customers in the real world will do. The same is true for any of the other main subsystems. The intent is only to describe what they do for this firm in a manner that is consistent with whatever theory is available from the social and physical sciences and with empirical observations about the behavior of their real-life counterparts. One important use of the simulation is to validate the individual models with respect to both the theory and the observations.

The most important part of this research effort is the study of the inter-relationships among the different activities. Management science and data processing specialists are now talking about the whole business firm and integrated data processing. "Let's look at the business as a whole," is a slogan of the day. But the whole is more than the sum of its parts, and a great deal must be known about the performance, the activities, and the transactions of these parts in order to study the interrelations among them. The Task Manufacturing Corporation is an attempt to study these interrelations through the simulation of the business from subsystems composed of individual units.

23.4   A BRIEF DESCRIPTION OF TMC

In order to set TMC in perspective with respect to size and scope, a very brief description is needed. The corporation employs about 400 people, 200 of whom are engaged in the direct labor activities of manufacturing a line of five related products in some combination of seven different operating departments. Four of these departments are machine shops: drill press, punch press, screw machine, and spot weld. The other three are finishing, assembly, and packaging. No single product uses all seven departments; only the packaging department deals with all five products. Final products are stocked in inventory in anticipation of sales which are made from a home office in Los Angeles to customers scattered geographically over the whole United States. Outside the immediate home office area, the sales outlets are generally large wholesalers or building-supply houses located in large cities. Near the home office, customers are also smaller wholesalers and both large and small retailers. At any one time, sales are made to between 150 and 200 customers.

Although the products have no real-life counterparts, they are thought of as items of the building-hardware type. The raw materials from which they are made are castings, steel strip, and steel bars. Both the strip and bars have different size specifications so that, altogether, eight different raw materials are carried in inventory and ordered from suppliers. The products do have manufacturing specifications, complete with blueprints, for use in production planning, tooling, and purchasing. The specifications for Product 2, a Stop Index Assembly, are shown on the drawing in Figure 23.1.

The products sell for around $1 each. Total annual sales volume for all products in the line is approximately $4 million. The corporation has $1 million of current assets and $1½ million of total assets. It has 55,000 shares of $10 par stock outstanding and no bonded debt. Annual earnings are about $2 per share. It has at present no policy for paying dividends.

This description makes the Task Manufacturing Corporation a small business firm by almost any definition.

23.5   EXAMPLE OF THE PRODUCTION PROCESS IN TMC

Limitation of space prevents a full discussion of all of the models used in TMC. The example given here in quite some detail is that of the production process.

The physical production of the products made by TMC involves the interaction of the employee and machine models. Individual employees work in each of the seven production departments. Individual machines are located in each of these departments. Employees are assigned to machines and scheduled to work on a particular product, and it is this combination of employee and machine that produces an output. Initially,

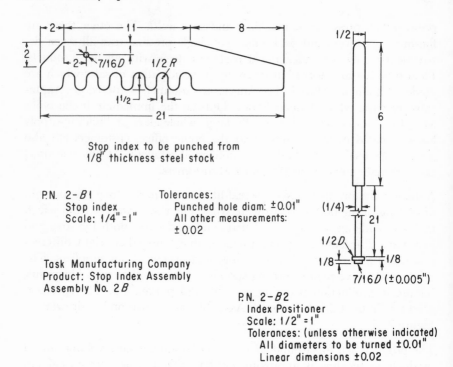

FIGURE 23.1 Stop index assembly specification drawing.

company policy provides that one employee is assigned to one machine and there is no excess labor force. There is excess capacity in the sense that machines in some departments are idle and not in use because they are not needed to produce the scheduled production. At some future time, this company policy may change and an excess of employees over machines may be desirable or inevitable.

The basic time unit in which TMC operates is one week. Once an employee is scheduled to work on a particular product, a particular machine, and for a defined work week, none of these conditions can be changed until the next week. To be consistent with the time unit, new employees are hired to start at the beginning of the week, and employees quit or are fired at the end of the week. Machines that need overhaul are taken off the production line at the end of the week and scheduled back at the beginning of a week after the overhaul is completed. Further, an initial condition is that work in process normally moves from one department to another at the end of the week, but this condition can be changed to lessen work-in-process shortages when the previous department has a finished supply on hand from the current week's production.

23.6   THE MACHINE MODEL

Punch presses, drill presses, screw machines, and spot welders are machines. In the finishing, assembly, and packaging operations, the use of "machine" is meant only to convey the notion of a production unit of some sort. All machines used in TMC look alike; i.e., they all have the same general model. They differ from each other with respect to the parameters which describe their behavior. The machine model reflects engineering design features and known data about machine operations. Parameters are selected that give realistic values to the simulated counterparts of real-life drill presses and punch presses working on products similar to those manufactured by TMC. The working tolerances are also realistic, as shown in Figure 23.1. Machine behavior is described by a model which involves both mathematical and statistical relationships. The most important characteristics are described in some detail but without any exact relationships being given.

TMC machines can break down. The probability that a machine will break down is an exponential function increasing with the age of the machine, the time since its last overhaul, the number of overhauls, and the rate of machine breakdown. The latter is included on the assumption that a machine showing a propensity to break down will break down more often than one without this propensity. In other words, a machine's own behavior modifies its future behavior. If a machine breaks down, the length of down time is determined by a random drawing from a Poisson process. If a machine runs, its efficiency (a new machine is rated as 1.00) is an exponential function decreasing with the age of the machine and the number of overhauls.

A machine may be pulled off the production line for overhaul at any time, but built into the model is a company policy that an overhaul is ordered automatically when the productive efficiency reaches a certain level, say, 0.70. The value of this level may be changed. The machine model is such that it implies company policies with respect not only to overhaul but also to replacement of old machines, to use of idle capacity (i.e., scheduling of idle machines with respect to age and operating efficiency), and to product assignment changes, which involve setup times.

One of the first uses of any model in TMC is its validation both with respect to theoretical considerations and known behavior. Figure 23.2 shows effective weekly operating hours of a single new machine with average parameter values for a period of eight years. The machine was scheduled for a standard day shift of 40 hours with no overtime.

The general shape of the curve is an exponential decreasing with time as was planned. The scale of the graph may be so small that minor variations are difficult to detect. Breakdowns occurred in the following weeks: 40, 64, 182, 249, 281, 295, 308, and 325.

The first overhaul took place automatically as a matter of policy in week 386 when the machine efficiency reached 0.70 or, on the graph, 28 effective hours. (Actually, 28.0 hours was first reported in week 383, but the efficiency was not down to exactly 0.70 and the reported 28.0 hours is a rounded value.)

Immediately following the overhaul in week 388, effective hours are four hours less than expected because a setup time is involved. Then, the machine efficiency increased to 0.90 (36 hours) but not back to the level of a new machine. It is a characteristic of the model that the efficiency increases after an overhaul, but to a lower level after each succeeding overhaul. This characteristic implies that there will come a time when it no longer pays to overhaul.

The behavior of this individual machine reflects both engineering features and known behavior of actual machines of the kind simulated here. It is known to the operators of TMC. No attempt is made to predict the behavior of real machines from this model. The model is merely a device to originate production transactions from individual machines in order to study a production system. The simulated machine behavior, at least in the author's opinion, appears to represent realistically actual machine behavior.

23.7 THE EMPLOYEE MODEL

The individual employees who work in the TMC production departments have the same general characteristics. They, like the machines, differ with respect to the values of their parameters. In general, employees can quit, be absent, be injured, and vary in their efficiency (for which 1.00 is assumed a normal, or standard). Their behavior is governed by mathematical and statistical functions of known characteristics.

For example, each new employee must learn to do his job. To reflect this, a learning curve is built into the model. The initial level of efficiency is primarily a function of the number of years of past experience. The average ultimate level an employee will reach is a function of accident and general health ratings. The rate at which he learns, i.e., proceeds from the initial level to the ultimate level, is a function of experience, education, and intelligence. The parameter values of each of the characteristics

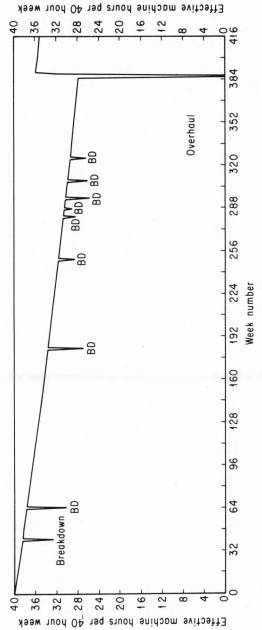

FIGURE 23.2 Effective machine hours per 40-hour week for eight years.

mentioned—accident, health, experience, education, and intelligence—are known from data recorded on an assumed employee application form. Some are a matter of record and entered by the applicant; others result from physical or psychological testing.

Once a new employee reaches his ultimate average efficiency level, his output is not constant at that level. The model is not deterministic in this sense. One examination given to employees is a psychological test for what is called "emotional stability." The value of this parameter causes an employee's efficiency to vary stochastically both in the amplitude and period of oscillation. An upper bound is placed on the efficiency. No fixed lower bound exists, but only a mechanism that forces employees to recover automatically from periods of very low efficiency if they do not quit or are not fired.

Figure 23.3 shows the effective production hours for an average employee working a standard 40-hour work week on the day shift with no overtime for eight years. His ability to quit (and be fired) has been suppressed for this test in order to insure that the eight-year period will be completed. He has the following parameter values:

Years of experience	5	
Intelligence	100	(scaled from 70–160)
Education	12	(high school graduate)
Accident	5	(scaled from 1–10)
Health	5	(scaled from 1–10)
Emotional stability	0.25	(scaled from 0.1–0.5)

In this eight-year period, the employee had four absences—in weeks 40, 166, 235, and 319—each of one-day duration. He was injured for three hours in week 264. Had the "quit" or "be-fired" characteristics not been suppressed, he would not have quit nor would he have been fired. It took him five weeks to reach the standard efficiency of 1.00, and except for absences and injuries, his efficiency fluctuated between 39 and 43 effective work hours per 40-hour week.

Employees with different parameters will behave differently from the typical one illustrated. TMC has a cross section of workers ranging from very good to very poor, from very stable to very erratic, and from old to new.

23.8   RUNNING THE PRODUCTION MODEL

Individual employee and machine behavior is known for typical units from a study of the outputs in Figures 23.1 and 23.2. In addition, stand-

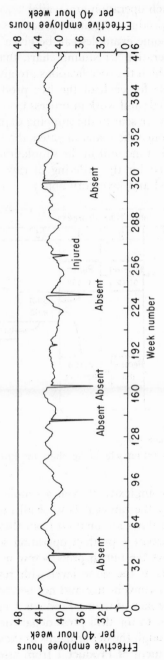

FIGURE 23.3 Effective employee hours per 40-hour week for eight years.

ard production data for each operation are available as well as the schedule of operations for each product. Again, it is not possible to report here all the relevant data, but some examples can be given. Figure 23.4 illustrates data of a typical operation scheduling chart, that for Product 2, a Stop Index assembly for which the specifications are given in Figure 23.1. A similar chart is available for each of the five products. It shows the *physical* flow of raw materials and work in process from the time of ordering until the finished goods are sent to the shipping department. The lead times (in weeks) are firm once the material enters the first production department, because the basic time unit in the simulation is one week. The variable lead time indicated for the ordering of raw materials is determined by the vendor model and inventory policy.

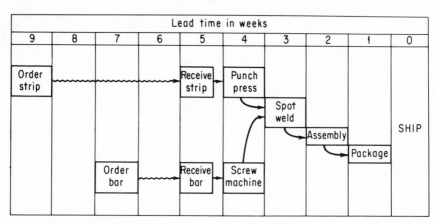

Legend:——► deliver to
     ~~~► Variable time link

FIGURE 23.4 Operation scheduling chart for Product 2.

To give some idea of the complexity of even a simple production model for a small firm, a chart of the physical flow of all materials is given in Figure 23.5. (Information flows are omitted from this figure.) This figure is a composite of the separate product operation scheduling charges. Although Figure 23.5 shows the punch press, screw machine, drill press, and spot weld departments at the same level with respect to this flow, they are drawn this way for convenience and not because work in process does not flow between some pair of them. Products 1 and 4, for example, move from the punch press to the drill press department. Neither is the flow necessarily directly through the departments as they are laid out here. One exception is the movement of Product 1 from assembly back to finishing and then on to packaging.

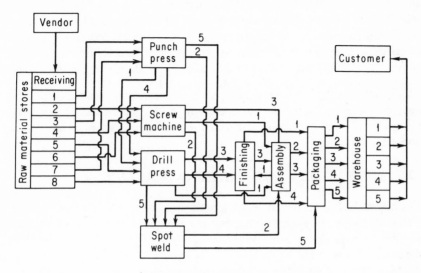

FIGURE 23.5 Physical flow of materials.

There are two parts to running the production process: planning and operation. Planning involves setting a production schedule based upon a sales forecast. This forecast may come from a computer model or from extensions of past sales data, or it may be given without any explanation. Operating results then come from a computer run with the employee and machine models scheduled to operate according to the plan. Reports are generated weekly to show the results and, in some instances, to explain or provide clues to the causes of seemingly exceptional behavior. On the basis of a comparison of the results and the plans, changes can be made, a new set of plans instituted, and the production model run for another period, etc., in an alternating sequence of planning and operating.

At present, changes in plans are made by people. No provision is made (it will ultimately be provided) to change plans by a built-in scheduling process. The production process can be run for several weeks with the same set of plans, i.e., a fixed schedule.

Without other models, one can study only a part of the physical aspects of production. With inventory and vendor models and an accounting system added, one may study the interrelationships between planning and operations with respect to features such as alternative schedules, overtime versus new employees, machine assignments, second shifts, machine replacement versus overhaul, hiring and firing, etc. Routine reports may not always give clues to causes of abnormal behavior. Because data are recorded on a transaction basis and kept in permanent files, special reports may be needed to explain a behavior in more detail. Ultimately, the firm will be run entirely on an exception principle, once enough is known to state rules that define exceptions and the actions to be taken.

People are brought into the simulation at an early stage not only because their presence simplifies the simulation in some hard areas (scheduling, for example), but to involve them in the use of simulation as an educational exercise.

23.9   EXTENSIONS AND ALTERNATIVE MODELS

The paper has discussed at some length employee and machine models. These represent one specification, but not the only one, for two basic subsystems of a business firm. With time, alternative models not only of these but of other subsystems should be available. In fact, a library of models is being planned from which one can pick and choose in order to simulate a complex system with desired characteristics.

The machine model described in this paper is rather uninteresting. Since it is a useful device for generating production transactions, a more elaborate specification of the same kind is probably not desirable. Alternatively, numerically controlled machine tools could be introduced. Such a model involves the design of an alternative plant with changes not only in the individual machine model, but also in the whole concept of the role of the individual employee and, therefore, in the employee model as well. One graduate student has already begun an investigation into this alternative, describing for a single product both the program needed to control a machine to produce the product and some estimates of the cost and numbers of such tools needed.

The present model for an employee is useful but rather mechanical. It does not incorporate or recognize researches into human behavior from the behavioral sciences. An alternative formulation which would take such research into account could be based upon the theory of employee behavior developed by March and Simon.* This model takes into account the motivations of satisfaction and dissatisfaction with the job, a search for alternatives, and the probability of finding such alternatives.

Even without going so far as to design a new employee model, additions to the present model may make it more interesting. Use can be made of

* March, J. G., and Simon, H. A., *Organizations*. New York: Wiley, 1958.

the emotional stability characteristic that is already a part of employee behavior to introduce a group effect so that individuals affect and are affected by the behavior of the group. Such an effect could be on both a departmental and plant-wide basis, depending upon the design.

As the simulation proceeds, more and more extensions and alternatives will present themselves; ultimately, a library of models for each subsystem will be available.

23.10   SUMMARY

Perhaps it is unfortunate that the final tone of this chapter must be hortatory rather than expository, but since this simulation is only just now developing, possible benefits and uses belong to the future. The models which were listed but not discussed in this chapter are beginning to fall into place: a customer model for sales data, a vendor model for raw materials, and accounting and inventory models. A standard cost system is available for appraising the results of operations, with specific data reported on a product and department basis in order to assess the performance of any particular set of plans. The intention is to have ultimately a simulated firm that may either be completely computer operated or permit the introduction of people into some of the key positions.

In addition to the use of TMC as a teaching device and as a research tool for the study of the interrelations among the different models is its use for the study of data and information processing. The nature and content of the data in individual transactions, the methods of processing such data, the design and information content of reports, all are areas which can be studied with this simulated firm.

A final paragraph should perhaps indicate why a computer is needed for a simulation of this kind. Case studies have provided a similar educational tool without a computer. Paper and pencil business games are available for many educational efforts. Why a large-scale digital computer in this simulation? A simulation which models subsystems of a complex system so as to give rise to individual transactions must use a computer for both the operation of the models and the processing of the data which they generate. Only with a large-scale data processing system can such a detailed simulation be attacked. Whether such a simulation is worthwhile is a question which only the future can answer. Only the present availability of such equipment makes possible even an attempt to find out whether a detailed simulation of the complete operations of a business firm is worthwhile.

ADDITIONAL READINGS

Alberts, W. E., System Simulation, *Proc. Seventh Annual Natl. Conf. AIIE.* Columbus, Ohio: AIIE, 1956.

Clarkson, G. P. S., and Simon, H. A., Simulation of Group Behavior, *Amer. Econ. Rev., 50,* December 1960, 4.

Cohen, K. J., *Computer Models of the Shoe, Leather, Hide Sequence.* Englewood Cliffs, N.J.: Prentice-Hall, Inc., 1960.

————, and Cyert, R. M., Computer Models in Dynamic Economics, *Behavioral Theory of the Firm,* Carnegie Institute of Technology, Working Paper *No. 20,* 1960.

Conway, R. W., Simulation in Profit Planning, *Report of System Simulation Symposium,* Malcolm, D. G., ed. Baltimore, Md.: Waverly Press, 1957.

————, and Johnson, B. M., *Problems of Digital Systems Simulation,* Fifth International Convention of the Institute of Management Sciences, October 1958.

————, and Maxwell, W. L., Some Problems of Digital Systems Simulation, *Management Science, 6,* October 1959, 1.

Cyert, R. M., and March, J. G., Research on a Behavioral Theory of the Firm, *Contributions to Scientific Research in Management,* Proceedings of the scientific program following the dedication of the Western Data Processing Center, University of California Graduate School of Business Administration, Los Angeles, Jan. 29–30, 1959.

Forrester, J. W., Industrial Dynamics—A Major Breakthrough for Decision-Makers, *Harvard Bus. Rev., 36,* July–August 1958, 4.

Harling, J., Simulation Techniques in Operational Research, *Operational Research Quar., 9,* March 1958, 1. Reprinted in *Operations Research, 6,* May–June 1958, 3.

Hoggatt, A. C., and Balderston, F. E., *Models for Simulation of an Intermediate Market.* Berkeley: Univ. California, June 24, 1958.

Jackson, J. R., Simulation Research on Job Shop Production, *Naval Research Logistic Quar., 4,* December 1957, 4.

Jennings, N. H., Computer Simulation of Peak Hour Operations in a Bus Terminal, *Management Science, 5,* October 1958, 1.

Kahn, H., and Mann, I., Techniques of Systems Analysis, *RM-1829.* The RAND Corp., Dec. 3, 1956.

Morgan, T. B., The People-Machine, *Harper's Magazine*, 222 (No. 1328), January 1961, 53–57.

Orcutt, G. H., Simulation of Economic Systems, *Amer. Econ. Rev.*, *50*, December 1960, 4.

————, Greenberger, M., Korbel, J., and Rivlin, A. H., *Microanalysis of Socioeconomic Systems—A Simulation Study*. New York: Harpers, 1961.

Shubik, M., Bibliography on Simulation, Gaming, Artificial Intelligence, and Allied Topics, *Jour. Amer. Stat. Assoc.*, *55*, December 1960, 292.

————, Simulation of Industry and Firm, *Amer. Econ. Rev.*, *50*, December 1960, 4.

Oliver Benson

24/SIMULATION OF INTERNATIONAL RELATIONS AND DIPLOMACY

*Oliver Benson is Professor
of Government, Chairman of the
Department of Government, and Chairman
of the International Studies Program
at the University of Oklahoma. He is a graduate
of the Institute of International
Studies of the University of Geneva,
where he received the degree*
Docteur ès sciences politiques *in 1936.
Author of a book on the diplomatic origins
of World War II and of some thirty
articles on current world politics, he served
for six years as editor of the*
Southwestern Social Science Quarterly.

As an academic field, international relations is relatively new. Usually offered in American colleges and universities in departments of political science, it is for the most part a post-World War I discipline. The older specialties, diplomatic history and international law, were blended with the newer study of power to create a more realistic set of concepts. Though definitions vary widely, and disagreement is sometimes violent, most academic workers in the field would agree, with different emphasis, that the subject is concerned with the interaction of those societal conglomerates habitually holding ultimate loyalty of the constituent individuals, or as in Hans Morgenthau's title, with *Politics among Nations*.[13]

24.1 QUANTITATIVE METHODS IN INTERNATIONAL RELATIONS

Research patterns in international relations are as various as the definitions, although the reader interested in computers, but incidentally familiar with typical works on diplomacy, may feel justifiable wonder at the presence of this particular chapter in this particular book. So too may the specialist in international relations. Nevertheless, quantitative elements have had at least a limited part in the work of many scholars, alongside the more traditional historical and legal studies, and the more modern analytical, socioeconomic, psychological, policy development, and problem-solving approaches.[5, 11]

24.1.1 Statistics. The average college textbook in international relations includes at least several tables of descriptive statistics on international trade, military establishments and costs, natural resources, and comparative data on various indicators of national strength. Such content is rarely given any inferential analysis or manipulation beyond the level of deriving percentages, but its inclusion suggests a continuing assumption that it is relevant. Outstanding among treatises using considerable quantities of statistics is Quincy Wright's major work, *A Study of War.* Wright also suggests a number of tentative general hypotheses in simple mathematical models.[22]

24.1.2 Capabilities Analysis. Measuring national power and war potential with a combination of statistical and analytical methods is a special field of research. The application of capabilities analysis has sharpened the long-standing concept of the balance of power, one of the time-honored "laws" of presumed universal applicability in diplomacy. Klaus Knorr's *War Potential of Nations* is an example.[9] He suggests that major account should be taken of resources, motivation, and administrative skills—a good indication of how concrete and imponderable factors are combined. Political geographers, notably Stephen B. Jones, have contributed both information and ideas to the task of analysis of the strategic implications of power distribution. Jones, like Knorr, stresses the importance of both "quantity modifiers" and "quality modifiers" of national strength.[6]

24.1.3 Decision-making Analysis. Application of the methods of sociologists and psychologists to international relations has greatly enriched its research equipment. The work of Richard C. Snyder [21] and his colleagues on decision making as a focus, and that of Herbert Simon and his associates [20] in the more generalized field of public administration, have forced a re-evaluation of methodology throughout the entire discipline of political science. Simon's *Models of Man* [19] is a more thoroughly mathematized treatment, employing formal models for the manipulation of social and psychological variables in the study of human and group behavior.

24.2   MATHEMATICAL METHODS

More strictly mathematical treatment is rare, but is represented by a growing number of research workers in international relations. The newness
of the field is indicated by the date (1939) of the first major mathematical monograph entirely concerned with international politics—that of
Lewis F. Richardson.[16]

24.2.1 *Calculus of Armament Contests.* Richardson concentrated his
attention on the spiral of armament races, developing a system of equations meant to represent each state's desire to exceed its rivals. Such a
system he showed to be unstable, since the equations are satisfied only if
all war potentials increase indefinitely and exponentially. He introduced
complications for parameters other than armament costs, expanded his
calculus to provide for n states, and supplied empirical runs for the periods
leading up to the two World Wars. Owing to the inclusion of two selections from his writing in the popular *The World of Mathematics,*[14] his
work is probably the purely mathematical treatment best known to the
general reader.

Maurice Ash, in a suggestion bearing some similarity to marginal economic analysis, postulates a "constant power curve" of maximal security,
which rises ever more steeply as reserves are exhausted.[1] He suggests
that a country's desperation increases as it approaches the end of its capacity to mobilize reserves: at a certain point, only war can redress the
balance. Applications based on the Ash approach might indicate the
probability of a war of desperation, such as (perhaps) the Israeli attack
on Egypt in 1956.

Arthur Burns, of the Australian National University, develops a similar
point by the use of "multiplier diagrams," verging on game theory but
in an essentially subjective treatment.[2] His system supplies hints as to
changes which come with varying degrees of information about the rival
and with the development of radically new weapons systems. The graphic
"rectangle of greatest danger" is plausibly found to be in a period of
secret armament with substantial forces, because of the uncertainty of
information available to the rivals.

24.2.2 *Game Theory.* It is a tribute both to mathematicians and political analysts that they have shown the greatest caution in attempts to use
game theory in the study of world politics, despite its superficially ap-

parent applicability. Morton Kaplan,[8] Thomas Schelling,[18] and others, have done preliminary work with its methods, which offer promise for the investigation of situations where goals partly conflict and partly coincide and where cognizant choice is based on evaluation of the possible outcomes. Rapoport [15] suggests that the study of large-scale human behavior may eventually require theoretical methods between the two extremes of Richardson's differential equations of physical determinism, on the one hand, and game theory's allowance for human choice, on the other.

24.2.3 General Applications. Several scholars suggest more broadly based systems of analysis to connect mathematical-statistical methods and the more traditional approaches. Quincy Wright [23] suggests that within the general field of international studies there be developed a small quantitatively oriented "discipline," parsimonious of assumptions, and so organized as to be self-correcting and self-improving. In his chapter "The Form of a Discipline of International Relations," he suggests a semimathematical model, wherein the available data, both objective and subjective, are manipulated to locate elements of the various states in a sort of twelve-dimensional space, on axes of flexibility, energy, strength, cooperation, technical advance, and resource abundance (the "capability field"), and of abstractness, objectivity, liberality, situation-orientation, affirmation, and manipulation (in a "value field"). He draws on objective data for about half of these locators, including population, trade, literacy, government employees, ranking administrators, income, national budgets, exchange of mail, energy production and resources, land area, education, and participation in international organizations. The other half of his data is based entirely on subjective judgments. By spotting successive changes in location, he would hope to develop vectors for the various states with reference to the twelve axes.

Karl Deutsch,[3] who has worked most energetically with actual data as applied to international relations, urges political scientists to give more time to processing and interpreting the great quantities of data they spend so much time acquiring. He has developed an analysis of international trade, using three 100×100 matrices processed on a computer, to detect trends of international interaction since World War II—a project which no tool less capable than the computer could perform, given the 30,000 matrix boxes involved. Deutsch has also suggested a variety of methods for establishing typologies of states, as well as of their interactions, by the arrangement of data deemed to bear on the stability and capabilities of governments. Some 75 categories of data, combined into 24 ratios, result in a tentative classification scheme which could serve as a starting point for examination of many hypotheses about international behavior.

24.3   SIMULATION

The complicated problems of war have long been studied under certain patterns of simulation, but only in recent years has the general field of diplomacy received similar analysis. Simulation is an artificial model of (hopefully) the most significant features and operating principles of reality, or in the felicitous phrase applied by the editors of *Harper's* to Simulmatics' electoral behavior simulation for the 1960 presidential campaign, "make-believe on mathematical principles." [12]

24.3.1 *Guetzkow's Inter-nation Simulation.* In the Northwestern University International Relations Program, Harold Guetzkow [4] has conducted a series of carefully designed and imaginative experiments with human actors playing the roles of internal and external decision makers in a setting of inter-nation interaction. The simulation was designed both for theoretical study and for instruction and contained patterns of internal pressures on decision makers as well as external problems. Precise rules were worked out, but considerable freedom of decision was left to the role players, making possible a study of their "quasi-nation" actions. Guetzkow has worked out a series of scales for measurement of a number of variable influences found to bear on decision, but at this writing the quantitative findings are considered too tentative for definitive conclusions.

24.3.2 A *"Balance of Power"* Game. At the Princeton Center of International Studies, Morton Kaplan, Arthur Burns, and Richard Quandt [7] devised a "possible set of rules" for a competitive game, intended to test a generalized model of a balance-of-power international system. Their theoretical analysis of the system postulated is rigorously abstract, so that exploration of the properties of the system could be carried out without qualitative influences from the real world. Their simulation, like Guetzkow's, is deemed still experimental, and they expressly disclaim any belief that their game can turn up positive principles. At most, they think, it may be useful in ruling out traditional beliefs about the "balance of power."

Though not exhaustive, this brief survey indicates that mathematization and quantification in international analysis certainly have a fascination for many scholars, including some of the most eminent in the discipline.

It is clear that further research along the lines blocked out by these studies can be based only on some minimal command of mathematical and quantitative method. It is equally clear that such research, if not guaranteed to be fruitful, at least offers some promise of usefulness.

24.4   THE SIMULATION PROGRAM: "A SIMPLE DIPLOMATIC GAME"

With the foregoing considerations in mind, the author has put together a somewhat crudely designed simulation program meant to duplicate some of the obvious features of international politics.[17] The remainder of this chapter describes the simulation. The reader is cautioned that the project is more an experiment in the introduction of computer techniques to the field of international relations than a serious research project. It is hoped that eventually valuable results may come, not specifically from this particular program, but from further applications of computer methods which it may suggest.

24.4.1 *How the Simulation Is Organized.* Development of the simulation program required arbitrary decisions on a number of elements in international politics on which no general agreement exists. For example, the two most crucial indexes derived in the program are those on "war potential" and "propensity to act" (a rough measure of aggressiveness). Although both concepts are common in international relations literature, quantification of them is certainly open to argument. The author emphasizes that he is not committed to the particular quantification formulas he has adopted, nor even to the idea that any system of indexing these qualities can give a reliable indicator. They are used in the program solely to find out whether valuable results can be obtained by tentative assumptions.

For an overview of the program, there follows a listing of the major routines employed, with a suggestion as to the purpose of each.

24.4.1.1 *The Storage Routine.* This stores all data employed in the program. These original data consist of nine war potential indicators (population, military age manpower, transportation, gross national product, gross national product *per capita,* energy production, steel production, literacy, and atomic capability) for each of nine major states; nine weights for gaging the relative importance of these factors; nine subjective indicators, for the same nine states, of "propensity to action" drawn from Quincy Wright's capability and analytical fields; weights for these; loca-

tion of the nine states and of nine small target states in latitude and longitude; alliance membership of the eighteen states; information about overseas military bases maintained by the nine major states; information about the mutual trade between the nine major states and the nine target states; information about the total trade of each of the eighteen states; a special notation of whether each of the nine major states is a nuclear power; a table of haversines for use in the determination of distance; a table of intensities of action for use in selection of counteractions; and a variety of alphanumeric codes for the final printout.

24.4.1.2 *The Preliminary Computation Routine.* This derives the war potential indexes, the "propensity" indexes, a deduction factor for low propensity, and a "value of the international situation" for each of nine actor states.

24.4.1.3 *The Action Routine.* This constitutes the heart of the program; it is initiated by an "action card," describing an action by one of the nine states against one of nine targets, and eventuates in a determination of a logical counteraction by each of the actors other than the one initiating action. The three processes next described are involved in this determination.

The Coalition Strength and Leadership routine selects the two strongest coalitions and their leaders, and defines the "nature of the universe" (according to the logic described in Figure 24.1) as "tight bipolar," "loose bipolar," or "balance of power."

The Selection of Counteractions routine consists of four sections. In the first, a distance routine (see Figure 24.5) yields an index of proximity. A trade index is computed as the average of total trade and mutual trade. Coalition status and presence of overseas bases are related to these in order to supply an "interest index," indicating the interest of each actor in the target. This composite interest index becomes one of three factors (intensity of action and original war potential index being the other two), whose product determines the presumed loss to each state (or gain to initiator of action). Selection of counteractions is then made, the action selected being that needed to redress loss.

The counteractions chosen will range in intensity from .100 to .900, the index representing presumed percentage of effort required to carry them out. In the Revision of Counteractions routine, four revisions may occur: (1) The index is lowered by the low propensity deduction (see Section 24.4.1.2). (2) It is lowered to .800 should the logic lead to .900, and the actor not be a nuclear power (.900 is the index for maximum intensity and is coded HBOMB in our program). (3) It is lowered to .700 should the logic lead to any higher index, should the state be an ally of the initiator of action, and the universe polar (.800 is the index identified as war, and our rules exclude war against an ally in any but a balance of power world). (4) "Nature of the universe" revisions complete this routine. In a loose or tight bipolar universe, the leaders of the two strongest coalitions counteract to recover relatively the same power they had before (i.e., the same percentage of total power); in a balance of power universe, all states counteract to recover relative power. In a tight bipolar world, only the two leaders act, their allies merely supporting them.

Finally, using the new strengths of the nine actor states, the program recomputes indexes based on 100 per cent and assigns these as the new values for use in future runs, in either a "competitive" game or a "stochastic" game, at the option of the user.

24.4.1.4 *Alliance Change on Loss Routine.* This part of the program maintains a count-box for each of the states. If the initiator of action is a leader of one of the two strongest coalitions, the routine is entered. If one of the leader's allies ends the cycle with a net loss, the ally's tally is increased by one. On three successive losses, an ally becomes a neutral, and a neutral joins the rival coalition. Losses resulting from the rival coalition leader's initiative restores the tally to zero. This feature of the program makes the coalition alignments unpredictable should the user select the "stochastic" game at the outset; should he select the *status quo* game, original coalition data are used.

24.4.1.5 *Competitive Game Routine and Printout.* An "alternator" (see Section 24.4.2.4) is used to determine which of two permissible players (or teams) is involved if the user has designated the run as a "competitive" game. Every second competitive run concludes by a comparison of the gain-loss ratio of the two initiators of action. If the first gained relatively more (or lost less) than the second, A is listed in the printout; if the second gained relatively more, B is indicated; if the gains (or losses) were equal, AB is the entry.

The printout reports the initial action, the counteractions selected by each of the other eight major states, the interest index, the new war potential index, the "value of the international situation," the new nature of the universe, and any alliance changes.

24.4.2 *Computer Techniques Used in the Simulation.* Without attempting a complete analysis of the program, it has seemed desirable to review a few of the more standard computer programing problems encountered in its preparation. This account may serve the double purpose of indicating some special features of the program and of expanding on the introduction to computer programing contained in Chapter 7.

24.4.2.1 *Branching.* Branch instructions are the computer's logic. On them depend some of the remarkable achievements so mystifying to the layman, as well as some of the purely "showy" demonstrations that have little relevance to the true purpose of the machine. Most machines employ similar branching devices; most used are tests to detect a zero and tests for the sign. The IBM 650 instructions BMI, NZU, and NZE, together with similar instructions for indexing registers, are typical. Upon receiving the instruction BMI (Branch on MInus), the program tests the accumulator for a minus sign; if the accumulator is minus, the program goes to one address for its next instruction; if not minus, it goes to another. The NZ instructions effect a similar branch by testing whether the accumulator is zero. By combining these two-way tests, the programer may achieve a complicated pattern of alternative branches.

As an example, in the branch for "nature of the universe," somewhat different principles of action should be applied depending on the relative distribution of strength among the nine major states, as well as within the two dominant coalitions. For consistency with certain general theory about power politics, a distinction is made among the "balance of power," the "loose bipolar," and the "tight bipolar" distributions. Having added together the war potential indexes of states in each coalition, and having arrayed the coalitions in order of strength (a routine described later in Figure 24.4), the program proceeds, in the section portrayed by Figure 24.1, to test the combined strength of the two most powerful groups. In addition to this test, a determination is made as to whether the strongest state in each coalition is dominant. The reader will note that the program fragment consists entirely of branches, denoted in flow chart convention by the oval boxes.

Another device effective for multiple branching is used in the original storage routine. Space is provided on the data cards for two different items of input information: (1) an instruction location and (2) the location in which to store the first of five data items contained sequentially in the first five spaces on the card. The multiple-multiple branch thus effected can handle any variety of categories and subcategories desired.

Translating machine language into plain words, the program to store a variety of data will be

  a. Read the card (results in storage of the eight "words" in a defined read region).

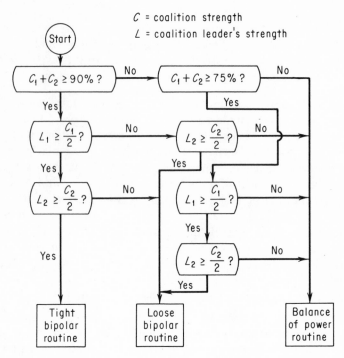

C = coalition strength
L = coalition leader's strength

FIGURE 24.1 Flow diagram of test for strength of coalition.

	Word 1	Word 2	Word 3	Word 4	Word 5	Word 6	Word 7	Word 8
	Card 1 Data 1	Data 2	Data 3	Data 4	Data 5	0000000000	0000000001	STORE INSTRUCTION
	Card 2 Data 6	Data 7	Data 8	Data 9	Data 10	0000000000	0000000006	STORE INSTRUCTION

FIGURE 24.2 Data card.

b. Obtain location of next instruction from word eight of the read region.

c. Store the five items of data in the first five words of the read region in five successive storage locations beginning with the location specified in word seven of the read region.

d. Read another card.

The sequence is terminated by a final "end of data" card coded as null except for the location of a terminating instruction in word eight. In our program, this relatively simple device stores all the original data listed above in 24.4.1.1.

24.4.2.2 *The Loop.* The loop is the programing device most significant to the computer's great power. Essentially it consists of a fixed or conditional number of iterations of a sequence of arithmetic-logical steps with modification of factors on each iteration. Following each iteration, a test is necessary to determine whether the required number of passes has been made. The test is usually made by a count-box, if the number of passes is fixed, or by reference to a maximum satisfactory error factor, if conditional. The count-box is actually a regular storage location, in which the program had previously entered the number of passes required. Following each iteration, this number is reduced by one; the zero branch test is used to terminate the loop and send the program to its next section. Most advanced computers provide special count-boxes, or "index registers," which make the programing of loops far simpler, though the basic logic remains the same.

Loops, and testing for their termination, occupy a special place among programing hazards. The beginner is urged to ponder carefully these words of McCracken.[10]

> Depending on the nature of the loop and of the test, it is possible to make a truly remarkable variety of mistakes in testing. If the loop should be carried out n times, it is quite easy to make mistakes which will result in doing it: (1) not at all; (2) $n - 1$ times; (3) $n + 1$ times; (4) $2n$ times; (5) until the power fails or the machine breaks down.

Most programs of any complexity will have nested loops, i.e., loops within loops; it is not unusual to have as many as five layers of such nested loops, but programs of that order are best left to the expert. The novice need only realize that such a program, once perfected, offers no more intrinsic difficulty for the computer than the simple adding of one and one.

Figure 24.3 shows an elementary application, drawn from our program, of looping and the testing of count-boxes. The problem was obtaining subtotals and a grand total of war potential data for subsequent computation into a war potential index for each of nine states. The program fragment represented by the chart does the job. Note that most of the steps represented are "logical" rather than arithmetic—they are concerned with setting up and applying the tests for number of iterations. The end result is a grand total in location SUM and the nine subtotals (sums of data times weight) in nine locations i. From these, the desired indexes are obtained in the next section of the program.

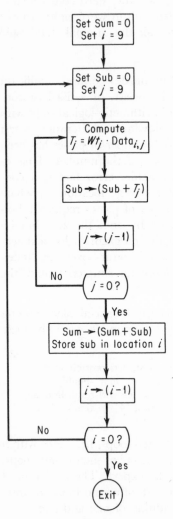

This may seem a great labor for a small result, but it must be remembered that neither the complexity of the factors nor the variety of arithmetic steps involved presents any greater problem than the simple addition and multiplication here performed.

As an example of a loop concerned almost entirely with logical operations, at one point in the program it is necessary to distinguish the leading power in each of the two strongest coalitions. The naked eye, observing written data, could accomplish this at a glance in the actual world of today. But our program is generalized, our computer a moron, and our data numerous. It is therefore necessary to prepare instructions following somewhat the pattern of Figure 24.4. (The fragment above, with it sequel, has provided us with indexes of strength, and our original data tell us the coalition affiliation of each state.)

FIGURE 24.3 Flow diagram illustrating the testing of count-boxes.

In this chart, C refers to the combined war potential indexes of the states in a given coalition; Cd, to the code number of the coalition (5 are provided for); Scd, to the same code numbers supplied in the original data to identify the coalition affiliation of the nine major states; Lcd, to the code number, determined in the program, of the leading member of a given coalition; W, to the war potential indexes of the nine major states.

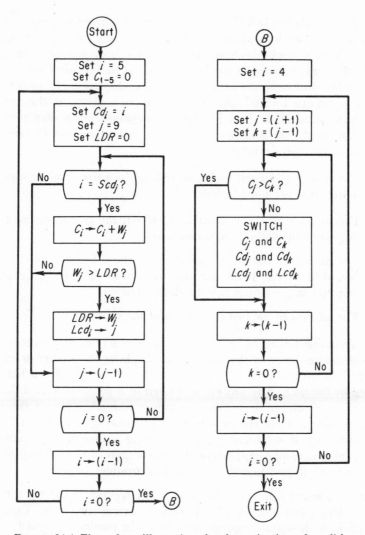

FIGURE 24.4 Flow chart illustrating the determination of coalition strength and leadership.

It may be noted that by substituting x for 4 in the first instruction of section B of the chart, the same routine could be used to arrange any given number of factors in an array in order of magnitude from largest to smallest, a device useful in many statistical applications.

24.4.2.3 *Subroutines.* For the beginning programer, the most welcome discovery is that much of his labor has already been performed. In any computer installation will be found a library of *subroutines,* expertly prepared program sections which may be tied into any program by suitable devices. Matrix multiplication, regression by least squares, chi-square tests, indeed any commonly used mathematical or statistical process, will be available, and more are being added daily. Moreover, by understanding the technique for including a subroutine in a program, the beginner acquires a useful method for identifying fragments of his own programs which are used over and over, and which may therefore become subroutines of his own devising.

The subroutine is addressed each time entered by a fixed *calling sequence.* The calling sequence must include:

a. The location of the instruction to which the programer wishes to exit when the subroutine is completed.

b. The numerical data to be processed by the subroutine, or the location of that data. If tabular material is to be processed sequentially, first and last locations may be designated.

c. The address of the first instruction of the subroutine.

The subroutine begins by storing the exit instruction. It proceeds to its efficient manipulation of the data indicated, places the answer or answers in locations promised in the writeup, and exits to the instruction prescribed by the user. Any process used often in a program may usually be reduced to a subroutine by the programer himself. Though the result will lack the nicety of the experts, the technique is useful for a lengthy fragment even if used only twice. In using subroutines prepared by others, the programer must follow the instructions of the writeup meticulously, or he will find himself in immediate trouble.

In the diplomatic simulation program, most repetitive patterns are handled by loops, but subroutines are used in several situations. Typical of a genuine mathematical manipulation is a sine routine employed as part of the process of determining distance between actor and target states, used in turn in the so-called interest index. In simplified form, the program for this is shown in Figure 24.5. (The reader may then check for later use in Section 24.4.2.5.) On each action card, nine haversines are derived, i.e., the program shown in the chart is contained within an outer loop set for nine iterations. Latitude and longitude for the eighteen states are supplied by the original data cards.

Another example is a programer's output subroutine, used to provide two sets of printouts: the original printout of nine lines descriptive of conditions at outset of action and the eventual printout of nine lines descriptive of counteractions and conditions resulting therefrom. Widely separated in the program, they nevertheless follow the same logical sequences, since the basic job in a printout is filling the appropriate words of the printout band needed to prepare a single line of output.

24.4.2.4 *Alternators.* The alternator is a special form of branch, used when two parts of a program are to be entered in regular alternation on successive passes. In the example shown in Figure 24.6, the program fluctuates regularly between the initial instructions of the first and final printout routines. Since these two sets of output are always printed in the same order, the situation calls for an alternator. Many devices are possible, but the "flip-flop" illustrated is a trick often used for accomplishing the purpose. We set a "+1" initially in a location coded here as ALTNR.

In IBM's SOAP symbolic programing language, this alternation is done by three simple instructions:

RSL	ALTNR
STL	ALTNR
BMI	FIRST FINAL

RSL is instruction 1 of the table; STL is instruction 2; BMI is the branch on minus.

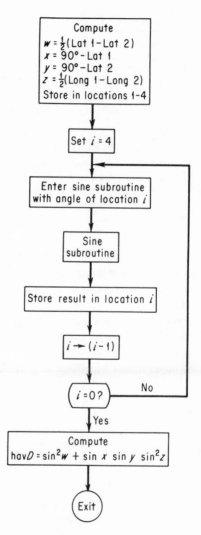

FIGURE 24.5 Flow chart illustrating the computation of the state "interest index."

24.4.2.5 *Table Look-Up.* The table look-up instruction is a feature of several machines, including the IBM 650, and where not provided can be programed. Essentially, it results in counting the locations from a fixed base to the location containing a number equal to, or higher than, an

Instruction	Content of "ALTNR"	Content of accumulator
(First Pass)		
1. Clear accumulator; subtract contents of "ALTNR" from it.	+1	−1
2. Store accumulator in "ALTNR."	−1	−1
3. Is accumulator negative? (Yes; branch to first printout)		
(Second Pass)		
1. Clear accumulator; subtract contents of "ALTNR" from it.	−1	+1
2. Store accumulator in "ALTNR."	+1	+1
3. Is accumulator negative? (No; branch to final printout)		

FIGURE 24.6 Alternators.

indicated number. This count is then entered in the accumulator, where it may be used as an address for any desired manipulation of the number sought. Often, table entries can be packed together with factors associated with each entry, so that when the desired entry is found, the factor associated with it can be used. In the distance routine described above, the assumption is made that the interest index of a state declines with distance. Suitable ingredients for the interest index are therefore packed as descending numbers in a table of ascending haversines, as in Figure 24.7.

TABLE LOOK-UP

Location	Contents	
	Haversine table	Interest factor
1200	002447	1000
1201	009549	0900
1202	020611	0800
1203	034549	0700
1204	050000	0600
1205	065451	0500
1206	079389	0400
1207	090451	0300
1208	097553	0200
1209	999999	0100

FIGURE 24.7

Once the look-up instruction reports the location of the haversine equal to, or greater than, the one which denotes the great circle arc between our actor and target states, the contents of that location are brought to the accumulator. By the simple "shift left six" instruction the six leading digits are discarded and the desired "interest" ingredient obtained. The solid bank of 9's in location 1209 is designed to stop the search, regardless of a possible error in computation of the haversine. Even safer would be a "stop" completely filled with 9's, since no higher factor would be possible, and thus the look-up instruction would certainly cease searching at this point. Depending on the exact purpose of the search, the 9's might serve to indicate an error, to switch the program to another table, or to send the program to another branch.

Another convenience of the table look-up is the possibility of storing associated factors in another table following the one searched. Since each entry in the associated table is separated by the same fixed number of locations from its corresponding entry in the base table, the count reported may be added to this fixed number to obtain the location of the desired factor. As an illustration, our simulation employs alphanumeric codes to indicate approximate intensity of diplomatic or military actions, and these are tabulated in sequence after the table of intensities (see Figure 24.8).

If the table look-up instruction is entered as "1959" to search for intensity 859, it will nevertheless begin the search at location 1950 (only certain locations are possible as initial table search bases). Instead of location 1958 being reported for an action of maximum intensity, however, the count will be added to the instruction actually entered, so that location 1967 will be reported. This is the location in which is stored a set of alphanumeric digits, translatable by a special feature of board wiring into the alphabetic code word "HBOMB," used in the program printout to suggest maximum intensity of action (the other code words represent, respectively: diplomatic protest, UN action, severing diplomatic relations, subversion campaign, boycott or reprisals, troop movements, full mobilization, and limited war).

24.4.3 *Trial Runs and Findings*. Since the simulation program is intended mainly to suggest and to test hypotheses about international interaction of states (most cautiously, be it emphasized), the reader is entitled to a report on what has been done in this direction. The limited runs thus far are in no sense conclusive of anything, least of all of the adequacy of the program, but with that warning, a few tentative principles seem to find certain support.

The method used in actual runs is to feed, as input, successive intensities of action by different major states against different target states and to

TABLE OF ASSOCIATED FACTORS

Location	Table of intensity	
1950	0000000100	
1951	0000000200	
1952	0000000300	
1953	0000000400	
1954	0000000500	
1955	0000000600	
1956	0000000700	
1957	0000000800	
1958	9999999999	
	Table of alphanumeric codes	Printout translation
1959	7269637282	KICKS
1960	8475618775	UNAXN
1961	8265856579	SEVER
1962	8284628583	SUBVT
1963	7779698273	PRISL
1964	8379767677	TROOP
1965	7476628975	MOBZN
1966	8661797383	WARLT
1967	6862767462	HBOMB

FIGURE 24.8

record the effects on the actor, his rivals, and his allies. The competitive feature of the game has been employed only for limited trials. On the basis of this use of the model, we can say that *with its assumptions,* the conclusions described below appear valid. The reader should consider them examples of the sort of work attempted, rather than as established conclusions.

24.4.3.1 *Strength Attracts.* There is a marked tendency for the strong to get stronger. This may be a direct result of a built-in bias, whereby the program arbitrarily assigns an advantage (though not a certain one) to the initiator of action. Even so, this bias is of less advantage to the second-rate powers than to the leaders.

24.4.3.2 *Maintaining Neutrality.* Even for strong powers, there is an apparent tendency toward coalition. The built-in pattern for computation of loss may be at fault and probably needs to be revised and refined with more subtle treatments. On the other hand, it may well be that no present possibility of precise measurement is reasonable for so subjective a set of attitudes as are bundled together in the isolationist syndrome.

24.4.3.3 *Action/Loss.* Moderate action yields less loss than does strong action. Logic might indicate that this is obvious, since complete inaction would lead to no loss whatever. But the program assigns a gain to the actor proportionate to the intensity of his action. Strong action should therefore bring greater gains. There seem to be just enough rules for revision of gains, assessment of costs, and penalties for evoking strong counteractions, so that uncertainty enters the picture. Indeed, at this stage of development of the simulation, the creation of this measure of uncertainty seems a considerable achievement. At least one feature of the real world is accurately portrayed!

24.5 ADVANTAGES AND LIMITATIONS OF THE SIMULATION

The reader who has traced through the foregoing fragments of the program can recognize that its main complications are logical rather than mathematical. The author claims no standing whatever in the mathematical guild and is aware that fundamental expansion of a project such as this will require close collaboration between mathematician and political scientist. Perhaps the most promising area for early inquiry is that of refining indicators for human factors of decision. In the program, these are represented in the propensity index, and are acknowledged to be most dubious.

Even with simple tools, elementary mathematics, and inadequate measurements, the program demonstrates what is possible in the way of data manipulation with the computer's aid. The speed and storage capacity of the machine are hardly taxed by the data thus far employed. In using the program, one is constantly reminded that much more information could be handled. There is an ever-present challenge to develop more sophisticated models for processing the extensive statistical compilations of relevant data available in such abundance today.

REFERENCES

1 Ash, M. A., An Analysis of Power, with Special Reference to International Politics, *World Politics, 3* (No. 2), January 1951, 218–37.

2 Burns, A., A Graphical Approach to Some Problems of the Arms Race, *Jour. Conflict Resolution, 3* (No. 4), December 1959, 327–42.

3 Deutsch, K., Toward an Inventory of Basic Trends and Patterns in Comparative Government and International Politics, *Amer. Pol. Sci. Rev., 54* (No. 1), March 1960, 34–57.

4 Guetzkow, H., A Use of Simulation in the Study of Inter-Nation Relations, *Behavioral Science, 4* (No. 3), July 1959, 183–91. Guetzkow has allowed the author to examine two mimeographed working papers developed in the project.

5 Hoffmann, S. H., ed., *Contemporary Theory in International Relations.* Englewood Cliffs, N.J.: Prentice-Hall, Inc., 1960.

6 Jones, S. B., The Power Inventory and National Strategy, *World Politics, 6* (No. 4), July 1954, 421–52.

7 Kaplan, M. A., Burns, A. L., and Quandt, R., Theoretical Analysis of the Balance of Power. Princeton Center of International Studies. (Mimeo.).

8 ———, *System and Process in International Politics.* New York: Wiley, 1957.

9 Knorr, K., *The War Potential of Nations.* Princeton, N.J.: Princeton Univ. Press, 1956.

10 McCracken, D. D., *Digital Computer Programming.* New York: Wiley, 1957, 77.

11 McLellan, D. S., Olson, W. C., and Sondermann, F. A., eds., *The Theory and Practice of International Relations.* Englewood Cliffs, N.J.: Prentice-Hall, Inc., 1960.

12 Morgan, T. B., The People-Machine, *Harper's, 222* (No. 1328), January 1961, 53.

13 Morgenthau, H., *Politics among Nations.* New York: Knopf, 1948.

14 Newman, J. R., ed., *The World of Mathematics.* New York: Simon and Schuster, *2,* 1956, 1240–63.

15 Rapoport, A., Lewis F. Richardson's Mathematical Theory of War, *Jour. Conflict Resolution, 1* (No. 3), September 1957, 249–99.

16 Richardson, L. F., Generalized Foreign Politics, *Brit. Jour. Psychol.*, 1939, (Monograph 23).

17 Rosenau, J. N., ed., *International Politics and Foreign Policy*. Glencoe, Ill.: The Free Press, 1961 (in press). This simulation was described in a paper by the author at the American Political Science Association in Washington, D.C., 1959. Another discussion of it, emphasizing aspects of interest to the specialist in international relations, will appear in *International Politics and Foreign Policy*. The author acknowledges a special debt to Harold Guetzkow, of Northwestern University, for his help and encouragement, and to the technical and professional staff of the University of Oklahoma Computer Laboratory (especially Richard Andree, William Viavant, and Harold Bradbury) for invaluable aid. Richard Brody, of San Francisco State College, assisted in planning the competitive branch of the game, particularly the mathematics.

18 Schelling, T. C., *The Strategy of Conflict*. Cambridge, Mass.: Harvard Univ. Press, 1960.

19 Simon, H. A., *Models of Man—Social and Rational*. New York: Wiley, 1957.

20 ————, Smithburg, D. W., and Thompson, V. A., *Public Administration*. New York: Knopf, 1950.

21 Snyder, R. C., Bruck, H. W., and Sapin, B., *Decision-Making as an Approach to the Study of International Politics*. Princeton University, Foreign Policy Analysis Project, 1954.

22 Wright, Q., *A Study of War*, 2 vols. Chicago: Univ. Chicago Press, 1942.

23 ————, *The Study of International Relations*. New York: Appleton-Century-Crofts, 1955, 531–603.

Harold Borko

25/A LOOK INTO THE FUTURE

*Harold Borko's interest in
electronic computers and their application
to the behavioral sciences arises from
his education and experience in
mathematics and psychology. His studies in the
field of mathematics and statistics led to an M.A.
degree in psychometrics at the University
of Southern California. A desire to apply as well as
explore basic psychological principles was
fulfilled by award of a Ph.D. in clinical psychology in
1952 at the same university. As a clinical
psychologist he served in the United
States Army until the latter part of 1956, when
he resigned his commission to accept employment with The RAND
Corporation. There, and later with System Development
Corporation, he worked on problems involving
the implementation of a system training program
for the Air Defense Command and used electronic
computers to design and produce training exercises
and to analyze the results of the
training program. At present, he is a member of the research
staff where he is studying the application
of computers to language-data processing and
information retrieval, with emphasis on automatic
machine abstracting and indexing of documents.
In September 1959, he organized and taught a course called
"The Use of Electronic Computers in Psychological
Research" at the University of Southern California.
This book had its origin in that course.*

What lies ahead in the field of data processing and computing? Whatever they may be, the developments will affect the lives of all of us. We must be concerned with: What lies ahead? Without being prophets or seers, when we analyze the happenings of yesterday and today, it seems reasonable that we should be able to make predictions about tomorrow. All science is based on the assumption that future events are determined by past occurrences. Difficulties arise when we make predictions without full knowledge of the pertinent facts. To the extent that this knowledge is lacking, our predictions err. Although we recognize that we are on shaky ground, the need seems to justify the risk; let us move boldly and look into the future.

25.1 ADVANCES IN HARDWARE DESIGN

25.1.1 *Greater Operating Speeds.* Undoubtedly there will be more computers tomorrow than there are today, but what will be their salient characteristics? There are general trends in computer design, and if we refer back to the chapter on the historical development and extend the trend line, we should be able to make some reasonable predictions. The desire for greater operating speeds dominates both the early history and the more recent developments in computer technology. As progress was made, speed of computation was reduced from hours to minutes and then seconds. Now we deal with milliseconds and microseconds, and we already have a new word in our vocabulary—the nanosecond, or one-billionth of a second. Unquestionably, the computers of the future will be faster than the machines presently available.

25.1.2 *Greater Storage Capacity.* Concomitant with greater speeds, our extrapolated trend lines clearly indicate that the computers of the future will have greatly increased storage capacities. Progress is already being made in this direction. Magnetic ferrite cores are being reduced in size, thus making it possible to package a greater storage capacity in a smaller physical area. Similarly, high density magnetic recording is being perfected so that more computer words can be stored in less space. Besides these improvements on the available hardware, a number of experimental memory devices are under development; one or more of these could lead to a greatly improved storage facility. One such system is a *diode-capacitor matrix* which stores words in a two-dimensional array and provides for parallel access. This system is more expensive than magnetic core memory, but it has many advantages, and as the price of components decreases, the system may become economically feasible. Also under development is a *ferroelectric storage system*. This device uses ferroelectric hysteresis in approximately the same manner as magnetic hysteresis is used by magnetic cores. The ferroelectric storage system is very compact, operates at a very fast rate, and uses very little power.

A prototype of a *thin film memory* has been designed and built at the Lincoln Laboratory of M.I.T. This experimental memory is constructed of $\frac{1}{16}$ inch circular spots, 600 angstroms * thick, and spaced ten to the inch. The memory contains 32 ten-bit words on two pieces of glass each holding a 16×16 array of spots. It is being installed in the control element of the TX-2 computer. Developmental work aimed at expanding the size of the unit is in progress.

A number of photographic storage systems are under development and these provide very interesting possibilities for future use. The Bell Telephone Laboratories are experimenting with the use of photographic plates as permanent memory stores for directory information and instructions for the telephone electronic switching system. Data are stored in the form of thousands of tiny clear dots on an otherwise opaque photographic area 2 inches square. These spots of clear and opaque film are scanned by a beam which is generated by a cathode ray tube and focused by a system of lenses. The memory has random access and can locate and read a 68-bit word in 2.5 microseconds.

IBM, in the course of its work on language translation, has coded a Russian-English machine translation dictionary onto a 10-inch glass disc. The binary coded data are arranged in 700 concentric tracks which are photographically printed on the outer edge of the disc. By the use of photo reduction processes, 30 million bits are stored on this single 10-inch revolving disc. In all probability, this compact, high-density, high-speed

---

* Angstrom is a unit of length equal to one hundred-millionth of a centimeter.

storage system soon will be adapted to other scientific and business data processing problems.

25.1.3 *Character Readers.* Although progress has been made in increasing the internal operating speed and storage capacity of the computer, the methods of providing input data have remained relatively unchanged. Information is first coded and punched onto cards or paper tape. It may then be converted to a magnetic tape format or directly used as an input to the computer. In either case, converting information into a coded computer format is a slow and expensive process. The advent of character reader devices portends a major breakthrough in this area. In essence, a character reading device is designed to convert data—words or numerals—into a computer code without human intervention. A number of such devices are currently available. Many banks are using magnetic character readers (see Section 5.1.4 and Figure 5.6). Using this machine requires that the original information be printed in magnetic ink and in a special type font. Another type of character reading device is employed by the major oil companies for use with their credit cards. This device does not require the use of magnetic ink, but it does specify specially designed characters (see Figure 17.1). Obviously, the next stage will be the design of equipment capable of scanning a page of ordinary type and automatically converting the information thereon to a code suitable for computer processing. Prototypes of such equipment have in fact been developed, and commercial models will be available within the next few years.

25.1.4 *Greater Reliability of Operation.* Currently, computers are used to process data which have been collected earlier. Thus two distinct steps are involved in the sequence of operations: first, the data are collected and coded; then, the data are processed. Since the two portions of the work are separated in time, the computer is always dealing with "old" data, such as yesterday's sales records. In most instances, this delay creates no hardship, because the results are still much more current than would have been possible without the use of the computer. There is, however, a growing trend to use the computer for "real-time" operational problems in which the data are processed as collected. The Air Defense SAGE System is an example of such use. In this application, the computer is used to monitor and update aircraft radar returns. But real-time operations are not limited to defense installations. The Remington-Rand UNIVAC 490 is a real-time system designed to provide business management with up-to-date operational information as it happens. This system is currently being used for airline reservation control, and it provides the airlines with accurate, instantaneous information of seat availability, cancellations, sales, and flight data.

The computer will be used to a greater extent than at present for real-time data processing. Before this prediction of future applications can come true, the computer must become a more reliable machine. In real-time operations, one cannot afford down time as a result of machine failure. This does not say that the present generation of computers is not reliable, but more time is spent on repairs and servicing than can be tolerated in economical real-time operations. Today's answer to this problem is found in duplexing the computer facilities, but this is an expensive solution. Future generations of computers will be more reliable and less subject to machine failure.

Some steps are already being taken in this direction, as can be inferred from the widespread use of transistorized printed circuit cards. These components are less subject to failure than are vacuum tubes. In the future—and the process has already started—the printed circuits will be manufactured in automated factories under computer control. Not only will automation cut costs, but component variability will be reduced and system reliability increased.

25.1.5 *Change in Machine Logic.* The very term "computer" implies the ability to calculate, i.e., to perform the standard arithmetic functions of addition, subtraction, multiplication, division, etc. Historically, this is what the machines were designed to do. But computers can do more, and the trend is to increase and improve upon their logical decision-making capabilities. At present, these improvements are being made within the framework of the traditional machine logic. But electronic data processing systems in the broadest sense of the term are not calculators but are symbol manipulators. In the future, machine logic will be designed to process efficiently natural language and symbols rather than merely to add numbers.

The first faltering steps in this direction are being taken now. Computers are being used to translate languages, to compose music, to simulate social organizations, etc. This trend will be accelerated as new logical components make their appearance.

25.1.6 *Increased Development of Special Purpose Computers.* In this area, the trend lines are not nearly as clear and defined as in the preceding areas. Nevertheless, present trends indicate that future designs will deemphasize the large, expensive general purpose computers and will feature the smaller, more economical special purpose machines. These computers will be designed to do a particular job and to do it quickly, reliably, and economically.

In the early stages of development there is a great need for large, highly flexible machines. There is a need for experimentation in order to define the problem properly and to discover the means for solving it. There is a need for flexibility and the capability of doing many things—even though this capability is not exploited to its fullest. A high price is paid for these unused features. With maturity, the problems are defined and the operational procedures become standardized. Therefore, as the computer industry moves out of its early infancy to a more mature phase of development, there will be less need for general purpose machines. The data processing systems of the future will contain a number of compatible, special purpose computers, all integrated and operating with great efficiency.

25.2   ADVANCES IN PROGRAMING LANGUAGES

We have seen many advances in the design of computer hardware. Not the least of these is the proliferation of new computers that are appearing on the market at an increasing rate. This fact is of great significance to the programer. One can study, work hard, and become an expert programer on one machine. Then, for any one of a number of reasons (the programer takes a job with another company having a different machine, or his own company changes machines, etc.), he is no longer an expert. True, there is some transfer of training, but the programer must start again to learn new codes and a new machine language. Were only a single individual to find himself in this situation, it would be merely sad; but since this has been the common experience of many programers, the waste in manpower and money is tragic.

25.2.1 *Problem-oriented Languages.* A need exists for a compatible system in which programs can be readily translatable from one machine to another. It is highly unlikely, and somewhat illogical, to expect competing manufacturers to design compatible hardware. It is logical, however, to standardize the programing language, and a great deal of effort is being spent in this direction. Standardization can be accomplished only by changing the emphasis from programing in machine language to programing in a problem-oriented language. This change of emphasis is beginning to occur and the trend will be accelerated in the future. ALGOL (*algo*rithmic programing *l*anguage), designed for scientific numerical calculations, appeared in 1958. Concurrently, COBOL (*common business oriented language*) was developed as an aid in the solution of business data processing problems. In addition, many manufacturers and some large user organizations are developing their own compilers specifically applicable to their own equipment and functions.

These problem-oriented languages are helpful, but they cannot be regarded as the panacea for all programing difficulties. They are costly to build and require many man-years of labor to perfect. The effort is worthwhile if the investment can be amortized over a number of years of operational use. But, occasionally, the computer becomes obsolete soon after the compiler for it has been designed. What is needed is an intermediate language—intermediate between the problem-oriented language and the machine language. (This concept was discussed in Section 7.3.) Some of the nation's most skilled programers are working in this area, and it is predicted that their efforts will soon bear fruit.

25.2.2 *Use of Natural Language.* Looking now to a distant future, we can glimpse some even more exciting developments. Programing codes are very precise, formal language structures by which the operator communicates with the computer. Codes are necessary because the computer and the programer do not speak the same language. Until now we have directed our effort toward teaching men the language of the machine; i.e., they learned to write the instructions in machine language. The problem-oriented language is a compromise approach by which both men and machine learn a third, or intermediate, language. Why not go the whole way and teach the machine to understand the natural language of man?

Before this can be accomplished, progress must be made toward the solution of two major problems. The first has to do with pattern recognition— i.e., the development of hardware capable of sensing and recognizing the different patterns which make up the numbers and letters of the alphabet. Some of the research in the field of perception and the use of the computer to generate and recognize patterns was described in Chapter 13. Section 25.1.3 pointed out that we already have a number of character-sensing devices that can "read" special type fonts, characters printed in magnetic ink, and even standard printed characters. Certainly progress is being made in this area. The second issue, and one more difficult to solve, involves programing the computer to interpret these sets of characters and to follow instructions or draw inferences. Chapters 15, 16, and 17 described research designed to study various aspects of language data processing and the simulation of cognitive functions and language behavior. Eventually these and similar studies will result in the development of a computer program which will enable the machine to interpret and respond to instructions written in natural language.

Pursuing this line of reasoning further into the future, we raise the obvious question: "Why do we have to limit our communications to the computer to written messages?" If the computer can be taught to interpret written symbols, why can't it interpret spoken language? Bell Telephone Laboratories and other research organizations are working in this area and are making good progress.

These are fascinating possibilities and they present some exciting challenges to research in general and programing in particular.

25.3 ADVANCES IN RESEARCH APPLICATIONS

The preceding chapters in Part 3 of this book described many specific applications of the computer as an aid in behavioral science research, and they suggested many additional research problems which would be amenable to solution by computer techniques. As a start in furthering research, our methods of data analysis must be refined. In psychology, both a univariate and a multivariate experimental design are used. More complex problems invariably require more sophisticated and more time-consuming statistical treatments. The computer has been of inestimable help in data analysis, and improvements in this area continue. The general model for multiple regression equations is one such example; the automation of factor analysis technique is another. Without the high-speed computer, canonical analysis would be impractical; now, its advantages are just beginning to be explored. The computer used as a high-speed calculator is enabling the researcher to apply a more rigorous mathematical treatment to his data.

When the computer is regarded as an aid in experimentation rather than as a calculating machine, whole new areas of application become possible. The computer can be used to generate data, as White did in his studies of perception. As studies using similar techniques proliferate, our knowledge of pattern recognition and perceptual phenomena will increase. New techniques of education are also being investigated by means of the computer, as are some of the basic theories of learning. In this area, too, the computer is functioning as a very powerful research tool.

One of the most difficult problems for scientific experimentation involves the higher mental processes of cognition, problem solving, and creativity. A musician cannot be put in a laboratory and told to compose a symphony while the psychologist observes the process. The computer makes this form of experimentation unnecessary, for if we can simulate the process, i.e., program the computer to compose music, the program becomes tantamount to a theory of musical composition. This concept is being explored, and obviously much more experimentation needs to be done before we can generalize to human creativity. Similar studies are being undertaken in the field of language data processing. Synthex describes an approach toward the development of a theory of human language behavior. Machine translation of languages is another aspect of this problem, and it has great practical as well as theoretical importance.

The computer can also be used in simulation studies to provide information on "brainlike" behavior and to advance medical science and diagnosis. It can also be used to simulate large social systems, business organizations, and even international relations. Research workers are exploring each of these areas. As our ability to simulate system behavior on a computer improves, so will our knowledge of human activities increase; and the psychologist will take another step toward his goal of being able to understand, predict, and control behavior.

25.4   GENERAL TRENDS

25.4.1 *Industry's Demand for Qualified People.* One of the most obvious trends in the computing industry is the increasing demand for qualified people. As more and more government agencies, universities, and industrial organizations order computers, the shortage of trained people will become critical. First is the need for logicians and mathematicians to conceive and design innovations in computer equipment. Then there is the need for trained engineers and technicians to build and service the ever-increasing number of new computers. Finally, and perhaps most critical, is the need for thousands of programers.

Industry is not blind to these needs, and some steps are being taken to meet these shortages. Universities throughout the country are offering special programs in computer engineering, including such courses as Logical Design of Digital Computers, Logic of Applications of Automatic Digital Computers, Introduction to Linear Programing, Programing Techniques of Selected Computers, etc.* Manufacturers are sponsoring training programs on their equipment, and some companies have their own internal training programs. All of this is excellent; yet it is a mixed blessing, for it means that a significant proportion of people now in com-

---

* These are actual titles of courses offered by University Extension, University of California at Los Angeles in the spring of 1961.

puting will be devoting a great deal of their time training new programers, designers, applications specialists, and maintenance men. The
obvious next question is, "Who will train the trainers?"

The situation is not hopeless, but an optimistic solution requires a different outlook. An analogy can be made between the automobile and the
computer. Undoubtedly, when the automobile first made its appearance
and some of its potentials were recognized, manufacturers and prospec-
tive industrial users worried about where they would obtain a sufficient
supply of trained drivers. Now, this is no longer a problem. Driving has
been simplified, and most people learn to drive a car. This analogy suggests that a similar process may take place in computer programing.
As computers become more common, college students will learn to use
them, just as today they learn to drive cars and use typewriters.

25.4.2 *Management's Demand for Qualified People*. To meet the immediate shortage of trained personnel, management will call upon psychologists and training experts to design the training programs. Not only
will it be necessary to train new people, but it will also be necessary to
retrain personnel presently employed by the organization. Take, for example, the crew presently operating an electronic accounting machine
(EAM card sort) installation. Can these same people be retrained to
program and operate electronic data processing machines (EDPM computer equipment)? On what basis will people be selected for training?
How shall the programs be organized to maximize positive transfer of
training? What are the criteria of a "good" programer? These and similar questions need answers and need them soon.

Besides the shortage of trained programing and operating personnel,
management has an even more critical shortage to face, and one still more
difficult to alleviate. This is the shortage of qualified managerial personnel—men who can recognize the need for computerized data processing systems and who have the knowledge and ability to integrate these
new tools into the existing corporate structure. Where will these people
come from? What formal qualifications should they possess, and what
training should they have?

Management faces a related and equally serious problem: the division of
labor between the man and the machine. In a man-machine system,
what shall be the function of the man, and what shall be the function
of the machine? Obviously, man should not be made to compete with
the computer any more than the ditch digger competes with the steam
shovel. But how does one arrive at an equitable, workable, and efficient
division of labor?

Management needs answers, and it needs qualified people to study the questions and provide the answers.

25.4.3 *Profession's Demand for Recognition and Accreditation.*

Many thousands of people are now making their living in one phase or another of the computer industry. They come from different disciplines and have diverse educational backgrounds and experience. Some have advanced degrees in mathematics, philosophy, physics, psychology, etc.; others are engineers; still others have no formal college education. Despite a common interest in the computer, these people do not have a common communication channel: an integrated professional organization of information specialists. The I.R.E. (Institute of Radio Engineers) speaks for some engineers, the ACM (Association for Computing Machinery) speaks for a group of data processors and programers. But the breadth of the field of information processing extends beyond engineering and programing. The diverse professional affiliations require an organization that will provide a common meeting ground and will help this expanding profession attain status. The critical shortage of qualified personnel has been emphasized; there is an equally great need for standards of competence and accreditation. A number of the leaders in the computer field have recognized the need. Daniel D. McCracken voiced similar views in *Datamation* early in 1960.[1] Professional recognition of the information specialist can be the expected result of the creation and continued support of an organization that provides for the exchange of ideas and the establishment of standards for accreditation among information specialists.

25.5   CONCLUSION

The preceding chapters of this book have dealt with some of the most important trends in the computer applications to behavioral science research. This work is being continued, and new projects are being started. In succeeding years, many advances will take place in the areas of statistical computation, language data processing, experimental psychology, and system simulation. Our lives will be greatly affected by continued expansion of computer technology. The computer is a powerful tool which can be a force for much good if properly used. Although the computer can solve many problems, it will not do man's thinking for him. It will also raise many problems that only enlightened men can solve. Of one thing, we can be sure, for those of us engaged in computer activities these next few years will be stimulating and productive.

REFERENCE

1 McCracken, D. D., The Human Side of Computing, *Datamation*, 7 (No. 1), 9–11.

GLOSSARY OF COMPUTER TERMS

This working glossary is not a comprehensive dictionary, nor do these definitions enjoy the status of industry-accepted standards. Usage in the computer field is subject to regional variations and modification in response to changes in equipment. However, these definitions should provide the reader with a key to the technical terminology in the field.

A

ACCESS, SPEED OF: a measure of performance of a computer memory or peripheral storage device; usually refers to the period of time (called access time) necessary to locate and transfer the contents of a specified storage location into a working register. *See* memory access time.

ACCESS ARM: (magnetic disc storage) mechanism to which read-write head is mounted, arranged to permit access to any disc in storage device or any track in multi-track disc.

ACCUMULATOR: a register to which information is transferred for manipulation; originally, the register in which sums were accumulated.

608

ACCURACY: freedom from error; the degree of exactness with which a quantity is known or observed (as contrasted with "precision," which is the degree of exactness with which a quantity is stated).

ACOUSTICAL DELAY LINE: a storage device in which acoustical pulses representing binary information are transmitted by means of elastic deformation of the delay line medium (quartz crystal, mercury, or magnetostrictive material); transmission through the medium delays a pulse, permitting circulation of a pulse train by connecting (through an amplifier and signal gate) the delay line output to its input.

ADDER: device (circuitry) producing the sum of two or more numbers delivered to it. *See* half adder *and* full adder.

ADDRESS: a label, usually numerical, that identifies a location in a storage or memory device.

ADDRESS LOGIC: the body of expressions defining the relationships and operations involved, by which a given computer keeps track of the addresses in which needed operands and subsequent instructions are to be found.

ALGORITHMS: procedures used by individuals or machines to solve problems by trying all possible alternatives. Algorithms necessarily lead to a solution, if one is possible, even though this solution may take years to accomplish. *See* heuristics.

ANALOG: a physical, mechanical, or electrical model (used for computation by analogous representation) corresponding in some respect to the original object or concept, with or upon which measurements or calculations are to be performed.

ANALOG COMPUTER: a computer using physically measurable variables (e.g., voltage, angular rotation, length) for calculating.

ANALYTIC ENGINE: a mechanical computing device designed by Charles Babbage (1792–1871); included provision for iterative loops and program transfers; never constructed.

"AND" GATE OR "AND" CIRCUIT: a circuit presenting an output if and only if every input is properly energized; performs the function of the logical "and." *See* "or" gate.

ARITHMETIC INSTRUCTION: a machine word or set of characters directing a computer to perform an arithmetic operation.

ARITHMETIC UNIT: that part of a computer performing arithmetic and logical operations.

AUTOMATIC PROGRAMING: any technique for equipping a computer to accept programs in languages other than machine language and to convert such programs automatically into machine language instructions. *See* compiler.

B

BAND: a group of recording tracks on a magnetic drum or disc.

BASE: any digit or number on which a number system is based (in the decimal system, ten; in the binary number system, two, etc.); the radix.

BINARY: involving two (digits, states, etc.).

BINARY-CODED DECIMAL (BCD): systems of representing decimal numbers as combinations of (usually) four binary digits (bits).

BINARY NUMBER SYSTEM: number system containing only two digits, based on powers of 2.

BIQUINARY: involving two and five; a system of notation representing a mixed base but utilizing binary digits.

BIT: binary digit; a one (1) or a zero (0), or the electrical, mechanical magnetic, or chemical representation of either in an automatic computer.

BLOCK: a group of machine words considered or transferred as a unit.

BOOLEAN ALGEBRA: a system of symbolic logic; an algebra of classes, propositions, on-off circuit elements, etc., associated by operators "and," "or," "not," "except," "if—then," etc.

BUFFER: device or technique for matching (usually) rate of information flow among computer system elements.

C

CATHODE RAY TUBE: a vacuum tube in which electrons emitted by a hot cathode are formed into a narrow beam or pencil and accelerated at high velocity toward a specially prepared screen which fluoresces at the point where the electrons strike; provides visual display of electronic signal information; can be used as a computer storage device. *See* electrostatic storage.

CHANNEL: a path along which information flows. In storage that is serial by character and parallel by bit (e.g., a magnetic tape or drum in some coded-decimal computers), a channel comprises several parallel tracks. In a circulating storage, a channel is one recirculating path containing a fixed number of words stored serially by word.

CHARACTER: any symbol, such as a number or a letter, or its machine representation that may be stored by, or used in, computer operations.

CIRCULATING MEMORY or REGISTER: a circuit in which a pulse train can be stored by circulation in a loop; volatile (information is lost when power is removed).

CLOCK: a primary source (pulse generator) for synchronizing signals in a computer; a reference pulse occurring at a specified rate, for synchronizing circuit operations in a digital computer.

CODE: a system for representing information and rules for representation; to prepare a set of instructions in computer language for a specific computer.

CODING: the act of preparing in code a list of instructions for successive computer operations required to solve a specific problem.

COMMAND: any coded representation to which computer circuits respond by executing a logical or arithmetic operation; also called the operation part of an instruction.

COMPILER: a program equipping the computer, for which it was designed, to accept programs in a problem-oriented language and to transform them into machine language instructions.

COMPUTER: any machine capable of performing numerical and logical manipulations; an automatic computer is one which performs sequences of operations on the basis of wired or initially stored instructions. *See also* analog computer, digital computer, *and* special-purpose computer.

COMPUTER-ORIENTED LANGUAGE: a language that conveniently expresses the operations of a particular computer or a class of computers. *See* machine language *and* problem-oriented language.

CONDITIONAL BRANCH, JUMP, or TRANSFER: an instruction specifying the condition under which the machine should deviate from the principal order of instruction execution in order to branch into an alternate order.

CONTINUOUS FUNCTION COMPUTER: analog computer; a computer forming required outputs on the basis of continuous input functions, as contrasted to digital computers, which require and operate on discrete digits.

CONTROL UNIT: that portion of the hardware of an automatic digital computer which directs the sequence of operations, interprets the coded instructions, and initiates the proper signals to the computer circuits to execute the instructions.

CORE MEMORY: a device for storage of information in a computer, each bit being stored as magnetic orientation of a ferromagnetic toroid. *See* magnetic core storage.

COUNTER: a circuit or device that can be incremented or decremented or reset to zero.

CYBERNETICS: studies comparing the performance of the nervous systems of man and animals to the control and communications functions of information-handling machines.

D

DATA WORD: an ordered set of characters which has at least one meaning and is stored and transferred by the computer circuits as a unit.

DEBUG: to isolate and remove malfunctions from a computer or mistakes from a program.

DECODE: to convert data from machine form into readable characters; to ascertain the intended meaning of the individual characters or group of characters in the pseudo-coded program.

DELAY LINE: device for producing a time delay of a signal. *See* acoustical delay line.

DELAY-LINE STORAGE: storage or memory device that consists of a delay line and the means for regenerating and reinserting information into the delay line.

DESTRUCTIVE READOUT: method of detecting the condition (generally binary) of a device used for information storage in an automatic computer, detection destroys the information.

DIFFERENCE ENGINE: a mechanical digital computer designed by Charles Babbage (1792–1871).

DIFFERENTIAL ANALYZER: an analog computer designed and used primarily for solving or "analyzing" differential equations.

DIGITAL: the quality of using numbers expressed in digits and in a scale of notation.

DIGITAL COMPUTER: a computer that performs mathematical operations with information, numerical or otherwise, represented in digital form.

DRUM MEMORY: a storage device in which information is stored in tracks and bands on the magnetic surface of a (usually) rotating drum. *See* magnetic drum.

DYNAMIC MEMORY or STORAGE: storage in which information circulates and is not randomly accessible, as in acoustic delay lines, magnetic drum, and circulating registers.

E

ELECTROMAGNETIC COMPUTER: a computer using relays, and electrical and mechanical devices, as the Mark I (Automatic Sequence Controlled Calculator).

ELECTRONIC COMPUTER: a computer which operates mainly by means of electronic devices (devices dealing with the motion, emission and behavior of currents of the electrons, particularly in vacuum tubes, gas or phototubes, and special conductors or semiconductors).

ELECTROSTATIC STORAGE: techniques and devices storing information as static (but changeable) charges, as on the screen of a cathode ray tube.

EXECUTE: phase of instruction processing in which the specified operation is performed on data obtained in fetch phase.

EXECUTIVE PROGRAM: a routine designed to process and to control other routines.

F

FEEDBACK: transmission of a fraction of the output of a machine, system, or process to the input, to which the fraction is added or subtracted. This procedure can result in self-correction and control of the process.

FETCH: phase of instruction processing during which required data are obtained for manipulation (and, sometimes, next instruction is transferred from storage to the instruction register).

FIXED POINT NOTATION: a system of representing all quantities (in a given computer or mode of computer operation) by the same number of digits, with the location of the radix point fixed. *See also* floating point notation.

FLOATING POINT NOTATION: a system of representing all quantities (in a given computer or mode of computer operation) by a fractional mantissa and an exponent to which the base is raised to determine the actual radix point location. *See also* fixed point notation.

FORTRAN: problem-oriented (mathematical) language and compilers for IBM 700-series computers; term coined from *formula trans*lation.

FOUR-ADDRESS INSTRUCTION: instruction specifying the operation and the addresses of four memory locations (in which may be stored three operands and the next instruction).

FLYBALL GOVERNOR: a mechanical speed control device based on the principle of centrifugal force, used in a wide variety of engines.

FULL ADDER: circuit accepting signals representing two digits to be added plus a signal representing a digit carried from next lower order stage, and producing full binary sum and carried digit. *See* half adder.

G

GATE: a circuit, the output of which is energized when and only when certain combinations of pulses appear at the input(s).

GENERAL-PURPOSE COMPUTER: a computer designed to solve a wide variety of problems whose exact nature may *not* be known before the machine is designed; contrasted with "special-purpose computer."

GENERATOR PROGRAM: program equipping a computer to generate machine language coding of programs written in a symbolic or problem-oriented language.

H

HALF ADDER: a circuit having two input channels and producing binary sum (and carried digit) outputs; does not accept carried digit from lower order stage. *See* full adder.

HARMONIC ANALYZER: a device for measuring the amplitude and phase of the various harmonic components of a periodic function.

HEURISTICS: techniques by means of which the individual (or machine) can be equipped to solve problems. If the heuristics are applicable, they will provide a short cut to the goal. However, heuristic methods cannot guarantee a solution and may lead to a blind alley. *See* algorithms.

HOLLERITH CODE: a system of punching holes in cards, to represent numerals and characters, for machine sorting and transfer of information into automatic computers; devised by Dr. H. Hollerith of the U.S. Census Bureau, *ca.* 1900.

I

INDEX REGISTER: a storage location used to retain numbers (increments) for modifying addresses; may be provided with automatic counting capability.

INHIBITOR CIRCUIT: a gate producing an output unless a given input (combination of input signals) appears; one whose output condition (produced by a particular input combination) inhibits subsequent signal transfer.

INPUT: information transferred into a circuit or device.

INPUT UNIT: the unit which takes into the computing system information from outside the system.

INSTRUCTION: a set of characters which defines an operation, together with one or more addresses (or no address), and which, as a unit, causes the computer to operate accordingly on the indicated operands.

INSTRUCTION CODE: an artificial language that expresses or describes instructions for a digital computer.

INTERNAL STORAGE: storage facilities forming an integral physical part of the computer and directly controlled by the computer; the total storage directly accessible to the computer.

J

JACQUARD TECHNIQUE: a technique devised by M. Jacquard to control, by means of punched cards, the pattern produced on a loom.

JUMP: an instruction which conditionally or unconditionally transfers or branches to the storage address specified. *See* transfer instruction.

L

LOGIC: generally, the science that deals with the principles and criteria of validity in thought and demonstration; specifically, the basic principles and applications of truth tables, the relations of propositions, the interconnection of on-off circuit elements, etc.; used to describe operation of a computer.

LOGICAL DESIGN: the symbolic statements describing design (interconnections) of computer circuits to produce required operation.

LOGICAL NET: circuitry interconnected to perform logical operations ("and," "or," and "not").

LOGIC OF MECHANISM (also MATHEMATICAL LOGIC): *See* logic.

M

MACHINE LANGUAGE: a vocabulary of "words" meaningful to a computer; strings of binary digits acceptable to and manipulatable by machine circuits; pulse trains setting and resetting computer circuits.

MAGNETIC CORE STORAGE: storage of binary information as magnetic orientation of a small ring of ferromagnetic material called a core; one core used for each bit in a register; random access to any addressable register; commonly, a single device stores between 8000 and 32,000 words.

MAGNETIC DISC STORAGE: storage of information on one or more discs having magnetizable surfaces and which rotate (on a common shaft); data accessible serially by bit on a single track or bit-parallel on several tracks (a band); commonly, a single device stores millions of words.

MAGNETIC DRUM: a rapidly rotating cylinder whose surface is coated with a magnetic material, on which information may be stored as discretely magnetized areas; registers arranged serially in tracks or in bands; commonly, a single device stores between 8000 and 250,000 words.

MAGNETIC READ-WRITE HEAD: a device for detecting (reading), recording, and erasing information in a magnetic storage medium; usually, a small electromagnet.

MAGNETIC TAPE: tape made of paper, metal, or plastic, coated or impregnated with magnetic material on which information may be stored as discretely magnetized areas.

MAGNETIC (THIN) FILM MEMORY: storage technique based on magnetic orientation of miniature deposits of ferromagnetic material on glass; characterized by extremly short access time (0.3 microsecond); commonly, a single device currently stores 128 words.

MARGINAL CHECKING: a system of testing circuits in a computer by varying certain operating parameters to detect tendencies toward malfunctions.

MATHEMATICAL MODEL: facsimile in mathematical terms; a body of mathematical statements describing a process, parameters, and their relationships to one another and to environments; useful for rigorously studying complex relationships, particularly with a computer.

MATRIX: in computer circuitry, a rectangular array forming a logical network of elements; usually functions as an encoder or a decoder.

MEMORY or STORAGE: any device into which units of information can be copied, which will hold this information and from which the information can be obtained at a later time.

MEMORY ACCESS TIME: a measure of time to communicate with a storage device; the time interval between the instant at which information is called for from storage and the instant at which delivery is completed, i.e., the read time. *See* access, speed of.

MODEL: a facsimile capturing the essence of one or more characteristics of the original, may be mathematical, physical, conceptual, etc. *See* mathematical model.

MULTIPLY TIME: the period in which a computer can perform a multiplication.

N

NAPIER'S BONES: a set of sticks or rods facilitating multiplication; arranged vertically on each stick are the products of one digit and each of ten digits of the decimal system.

NONVOLATILE MEMORY: any storage medium that retains information in the absence of power; e.g., magnetic tapes, drums, or cores.

O

OCTAL NUMBER SYSTEM (also OCTAL NOTATION): the scale of notation having the base 8; convenient in dealing with binary numbers because a group of three binary digits (beginning in digit position adjacent to the radix point) can be "read" as an octal digit (000 = 0; 001 = 1; 010 = 2; 011 = 3; 100 = 4; 101 = 5; 110 = 6; and 111 = 7).

OFF-LINE: equipment whose operation, while part of a computer system, is not under direct control of the computer; tasks performed by such equipment as in conversion of information on tape into card decks, etc. *See also* on-line.

ONE-ADDRESS (also SINGLE-ADDRESS) INSTRUCTION: an instruction consisting of an operation and exactly one address.

ONE-AND-ONE-HALF-ADDRESS INSTRUCTION: instruction specifying operation, address of one operand, and address of next instruction.

ON-LINE: equipment whose operation is under direct control of the computer; tasks performed under direct computer control. *See also* off-line.

OPERAND: a quantity entering into or arising from an operation.

OPERATION: the part of an instruction that usually designates the kind of task to be performed, but not the location of the operands. *See also* instruction code.

"OR" GATE OR "OR" CIRCUIT: a gate or circuit having the property that it produces an output when any (acceptable) input is available. *See* "and" gate.

OUTPUT: information transferred out of a circuit or device.

OUTPUT UNIT: the unit which delivers information outside the computer in a usable form.

P

PARALLEL COMPUTER: a computer in which all bits, or characters, or words are essentially equally accessible for manipulation; or in which arithmetic is performed on all digits in parallel (rather than serially on digits of successively higher powers).

PARITY: a method for increasing the code representation (pulse pattern) of a character handled by and stored in a computer in a manner that facilitates checking the accuracy of character transfers and, in some cases, correcting errors created during transfer.

PROBLEM ANALYSIS: in computer programing, precisely formulating a problem, defining the scope of investigation, stating hypotheses, and establishing statistical techniques.

PROBLEM-ORIENTED LANGUAGE: an artificial language (vocabulary and rules) conveniently expressing relationships of a particular problem or class of problems and the solution method. *See also* symbolic language, computer-oriented language, *and* machine language.

PROGRAM: a set of instructions arranged in proper sequence to cause a computer to perform a desired set of operations.

PROGRAM COUNTER (also SEQUENCE REGISTER): a device in which is recorded the name or number of the storage location of the instruction to be executed following that in process.

PROGRAMING: the procedures contributing to development of a set of instructions for computer solution of a problem; includes problem analysis, program design, coding, and testing.

PUNCHED CARDS: (80- or 90-column) a card of constant size and shape designed for punching holes in meaningful patterns; can be used for storing data, and can be handled mechanically. The punched holes are usually sensed electrically by wire brushes, mechanically by metal fingers, or photo-electrically by photocells.

PUNCHED PAPER TAPE: paper or plastic tape perforated in character groups (cells) along length; for introducing information into and for output from an automatic computing system.

R

RANDOM ACCESS: storage characteristic in which the time required to access the next position from which information is to be obtained is in no way dependent on the position last accessed.

READ: to sense the information contained in patterns of holes punched into cards or tape, or of magnetized areas on discs, drums, and tapes, etc. *See also* write.

REAL-TIME OPERATION: operation in which an event is controlled by information generated by the event. The finite time involved in processing may be compensated by extrapolating and cyclically correcting as the conditions being measured change.

REGISTER: a device that stores information, often one subset (such as a word) of the total information in a digital computer. *See also* storage.

ROUTINE (also PROGRAM or SUBPROGRAM): a set of coded instructions arranged in proper sequence to direct a computer to perform a desired operation or series of operations.

S

SAGE: acronym standing for Semi-Automatic Ground Environment; a comprehensive electronic data processing system used in air defense.

SEQUENCE REGISTER: register containing name or number of location in which is stored the next instruction to be executed. In a one-address machine, this is a counter incremented by one as the present instruction is fetched for execution. Branch instructions can change the contents of the register if the test specified for branching is passed.

SERIAL COMPUTER: a computer which reads out of or writes into storage one bit at a time, performing arithmetic serially on successively higher power positions in numbers.

SERVOMECHANISM: a system, usually combining electronic, electric, and mechanical elements, in which feedback is used to maintain constant performance of the system.

SIMULATION: representation of necessary elements of some object, phenomena, system, or environment facilitating control and study (often by or involving an automatic computer).

SIMULATOR: a computer or model which represents a system or phenomenon and which mirrors or maps the effects of various changes in the original, enabling the researcher to study, analyze, and understand the original by means of the behavior of the model; specifically, a program enabling one computer to simulate another—e.g., to permit design of operational programs for a computer not yet constructed.

SINGLE-ADDRESS INSTRUCTION: *See* one-address instruction.

SOLID-STATE COMPUTER: a computer which uses the magnetic, electric, and other properties of solid materials—e.g., magnetic cores, transistors, magnetic amplifiers, crystal diodes—as opposed to vacuum or gaseous devices as tubes.

SPECIAL-PURPOSE COMPUTER: a computer designed to solve a restricted class of problems—for example, aiming a large telescope in an astronomical observatory, controlling petroleum processing in an oil refinery, navigating an aircraft.

STATIC STORAGE: storage in which information is fixed in space, as a flip-flop or magnetic core.

STORAGE (also MEMORY or STORE): any device used to store information. *See* memory, magnetic disc storage, ultrasonic delay line, drum memory, magnetic core storage, magnetic film memory.

STORAGE CAPACITY: the amount of information that the principal internal storage, or memory, device of a computer can retain; often measured in the number of words that can be retained, given the number of digits and the base of the standard word; customarily expressed in *bits* when comparisons among devices are made.

SUBROUTINE: a subunit of a routine; a short or repeated sequence of instructions; often written in relative or symbolic coding even when the routine to which it belongs is not.

SYMBOLIC LANGUAGE: (in computers) a special language convenient for the programer in preparing computer instructions; converted (one-to-one) by the assembly program into machine language. *See also* problem-oriented language *and* machine language.

T

THREE-ADDRESS INSTRUCTION: an instruction that includes an operation and specifies the location of three registers: two operands and a location for the result of the operation; or two operands and the location of the next instruction; or one operand, the location for the result, and the location of the next instruction.

TIME-SHARING: technique allowing execution of two or more functions essentially at the same time, by allocating (in rotation, for instance) small divisions of the total time for the performance of each function.

TRANSFER INSTRUCTION: a set of characters interpreted by a computer as a direction to "transfer" or branch or jump to a specified location; also a direction to transfer (blocks of) data between memory and external storage.

TRANSLATOR PROGRAM: equips a computer to accept a program *not* in machine language and transform it into the machine language used by it or by another computer.

TWO-ADDRESS INSTRUCTION: an instruction specifying an operation and the location of two registers.

U

ULTRASONIC DELAY LINE: a device capable of transmitting retarded sound pulses, the transmission of which is accomplished by wave patterns of elastic deformation. *See* acoustic delay line.

V

VOLATILE MEMORY: storage in which information vanishes when power is removed, as in mercury delay-line memory, electrostatic storage tubes.

W

WIRE MATRIX PRINTER: an output mechanism which prints by transferring an image corresponding to the pattern of wires energized in a matrix (usually 5 wires in horizontal and 7 in vertical dimensions; one matrix per character in a line, often 120 per line).

WORD FORMAT: the specified arrangement of digits, characters, fields, lines, etc. in a meaningful coded set.

WRITE: to introduce information, usually into some form of storage. *See also* read.

Glossary prepared by Louise Schultz.

INDEX

The index is divided into a list of the names cited and a separate subject index. Italicized numbers in the index to names refer to pages on which biographical data are provided or on which a work is listed. Glossary page numbers do not appear in the subject index.

SUBJECT INDEX

Abacus, 32, 35
  contest versus calculator, 33
Abstracting, automatic, 370
Access arm, 83
ACM, 126, 606
Accumulator (register), 45, 121, 128
Acoustical delay line, 86
Adding machine, 35
Address, 75, 120
Agreement analysis, 160, 169, 191
Airline reservation control, 599
ALDP (*see* language-data processing)
ALGOL, 126, 601
Algorithmic methods, 15
Analog computers, 23, 464, 499
Analog mechanical devices, 29
Analog simulation, 499, 535
Analysis of variance, 205, 213
Analytic engine, 39
Analytic rotation, 181

Analytical oblique methods, 255
Analytical orthogonal rotation, 250
"and" gate, 104
Anesthetic machine, 505
Arithmetic mean, 88, 127
Arithmetic operations, 50, 120
Arithmetic (processing) unit, 61, 87, 121
Artificial intelligence, 355
Auditory patterns, computer-produced, 294
Autistic thinking, 18
  definition, 14
Automated teaching, 8, 308
  lesson preparation, 317
  lesson presentation, 316
Automatic abstracting, 370
Automatic computers, 41
Automatic control, 8
Automatic indexing, 370

NAMES INDEX